CANADIAN MARKETS

for

Writers and Photographers

Edited by
Melanie E. Rockett

Assistant Editor
Lorna J. McElhinney

PROOF POSITIVE PRODUCTIONS LTD.

Canadian Cataloguing in Publication Data

Main entry under title:

Canadian markets for writers & photographers

Includes index.
ISBN 0-921528-04-3

1. Authorship--Marketing--Directories. 2. Photography--Marketing--Directories. 3. Publishers and publishing--Canada--Directories. 4. Canadian periodicals--Directories. 5. Authorship--Marketing--Handbooks, manuals, etc. I. Rockett, Melanie E. (Melanie Elizabeth)
PN161.C3 1995   070.5'2'02571   C95-910572-7

Printed and bound in Canada

Orders and inquiries to:

Proof Positive Productions Ltd.
#1330, 194 - 3803 Calgary Trail
Edmonton, Alberta
CANADA T6J 5M8
phone: (403) 435-7831   fax: (403) 434-2888

Distributed to the book trade by:
Sandhill Book Marketing
#99 - 1270 Ellis Street
Kelowna, BC V1Y 1Z4
Phone: (604) 763-1406 Fax: (604) 763-4051

TABLE OF CONTENTS

INTRODUCTION

In 1991 we published the first edition of *Where to Sell Your Photographs in Canada*. Four years, and three editions later requests for more listings and more information from both photographers and writers have resulted in the expansion, revision and renaming of our original ... and here it is, the first edition of *Canadian Markets for Writers and Photographers*. In it we offer you the most complete and up-to-date listings of magazines, publishers, stock agencies, newspapers and resources available.

The listings include information provided by editors, publishers and buyers. We have made over 4,500 phone calls in order to complete the information in this book. As of the day we go to press, every listing is up-to-date and accurate. Our 4,500 phone calls have resulted in over 1,700 listings. At a minimum we confirmed the address, phone numbers and contact names for each of the listings. Where possible we obtained additional information including the kinds of material purchased, prices paid, and direct quotes from our information sources.

In addition to the 1,700 listings, we have also provided you with a resource section filled with names and information on organizations, groups, books, products and newsletters.

Articles by working professionals on their experiences in the marketplace and advice garnered from years of experience may give you inspiration and encouragement to keep on going. It is possible to sell your work, it is possible to make a living doing what you love. Melanie Isaac writes about the process of getting her first romance novel published and Catherine Senecal tells us about her travel writing experiences. You will find out how to get the most out of your learning experiences and how to negotiate the best price for your work.

As this book goes to press we are already at work on our next edition. If you have any information that could help us expand and improve the next edition, we will happily receive it. We need names, addresses, phone numbers and any other information you can provide us with (a xerox copy of the cover and masthead would be very useful).

We'd also like to hear about your sales successes. It gives us great joy to be able to help you make a new contact and a sale. It is wonderful to be able to open up a Canadian magazine or peruse the lists of upcoming books and recognize the names of our customers. If you have a sales story that may be of interest and inspiration to other writers and photographers, feel free to submit it for our next edition. If you want to get on our mailing list, or tell us about your experiences with using this directory, please write us. Keep your letters coming.

The key to pursuing a career in writing and/or photography is in your hand; read it, make notes in it, enjoy it, but above all, make it happen by using it!

Melanie E. Rockett
Editor

FOCUS ON

PHOTO DIGEST
THE PHOTOGRAPHER'S
MAGAZINE

- **PHOTO DESTINATIONS**
- **PHOTO EQUIPEMENT**
- **PHOTO DIMENSIONS**
- **PHOTO TECHNIQUE**
- **DIGITAL IMAGING**
- **NATURE NOTES**
- **DARKROOM**
- **PORTFOLIO**
    - **Reader's images**
    - **Showtime**
    - **Gallery**
    - **Springboard**

HOW TO USE CANADIAN MARKETS

Before making queries or submissions, read the information in this section on how to make the most effective use of the listings.

The listings in *Canadian Markets* have been divided into several sections: magazines, publishers, stock agencies and newspapers. The information differs from section to section depending on the needs of the companies or publication in the listing.

Information was obtained directly from editors, publishers or company contacts. It reflects what they want and need. *Canadian Markets* was up-to-date and accurate as it went to press. However, since people and companies move frequently, and pay rates and needs change rapidly, it is up to you to confirm addresses and to iron out the fine details of a sale; each and every time you make a sale.

SASE refers to self-addressed stamped envelope. Most magazines and publishers receive huge stacks of unsolicited submissions daily. They can not afford to reply to your questions or return your submissions unless they are provided with the means to do so. Along with your submissions, or request for guidelines, catalogues and samples, you must include a stamped self-addressed envelope that is large enough to accommodate the returning material. If you are requesting a sample copy of the publication you must send a large envelope. Nine by twelve inches is usually sufficient. You must also include enough postage. We recommend $1.40 or even $2.00. If you are making a submission, get it weighed at a post-office and include enough postage for its return. Because of today's computer technology, some writers will find it cheaper to print out a new copy of their work rather than having copies returned. In this case enclose a #10 SASE so that the editor can let you know whether or not your material is suitable. We advise photographers to use insured, registered mail or couriers if they are sending originals. What's a few extra bucks compared to the loss of 20 or even a hundred of your precious slides.

With the exception of the article on negotiating, all numbers and quotes are in Canadian dollars. If you are submitting material from outside Canada, you will have to use **International Reply Coupons** in place of stamps, or somehow obtain Canadian stamps. International Reply Coupons (**IRCs**) are available from most American and overseas post offices. You may have to send for current Canadian postal rates since they differ significantly from rates in other countries. To obtain current postal rates send a request to the Post Master of any major Canadian city.

Some publishers have a policy of not returning unsolicited material even if an SASE is enclosed. If the listing states "Do not send unsolicited material," then don't do it. If you do, don't expect to ever see your material again. One editor told us that unsolicited material automatically went into the shredder. This might not be a tragedy if you are sending a computer generated article, but it is a tragedy if you included the original slides from your expedition to the jungles of Borneo! The receiver of unsolicited mail is under no legal obligation to return your materials. Please do not send any material, other than a query letter and samples that you do not expect to be returned. When an editor asks to see something you may still be submitting your work on spec but your article or photos are now considered to be solicited.

Over the years we have encountered much confusion over "**solicited**" and "**unsolicited**." If you know what they mean skip this paragraph, if you need clarification read on. In the simplest of terms solicited means "asked for" and unsolicited means "not asked for." If you come back from your trip to Borneo, write an article on your experiences, package it up with a few of your best slides and send it to the editor of *Leisure World*, you are sending an unsolicited package. The editor has not asked for it and therefore has no obligation to open it, look at it or return it. If, however, an editor phones, faxes or writes you asking you to send your article, then your article has been asked for, or solicited. In most cases an editor will ask an unknown writer or photographer to submit their material on spec, which means that they are not under any obligation to buy your material ... they are just asking to take a look. Your cover letter should state the fact that the editor has asked for the material to be submitted. The key to getting "solicited" is the **query** letter, you will see it often in the listings. Keep it brief; in one or two paragraphs let the editor know what you are planning on writing about and why their readers should be interested. Include a one paragraph bio of your writing experience and/or your qualifications to write the article. In the same package you might include one or two short sample articles or xeroxes of published articles. If you have photos, enclose a few copies (not originals). Enclose a SASE and wait patiently. Proceed to send the entire article and photos only if and when asked.

Listings consist of the following:

Circulation: The number of copies a magazine distributes. This has an obvious impact on a publications budget and their ability to purchase articles and photos. Generally, the larger the circulation the higher the pay. Some of the smaller magazines don't pay at all ... while others pay rather handsomely.

Established: How many years has the firm been in business? Magazines and publishers come and go, the first few years in business are often the riskiest.

Description: This is a general description of the magazine or publisher. The kinds of material they publish, the types of articles they use. In the publishers section we tried to give you examples of recent publications so you can get them at your local bookstore or look them up in the library.

Writers: This section includes information specific to writers. Average article lengths, pay rates, etc.

Photographers: This section includes information specific to photographers. Formats used, pay rates, submission guidelines, the requirements for model releases and captions.

Notes: If information is applicable to both writes and photographers we put it in this section. For example if both photo and writers' guidelines are available it appears in this section. If the magazine buys first North American serial rights for both photography and articles it appears in this section. This section also includes general quotes from the editors, publishers or buyers, including their wants and needs for coming years.

Quotes: Quotes are a great insight into the personality of the buyers. They are as accurate as we could get them.

Photo and Writers' guidelines: If they are available, get them before making any queries or submissions. Follow the directions; most magazines and publishers would appreciate SASEs.

Transparency: Transparency is the term for positive film. 35mm slides, 2¼ slides, other medium format sizes, 4x5's and 8x10 chomes or colour reversal films are all referred to as transparencies.

Trade magazine: Consumer magazines are usually those found on magazine racks. Trade magazines are normally considered to be "magazines for the trade" or magazines published for specialty interest groups or business groups. So a photo magazine such as *Photo Digest, Photo Selection* or *Photo Life* can be found on magazine racks and are considered to be consumer magazines. *Photo Retailer* and *Photo Dealer News* are trade magazines because they are highly specialized magazines distributed to photo businesses.

Trade books: Large publishers often run a number of divisions. These can include mass market paperback; fiction; educational and professional; and children's divisions. Each of these categories may sell to different markets. Educational books sell to schools, colleges and university book stores ... and would not sell in a regular bookstore; mass market paperbacks are sold in drug stores and supermarkets. Trade books are normally the category of books you would find in a regular book store.

FACE THE FACTS

FRANS LANTING/FIRST LIGHT

If you're serious about your photography, the best way to improve is with a subscription to *Photo Life*. In every issue, you'll find no-nonsense equipment pieces, helpful technical stories, great images, profiles ... in short, everything you need to face the world of Canadian photography with an informed eye.

We also do our best to reveal the stories behind the images. How, you might wonder, did the photographer catch an ostrich with its head in the sand, since that old cliché is a myth — ostriches don't really do that. At least live, non-stuffed ostriches don't.

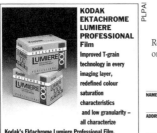

TRAVEL WRITING AND PHOTOGRAPHY
by Catherine M. Senecal

I am a professional travel writer and photographer based in Winnipeg. Hundreds of my illustrated articles have been published in magazines and newspapers primarily in North America and Australia, and in five other countries as well. My monthly travel columns appear in city magazines in Edmonton and Winnipeg, and I am a regular travel correspondent for a major Australian newspaper. Several photo\text packages are syndicated through Fotopress International.

Ten publications have used my photo of "boys paddling" to illustrate an article about a river barge trip down the Zaire River in Africa. When I took the trip, I had no idea I would eventually write a story about the journey. As a result, I am extra cautious with the very few images I shot on the trip. So far, the combined photo/text package has earned me more than $2,500. As is the case with many writers and photographers, it is imperative that I sell my work again and again to non-competing markets.

I now have a relatively small stock collection of more than two thousand captioned 35mm slides from visits to Alaska, Brazil, Kenya, Zaire, Zambia, Tanzania, Barbados, British Virgin Islands, Holland, Israel, Mexico, Indonesia, Malaysia, South Dakota, North Carolina, British Columbia, Manitoba and Ontario. They depict outdoor activities, geographical features, markets, buildings, people, wildlife and more. It is sometimes surprising to learn how my travel photos are used. For example, I photographed a teenage boy and girl arm in arm on a busy street in

Jerusalem one night. A high school magazine used it to illustrate sexual practices in other cultures.

I choose a destination based on whether I think forthcoming articles and photographs will garner a high demand, thereby increasing their likelihood for repeat sales. While I paid for my own travel earlier in my career and still do today, I now accept travel industry invitations to research destinations at subsidized rates. This still doesn't make it easy to be profitable, but it helps enormously.

I have been selling articles full time for the last three years and have only recently started marketing my images separately. To do this include a slide faxback sheet with all article mail outs. Editors can keep the faxback sheet on file and request slides at a later date. On the back of this sheet is an index of existing and upcoming travel articles for publication. Editors are much more interested in your articles if you can provide high-quality images to illustrate them. Some editors will ask to see your images first before committing to using the article. I find that the majority of editors use slides instead of prints, although many can use either. Few editors are equipped to receive articles by modem but many like to receive them on diskettes.

A crowd from a large village greets the
Zaire River barge on its journey down river.

Instead of duplicating my best slides, I've learned that it is much easier and cheaper *and smarter* to shoot the same image several times while I'm *right* there floating in the Dead Sea or jeeping across the Pantanal wetlands in Brazil. I work with a Nikon F-601 with 35mm to 70mm zoom lens and a Pentax P5 with 50mm, 28mm, and 75-200mm lenses using mostly Kodachrome 64, Lumiere or Fujichrome Velvia film. I usually shoot a couple of rolls of black-and-white film to satisfy a few publications that use it exclusively.

Although I do not include slides with manuscript submissions to every newspaper, many editors will not look at my material unless I include at least six slides. So in a mail-out to 50 newspapers, I may put together a dozen slide packs of six to 12 slides to accompany those articles. Then, I still need to have a diverse selection on hand for the other newspaper editors who call requesting slides -- anywhere from 12 and up. All are captioned and marked with a copyright symbol, my name, address and telephone number. I always include a SASE (self-addressed stamped envelope) and rarely send out original slides I must see again.

Two top books for travel writers and photographers include *The Travel Writer's Guide* (Prima Publishing) by Gordon Burgett and *A Guide to Travel Writing & Photography* by Carl and Ann Purcell (Writer's Digest Books).

Catherine Senecal on location in the Pantanal wetlands of Brazil

Before he became a bestselling author, John Grisham woke each day at 5:00 AM, scribbled notes on a legal pad between sessions in court, mailed 26 submissions...

and subscribed to WRITER'S DIGEST.

In fact, it was an article on the rules of suspense that gave Grisham the boost he needed to put pen to paper. "Once I finished *A Time to Kill*," he says, "I was fairly confident about how to send it off because I had read so much about it in WD. And their advice worked."

Each month WRITER'S DIGEST helps thousands of writers hone their skills and find the best-paying markets for their work. You'll find page after page of solid advice for writing stories, articles, poems, screenplays...suspense novels, too.

Invest in your career as a writer and start a subscription to WD today. You'll save more than $18 off the newsstand rate, <u>and</u> get a free copy of **Getting Published: What Every Writer Needs to Know.** A handy guide packed with essential information for writers who want to see their work in print.

THE JOYS OF LEARNING

In this day and age of non-stop, rapidly accelerating change a commitment to continual learning is a must. If you stop learning you will be left far behind. What is the information highway anyway? Turn on a computer? Not me! Faxes, modems, cyberspace, virtual reality, digital photography. There are times when learning is a painful necessity ... when it stretches you to your limits and you are convinced you will never get it. And there are times when learning can be pure, unadulterated pleasure. Fun!

Writers and photographers are amongst the lucky. Numerous opportunities exist not only to learn ... but to have an enormous amount of fun learning. There are hundreds of opportunities to learn from the best writers and photographers in Canada, the best in North America, the best in the world. Opportunities to travel, to see our wonderful country, and to meet wonderful people who are interested in the same subject, and who want to learn too!

Being part of a non-competitive, informal group with a similar interest is more than just a learning experience. It is a means of gaining enthusiasm, anticipation and the opportunity to express yourself. It is a venue to discover new ideas and techniques, recharge your creative juices, your imagination and provides great fellowship. Some workshops or tours may involve long hours and hard work, but the results can be worth it.

One of the biggest challenges is in deciding what trip or seminar to take ... where you want to go, who you want to learn from, what skills you want to learn. Learning about something you love really ought to be pure pleasure and it can be if you ask the right questions and choose carefully.

Dale Wilson, a noted Canadian photographer and contributing editor to Photo Digest magazine talks about the kinds of questions you ought to be asking.

Go Ahead ... Be a Pest .... ASK!!!

When I first started my photo tour business, I approached my itineraries in a manner which any one of my guests might. What would I want should I be the tour participant? It came to light that photographers are generally an eclectic lot and it was near impossible to satisfy all with a single tour. Therefore many tours are designed with specific photographic styles in mind. It is up to you to find one that meets your aspirations.

Once a geographic destination has been decided upon, you must seek literature from the various companies offering excursions to that area. Study that printed matter religiously. Learn how many people will be allowed to participate; the kind of accommodations there will be; what meals are included; what type of ground transportation will be provided; how many pieces of luggage will you be permitted to bring; whether gratuities are included; if photographic instruction is to be provided; and most importantly - who is the tour leader? Be objective about yourself and your needs, if you think the best room at the Holiday Inn is camping out, and you wouldn't dream of walking the golf course, do you really want to go on that two week trek?

Once you know who the tour leaders are, start looking for samples of their published work. Is their style compatible to yours? Or, is theirs a style you would like to study further? When you telephone the tour office, ask to speak to the tour leader and enquire about an image which interests you. If the leader avoids the topic of how that particular photograph was approached, you can almost bet this will not be a tour laden with educational opportunity. Find another tour company.

Equally important, if not more so, is the tour leader's familiarity with the destination. You can book yourself on a tour with the best photographers in the world, but if they are not familiar with the area you would perhaps be better served by exploring on your own. The resident tour leader knows not only the best areas, but also the best time of day to be at a location. Although I would love to travel to exotic locations around the world, it was for this very reason my tours are set in Atlantic Canada. Ask if the itinerary was designed by the tour leader, and accept a tour designed by a photographer as a minimum.

You must also be aware that there is indeed a difference between a workshop and a tour. Basically put, the photo tour is just that - a tour. And yes, the tour leader will in all likelihood be taking photographs (unless they are a resident and have photographed the area countless times). A workshop on the other hand, is an avenue of education and in all likelihood the leader will not be making photographs.

This is **your** trip. Investigate and do your homework. Compare not only the administration of the tour companies, but also the tour leaders. Ask the right questions, be prepared and choose wisely. You will return with not only lots of pleasing photographs but with lots of pleasant memories as well.

Here's a summary of the questions you should be asking.

HOW FAMILIAR IS THE TOUR LEADER WITH THE AREA?
If a tour leader isn't familiar with the area they are taking you to, what are you paying them for? Your leader should be able to take you to the best spots at the perfect time of day.

DOES THE TOUR LEADER HAVE A VESTED INTEREST IN THE TOUR COMPANY?
You may not get a straight answer on this one, but ask anyway. You can bet your bottom dollar that should the tour leader be a principle owner in the tour company, you are going to get your monies worth. Word-of-mouth can mean a company's success or its demise.

WAS THE ITINERARY DRAFTED BY A PHOTOGRAPHER?
When I started my photo tour business last year, I contracted a tourism business to package my trips. Upon reviewing the material submitted to my office I was appalled. Who could be so stunned to think a photographer would have breakfast at 8:00 am and finish their day at 4:30 pm? We are photographers who must be up and ready for sunrise, and tourism industry related "experts" simply don't know this. Established photo tour companies are expert in drafting itineraries tailored for photographers.

WILL THE TOUR LEADER BE TAKING PICTURES?
Local tour leaders will already have photos from all of the locations you will visit, and they will be more interested in providing assistance to the tour participants.

WHAT ARE THE TOUR LEADER'S CREDENTIALS? WHAT DO THEY KNOW ABOUT THE AREA YOU WILL BE TOURING?
This is a question which must be asked, and provides for some varied responses. You can only listen to the reply and see if the tour leader is pushing the right buttons. Be careful. I recently learned of a tour whose highlight was to be Cape Breton Island's Louisbourgh Castle. The organizer wanted to know where I got off telling him the Castle closed after the last week-end in September. His tour was going to be there in October. Oh well, I tried!

IS THE TOUR LEADER WILLING TO SHARE TECHNIQUES AND SKILLS?
Be wary of the professional who is not willing to share their techniques and skills. Get examples of your tour leaders work and ask how they approached that particular subject. If they won't tell you, and if you want to learn, its time to find another tour!

WHAT IS INCLUDED IN THE PACKAGE PRICE?
This question should be answered in the tour literature, but read it carefully. Most importantly ask *what is not included?* Many tour operators don't include meals. The price often does not include getting to the preliminary staging ground. Make sure you know what meals, accommodations, gratuities, ground expenses, charter fees and taxes are provided for.

All questions, asked? Trip booked? Have a great time!

Dale Wilson, now a resident of Nova Scotia has lived and travelled extensively in Newfoundland. His Maritime tours are designed to give you the best photographic opportunities available. Wilson's Newfoundland tour takes you through the Avalon Peninsula. Photo opportunities include the humpback whales of Whitless Bay, Woodland Caribou herds and giant colonies of nesting Gannets. His coastal Nova Scotia tour focuses on a maritime coastal motif and an autumn tour concentrates on the wonderful colours of fall foliage in Cape Breton. As you have probably guessed, he is intimately familiar with the locations he takes his tour guests through. Call for a brochure or for more information.

Dale Wilson Photography Tours
Phone: (902) 465-2750

Here are a few other courses and tours you may be interested in getting more information on. Additionally you will want to investigate the workshops put on by your local (and national) writers and photographers associations.

Spirit of the West Photo Ventures offers a number of "staged photo opportunities." Visit the Douglas Lank ranch, Canada's largest working cattle ranch to photograph cow camps, horse roping, campfire and horse riding demonstrations. Working cowboy models will provide you with a full range of photo opportunities. 1995 events include Horse Drives, A Horse Drive with Paul Lazarski, a NAPA Columbia Gorge photo event, Life on a Ranch, Harvest Time in the Palouse and more. Write or call for details and a brochure.

Spirit of the West Photo Ventures   Phone: (604) 855-4848
Leona Isaak   Fax: (604) 859-6288
31858 Hopedale
Clearbrook, BC   V2T 2G7

Ecosummer Expeditions has numerous sea kayaking, trekking, canoeing, rafting, exploration and photo tours and workshops available. Photo tours and workshops are conducted by Paul Lazarski and resident tour leaders. There are dozens of tours and workshops to choose from, a few examples include: High Arctic, Ellesmere & Devon; Land of Fire & Ice, Iceland; Icebergs, East Greenland; Lake Powell Kayaking, Arizona; Rafting the Colorado; California Poppies; Waterton & Glacier, the Rockies. Call or write for brochures and information.

Ecosummer Expeditions   Phone: (604) 669-7741
1516 Duranleau Street   1-800-465-8884
Vancouver, BC   V6H 3S4

Join photographers Don Cole Harvey and Ingrid Wypkema for photography tours into remote high alpine meadows and landscapes only accessible by helicopter. The workshops are given in the wilderness ranges of the *Cariboo and Monashee Mountains*. Lodging is at a first-class resort. For more information phone, fax or write:

Cariboo and Monashee Mountain   Phone: (604) 673-8400
Workshops   Fax: (604) 673-8488
Don Cole Harvey or Inrid Wypkema
Box 11
Blue River, BC   V0E 1J0

Great Canadian Ecoventures leads expeditions to the most remote regions of Canada, designed to offer the very best photographic opportunities for a variety of species in their natural habitat. Once in Yellowknife you board a float aircraft to fly you to the wildlife basecamp. A choice of daily field programmes are featured, led by some of the best naturalist trip leaders and wildlife photographers in the world.

The expeditions are relaxed and informal and are educational and rich with native cultural and natural history, archaeology, and feature excellent wildlife and incredible Arctic landscapes! A few samples: Dances with Wolves; and Musk-Ox and Gyrfalcon. Some of the canoeing trips offered are the Haunted Kazan, Canoe/Raft the Nahanni River or Soper River and Baffin Island. Write for brochures and information.

Great Canadian Ecoventures
Box 25181
Winnipeg, MB   R2V 4C8

Phone: 1-800-667-9453
Fax: (604) 733-8657

Write-On Holidays tours for writers are organized and led by experienced workshop leader Joyce Gariepy. Learn the art of writing and getting published while having the time of your life. Gariepy personally leads you to all the special places a writer would want to visit while on tour. The tours and itinerary change from year to year. In past years tours have be held throughout Canada, the US, Europe and on luxury cruise ships. Call for information.

Write-On Holidays
Joyce Gariepy

Phone/Fax: (403) 438-6335

AND THEN HE KISSED HER: BREAKING INTO THE ROMANCE MARKET
by Melanie Isaac

Romances lead us, safely, to joy. -- Lisa G. Brown

Blame it on Rhett and Scarlett.

I wish I could say that the reason I began to write romance novels had something to do with the fiery characters and timeless plotline of Margaret Mitchell's *Gone With the Wind*. Or the tragic consequences of young love in Shakespeare's *Romeo and Juliet*. I'd even mention Danielle Steel if I thought it would ennoble my cause. If the truth be known, however, I turned to writing romance because it was lucrative, stylistically simplistic and wide-open to new authors.

Or so I thought.

I'd researched the romance field before I wrote my first word. In the early 1990s, the market was expanding, profits were rising and editors were frantic for manuscripts. These days the figures are even more impressive. Romance novels make up almost 50% of mass market paperback sales with more than 140 new titles hitting the shelves every month. That translates into $884 million in North American sales. The proliferation of such subgenres as romantic suspense, futuristic romance, paranormal romance and ethnic romance has enlivened the market and attracted readership beyond purist romance circles. Currently, no other sector of the publishing world is as healthy as romance.

Or as competitive. Scratch the surface of your best friend or your mother or your hairdresser and you're apt to uncover a would-be romance writer. Even men are not immune to the lure. This overwhelming interest is reflected in the flood of manuscripts that Harlequin, Silhouette and other romance publishing houses receive each year, manuscripts that are increasingly well-written, innovative and compelling. It was into this maelstrom that I cast myself when I submitted my romantic suspense novel, *Lying Eyes*, to Harlequin Intrigue in 1991.

I'd done my homework then, too. Prior to mailing out the manuscript, I'd contacted the senior editor with a query letter and a story synopsis as per the publishing guidelines that Harlequin provides free-of-charge to all interested writers. When I received a letter from the Intrigue editor asking to see my story, I made a clean copy of the manuscript and marched down to the nearest post office, confident that I knew what I was getting into. Even so, submitting the completed manuscript felt a little like casting my first-born, naked and vulnerable, out into the world. The envelope practically whimpered when I handed it to the postal clerk. I often felt like whimpering myself as I waited for a response during the long months that followed.

Harlequin estimates it takes fourteen weeks from the time it received a manuscript to the time it makes an effort to go to the contract. Of course, the exception often disproved the rule and I proved to be the exception. Ninety-six weeks passed before my editor called me with an offer, during which time I second-guessed the merits of my story and the quality of my writing so often I made myself dizzy.

Once the call came through, I barely had enough time to shout the good news from the rooftops before I plunged into a whirlwind of revisions, editor-generated line and copy edits and proof-reading sessions of the revised story. Each step of the process was set out in a comprehensive contract almost twenty pages in length. What the contact didn't cover, my editor did, from explaining the input required of me by the art department in preparing the book cover art to making suggestions for a new title more in keeping with the suspenseful tone of the Intrigue line of books.

The most enjoyable task at this stage was selecting my pen name, a request made of all new Harlequin writers. By acquiring sole rights to the pen name, the company feels its' writers may be less apt to stray to other publishing houses, taking their often substantial numbers of devoted readers with them. I'd had my pen name, Erika Rand, picked out for years. Poll any aspiring romance writer and she'll probably tell you the same thing. In those dark hours, when the prospects of being published seem the bleakest, a catchy pen name, like a good mantra, can ward off all self-doubt.

Lying Eyes was published in January, 1994. Since then, I've had a romance novella published (co-written with my sister under the name Maddie Price), lectured to writer's groups and taught romance writing to adult education classes. In between the public speaking and the collaboration, I've continued to work on my next two novels for Harlequin Intrigue. It's a little easier this time around. This time I have my own editor, some experience under my belt and a better understanding of the publishing world. Still, there are no guarantees in this business. An old saying reminds me that you are only as good as your last book.

Am I up to the challenge?

You bet I am. The first time I walked into a bookstore and saw my romance novel on the shelf, nine months after my editor first phoned me, I fell in love: with the genre of romance, with the challenge of creating a well-crafted story, with the legions of other writers, published and unpublished, who are trying to make a difference with their work in a field that is often disparaged and ridiculed as lucrative but simplistic.

I used to be one of those detractors but I've changed my tune.

Blame it all on romance.

FAITES LA MISE AU POINT

AVEC PHOTO SÉLECTION
LE MAGAZINE QUÉBÉCOIS DE LA PHOTOGRAPHIE

- **DESTINATIONS PHOTO**
- **ÉQUIPEMENT PHOTO**
- **TECHNIQUES PHOTO**
- **IMAGE NUMÉRIQUE**
- **CHAMBRE NOIRE**
- **NATURE EN VUE**
- **PORTFOLIOS**
    - **Images de lecteurs**
    - **Expo**
    - **Galerie**
    - **Tremplin**

SELL YOUR RIGHTS NOT YOUR SOUL!

Nothing causes more confusion, more angst or concern than COPYRIGHT. This article only touches on the subject and is in no way meant to be the definitive guide to copyright. I would highly recommend that all writers, photographers and editors get the following book for their reference shelf. *Canadian Copyright Law* by Lesley Ellen Harris. The newly revised 1995 edition contains information on digital photography and electronic rights. The book includes a copy of the Canadian Copyright Act and a comparison of Canadian and American copyright, which is very helpful.

The Copyright Act protects two kinds of rights: economic rights and moral rights. Economic rights are normally what people refer to when speaking of copyright. Economic rights refer to the right of a copyright owner to reproduce a work or to authorize others to reproduce the work. These are the rights which are exchanged for money. Moral rights protect the reputation and "name" of the creator. Moral rights cannot be exchanged for money nor can they be assigned to anyone else but the creator. Moral rights include such things as using pseudonyms, and changing the look or context of an author's or photographer's work without permission. These rights are going to come into question more with the advent of digital photography and computer manipulation of images.

Although copyright is automatic on creation, you can voluntarily register your work in order to officially establish ownership.

In Canada, it is not legally necessary to place your copyright notice on your articles or photographs, however, if you wish to retain copyright protection under the Universal Copyright Convention (USA, France, Etc.), you should mark your work with the copyright symbol ©, followed by your proper name and the date of first publication. If the work has not yet been published, you can leave the date blank, ie. 19__. Some writers and photographers feel uncomfortable about using a date because it may depreciate the market value of their work. To get around this you can mark the date in Roman numerals (few people will bother to translate). Writers can protect their work and establish copyright by sending themselves a registered letter containing their article, or book. Don't open it when it arrives, and be sure to keep the registration information with the envelope. Keep your registered envelope on file in case you ever need to prove authorship. Only open the registered letter in court, in front of a judge.

After you've done everything you can to protect your work, it's time to get to the business of selling. What rights can you sell, what rights do you wish to sell? Keep in mind that the amount of money you make is directly related to the rights you are selling.

You may divide up and sell the rights to publish or use your work in any number of ways. This includes selling "rights" either in whole or in part. For example the author of a book can sell the rights to publish the entire book, can sell the translation rights for the book, can sell the book chapters separately to magazines, can sell the movie rights, the audio rights, etc. A photographer can sell publication rights and exhibition rights as well.

Territory is also negotiable. For example both photographers and writers could sell rights worldwide or in North America or in Canada. A commonly asked for right is "First North American Serial right" which means the right to publish an article or photograph in a magazine and to be the first in North America to do so. Writers who are good negotiators might be able to sell first Canadian serial rights (English language), and first American serial rights (English language), and still be able to sell rights for French, Spanish etc. etc. Once the "first rights" have been exercised, you can still sell "one-time rights" indefinitely.

Your copyright can extend up to 50 years after your death (it becomes part of your estate). So another part of copyright that is negotiable is "time." A photographer for example can assign "exhibition rights" for a certain length of time.

Your agreement for assignment of rights MUST be in writing.

In the course of compiling this book we talked to thousands of editors across the country. Many of the editors were very professional and were a delight to deal with. It became clear however, that there are also editors out there who are completely unaware that copyright exists, let alone understand the concept of "rights." We ran across editors who regularly receive work from writers who do not expect to be paid. We talked with one editor who was incensed to learn (after he published an article) that the writer wanted to be paid. Our advice is to enclose a cover letter with each article you submit. The cover letter must state the rights you are selling. If you are open to negotiation state that … if you are not, let the editor know your selling price. Don't assume anything. Don't assume that because someone is called an editor they know anything about copyright. We often hear the phrase "buyer beware." In this case I would caution sellers to study up on copyright, understand it as fully as you can, and be prepared to educate and negotiate. Don't give your rights away, and keep everything "professional" which means IN WRITING! Seller beware!

Knowing your rights and learning to negotiate skilfully will enable you to sell an article or photograph indefinitely. If you sell "all rights" you can never again sell that article or photograph. So be careful about what you sell. If someone asks for "all rights" it may be because they are unfamiliar with the other options available. After all if they are publishing a magazine, do they really want the "movie" rights to your article? Do you want to give away "movie" rights or foreign translation rights to your book? Part of being in business is negotiating.

Here are some of the more common rights you might negotiate.

Serial rights refers to a magazine or periodical. Be careful because some editors also use serial to refer to "sister" publication. This may be an issue especially with French and English rights.

First rights mean that the publication is buying the privilege of being the first to publish your article or photos. A commonly asked for combination of rights is "first North American serial rights" which means you are selling the publication the right to be the first to publish your work in a serial (magazine), and that the distribution of the serial is throughout North America.

Exclusive rights refer to a type of market. An example of this may be the calendar market. Selling exclusive rights would prevent you from re-selling the photos to any other publisher for use in a calendar. You could however, sell the photo for use in a text book or magazine.

One-time rights are very desirable for both writers and photographers. It means that the publisher buys the right to publish the work only once. You are free to sell your photos again and again, as long as each time you sell only one-time rights. Though one-time rights really opens up doorways for you, it still pays to be careful. You don't want to antagonize your favourite editor by having the same article, or photo coming out exactly at the same time in a competing publication. If however you have the only photo of an earth shattering news-breaking event, go ahead and make the most of it. Sell it to every newspaper, magazine, tv station you can... just let them know you are doing it!

The sale of *all rights* is particularly common when dealing with "work for hire," and government assignments. The publisher (employer) buys the work and all rights from you and is no longer obligated to pay for subsequent use. You are selling your work completely and unconditionally. We had many magazine editors tell us they wanted to purchase all rights. Our advice is don't do it! First North American serial rights gives them plenty of exclusivity. Some editors assume that if they hire on assignment, they outright own your article or photographs. This is not so ... unless, you sell them all rights or, unless you sign a "work for hire" agreement. Be careful. Some firms have been known to send a cheque with a "work for hire" statement on the back. As soon as you sign the cheque, you've signed the agreement.

The more rights you sell, the higher your price should be. Remember, if you sell all rights you may lose out in the long term so keep this in mind and don't undersell what you've worked so hard to create.

NEGOTIATING IS THE KEY TO SELLING YOUR PHOTOS
by Vince Streano

I sell many of my own stock photos from my office in Anacortes, Washington. Most people are amazed when I tell them my average sale price for the past two years is over $900. I am able to get the prices I do because I do not simply look up a price for a particular stock usage on a chart. First I determine the value my images will have to the client, and the uniqueness my images have in the market place. I then base my negotiations on those decisions. This makes every negotiation I do unique.

Negotiating skills are the most important skills you can learn in addition to you photography skills. Good negotiators can dramatically increase their earning power, while people with poor negotiating skills lose money every day. It's important to think of each and every negotiation as a contest, where both participants can come out winners. It takes a skilful negotiator to achieve this result. In other businesses most negotiations take place face to face. In this type of negotiation you can read you opponents expressions and body language, and gauge their reactions to what you are saying. Unfortunately, most, if not all, negotiating for stock images takes place over the phone. Phone negotiations require special skills in order to be successful.

Many photographers feel they cannot get the same prices for a usage as other "big" name photographers because they do not have the reputation. That may be true in assignment photography. But the beauty of stock photography is everyone is equal, and the strength of the image and the skill of the negotiator are the sole determining factors for the price. It does not matter if you are just beginning, of have been in the business for twenty-five years. If you are a skilful negotiator and the client wants your image, you should get the highest price possible.

Others feel once you have a picture in your files, you should sell it for whatever you can get. A client calls and offers you $100 and even though you know the usage should cost $400 you sell it for less. After all $100 is better than nothing. I do not agree. First you have to be able to recover your expenses on that shoot. If you continue to sell shots for less than the market value, you'll find you won't be able to recover your expenses. Remember there are many shoots that never sell a picture, and you have to recoup those expenses also. Secondly, by lowering your prices you are perpetuating a downward price spiral. The next time the art director calls, he'll only offer $75, then $50. Where would it stop?

WHAT IS THE RIGHT PRICE?

Unfortunately there is no "right price" when it comes to pricing your photos for a certain usage. Prices very depending on who is quoting them, the picture that is being priced, the skill of the negotiator, and the value of the picture to the client. The best price for you is the price that enables you to continue in your business and show a profit.

In a recent survey of nine stock agencies, I asked the price of a picture for a brochure with a print run of 40,000. I wanted a price for a 1.2 page inside and for a cover. Of the nine agencies I surveyed, the prices that were quoted ranged from a high of $670 for the 1.2 page to a low of $275. For the cover, the prices ranged from $1240 down to $800. So you can see pricing is not an exact science.

You just want to make sure your prices are within industry standards, preferably the upper end.

STOCK PHOTOGRAPHY EXPENSES

The first thing you have to know about pricing your work is what it costs you to do business. By knowing what is costs each year to operate your stock business, you can then set goals for your income.

Here is one example of the expenses of a very small stock photography business: Postage and shipping $750; Office supplies $1,500; Stationery and printing $750; Phone $2,400; Photo equipment $3,000; Film and processing (750 rolls) $11,250; Insurance $1,500; Marketing $5,000; Production expenses (models, props) $7,500; Travelling expenses $10,000; Labour $7,500; **TOTAL:** $51,150

At approximately $50,000 in yearly expenses, you need to make 100 sales a year with an average sale of $500 each. Or 290 sales a year with a stock agency at an average of $350 each (assuming you receive 50%), just to break even. Hopefully we're not in this business just to break even.

GENERAL TIPS FOR GETTING STARTED

First, you never want to give a price off the top of your head. If a client calls to ask for a price, get as much information as possible and tell them you will research it and call back. Second, when you do call back, prepare for the negotiation. Know what your price is and be able to defend it. Also know the price you won't go below in case you are forced to go lower. Remember, never lower your price without a good reason. If you do, the next time your client will expect you to lower your price again just because they asked.

Third, remember that the most powerful word you have in any negotiation is "NO". Know what your limits are, and don't go below them. If the picture is unique and powerful, you will get your price. I am not saying you will make a sale every time you negotiate. If you do, you're doing something wrong and selling your work too cheap. I've had many negotiations where the client said they would not pay my asking price, then call back later to buy the usage. Just hang in there and be polite. Believe me, it works.

And last, remember good negotiating techniques take practice. Do some role playing. Find a friend who will act as a client, and practice your negotiating. Before long you will find you are getting prices for your pictures you only dreamed possible.

Vince Streano has been a professional photographer, selling his own stock for over 20 years. In 1992 Vince completed a second term as National President of ASMP. You can get more detailed negotiating tips from Vince in fotoQuote, the computer program for pricing and selling your stock photography. In fotoQuote you also get industry standard prices for over 1500 usages. To order fotoQuote call the Cradoc Corporation toll free at 1-800-679-0202 or order through the Creative Source Bookshop at 1-800-361-2349.

NATIONAL ASSOCIATION fOR PHOTOGRAPHIC ART (N.A.P.A.)

You can be a part of this important Canada-wide organization!

* **SUPPORT** photography as an Art Form.

* **RECEIVE** the latest in News on photography in our two publications, Foto Flash Journal and Camera Canada Magazine.

* **GAIN** recognition through NAPA's Honours and Awards program (ANAPA, FNAPA).

* **ATTEND** our annual, national event, Camera Canada College.

* **EXPLORE** new techniques by enjoying our Slide Sets and Video Library.

* **PARTICIPATE** in our Nature Slide, Pictorial Slide and Print Competitions.

* **ENHANCE** your image quality by allowing us to critique your work within our Novice or Advanced Evaluation Services.

* **ENJOY** our Print and Slide Circuits at your request.

* **DEVELOP** skills through Workshops, Seminars and Field Trips.

JOIN US FOR THE FUN OF IT!

Write to: NAPA HEAD OFFICE, 31858 Hopedale Avenue, Clearbrook, B.C., V2T 2G7   (604) 855-4848

ORGANIZATIONS AND ASSOCIATIONS

FOR WRITERS

The purpose of the following organizations and associations is to encourage writers and photographers by providing a community of people with similar interests, information and feedback. Some of the organizations welcome beginners, others focus only on professionals and their concerns.

ROMANCE WRITERS OF AMERICA
13700 Veterans Memorial, Suite 315
Houston, Texas
USA 77014-1023
Phone: (713) 440-6885
Fax: (713) 440-7510

A worldwide network of more than 7,600 romance writers of varying levels of expertise; from brand new beginners to multi-published New York Times Bestselling authors. RWA is committed to excellence in romantic fiction, to helping writers become published and establish careers in the romance genre, and to providing continuing support for authors within the romance publishing industry. Most members belong to one or more of 130+ chapters across the US and Canada, where they meet and network with other RWA members. *Outreach*, allows those who live too far from a chapter to take part in a network-by-mail. Published authors are invited to belong to the *Published Authors Network* for no additional charge.

An annual conference held each July includes workshops of all levels; opportunities to network with agents, editors and other writers and numerous awards for both published and unpublished authors. Other membership benefits include a Professional Relations Committee, which acts as a "Better Business Bureau" for members to check out agents and editors.

Magazine: *Romance Writers' Report* contains in-depth articles for the professional writer, as well as market news, upcoming contests and conferences and more. Published bimonthly and included with your membership fees.

Membership: Anyone may join.

Local romance organizations include:

Romance Writers of Edmonton
Box 52063 Garneau Post Office
Edmonton, AB
T6G 2T5
New Member Coordinator: Peggy Morgan (403) 439-0398.

Alberta Romance Writers' Association
223-12th Avenue S.W.
Calgary, AB
T2R 0G9

Saskatoon Romance Writers
326 J.J. Thiessen Way
Saskatoon, SA

Greater Vancouver Chapter of the Romance Writers of America
#51 9012 Walnut Grove Drive
Langley, BC
V1M 2K3

CANSCAIP
35 Spadina Road
Toronto, ON
M5R 2S9

Canadian Society of Children's Authors, Illustrators and Performers

CANSCAIP is a society of professionals in the field of children's culture. The aims of the organization are to create awareness of Canadian children's literature; to promote the growth of children's literature; to provide a meeting place for members and friends; to establish communication with publishers and CANSCAIP members; to encourage the development of new writers, illustrators and performers; to publicize the work of members; and to promote English-French and French-English translation of members' works.

This organization participates in children's cultural and creative arts festivals; consults with schools; arranges a travelling art exhibit and an annual workshop.

Newsletter: *CANSCAIP News* published quarterly with profiles of members, new items and market reports.

Other publications include: *CANSCAIP TRAVELS* - a listing of members who are available for visits to libraries and schools.

To become a MEMBER you must be a professional in the field of children's culture; writing, illustrating or performing. Annual fees include a subscription to the newsletter and a free copy of *The CANSCAIP Companion: A Biographical Record of Canadian Children's Authors, Illustrators and Performers*. Anyone interested in Canadian children's literature (teachers, librarians, editors, publishers, beginners) can become a FRIEND and receive a subscription to the newsletter.

OUTDOOR WRITERS OF CANADA
Box 1839
Peterborough, ON
K9J 7X6
(705) 743-7052

The objectives of the Outdoor Writers of Canada are to stimulate interest in and appreciation of the outdoors; to stimulate high standards of craftsmanship among professionals concerned with the portrayal of outdoor life; to cooperate with government agencies and others in support of the best possible use of Canada's natural resources.

Membership includes a newsletter and an annual directory.

PERIODICAL WRITERS ASSOCIATION OF CANADA
54 Wolseley Street, 2nd Floor
Toronto, ON
M5T 1A5
(416) 504-1645
(416) 947-0159 fax

Incorporated in 1976, The Periodical Writers Association of Canada (PWAC) was established to promote and protect the rights of professional freelance journalists.

Membership in this organization includes vital networking opportunities with regular workshops and seminars, and the chance to attend the annual general meeting. An annual Directory of Members and an array of professional development material. A voice in addressing legal, political and business issues of concern to writers as well as the services of the PWAC mediation committees if you have a grievance with a publication. Discount rates on business supplies, membership to CanCopy (the Canadian Copyright Licensing Agency) and tax deductible PWAC membership dues.

Newsletter: A subscription to *PWA Contact*, the writers' grapevine with new markets, awards, grants, writer's events and resources is also included in your membership.

SF CANADA: SPECULATIVE FICTION WRITERS
2nd Floor, 11759 Groat Road
Edmonton, AB
T5M 3K6
(403) 441-6775

SF CANADA is a professional organization of Canadian speculative fiction writers. The goals of the organization are to foster a sense of community and improve communication among SF writers; to lobby on behalf of SF writers in Canada and promote positive social action; to foster the growth of quality writing and to encourage the bilingual translation of speculative writing.

Membership is open to any Canadian writer who has had a novel (not self-published) or at least two pieces of speculative short fiction or three poems professionally published. "Professionally published" is defined as "any work published by an accepted publisher and for which the writer receives cash payment." An "accepted publisher" includes "any periodical with a circulation of at least 300 copies with at least two issues published." Minimum payment of 1¢ per word is required. For scriptwriting, radio drama or theatrical production, the item in question must have been professionally produced or performed. Each membership candidate is assessed individually.

The bimonthly newsletter, *Communiqué*, is available by subscription to non-members. Its companion piece *Top Secret* is for members only.

CANADIAN AUTHORS ASSOCIATION
275 Slater Street Suite 500
Ottawa, ON
K1P 5H9
(613) 233-2846
(613) 235-8237 fax

The Canadian Authors Association (CAA) works with and for beginning writers and seasoned professionals. Branch programs are offered in 16 centres across Canada.

The mandate of the CAA is to help members develop writing skills through workshops and critique sessions; to develop marketing skills through branch and national workshops; to protect the interests of writers through an informal grievance committee; to promote Canadian writing with its awards program and information on contests throughout Canada; and to unite Canadian writers and offer them the opportunity to mingle with peers and learn more about their craft.

Membership includes four issues of *Canadian Author* and *National Newsline*; the recent edition of *The Canadian Writer's Guide*; and national office referrals for members seeking information on editors, workshops, seminars and literary awards.

THE WRITERS' UNION OF CANADA
24 Ryerson Avenue
Toronto, ON
M5T 2P3
(416) 868-6914
(416) 860-0826 fax

The Writers' Union is a national organization of almost 1,000 writers who have published at least one book for the general reading public with a trade or university publisher.

Formed in 1973, the Union is a dynamic organization of professional book writers from all provinces and territories. The union is dedicated to enhancing writers' working conditions, protecting their rights, and enabling them to communicate with their colleagues across the country and beyond.

A wide range of services is included in the membership. Assistance and advice are given on contracts, grievances and other professional matters. There are opportunities to participate in the Union-administered Canada Council National Public Reading Program and the Ontario Arts Council Writers-in-the-Schools Program. The Union has an optional insurance plan and maintains an optional referral list for incoming inquiries. Membership includes union reports and a listing in *Who's Who in The Writers' Union of Canada: A Directory of Members*.

Newsletter: A monthly newsletter and mailing contains up-to-date information on markets, contracts, legislation, lobbying and a members' forum.

THE EDITORS' ASSOCIATION OF CANADA
35 Spadina Road
Toronto, ON
M5R 2S9
(416) 975-1379
(416) 975-1839 fax

The Editors' Association of Canada (EAC) is a national body of both English and French language editors, with more than 700 members. This organization sponsors professional development seminars taught by top editors from across the country; provides networking opportunities; promotes and maintains high standards of editing and publishing in Canada; establishes guidelines to help editors secure fair pay and foster good working conditions; and cooperates with other publishing associations in areas of common concern.

Members include a broad range of people in publishing, from proofreaders, copy editors and researchers to production editors, substantive editors, and desktop publishers.

EAC offers monthly membership meetings in Victoria, Edmonton, Vancouver, Toronto, Ottawa and Montreal; a discount on the volumes of *Meeting Editorial Standards*, a set of editorial self-tests; and discounts on other EAC publications.

To qualify for voting membership, an editor must have completed at least 500 hours of paid editing over the past year. Associate membership, which allows participation in all programs and benefits except for voting privileges, is open to anyone with an interest in editing.

Newsletter: *Active Voice* brings news and reviews to members across the country.

THE WRITERS GUILD OF CANADA
35 McCaul Street, Suite 300
Toronto, ON
M5T 1V7
(416) 979-7907
(416) 979-9273 fax

The Writers Guild of Canada (WCG) is a professional union representing more than 1,200 writers in television, film, video, radio and the recorded media; including dramatic programs of any kind, situation comedies, variety, documentaries, any form of entertainment program, industrials, corporate videos, educational and children's programs.

The Guild was created on April 15th 1991 by vote of the writer members of the Alliance of Canadian Cinema, Television and Radio Artists (ACTRA). The ACTRA Alliance now consists of three Members - the Writers Guild of Canada, the ACTRA Performers Guild and the ACTRA Media Guild.

WCG membership provides industry-standard writing contracts; helps collect script fees and royalties; resolves disputes over working conditions and writing credits; organizes professional activities; lobbies governments on behalf of writers; provides copyright information and a script registration service; publishes the *WCG News*, a quarterly newsletter; and offers insurance and RRSP plans. Writers become eligible to join the WGC on signing a writing contract under one of the Guild's collective agreements.

THE FEDERATION OF BRITISH COLUMBIA WRITERS
Box 2206
Vancouver, BC   V6B 3W2
(604) 683-2057
(604) 683-8269 fax

If you are a writer in British Columbia you need the Federation of BC Writers - and we need you. The Federation of BC Writers is a non-profit organization of professional and emerging writers of all genres. We are governed by a board of directors elected from around the province. As BC's largest writer's organization, our mandate is to service the needs of established and emerging writers in the province. The Federation helps to improve working conditions and expand support programs for writers. We provide members with up-to-date information that helps them find the largest audience for their work.

The Federation keeps you in touch with your writing colleagues across the province. We have current information on federal, provincial and municipal events of importance to writers.

Newsletter: As a member you recieve *Wordworks*, our quarterly newsletter, full of the latest information about writer's markets, political trends, awards, literary activities and marketing tips.

SASKATCHEWAN WRITERS GUILD
Box 3986
Regina, SK
S4P 3R9
(306) 757-6310
(306) 565-8554 fax

Founded in 1969, the Saskatchewan Writers Guild (SWG) is a province-wide organization representing writers in all disciplines and at all levels of development. It is one of the largest writers organizations in the country, with a membership of over 700.

The Guild works to foster excellence in writing and to promote public awareness of Saskatchewan literature. It acts as an advocate for writers, encourages the development of young writers and strives to improve public access to Saskatchewan writers and their work.

Membership provides many programs and workshops, awards and scholarships, and indispensable information found in various publication including *Freelance*, the monthly newsmagazine, *Grain*, an international literary journal and *WindScript*, the best of Saskatchewan high school students' poems, stories and visual art. Membership is open to all writers, teachers, librarians, publishers, booksellers, students and others with an interest in Saskatchewan literature.

ALBERTA CHRISTIAN WRITERS' FELLOWSHIP
Marcia Laycock
4217 - 46 Street
Ponoka, AB T4J 1C1

The ACWF is an organization formed for the encouragement of better writing, and for the fellowship of Christian writers throughout Alberta.

The ACWF day workshop in the spring of each year allows writers to meet and talk with other Christians who share their desire to use the writing gift to glorify God.

The annual ACWF fall conference features some of the best Christian writers and speakers in North America. Past speakers have included Janette Oke, Bernard Palmer and Maxine Hancock.

Membership includes a quarterly newsletter *Fellowscript,* full of news and writing tips. Membership is $30 per year, and includes special discounts on ACWF workshops and conferences.

THE WRITERS' FEDERATION OF NEW BRUNSWICK
Box 37, Station A
103 Church Street
Fredericton, NB
E3B 4Y2
(506) 459-7228

The Writers' Federation of New Brunswick was founded in 1983 to promote and publicly recognize the works of New Brunswick writers while at the same time promoting a sense of camaraderie. The aim of the Federation is to assist members at all stages of their development by providing a writers' newsletter, writers-in-residence, information referral and manuscript readings.

Free artistic expression is encouraged through various activities: readings, workshops and literary salons, a literary competition, book launchings, support of a Writers in Schools Programme, and participation in National Book Festival Week.

A variety of membership options from the Basic Annual Membership to the Lifetime Member are available to anyone who has an interest in writing and supports the aims of the Federation.

Newsletter: Members receive *Writers News*, published in co-operation with the Writers' Federation of Nova Scotia, and *The New Brunswick ink*, the official membership newsletter.

WRITERS' ALLIANCE OF NEWFOUNDLAND AND LABRADOR
Box 2681
St. John's, NF A1C 5M5
(709) 739-5215

The Writers' Alliance of Newfoundland and Labrador serves the needs of writers in the territory, and develops and promotes the role of writers in society. With a membership of over 160 members its aims are to create links among the writers of Newfoundland and Labrador; to promote freedom of expression and fight censorship in the province; to lobby all levels of government on behalf of writers; to foster writing through workshops, meetings and readings; to establish a liaison with educational institutions to promote creative writing programs; to draw up guidelines and circulate information on contracts, marketing and remuneration for writers; and to keep writers informed about the provincial and national award-granting bodies.

Members have access to various resources and facilities; can attend workshops, local readings and conferences on various writing genres; obtain free information on contracts, publishing etc.; and receive a *Resource Manual for Writers* as well as a free listing in the *WANL Freelance* brochure distributed to prospective employers of freelance writers.

Newsletter: Membership includes a subscription to the newsletter *Word*.

THE WRITERS' FEDERATION OF NOVA SCOTIA
Suite 901, 1809 Barrington Street
Halifax, NS
B3J 3K8
(902) 423-8116
(902) 422-0881 fax

The Writer's Federation of Nova Scotia (WFNS) was established in 1975 to foster creative writing and the profession of writing in Nova Scotia; to provide advice and assistance to writers at all stages of their careers; to encourage greater public recognition of Nova Scotia writers and their achievements; and to enhance the literary arts in our regional and national culture.

The Federation offers its members the fellowship of other writers across Canada and a national and local forum for professional discussion. A number of specific professional services includes: help with contracts; a monthly newsletter; touring opportunities; volunteer group life and health insurance; copies of reports and publications dealing with such topics as literary estates and archives, income tax law, literary agent agreements, grants and competition, anthology rates, and a model trade book contract. These publications are also available to non-members; a price list is available upon request. Membership is open to anyone who writes.

Newsletter: A subscription to *Eastword* is included in the membership fee.

ISLAND WRITERS' ASSOCIATION
Box 1204
Charlottetown, PEI
C1A 7M8
Contact: Julie Wilson
(902) 566-9748

A small local and informal group of writers who meet 4 to 5 times a year. The group has been in existence for over 15 years. Members are professional writers. Occasionally puts on writing workshops.

THE WRITERS GUILD OF ALBERTA
3rd Floor, Percy Page Centre
11759 Groat Road
Edmonton, AB
T5M 3K6
(403) 422-8174

The Writers Guild of Alberta was formed in 1980 to provide a meeting ground and collective voice for the writers of Alberta. Membership includes 700 writers from every genre and at every level of expertise. The Guild acts as a strong representative voice with the public and with every level of government. The Guild has helped give Alberta writers a sense of unity and has contributed to an awareness of community with other writers' organizations across the country.

Membership includes reduced rates for manuscript reading service; assurance that your views and interests are represented to all government and community levels; camaraderie and support of other writers; reduced rates for workshops; access to resource centres and many other benefits.

Newsletter: Members receive a one year subscription to the *Westword* newsletter with information on markets, literary events, books released, awards etc.

THE MANITOBA WRITERS' GUILD
206-100 Arthur Street
Winnipeg, MB
R3B 1H3
(204) 942-6134

The Manitoba Writers' Guild was inaugurated in August 1981 as a grassroots organization created for, and by, Manitoba writers of all disciplines and at every level of writing. The Guild has grown to over 400 members and continues to expand services and programming to find, develop, and promote literary talent across the province.

The primary aim of the Guild is to promote and advance the art of writing, in all its forms, in the province of Manitoba.

Membership programs and services include: access to the Mentor Program where promising new writers are teamed with experienced mentors; *The Writers' Handbook*, a comprehensive manual offering concise information, articles and advice from some of Manitoba's most celebrated authors; The Manitoba Workshop series consisting of one-day sessions on various topics such as short story development and narrative strategies; nominal rental of studio space; a Reading Series showcasing local writers and the Annual Literary Conference; access to the Writers' Resource Centre and numerous other offerings.

Newsletter: Members receive *WordWrap*, a Guild newsletter filled with information about copyright, markets, competitions and events news.

FOR PHOTOGRAPHERS

CANADIAN ASSOCIATION OF PHOTOGRAPHERS & ILLUSTRATORS IN COMMUNICATION (CAPIC)
100 Broadview Ave. Suite 322
Toronto, ON
M4M 2E8
Phone: (416) 462-3700
Fax: (416) 462-3678

A national association dedicated to promoting the interests of photographers and illustrators in the communication arts industry. Works at the standardization of business practices, copyright concerns, professional standards and support services. Promotes visual excellence and a sense of fellowship among members.

Local chapters are located in Vancouver, Calgary, Toronto, Ottawa, Montreal and Halifax.

NATIONAL ASSOCIATION FOR PHOTOGRAPHIC ART
31858 Hopedale Avenue
Clearbook, BC
V2T 2G7
(604) 855-4848

The National Association for Photographic Art (NAPA) is a Canadian-based forum for both amateur and professional photographers who wish to share their views and insights with others both locally and across the country. NAPA works to promote photography as an art form to the general public. Local chapters are located throughout Canada.

Benefits of membership include *Foto Flash*, a quarterly newsletter; *Camera Canada Magazine*, a publication of fine photographic art; access to slide sets with written commentary for home viewing and study; loans from the video library on a wide range of photographic topics selected to help you improve your enjoyment of photography; evaluations of photographs for both novice and experienced photographers.

NAPA also hosts competitions, workshops, field trips, and instructional programs in the form of Camera Canada College.

Memberships are available to individuals, families, groups, camera clubs, libraries and photo businesses.

PROFESSIONAL PHOTOGRAPHERS OF CANADA
Box 2740
St. Mary, ON
N4X 1A5
Phone/Fax: (819) 643-5177

A national organization of professional photographers. Chapters across Canada meet regularly to discuss business related issues. Members receive a magazine, annual directory and may attend workshops, seminars and an annual conference.

FREELANCERS' PRESS ASSOCIATION
3946 Steeles Avenue East
RR#8 Brampton, ON
L6T 3Y7
(905) 793-9554
(905) 793-7636 fax

Established in 1986 for the purpose of helping talented amateur photographers turn professional, and then helping those new professionals survive, and thrive, in the competitive world of professional photography. We are an alliance of amateur and working professional photographers united in our goals of earning income, while building our reputations and establishing our credibility as full or part-time freelancers.

Membership includes the *Freelancer* newsletter 10 times a year. The newsletter is packed with proven ideas, hints and tips and is specifically written to help its readers turn their photograph skills into income and photo credits.

Photographers in, or visiting the Toronto area, can attend the regular working breakfasts. Call (905) 793-9554 to book a seat.

Send $2.00 for an information package.

GUILFOYLE REPORT
AG Editions Inc.
41 Union Square West #523
New York, NY 10003
(212) 929-0959

The Guilfoyle Report is a marketing newsletter for nature photographers. Each issue of the report features current photo wants, new markets and future trends. Includes publication profiles, industry news, address and personnel changes. Issued 10 times a year. Edited by Ann Guilfoyle, a respected authority on the business of nature photography and a former editor/founder of *Audubon*.

AG Editions also publishes *The Green Book* and *The Blue Book* directories of stock photography.

PHOTOSOURCE INTERNATIONAL
Pine Lake Farm
Osceola, WI 54020 USA
Phone: (715) 248-3800
Fax: (715) 248-7394
Credit Card Order Desk: 1-800-624-0266

Photosource International publishes a number of newsletters aimed at stock photographers. The newsletters are available in hard copy, by fax or by computer modem. If you are serious about selling your work across North America call for their information package.

PhotoLetter: Monthly market listings.
PhotoMarket: Twice a month listings available by fax or modem.
PhotoBulletin: Weekly market service. Professional photographers must apply.
PhotoStockNotes: Monthly newsletter on the stock photo industry.

BOOK RESOURCES FOR WRITERS AND PHOTOGRAPHERS

The following books will be of interest to writers and photographers at all levels of experience. They may be available through your local library or book store. They are also available through the Creative Source Bookshop, a Canadian mail-order bookshop catering to writers, photographers and artists. A free catalogue of hundreds of writing and photography books is available by phoning 1-800-361-2349.

HOW TO OPEN AND OPERATE A HOME-BASED PHOTOGRAPHY BUSINESS by Ken Oberrecht. This thorough and informative book discusses every aspect of what it takes to run a successful home-based business. The author carefully details all the considerations that must be addressed by the amateur photographer who wants to turn pro. This book is jam packed with reality based information and is a must for anyone considering photography as a part-time or full-time business. #P-0565

PRICING PHOTOGRAPHY by Michael Heron & David MacTavish. A guide to determining what your photography is worth and getting a fair price for it. Over 50 pages of clear, easy-to-read pricing charts for assignment and stock photography. The authors remove the cloak of mystery that surrounds pricing and negotiating your photography fees. The authors cover negotiating principles, factors that enter into pricing assignments or stock photography. They show you how to write a usage rights statement, how to do assignment price calculations, and how to price stock. They also give you pricing charts that guide you in setting your own prices depending on your level of experience, reputation, and geographical location. #P-507

BUSINESS AND LEGAL FORMS FOR PHOTOGRAPHERS by Ted Crawford. Here is a complete set of business and legal forms to meet every need as well as advice on how to negotiate and standard contractual provisions. Unique negotiation checklists guide the photographers to the best deal - even if the other party has drafted the contract! Included are an estimate form, confirmation of assignment, invoice, agency contract, collaboration agreement, privacy release, property release, permission form, lecture agreement, contracts for weddings and portraits, contracts for sales through a gallery, licensing agreements, stock photography contracts, transfers of copyright and more. If you've ever had questions about how to protect yourself legally, this book will probably cover it!   #P0439

PHOTO RELEASE CARDS These handy 3" x 5" cards are perfect for carrying around in your camera bag or pocket. When you get home, or to the office, you can simply file them by number, date or the subject's last name. The cards come in packages of 100 and contain an easy to read and non-threatening photo release that will suffice for most occasions including editorial use. The release is on one side, on the opposite side is room for your descriptive and filing information. Note: If you work with professional models, you will need a more comprehensive contract. #P-0300

THE PERFECT PORTFOLIO by Henriette Brackman. A finely tailored portfolio is the most important sales tool for anyone who wants to sell his or her photographs. The author provides step-by-step instructions for creating a personal portfolio that will start your career off right and keep it going. Henrietta Brackman is a photographer's consultant who specializes in portfolio planning. The book includes chapters on developing a powerful portfolio; analyzing the markets and where you fit; understanding how clients think; the best form of presentation; how to rise above your competition; choosing your best pictures; choosing your most saleable pictures; and arranging your portfolio for flow, sequences, transitions and pacing. The entire book is heavily illustrated with examples of how to do it and how not to do it ... and why. #P-0423

TRAVEL WRITING AND PHOTOGRAPHY Ann and Carl Purcell are seasoned travel writers and photographers, who now share their experiences with you. They show how you can travel the world and get paid for it! From where to find saleable ideas and how to sell them ... to the getting started basics, their advice is based on years of experience in the field. They talk about the mechanics of travelling with equipment, tell you where and how to get information and the process of designing a well laid out story. And they provide you with sample articles and photos ... A well thought-out and laid out book for those with a spirit of adventure. #P-0277

SHOOTING FOR STOCK by George Schaub. All about how to create, organize and market photographs that will sell again and again. A comprehensive book on taking photos of everyday activities and earning top dollars selling them. Schaub covers the stock business starting from how to organize your photo files and edit your own work to setting prices. He talks about all the different markets (editorial, trade and speciality publications; consumer magazines; textbooks; greeting cards; and advertising) and tells you what they want and how to approach them. Best of all he shows you (photos) what a submission package looks like; tells you what different rights you can sell; gives you examples of submission forms and invoices; and shows how to caption and label your photos for submission. #P-0481

PHOTOGRAPHING PEOPLE FOR STOCK: HOW TO TAKE PICTURES THAT SELL AGAIN AND AGAIN by Nancy Brown. Nancy Brown is one of the most profitable stock shooters for one of the world's largest stock photo agencies. In this book, the first to focus exclusively on photographing people for stock, she reveals the secrets of her success and shows how anyone can turn a flair for capturing people on film into a lucrative career. Brown provides a richly illustrated catalogue of the most popular categories of "people stock": lifestyle images, simple head shots, mood pictures, health and beauty shots, travel pictures and photos of children and babies. She explains how to style for European as well as North American markets. If you want to really make money in stock photography, you should be shooting people ... this book tells you why and how. #P-475

STOCK PHOTOGRAPHY; THE COMPLETE GUIDE by Ann and Carl Purcell. Two highly successful stock photographers talk about a wide range of topics including: what kind of money photographers can expect to make from stock; how to determine what is a good stock picture; model releases, submission forms and holding fees; differences between editorial and advertising style; stock photo composition; how to edit, caption and organize slides into categories; new technology;

copyright issues and protecting against misuse of your images. Illustrated with dozens of examples of the author's fabulous photos. #P-0485

THE PROFESSIONAL PHOTOGRAPHER'S GUIDE TO SHOOTING AND SELLING NATURE & WILDLIFE PHOTOS by Jim Zucherman. This book, consisting of over 250 full-colour photos shows aspiring nature and wildlife photographers how to succeed in the market place. Each photo is captioned with detailed explanations of where it was shot, how it was shot, and the easiest way for the reader to achieve the same effects. Photographers will learn: what the most popular subjects are and why; how to work with zoo curators, biologists and specialists; how to make a "powerful presentation" including how to write query letters, advice on equipment and how to set up a portfolio, and detailed information on appropriate markets for nature photos. #P-0255

SELL & RE-SELL YOUR PHOTOS is an industry classic! This highly recommended book by Rohn Engh has been one of my bibles for years and should be on your own bookshelf now! Engh helps photographers sell photographs by mail to every type of market. He begins with the premise that you should and have to specialize, from there he helps you develop a marketing plan for your market speciality. The book also includes useful information about pricing, and how to organize yourself and your photos. Illustrations include photos that have been sold dozens ... even hundreds of times. Highly recommended. # P-0217

HOW TO SHOOT STOCK PHOTOS THAT SELL is written by Michael Heron, a photographer who runs her own stock business and who is represented by a variety of international stock agencies. Numerous saleable subjects for stock photography are ignored, even by the pros. The stock assignments in this book are designed to help photographers fill those gaps by building an integrated file of currently unavailable stock subjects. This book also includes information on the technical aspects of stock, how to plan and produce a shoot, selling stock to an agency, marketing and promotion, legal protection and a list of organizations, workshops and seminars. Highly recommended. #P-0215

PUBLISHING YOUR ART AS CARDS, POSTERS AND CALENDARS by Harold Davis. This is the second edition of the only book we have seen to cover the production and publishing of the paper-products market: cards, posters and calendars. Inside you will find information on: the economics of self-publishing; the print reproduction process; dealing with printers; markets; creating a publication design; how to submit work to other publishers; managing your business; creating successful imagery; finding a publisher; finding sales reps and much, much more. *Publishing Your Art as Cards, Posters and Calendars* is a complete guide to creating, designing and marketing art. It provides a detailed road map for both the self-publisher and for those who choose to have their work published by others. #P-0577

CANADIAN COPYRIGHT LAW by Lesley Harris.
A guide for writer's, musicians, visual artists, filmmakers, publishers, editors, teachers, librarians, students, lawyers and business people. If you create a work (a written document, a recording, a sketch, a photograph), you must know how your work can be legally protected. If you use a work created by someone else

(photocopy it, videotape it etc.) you must ensure that your use complies with copyright law. **Canadian Copyright Law** discusses the current copyright law, in everyday language, including its fundamental principles, the legal rights it protects, and the obligations it creates. This second edition also includes issues related to multimedia works and the Internet. It covers revisions to the Canadian Copyright Act, NAFTA and GATT, intellectual property, moral rights and Cancopy. **#W-0473**

HOW TO OPEN AND OPERATE A HOME-BASED WRITING BUSINESS by Lucy V. Parker. With hands-on techniques and a friendly, personal approach, this indispensable guide brings out the business genius in writers, designers, and other creative types. The author tells you how to unearth the hidden market in local, everyday jobs, along with a list of the types of clients who buy writing and desktop design services in most communities. Detailed chapters on marketing and selling help demystify these vital functions. Aspiring entrepreneurs will also find sound advice on: dovetailing personal skills with those of colleagues to offer clients a full desktop publishing package; purchasing equipment; obtaining licenses and dealing with tax and insurance considerations; and determining pricing. The author works out of her home office in Orange, California. **#W-0449**

HOW TO MAKE MONEY FROM FREELANCE WRITING by Andrew Crofts. The author will tell you: how to get started; what to write about; how to sell what you've written; how to get commissioned; how to interview people for articles and how to overcome the blocks and barriers to becoming a great freelance writer. The book covers all aspects of writing - fiction, short stories, travel, newspaper and magazine journalism, TV and radio scripts and ghostwriting. **#W-0407**

COMPLETE GUIDE TO SELF-PUBLISHING by Tom & Marilyn Ross. 3RD EDITION completely revised, expanded and updated. Writers who want full control over their careers can get it by self-publishing. This book tells you how. Writers will be given an insight into the publishing industry and how it works ... so that they can make it work for them. Includes: step-by-step guidance on every aspect of publishing and marketing a book; current advice for using a computer to cut costs and save time; production tips that can halve design and printing costs; proven sales letters, cover designs, catalogue sheets and forms; proven marketing strategies for publicity, advertising and sales. Includes a Canadian resource section. **#W-0359**

HOW TO WRITE AND SELL CHILDREN'S PICTURE BOOKS by Jean E. Karl. Step-by-step Jean Karl takes you through the process of penning and publishing a picture book. A real writer's guide, with insight on what makes a picture book good and how to put stories on paper - whether they're retellings of wonderful old tales or splendid new yarns, nonfiction or poetry. Packed with advice that will help you bring your ideas to life and put big smiles on little faces. Also contains advice on how to find the right publishers, how to approach them, how not to approach them, and what happens then. **#W-0451**

MAGAZINE WRITING THAT SELLS by Don McKinney. Through McKinney's solid, clear teaching and examples by top-notch writers, you will learn how to: uncover the best ideas and match them with right magazines; write an irresistible query letter sure to catch the editor's attention; conduct an interview and gather facts from other sources (including on-line and CD-ROM); write evocative articles, complete with reader-grabbing leads, powerful endings and smooth transitions. Includes an inspiring chapter of successful writers and their stories and a chapter where leading editors reveal what they expect. #W-0455

HOW TO WRITE A BOOK PROPOSAL by Michael Larsen. The author gives you a clear, thorough explanation of the kinds of book proposals writers should submit and how to determine which publishers to submit to. Larsen provides samples, addresses for further help and a "hot tips" section. #W-0437

THE BUSINESS OF WRITING: The Canadian Guide for Writers and Editors by Dyanne Rivers. Writing and editing is a business, just like any other. Making a living from your efforts is far more satisfying than starving in a garret and writing by candlelight! *The Business of Writing* offers a no-nonsense approach to the practical and business aspects of freelance writing and editing in Canada. It guides the novice freelancer through self-promotion; accounting; bookkeeping; writing proposals and query letters; making contracts; negotiating prices and delivering your work on time and on budget. One of the oh-so-few Canadian books on writing! #W-0475

INSIDER'S GUIDE TO BOOK EDITORS, PUBLISHERS AND LITERARY AGENTS by Jeff Herman. Gives authors the inside scoop on the names and interest areas of acquisition editors. This vital information makes all the difference when submitting a book proposal to the American markets. Now in its fourth edition, this book has been fully revised to keep on top of the rapidly changing publishing world. Who moved where, and who is gone for good - it's all here in one big volume. The author owns a literary agency in New York City. #W-0479

HOW TO MAKE $50,000 A YEAR OR MORE AS A FREE-LANCE BUSINESS WRITER by Paul D. Davis. The business of business writing is a well-kept secret, and the unknown group of writers who make big sums of money doing it would certainly prefer it stays that way! Fortunately, this nuts-and-bolts guide will teach aspiring business writers everything they need to know to get started. Beginning with a clear explanation of what a business writer does, Davis goes on to explain how to find business, keep clients happy, and manage time effectively. Davis also outlines the four most common mistakes make by novice business writers and how to avoid them. #W-0483

HOW TO SELL 75% OF YOUR FREELANCE WRITING by Gordon Burgett. Amateurs write, then try to sell. Professionals sell before they write. This is just one of the truths about publishing revealed in this comprehensive book on the art of getting published repeatedly and successfully. Burgett teaches the reader how to turn a frustrating avocation into a lucrative profession. Among the areas covered are: choosing and defining a topic; conducting a feasibility study; dealing with copyrights and other rights; making multiple sales through reprints, rewrites, mixed markets and overseas sales. #W-0485

NATIONAL WRITERS UNION GUIDE TO FREELANCE RATES & STANDARD PRACTICE by the American National Writers Union. The first professional writers' guide based on an independent survey of working writers, as well as interviews with agents, editors and publishers. This book offers a real-life look at fees, contracts and working conditions, alongside fair and clear recommendations tailored to six major freelance markets: journalism; books; technical writing; corporate communications; small press magazines; academic writing. Also explores such issues as copyright in the electronic future and censorship. The National Writers Union has 4,000 members and twelve local chapters throughout the U.S. It is committed to protecting the rights and improving the economic conditions of freelance writers. If you are selling work in the US this is a valuable resource. #W-0467

SHIFT YOUR WRITING CAREER INTO HIGH GEAR by Gene Perret. Teaches writers to expand their writing horizons, capitalize on previous sales and become versatile, well-rounded and successful writers. This practical yet inspirational guide is divided into three major sections: "Look to Yourself" - encourages you to investigate your own attitudes and expectations; "Look to Your Writing" - what you can learn from your past to influence future sales ... how can you improve your quality and quantity?; "Look to Your Marketing" covers how to promote and sell your work, stimulate old markets and discover new ones. #W-0381

BUSINESS AND LEGAL FORMS FOR AUTHORS AND SELF-PUBLISHERS by Tad Crawford. This is a complete set of business and legal forms, including sample contracts, for your every need as an author or self-publisher. You'll find one copy each of 17 different forms, each with step-by-step instructions on how to fill it out. You'll also find perforated tear-out pages of each form for your own personal use. A few of the forms this success kit contains includes: estimate forms; contract with a literary agent; book publishing contract; collaboration agreement; privacy release; permission to use copyrighted work form; nondisclosure agreement for submitting ideas; contract with a book designer; contract with a printer; and transfer of copyright. #W-0357

HOW TO WRITE IRRESISTIBLE QUERY LETTERS by Lisa Collier Cool. A good query letter sent to the right editor will not only increase your chances of a sale - it's also the most effective way to pre-sell your idea. That way you can write your article or nonfiction book with the confidence of knowing it's good, it's wanted and it's going to be paid for and published! Practical advice on how to craft powerfully persuasive letters that connect with an editor's imagination - and sell your work. Learn how to: recognize, develop, target and pre-sell your ideas; select the strongest slant for your book or article; hook an editor with a tantalizing lead; shape a summary that stokes the editor's desire to buy; rejection-proof your query by weeding out subtle mistakes that can sabotage a sale; sell yourself as *the writer* for the subject. Lots of good examples! #W-0311

MAGAZINES

If you can think of a subject, there's likely to be a magazine to go along with it. As you look though the hundreds of magazine listings you'll find everything from computers and technology to living off the land and gardening without chemicals. Consumer magazines are becoming more diversified with Computer magazines as the successful new kids on the block and the old standbys ... gardening, house decorating, women's and men's magazines. Unless you visit your local library you may never see the diversity of trade magazines published for hundreds of special interest groups, industry groups and associations.

If you are going to be successful at selling your writing or photography to magazines you must approach them professionally. Never approach an editor without first having examined several back copies of the magazine. When you make a query you are asking the editor for his or her time. You are asking them to take the time to talk to you or read and consider your query. Don't expect them to do your homework for you. Read the publication. Examine it for editorial focus, for tone and for content level. Do word counts on the articles. Figure out who the audience is.

Don't forget about your "own back yard." Write about and photograph what you are familiar with. If you work in the construction industry, yes it's great to get out into nature and commune with the bears, but you may be ignoring all the construction related magazines and markets. Your career could be positioning you as an industry writer or photographer and conversely, your industry writing or photography could be helping you with your career.

Writers and photographers who query inappropriately, are not only wasting their time and setting themselves up for automatic rejection, they are making it harder for those that follow. It is sometimes faster and easier to write the entire article than it is to write a query. The fact is most editors do not have time to read entire articles. They want you to sum things up in a nice, tidy, one-page query that tells them what the article is about, why they should care and what your qualifications for writing the article are. If you are unsure about what a query is, or what its purpose is, ask people in your writing or photo group to help you, or get one or more of the marketing books on query letters. (see the resource section).

There are over a thousand Canadian magazine markets. Some of them do not want to be approached. We've let you know where the "no markets" and "so, so markets" are, so you don't waste your time or money. Once you've chosen a market, and researched it thoroughly, make your pitch and don't get discouraged. Editors are busy people, and often their priorities are not your priorities. One of the articles in this book was written by a writer who queried well over 18 months ago! The query was short, it was professional, it was accompanied by non-returnable photo samples and it quietly stayed in the filing cabinet until needed.

Professionalism shows; once a query has been accepted be sure you can follow through with what you promised, when you promised it. Editors love to find writers they can count on. If you prove yourself to be a good writer, work professionally and keep your time commitments, editors will be only too happy to take your phone calls, put your query on top of the stack, and make you one of their regulars.

ABILITIES
444 Yonge Street
Toronto, ON M5B 2H4

DESCRIPTION: Published by Canadian Abilities Foundation. Lifestyle magazine for people with disabilities. Published quarterly. Articles include products, sports, education, travel, health and more.

ABOVE AND BEYOND
Box 2348
Yellowknife, NT X1A 2P7

PHONE: (403) 873-2299
FAX: (403) 873-2295

CONTACT: Jake Ootes **DESCRIPTION:** Published by Jake Ootes. Circulation 30,000. Magazine focuses on the Arctic, NWT, Northern Quebec and Greenland. Full-colour in-flight magazine, published quarterly. Established in 1988.
WRITERS: 20% freelance written. Purchases approximately 8 articles per year. Pays 20¢ per word for articles no more than 1,500 words. Byline given. Writers are not hired on assignment. Send completed articles on spec. Guidelines are available.
PHOTOGRAPHERS: We prefer text/photo packages.
NOTES: Purchases one-time rights. Returns unsolicited materials with a SASE. Does not consider previously published work or simultaneous submissions. Sample copies of this publication are available for $14.

ACADIENSIS: JOURNAL OF THE HISTORY OF THE ATLANTIC REGION
Box 4400, University of New Brunswick
Fredericton, NB E3B 5A3

PHONE: (506) 453-4978
FAX: (506) 453-4599

CONTACT: Gail Campbell, Editor **DESCRIPTION:** Published by University of New Brunswick. Circulation 850. Published twice a year in English and in French. Articles include: academic research, review articles, documents, and notes. Established in 1971.
WRITERS: Unable to pay for articles but inquiries welcome.
PHOTOGRAPHERS: Photography is not used.

THE ACCOMMODATOR
1520 Trinity Drive, Suites 11 & 12
Mississauga, ON L5T 1N9

NOTES: Could not locate.

ACHIEVING A HEALTHY ENVIRONMENT
311 Richmond Road #200
Ottawa, ON K1Z 6X3

PHONE: (613) 728-2730
FAX: (613) 725-9855

CONTACT: Robert Smith, Editor **DESCRIPTION:** Published by O'Brian Publishing. Circulation 1,300,000. Published quarterly.

ACHIEVING HEALTH: NO LONGER PUBLISHED

ACTIF
4200 boul St Laurent #510
Montreal, PQ H2W 2R2

PHONE: (514) 843-9191
FAX: (514) 843-3604

CONTACT: Stéphane Leroy, Editor **DESCRIPTION:** Published by Les Editions Edibec Inc. French publication containing articles which clearly and easily explain the law to citizens. Published 11 times a year. Established in 1988.
WRITERS: Writers are usually lawyers or notaries.
PHOTOGRAPHERS: Purchases some photography from stock.

THE ACTIVE GENERATION
Box 1600
Bracebridge, ON P1L 1V6

PHONE: (705) 645-4463
FAX: (705) 645-3928

CONTACT: Dave Opavsky, Editor **DESCRIPTION:** Published by Muskoka Publications Group Inc. Circulation 13,100. Seniors paper published 6 times a year. Established in 1989.

L'ACTUALITE
1001, boul. de Maisonneauve Ouest
11th Floor
Montreal, PQ H3A 3E1

PHONE: (514) 845-5141
FAX: (514) 845-3879

CONTACT: Jean Paré **DESCRIPTION:** Circulation 219,000. French language general interest magazine; public affairs, economics, architecture, arts, trends. A mirror of French Canadian Society. This publication offers a global perspective on events and newsmakers. Published 20 times a year. Established in 1976.
WRITERS: "We do purchase freelance. Write to the editor and provide an outline. The minimum pay rate is $80-100 per page."
PHOTOGRAPHERS: "Contact the artistic director, Jocelyne Fournel." Hires on assignment and buys from stock. Uses approximately 50 photos per issue, buys 1,000 per year. 50% are assigned to freelancers, 50% are purchased from stock, 5% are purchased as part of a text/photo package. Pays: $80-125 for b&w, $100 minimum for colour, $125 minimum (per photo) for text/photo package. Model releases and captions required. To make contact send subject list - IMPORTANT. Also send sample portfolio. This will be kept on file for possible assignments. Previously published work and simultaneous submissions considered. Photo guidelines are available. b&w: 8x10 glossy prints. Colour: 35mm, 2¼x2¼, 4x5 and 8x10 transparencies, and 8x10 prints. Credit line is given. "Photographers are assigned by the photo editor according to the type of article and how it is to be played. We can easily identify pictures that are taken in USA. We prefer not to include these shots in our magazine."
NOTES: Purchases first North American serial rights. Copies are available on newsstands.

ACTUALITE CANADA
366 Adelaide Street #606
Toronto, ON M5V 1R9

PHONE: (416) 599-9900
FAX: (416) 599-9700

CONTACT: Linda Kroboth, Editor **DESCRIPTION:** Published by News Canada Inc. Circulation 1,250 . "We are a media news service publication distributed to newspaper editors." Published monthly. Established in 1981.

NOTES: "Everything is done in-house and all of the copy and photos are supplied by our clients."

L'ACTUALITE MEDICALE
1001 boul. de Maisonneuve Ouest #1001
Montreal, PQ H3A 3E1

PHONE: (514) 843-2542
FAX: (514) 845-2063

CONTACT: Daniéle Rudel-Tessier **DESCRIPTION:** Published by Jacques Lafontaine. Circulation 18,000. French publication serving the medical profession with clinical news and columns on lifestyle, management and economy. Issued 44 times a year. Established in 1980.

L'ACTUALITE PHARMACEUTIQUE
1001 boul. de Maisonneuve Ouest #1000
Montreal, PQ H3A 3E1

PHONE: (514) 843-2542
FAX: (514) 845-2063

CONTACT: Daniéle Rudel-Tessier **DESCRIPTION:** Published by Chantal Goudreau. Circulation 5,600. French language publication. Published monthly and sent to all Quebec pharmacists. Covers professional news, reports on legal changes, new merchandising techniques etc. Established in 1993.

L'ACTUEL
1043 Tiffin
Lonqueuil, PQ J4P 3G7

PHONE: (514) 442-3983
FAX: (514) 442-4363

CONTACT: Suzanne Paquim **DESCRIPTION:** French language publication. Published 7 times a year. Established in 1990.

ACUMEN MAGAZINE
111 Avenue Road
Toronto, ON M5R 3J8

PHONE: (416) 962-9184
FAX: (416) 962-2380

CONTACT: Kathleen Hurd, Editor **DESCRIPTION:** Circulation 120,00. "A business magazine for business men who travel a fair amount."
NOTES: "We have been so totally overwhelmed with people sending work to us that we have a very limited use for freelance material now. That includes both writing and photography. If someone is to contact me I don't want a resumé, I want a fax of a specific query given in as few words as possible."

THE AD-VISER
1320-36 Street North
Lethbridge, AB T1H 5H8

PHONE: (403) 328-5114
FAX: (403) 328-5443

DESCRIPTION: Published by Robins Southern Printing. Circulation 21,000. A farm and ranch publication. Published bi-weekly. Established in 1982.
NOTES: No freelance work is purchased for this publication.

ADBUSTERS QUARTERLY

1243 West 7th Avenue
Vancouver, BC   V6H 1B7

PHONE: (604) 736-9401
FAX: (604) 737-6021

CONTACT: Kalle Lasn, Publisher   **DESCRIPTION:** Published by Adbusters Media Foundation. Circulation 20,000. "We call ourselves the journal of the mental environment. We produce ad parodies and articles that look at the media and how it affects our social culture. Everything from environment, economics, health, fashion, cyberspace. We feel that the billions of dollars that corporate America spends on advertising does affect our mental environment. We look at the effects of media and question whether or not the media can be held accountable. A journalist in Vancouver called us the *Green Peace* of the mental environment. We are largely read by teachers, people in the industry, environmentalists." Published quarterly. Established in 1989.
WRITERS: 75% freelance written. Purchases 200 articles per year. Byline given. Purchases fiction, non-fiction, poetry and fillers. Hires writers on assignment and pays expenses. Prefers articles from 100-2,000 words. Pays approximately $50 for a page of published text. Guidelines available along with a sample issue.
PHOTOGRAPHERS: "Yes we buy photos, artwork, graphic artwork, cartoons." Pays $100 for a published page. For photography contact Terry Sunderland. Photo guidelines are not available.
NOTES: Please send large SASE and $5.75 for a sample issue. Purchases first North American serial rights. Does not return unsolicited materials. Does not consider previously published work. Considers simultaneous submissions. Media Foundation has a television production arm called Power Shift.

ADNEWS

2 Lansing Square #1003
Willowdale, ON   M2J 4P8

PHONE: (416) 498-5164
FAX: (416) 498-6845

CONTACT: Mike Deibert, Editor   **DESCRIPTION:** Published by Robert A. Bale. Circulation 6,400. Advertising industry publication distributed to advertising agency personnel. Published daily Monday to Friday. Established 1981.
NOTES: Does not purchase freelance work.

THE ADVOCATE

4765 Pilot House Road
West Vancouver, BC   V7W 1J2

PHONE: (604) 925-2122
FAX: (604) 925-2065

CONTACT: David Roberts   **DESCRIPTION:** Circulation 9,000. A legal magazine aimed at people in the legal profession. Published 6 times a year. Established in 1943.
WRITERS: Does not purchase articles or hire freelancers on assignment. Articles are submitted by members of the legal profession and are not paid for.
PHOTOGRAPHERS: Does not use photography.

AEROSCOPE: NO LONGER PUBLISHED

LES AFFAIRES
1100 René-Levesque Blvd W 24 fl.   **PHONE:** (514) 392-9000
Montreal, PQ H3B 4X9   **FAX:** (514) 392-4723

CONTACT: Jean-Paul Gagné   **DESCRIPTION:** Published by Transcontinental Publications. Circulation 91,000. French business publication including financial markets, real estate etc. Published 50 times a year. Established in 1928.
WRITERS: "We purchase more material in the winter, less in the summer, on average 10 articles per issue. We are interested in freelancers from Quebec. We have quite a large group of freelancers we call upon for certain subjects. Freelancers can write us a query letter or they can phone. We are looking for marketing articles which feature Quebec companies. Our own journalists cover finance and real estate." Guidelines are available to freelancers who write frequently.
PHOTOGRAPHERS: "We have an in-house photographer so we don't purchase anything."
NOTES: Does not consider previously published work.

AFRICAN IDENTITY
236 Albion Road #1910   **PHONE:** (416) 743-1900
Rexdale, ON M9W 6A6   **FAX:** (416) 923-1599

CONTACT: George Marcells, Managing Editor   **DESCRIPTION:** Published by Afrimedia Publications. Published monthly. Established in 1993.

AFTERMARKET CANADA
2050-Speers Road #1   **PHONE:** (905) 847-0277
Oakville, ON L6L 2X8   **FAX:** (905) 847-7752

CONTACT: Steve Manning, Editor   **DESCRIPTION:** Published by SGB Communications. A monthly trade publication for automotive aftermarket parts. Contains marketing stories and technical support stories from auto parts manufacturers. Established in 1984.
WRITERS: All work is done by trade writers. Rarely hires outside freelance writers.
PHOTOGRAPHERS: All photographs are supplied by manufacturers.

AGENDA WORLD
Box 146
Pointe Claire, PQ H9R 4NS

NOTES: NO LONGER PUBLISHED

AGENT CANADA
1199 West Pender Street #240
Vancouver, BC V6E 2R1

NOTES: Couldn't locate. Phone number is not in service (604) 688-0481.

AGRI BOOK MAGAZINE

145 Thames Road West, Box 1060
Exeter, ON N0M 1S3

PHONE: (519) 235-2400
FAX: (519) 235-0798

CONTACT: Peter Darbishire, Managing Editor   **DESCRIPTION:** Published by AIS Communications . "Agricultural trade magazine that covers field and production management issues in agriculture. Publishes 5 very specialized issues per year. One for potato growers, one for bean growers, one for corn growers and one for farm drainage contractors and a Western edition called Top Crop Manager."
WRITERS: "We purchase freelance work very infrequently. Generally speaking with all of our publications we don't do much with unsolicited material. We tend to keep a stable of freelancers handy. If there's a hole or if we need something done in a certain area we either put it into our travel plans or call on our freelancers. We work 12 months in advance and generally our stories are not time-sensitive. Contact us by mail or fax. If writers have a suggestion I'll take a look at it. I am not in a position where I am really clamouring for stories."
NOTES: Also publishes Canadian Rental Service, Glass Canada and Water Well.

AGRI-COM

Box 220, 2474 Champlain Street
Clarence Creek, ON K0A 1N0

PHONE: (613) 488-2651
FAX: (613) 488-2541

CONTACT: Pierre Glaude, Editor   **DESCRIPTION:** Circulation 5,300. French agricultural tabloid published 22 times a year. Established in 1983.
PHOTOGRAPHERS: Photography done in-house.
Average article is half a tabloid page and pays about $100. Has approximately a $6,000 budget for freelance writers for the year. "We are a non-profit organization so our budget is not very big."

AGRISCIENCE

151 Slater Street #907
Ottawa, ON K1P 5H4

PHONE: (613) 232-9459
FAX: (613) 594-5190

CONTACT: Brenda Heald, Editor   **DESCRIPTION:** Circulation 5,500. Published bi-monthly. Established in 1934.
WRITERS: Byline given for non-fiction work of around 500 words. Writers' guidelines are available.
PHOTOGRAPHERS: 90% received in text/photo packages, 10% from stock. Purchases approximately 6 photos per year, 1 per issue. Uses 35mm colour transparencies and 5x7 b&w glossy. Model releases are not necessary, captions are required and credit line is given. Pay negotiated. Photo guidelines are not available. Approach publication by sending subject list.
NOTES: Sample copies free upon request. Purchases one-time rights. Returns unsolicited materials with a SASE. Considers previously published work and simultaneous submissions.

AIR TRANSPORT MANAGEMENT

310 Dupont Street
Toronto, ON M5R 1V9

NOTES: NO LONGER PUBLISHED

AIRFORCE

Box 2460 Station D, 100 Metcalfe Street
Ottawa, ON K1P 5W6

PHONE: (613) 992-5184
FAX: (613) 995-2196

CONTACT: Vic Johnson, Editor   **DESCRIPTION:** Published by Air Force Association of Canada. Circulation 30,000. This magazine is heavily oriented to the aviation and military industry. Published quarterly. Established in 1977.

WRITERS: Articles are submitted free of charge.

PHOTOGRAPHERS: Doesn't purchase photos.

AIRPORTS NORTH AMERICA

1625 Ingleton Avenue
Burnaby, BC V5C 4L8

PHONE: (604) 298-3004
FAX: (604) 291-1906

CONTACT: Toni Dabbs   **DESCRIPTION:** Published by Heri Baum. Circulation 17,300. This magazine publishes information about airport products. Published quarterly. Established in 1993.

WRITERS: Does not use freelance articles or hire on assignment. All articles are written in-house or are furnished by the product manufacturers.

PHOTOGRAPHERS: Does not purchase photography.

ALBERTA BEEF

2915 - 19 Street NE, #202
Calgary, AB T2E 7A2

PHONE: (403) 250-1090
FAX: (403) 291-9546

CONTACT: Garth McClintock, Editor   **DESCRIPTION:** Published by Garth McClintock. Circulation 13,800. This magazine is directed toward commercial cattlemen of Alberta. We carry several profile stories about cattlemen and stories on herd health, management, etc. Published monthly. Established in 1976.

WRITERS: We do use freelance articles. Rights etc. are negotiated. "We purchase approximately one article a month."

PHOTOGRAPHERS: Does not buy photographs. "Normally the pictures we use are part of a text/photo package or are taken by staff."

NOTES: "Writers would have to have a fairly decent knowledge of the cattle industry."

ALBERTA BUSINESS

2207 Hanselman Court
Saskatoon, SK S7L 6A8

PHONE: (306) 244-5668
FAX: (306) 653-4515

CONTACT: Heather Sterling, Editor   **DESCRIPTION:** Published by Sunrise Publishing. Circulation 11,000. "We like to cover all facets of business and the economy. For each issue we pick an editorial theme and focus on a sector of the economy. We are entertaining as well as fact-informative. We report on new businesses, inventive ideas that businesses have come up with and those who are prospering in spite of certain situations." Published twice a year. Established in 1994.

WRITERS: "Feature stories are 1,500-2,500 words and our In Business section is 300-400 words. We pay around 20¢ a word, it's negotiable. We hire writers on assignment. Bylines are given. Phone or fax us, it doesn't matter. We do occasionally accept articles on spec. We are open to articles about the ingenuity of a business itself or the people behind the business. As you read the article you should be able to make a type of check list in your mind that will help other businesses. Our publication focuses on business profitability and productivity and the bottom-line for both large and small businesses." Guidelines are not available.

PHOTOGRAPHERS: "If a freelance writer who is hired on assignment is not confident of their photographic abilities we will hire a photographer. We use both colour and black & white. We prefer prints for individual photos. Payment is negotiated." Contact by phone or fax. Photo guidelines are not available.

NOTES: "We are open to freelance writers and photographers calling us with story ideas or photographs that may work." Purchases first North American serial rights. Sample copies of this publication are available free upon request to those in the industry. Considers previously published work, depending on where it appeared.

ALBERTA CONSTRUCTION

124 West 8th Street North
North Vancouver, BC   V7M 3H2

PHONE: (604) 985-8711
FAX: (604) 985-7399

CONTACT: Wendy Melanson, Editor   **DESCRIPTION:** Published by Naylor Communications; Association magazine. Published quarterly. Established in 1978.

THE ALBERTA DOCTORS' DIGEST

12230 - 106 Avenue
Edmonton, AB   T5N 3Z1

PHONE: (403) 482-2626
FAX: (403) 482-5445

CONTACT: Donna Schultz, Editor   **DESCRIPTION:** Published by Alberta Medical Association. Circulation 5,600. This magazine addresses the political, financial, legal and ethical issues facing the medical profession in Alberta. Published bi-monthly. Established in 1976.

WRITERS: "Purchasing freelance material is always a possibility, but we haven't done so for some time. We are interested in articles falling into our mandate. If we purchased articles, pay rates would be negotiated. Normal article length is 750 words." Writers' guidelines are available. Send SASE.

PHOTOGRAPHERS: "Because of costs we have not been hiring lately. We have been considering using stock in the future. If freelancers are interested in submitting stock we would consider it." Pay would have to be negotiated. "We are trying to keep costs down."

ALBERTA FARM AND RANCH

4000-19th Street NE
Calgary, AB   T2E 6P8

NOTES: NO LONGER PUBLISHED

ALBERTA FARM LIFE

5929 - 48 Avenue
Red Deer, AB   T4N 6R4

PHONE: (403) 346-3356
FAX: (403) 347-6620

CONTACT: Keith Rideout   **DESCRIPTION:** Circulation 72,000. A farm oriented bi-monthly directed to all the farms and ranches in Alberta.
NOTES: "We almost never purchase freelance material. The magazine is done in-house."

ALBERTA FISHING GUIDE
5571 - 45 Street, #6C
Red Deer, AB T4N 1L2

PHONE: (403) 347-5079
FAX: (403) 341-5454

CONTACT: Ann Mitchell **DESCRIPTION:** Published by Barry Mitchell. Circulation 26,000. Guide book for fishermen in Alberta, lists about 1,300 fishing waters in Alberta with directions on how to get there. Includes articles of interest to fishermen. Published annually. Established in 1971. Sample opy is available for $4.95 with 9x12" SASE, $7.95 to U.S.
WRITERS: "We purchase 14 articles a year. We prefer text/photo packages. Length 1,800 words. Articles must be about fishing in Alberta. We do not accept previously published work or simultaneous submissions. Purchases one-time rights. Pay rates: 15¢ a word and photos are included with that.
PHOTOGRAPHERS: Buys 50 photos annually, a large percentage are purchased as part of a text/photo package. Purchases from stock, does not hire on assignment. Purchases one-time rights. Pay is negotiable, $250 for a colour cover. Send query letter with a resumé, business card and detailed subject list of fishing/sports related photos. Unsolicited material will be returned with SASE. Neither previously published work or simultaneous submissions will be considered. Photo guidelines are not available. Uses colour: 35mm transparencies or prints. Credit line is given. Needs: "We are always looking for good scenery shots with fishermen in them and lots of action. No kids, no dogs. Mountain scenery is always nice. No winter or fall shots."
NOTES: Publication comes out in March so "we need material in October, November 15 is our deadline."

ALBERTA REPORT
17327 - 106A Avenue
Edmonton, AB T5S 1M7

PHONE: (403) 486-2277
FAX: (403) 489-3280

CONTACT: Paul Bunner, Executive Editor **DESCRIPTION:** Published by United Western Communications. Circulation 41,000. Consumer magazine covers local, provincial, and national news weekly. Also covers government, business, law, education, resources, arts, sports, agriculture, religion, and people of Alberta. Published weekly. Established in 1973.
WRITERS: "We don't often assign articles to unknown writers. Most is on assignment. We like writers to do a few articles first. Contact the executive editor with writing samples."
PHOTOGRAPHERS: "We have a network of freelance photographers in different cities. New photographers can contact us so we can look at their work."
NOTES: Sample copies of this publication are available free upon request. Also publishes BC Report and Western Report.

ALBERTA WILD ROSE QUARTER HORSE JOURNAL see Horses All

ALBERTA WOMEN
101-6 Avenue SW
Calgary, AB T2P 3P4

NOTES: Could not locate.

ALIES DE LA MODE
50 De Lauzon
Boucherville, PQ J4B 1E6

PHONE: (514) 449-1313
FAX: (514) 449-1317

CONTACT: Juliette Ruer, Editor   **DESCRIPTION:** Circulation 75,000. French language publication aimed at women. Published 6 times a year. Established in 1988.

L'ALIMENTATION
1298 St-Zotique
Montreal, PQ H2S 1N7

PHONE: (514) 271-6922
FAX: (514) 271-1308

CONTACT: Francoise Pitt   **DESCRIPTION:** Published by Les Editions du Marchand Quebecois Inc. Circulation 14,600. French publication. Published 11 times a year for Quebec's grocery industry. Established in 1961.
NOTES: This publication is not purchasing freelance material at this time. Was formerly Le Depanneur.

ALIVE - CANADIAN JOURNAL OF HEALTH AND NUTRITION
7436 Fraser Park Drive
Burnaby, BC V5J 5B9

PHONE: (604) 435-1919
FAX: (604) 435-4888

CONTACT: Rhody Lake, Editor   **DESCRIPTION:** Published by Canadian Health Reform Products, Siegfried Gursche. Circulation 138,000. Features articles on health, foods, nutrition, vitamin and mineral therapy, herbal medicine, self-help health information, ecology, natural living and natural health and beauty care. Published 11 times a year.
WRITERS: "We publish articles and books. We look for material on natural health and natural healing. Writers' guidelines are available. Contact the editor or publisher in writing with a query letter."
PHOTOGRAPHERS: Buys up to 40 photos annually, 5-8 per issue. 40-60% from freelance photographers. Does not hire on assignment. Pays $25-$75 for b&w, $40-$15 for colour. Purchases one-time rights. Send a query letter with a subject list of stock photography, resumé, business card and tear sheets. Unsolicited submissions returned with SASE. Will consider simultaneous submissions. Previously published work will be considered. Model releases are required and captions are preferred. Photo guidelines are available.
NOTES: Sample copies of this publication are available free upon request on a limited basis.

ALPHABET CITY
Box 387 Station P
Toronto, ON M5S 2S9

NOTES: Could not locate.

ALTERNATIVES: PERSPECTIVES ON SOCIETY, TECHNOLOGY AND ENVIRONMENT

University of Waterloo
Faculty of Environmental Studies
Waterloo, ON N2L 3G1

PHONE: (519) 885-1211 ext. 6783
FAX: (519) 746-0292

CONTACT: Robert Gibson, Editor **DESCRIPTION:** Circulation 4,000. "An academic journal on environmental issues." Issues confront problems facing our natural and social environment and thought-provoking, well-researched feature articles go beyond band-aid solutions for a wide range of environmental concerns. Also publishes short news reports, books reviews, and humour. Established in 1971.
WRITERS: "We do accept freelance work however we don't pay our writers. We would gladly distribute guidelines for contributors and we will look at anything that people send in. Our feature articles are about 4,000 words. Report length articles are 750-1,000 words."
PHOTOGRAPHERS: "We do use photography but our needs are very specific so we seek it out ourselves. We do pay for images. We know what we are looking for so we contact the people or agencies that are likely to have what we need."
NOTES: Sample copies of this publication are available free upon request.

ALUMI-NEWS

Box 400, Victoria Station
Westmount, PQ H3Z 2V8

PHONE: (514) 489-4941
FAX: (514) 489-5505

CONTACT: Frank O'Brien, Editor **DESCRIPTION:** Circulation 18,400. Focuses on renovation, construction and energy conservation. Published bi-monthly in English and French. Established in 1976.
NOTES: May buy photos or articles on occasion.

ANGLER & HUNTER

Box 1541
Peterborough, ON K9J 7H7

NOTES: Couldn't locate. Phone number is not in service (705) 748-3891.

ANGLICAN

135 Adelaide Street East
Toronto, ON M5C 1L8

PHONE: (416) 363-6021
FAX: (416) 363-7678

CONTACT: Stuart Mann, Editor **DESCRIPTION:** Published by The Anglican Diocese of Toronto. Circulation 46,000. Religious publication published monthly. Established in 1953.
WRITERS: 75% freelance written. Byline given. Purchases non-fiction and hires writers on assignment but doesn't pay expenses. Kill fee is not paid if article is cancelled. Average pay is $75 per article. Writers' guidelines are not available. Contact magazine by sending query letter. "You must read the publication to know what we want. We are looking for news about Anglicans in the Diocese of Toronto. Human feature stories are most sought after. All material must be about Anglicans in the Diocese of Toronto."
PHOTOGRAPHERS: Purchases approximately 30 photos annually, 3 per issue. Hires photographers on assignment 40% of the time, 60% of photos are included in text\photo packages. Uses b&w 5x7 and 8x10 glossy. Pays $15.75 per photo. Credit line is given.

Contact by sending sample portfolio to Patti Spezzaferro. Photographer's guidelines are not available. "We like a photograph to reach out and grab our audience. Something never seen before. We trust our photographers here and give them as much freedom as possible to be as creative as possible. Hate seeing group fire and shoot shots."

NOTES: For a sample copy send 9x12" SASE with appropriate postage. Purchases one-time rights and first North American serial rights. Returns unsolicited materials if a SASE is enclosed. Considers previously published work and simultaneous submissions.

THE ANGLICAN JOURNAL/JOURNAL ANGLICAN

600 Jarvis Street   **PHONE:** (416) 942-9192
Toronto, ON M4Y 2J6   Editorial office: (416) 924-9199 ext. 304
     FAX: (416) 921-4452

CONTACT: Carolyn Purden, Editor   **DESCRIPTION:** Published by Anglican Church of Canada. Circulation 265,000. "We are the national newspaper of the Anglican Church of Canada and are also the largest denominational publication in Canada. We have 20 publishing partners which are regional diocesan newspapers. Our national news is inserted into the regional papers." Published 10 times a year. Established in 1989.

WRITERS: "Articles should be of interest to a national audience. They are usually about a national event, a local happening which reflects the larger picture, or a local happening which is relatively unusual. We have regular columnists and feature areas including an across-Canada page which consists of church and news briefs. The world page contains world news briefs. A page entitled *Reflections* consists of articles which offer theological or spiritual insights into issues of interest to church or society. Please submit a query before proceeding with an article. If we commission it, we pay upon publication. Rates range from $75 to $500. Articles on Macintosh disks are welcome. We do occasional book reviews on spiritual and theological books. We have a few regular writers, usually lay people who travel a lot. We look for international stories about what is going on in the Anglican church. We also have a sound and screen page, a movie and music reviewer but those are done by regular columnists. We like to be approached with query letters or at least a query call. Occasionally we take articles on spec if they fit our needs." Guidelines are available.

PHOTOGRAPHERS: "We don't purchase a lot, only if a freelancer is doing a story for us and they can supply black and white or colour photos." Glossy 8x10s are preferred. Guidelines are included in the writers' guidelines.

NOTES: Considers previously published work. Sample copies of this publication are available free upon request with the guidelines. Formerly Canadian Churchman.

ANGUS TIMES

Box 3209
Regina, SK S4P 3H1

NOTES: Couldn't locate. Phone number is not in service (306) 757-5539.

ANNALS OF SAINTE ANNE dE BEAUPRE

Box 1000 Basilica of Sainte Anne   **PHONE:** (418) 827-4538
Ste-Anne-de-Beaupre, PQ G0A 3C0   **FAX:** (418) 827-4530

CONTACT: Roch Achard, Editor   **DESCRIPTION:** Circulation 42,000. Published for the English speaking groups in the area. Promotes Christian family values.

WRITERS: "The majority of our writers are freelance, 60%. Articles are between 1,200-1,500 words paying 4¢ a word. Query with a letter."
PHOTOGRAPHERS: "It's not a regular practice for us to buy from freelancer photographers."
NOTES: Also publishes a French version called Review Sainte Anne de Beaupre.

THE ANTIGONISH REVIEW

St. Francis Xavier University, Box 5000   **PHONE:** (902) 867-3962
Antigonish, NS B2G 2W5   **FAX:** (902) 867-5153

CONTACT: George Sanderson, Editor   **DESCRIPTION:** Published by St. Francis Xavier University. Circulation 750. Literary publication features poetry, fiction, reviews and critical articles from Canada and abroad. Each issue contains the work of 20-30 poets, 5-6 fiction writers, reviews of 10-15 books and 2-3 articles directed at a general audience. Established in 1970. Published quarterly.
WRITERS: Does not purchase articles but occasionally hires on assignment and gives a byline. Average length for an article is 2,500-6,500 words, which pays $100. A $50 kill fee is offered if the article is cancelled. Contact with a query letter. Writers' guidelines are available.
PHOTOGRAPHERS: Photo guidelines are not available.
NOTES: Sample copies of this publication are available for $3. Returns unsolicited materials with a SASE. Does not consider previously published work or simultaneous submissions.

ANTIQUE SHOWCASE

Box 9   **PHONE:** (705) 484-1668
Brechin, ON L0K 1B0   **FAX:** (705) 484-1681

CONTACT: Barbara Sutton-Smith   **DESCRIPTION:** Published by Peter Sutton-Smith. Circulation 4,400. Aimed at antique lovers and collectors, this publication's diverse articles focus on helpful information for seasoned and beginner collectors. Keeps reader informed on state of the market. Published 9 times a year. Established in 1963.
WRITERS: Regular features include museum exhibitions and acquisitions, book reviews and show calendars. This publication is mainly written in-house. Supplementary articles are supplied by museums etc. Does purchase approximately 3-4 articles per issue and pays by the column inch (two sizes).
PHOTOGRAPHERS: Prefers photos with articles. "It is difficult to purchase stock photos as they often have to be researched at the library."
NOTES: Fees for both writers and photographers are negotiable and depend on the level of the creators expertise.

ANTIQUES

Box 75114, 20 Bloor Street East
Toronto, ON M4W 3T3

NOTES: Could not locate.

L'APERCU/REVUE
920 Yonge Street 6 Floor
Toronto, ON
M4W 3C7

PHONE: (416) 961-1028
FAX:(416) 924-4408

CONTACT: Lori Knowles, Editor **DESCRIPTION:** French language publication. Published annually by the Canadian Construction Association.
NOTES: Does not use freelance material.

APPAREL
1 Pacifique Street
Ste. Anne de Bellevue, PQ H9X 1C5

PHONE: (514) 457-2347
FAX: (514) 457-2147

CONTACT: Gillian Crosby, Editor **DESCRIPTION:** Published by CTJ Inc. Publishes profiles and features of Canadian apparel manufacturers, suppliers and retailers. Contains apparel industry news and trend reports. Published 6 times a year. Established in 1977.
WRITERS: "We purchase 1-2 articles per issue both assigned and on spec. Contact us by mail with story ideas and samples of work. We are always interested in current articles from other areas than Toronto or Vancouver.
PHOTOGRAPHERS: No photography is purchased.
NOTES: Sample copies of this publication are available free upon request.

APPLIED ARTS MAGAZINE
885 Don Mills Road, Suite 324
Don Mills, ON M3C 1V9

PHONE: (416) 510-0909
FAX: (416) 510-0913

CONTACT: Peter Giffen, Editor **DESCRIPTION:** Published by Applied Arts Inc. Circulation 11,000. Features work of communication professionals, graphic designers, illustrators, and photographers. Combines the solid information of a trade journal with the graphic excitement of a consumer magazine. Published five times a year.
WRITERS: May occasionally use freelance work. Please send examples of previously published work.
PHOTOGRAPHERS: To contact, please send samples of work. Guidelines are not available.
NOTES: Also publishes Electronic Link Magazine.

AQUATIC LINK
920 Yonge Street 6 Fl.
Toronto, ON M4W 3C7

PHONE: (416) 961-1028
FAX: (416) 924-4408

CONTACT: Lori Knowles, Editor **DESCRIPTION:** Published by Naylor Communications. Contains news and trends of pool and waterfront maintenance and recreation. Published bi-annually.
WRITERS: 50% freelance written. Writers are hired on assignment and negotiated expenses are paid while on assignment. Byline given. Average article length 1,500-2,000 words. Fees are negotiable. A 33% kill fee is offered if an article is cancelled. "No unsolicited material please. Send query with resumé and business card and a SASE for guidelines and sample copy."
PHOTOGRAPHERS: 50% assigned to in-house photographers, 25% assigned to freelance photographers and 25% purchased from stock. Colour formats used: 35mm transparencies, 2¼x2¼ transparencies, 4x5 transparencies, 5x7 colour prints, and 8x10 colour prints.

b&w formats used: 5x7 prints, 8x10 prints, glossy and matte. Model releases are not necessary but captions are required. Fees negotiable. Credit line is given. New photographers should send query letter, subject list, brochure, flyers or tear sheet, resumé and business card. Photographer's guidelines are not available.
NOTES: For a sample copy send 9x12" SASE with appropriate postage. Purchases one-time rights. Doesn't return unsolicited materials with a SASE. Considers previously published work and simultaneous submissions.

ARC
Box 7368
Ottawa, ON K1L 8E4

NOTES: Couldn't locate. Phone number is not in service (613) 789-9430.

ARCHITECTURAL ENGINEERING CONSTRUCTION MAGAZINE
395 Matheson Blvd. East
Mississauga, ON
L4Z 2H2

NOTES: NO LONGER PUBLISHED

ARCHITECTURE CONCEPT
Box 1010   **PHONE:** (819) 752-4243
Victoriaville, PQ G6P 8Y1   **FAX:** (819) 758-8812

CONTACT: Claude Roy, Editor   **DESCRIPTION:** Published by Editions C.R. Inc. Circulation 4,400. French language publication. Focuses on architecture. Issued quarterly. Established in 1945.

ARCH●TYPE
40 Orchard View Boul.
Toronto, ON M5S 2S9

DESCRIPTION: Published by Advocacy Resource Centre for the Handicapped (ARCH). A bi-monthly publication defending the rights of people with disabilities. Provides current information to service providers, professionals, unions and families.

ARCTIC
Arctic Institute of North America   **PHONE:** (403) 220-7515
University of Calgary   **FAX:** (403) 282-0085
2500 University Drive NW
Calgary, AB T2N 1N4

CONTACT: Karen McCullough **DESCRIPTION:** Circulation 1,500 individuals, 500 businesses and libraries. A quarterly multi-disciplinary journal dedicated to the international dissemination of research results and current thought relevant to northern areas of the world. Publishes peer-reviewed papers as well as book reviews and profiles of northern people, places and things. Abstracts are published in English, French and Russian.

WRITERS: "People submit scholarly articles and they are sent out for peer review. We have mandatory page charges. They should submit material to the editor." Writers' guidelines are available.
NOTES: Sample copies of this publication are available free, depending upon availability.

ARCTIC CIRCLE: NO LONGER PUBLISHED

ARTERE
505 Boul del Maisonneuve W #400   **PHONE:** (514) 842-4861
Montreal, PQ H3A 3C2   **FAX:** (514) 282-4289

CONTACT: Raymond Roberge   **DESCRIPTION:** Published by L'Assn des hopitaux du Québec. Circulation 7,000. French language publication. Targets managers and trustees of hospital boards in Quebec. Published 10 times a year. Established in 1983.
NOTES: Does not purchase freelance material.

ARTFOCUS MAGAZINE
Box 1063, Station F   **PHONE:** (416) 925-5564
Toronto, ON M4Y 2J7   **FAX:** (416) 925-2972

CONTACT: Pat Fleisher, Editor   **DESCRIPTION:** Circulation 6,000-8,000. "A full-colour quarterly review of the visual arts in Canada." Focuses on reviews of art, artists, and galleries from across Canada plus in-depth feature articles on media and techniques for artists.
WRITERS: "We purchase 6-8 articles per issue. Pay rates range from $50-$150 depending on the length. We are looking for people who have credentials as art historians or who have done some serious art writing in other publications. Our readers are in the art history area and will only accept writing from knowledgeable writers. The best thing for a freelancer to do is write me a letter and send samples of their previously published work or something that will give me an idea of their language style and taste in art."
PHOTOGRAPHERS: "Photography is usually provided by the art gallery."
NOTES: Sample copies of this publication are available free upon request. Send a $1.50 SASE, please be patient. Formerly called ArtPost. Purchases first North American serial rights. Does not consider previously published work.

ARTHRITIS NEWS
The Arthritis Society, 250 Bloor Street   **PHONE:** (416) 967-1414
East #901   **FAX:** (416) 967-7171
Toronto, ON M4W 3P2

CONTACT: Dennis Jeanes, Editor   **DESCRIPTION:** Circulation 17,000. A quarterly magazine featuring research news, coping skills for those with arthritis and treatment information. Is of interest to both health care professionals and the lay person.
WRITERS: "Some freelance material is purchased. We have 4-5 freelancers who do most of our writing. Direct a query letter to the editor."
PHOTOGRAPHERS: "We have a regular photographer but interested photographers can contact us with a query letter."

NOTES: Sample copies of this publication are available free upon request. "We publish first-time rights and have rights for the first 6 months after publishing." Also published in French as ArthroExpress.

ARTICHOKE
238 - 5th Avenue NE, #402
Calgary, AB T2E 0K6

NOTES: Couldn't locate. Phone number is not in service (403) 276-8612.

ARTPOST see Artfocus Magazine

ARTSATLANTIC
145 Richmond Street   **PHONE:** (902) 628-6138
Charlottetown, PE C1A 1J1   **FAX:** (902) 566-4648

CONTACT: Joseph Sherman, Editor   **DESCRIPTION:** Published by Confederation Centre of the Arts. Circulation 3,500. "A multi-disciplinary arts magazine with an emphasis on visual arts, and performance arts (dance, music). We look at crafts, cultural issues, heritage issues, and occasionally architecture. The mandate of the publication begins with Atlantic Canada or its artists. We cover issues that are not necessarily geographically connected but which affect the cultural community." Each issue contains feature articles, dozens of incisive reviews, arts news from all over, and an activities calendar. Published three times a year. Established in 1977.
WRITERS: "Most of our articles are commissioned. We do not discount the receipt of unsolicited materials. We rely on contract and commission. We are open to queries from freelancers. If freelancers submit articles we consider them but its not our normal way of business. Writers are more likely to find an opening if they have a suggestion based on their understanding of what the magazine does."
PHOTOGRAPHERS: Hires freelancers on assignment. Occasionally publishes photography/art portfolios. "We are less open to queries from photographers because most of the photography is very specific to the article and is therefore assigned. There is relatively small opportunity for the freelance photographer in terms of producing the kinds of images that we would use in an arts publication. We are not doing a Canadian Geographic type thing where we are looking for photos of Georgian Bay. Photos are specific to exhibitions or individuals who happen to be artists."
NOTES: This magazine is open to ideas from writers. Most photography is on assignment. Photography/art portfolios are considered. Its important to review the publication before submitting anything.

ASSOCIATION
250 The Esplanade #201   **PHONE:** (416) 867-1042
Toronto, ON M5A 1J2   **FAX:** (416) 867-1115

CONTACT: Andrea Kuch, Editor **DESCRIPTION:** Published by August Communications. Circulation 3,800. A national publication endorsed by the Canadian Society of Association Executives. Published bi-monthly in English and French for Association executives and staff. Established in 1974.

WRITERS: "Some freelance work is purchased. There is no standard length and the rate is negotiable. Contact the editor with a query letter. We do take pitched articles from time to time."
PHOTOGRAPHERS: "We occasionally purchase photography." Contact the editor with a letter of inquiry.
NOTES: Sample copies available for serious potential writers. Also publishes Canadian Retailer, University Manager and Vision.

ATA MAGAZINE
11010 - 142 Street
Edmonton, AB T5N 2R1

PHONE: (403) 453-2411
FAX: (403) 455-6481

CONTACT: Timothy Johnston, Editor   **DESCRIPTION:** Published by Alberta Teacher's Association. Circulation 39,500. Magazine for educators. Features regular columns, professional development information and articles on issues of concern to teachers. Includes book reviews. Published quarterly. Established in 1920.
WRITERS: "People can submit articles. We confirm that we have received them. Appropriate articles are selected in an editorial meeting. The final payment is negotiated but generally unsolicited articles are $75. Length varies from 500-700 words." Guidelines are available.
PHOTOGRAPHERS: "Some photography is purchased." Send a query letter to Raymond Gariepy.
NOTES: Sample copies of this publication are available free upon request.

ATHLETICS
1185 Eglinton Avenue East
North York, ON M3C 3C6

PHONE: (416) 426-7215
FAX: (416) 426-7358

CONTACT: Greg Lockhart, Editor   **DESCRIPTION:** Published by Cecil Smith. Circulation 7,000. Canada's track and field magazine for families. Articles on diet, training and athletes. Covers national and international events and publishes profiles and ranking lists. Published nine times a year.

THE ATLANTIC BAPTIST
Box 756
Kentville, NS B4N 3X9

PHONE: (902) 681-6868
FAX: (902) 681-0315

CONTACT: Michael Lipe, Editor   **DESCRIPTION:** Published by Atlantic Baptist Convention Board of Publication. Circulation 7,200. A monthly general interest magazine containing features, news and devotional materials for Christians of all ages. Major focus is on Baptists in Canada and throughout the world. Established in 1827.
WRITERS: 10% freelance written. Doesn't hire writers on assignment. Purchases approximately 5-10 non-fiction articles per year. Byline given. Average article length 750-1,000 words. Pays $30 per article. Writers' guidelines are available. "We are a general interest magazine, with material for all ages. The single most important aspect of our content is that it be Christian. 95% of our readers are Baptists. We do not publish poetry or charismatic-oriented material." Make contact by sending a query letter.
PHOTOGRAPHERS: 100% assigned to in-house photographers.
NOTES: Purchases one-time rights. Returns unsolicited materials with a SASE. Considers previously published work and simultaneous submissions.

ATLANTIC BUSINESS REPORT
599 Main Street #203   **PHONE:** (506) 857-9696
Moncton, NB E1C 1C8   **FAX:** (506) 859-7395
                                        EMAIL abjpubl@nbnet.nb.ca
CONTACT: Ron Levesque   **DESCRIPTION:** Published by ABJ Publishing Inc. Circulation 7,000. Monthly business publication. We like to focus on the positive aspects of businesses in Atlantic Canada. Articles range from business news to success stories with particular emphasis on how they achieved their success. Established in 1991.
WRITERS: 90% freelance written. A byline is given. Hires writers on assignment and pays expenses. Pays 15¢ per word for articles averaging 750 words in length. A 50% kill fee is paid if an article is cancelled. "Writers should query with their own story ideas. Your ideas will not be assigned to someone else or produced in-house. We want writers who show initiative, and who can take good photos." Regular features include business strategies, environment, and finance. Columns include leadership, computers, information technology, woman to woman, and coffee break. Fees for columns are negotiable. Writers' guidelines are available. Contact with a resumé and business card or send resumé via email.
PHOTOGRAPHERS: Purchases approximately 100 photos annually. 20% assigned to in-house photographers. 80% included in text/photo package. Purchases approximately 40 photos annually. Accepts 5x7 and 8x10 colour prints and 8x10 and 5x7 b&w glossy prints. Model releases are not necessary but captions are required. Pays $15 for photos and $35 for the cover. Credit line must be negotiated. Please send query letter, subject list and sample portfolio of 3-4 photos. "Most of the photography we buy is included in the writer's submission - part of the deal." Photo guidelines are not available.
NOTES: For a sample copy send 9x12" SASE with 88¢ postage. Purchases first North American serial rights. Returns unsolicited materials with a SASE. Does not consider previously published work or simultaneous submissions. Also publishes The Brunswick Business Journal.

ATLANTIC CHAMBER JOURNAL
309 Amirault Street   **PHONE:** (506) 858-8710
Dieppe, NB E1A 1G1   **FAX:** (506) 858-1707

CONTACT: Elie Richard   **DESCRIPTION:** Published by Eastcan Publications. Circulation 9,000. A regional business magazine serving Atlantic Canada since 1987. We are aboard the regional airlines, marine atlantic vessels and Via Rail." Published bi-monthly.
WRITERS: "I very seldom buy work because we have a number of writers waiting in the wings. I have 8-10 contributing writers and I always have 4 or 5 who want to write for us. I can't fit them all in. I do accept queries, either by letter or fax. I seldom have to pay, writers often want the exposure and the opportunity to express their views. Our guidelines are pretty wide, as long as articles fit into the general subheading of regional business. We want our articles to be of interest to our readership. That can be everything from how to invest funds to business expansion or development plans in the region."
PHOTOGRAPHERS: "We maybe purchase something once or twice a year, very seldom."
NOTES: Sample copies are available upon request.

ATLANTIC CONSTRUCTION JOURNAL
6029 Cunard Street   **PHONE:** (902) 420-0437
Halifax, NS B3K 1E5   **FAX:** (902) 423-8212

CONTACT: Ken Partridge, Editor   **DESCRIPTION:** Published by Bilby Holdings. Circulation 25,000. Circulated throughout all four Atlantic provinces. Publication aimed

at Atlantic Canada's construction industry. Focuses on new constructions projects, contracts, as well as safety issues and government policy issues that pertain to construction. Published quarterly. Established in 1988.
WRITERS: "We do purchase some work, 10-20% freelance. I prefer to assign however I do accept query letters by mail or fax. Average article length is 500 words. For new writers the rate is 10¢ a word. Once we have some experience with a writer we will slowly increase the rate. I want to see articles on my topic areas. I like to see an inquiry first."
PHOTOGRAPHERS: "We purchase very little photography."
NOTES: Considers previously published work. Sample copies of this publication are available free upon request. Purchases one-time rights. Also publishes Atlantic Transportation Journal and Nova Scotia Business Journal.

ATLANTIC COOPERATOR
Box 1386   **PHONE:** (902) 863-2776
Antigonish, NS B2G 2L7   **FAX:** (902) 863-8077

CONTACT: Brenda MacKinnon, Editor   **DESCRIPTION:** Published by Atlantic Co-operative Publishers. Circulation 61,000. Publication focuses on all levels of co-ops; consumer, credit unions, worker, housing, producer, marketing etc. in the Atlantic region. Published bi-monthly. Established in 1939.
WRITERS: Buys 500 articles per year and is 98% freelance written. Average pay rate is $150 per article. Average length 700-800 words. Features can be from 500-2,000 words. Concerned with five areas: co-operatives, the environment/sustainable development, consumers, social justice and community development. The most popular topics are innovations, news items, consumer information and commentary on regional issues. Queries should be 50-100 words and include a theme, angle, sources, length, expected expenses and when the first draft can be delivered. Guidelines are available.
PHOTOGRAPHERS: Prefers photos with stories. Purchases about 20 photos per issue. 95% of photos are assigned to free-lance photographers. Prefers 5x7 colour prints and 5x7 b&w prints. Captions are preferred and credit line is given. Pays $20 for b&w photos. Photo guidelines are available.
NOTES: Sample copy free upon request. Purchases first North American serial rights. Considers previously published work and simultaneous submissions. Returns unsolicited materials with a SASE.

ATLANTIC FIREFIGHTER
34 Spring Street   **PHONE:** (902) 667-5102
Amherst, NS B4H 1R9   **FAX:** (902) 667-0419

CONTACT: Dorothy Brown, Editor   **DESCRIPTION:** Published by Cumberland Publishing Ltd. "We are a trade newspaper that goes into virtually every fire hall in the Atlantic region. We do all kinds of stories; human interest, firefighting experiences and hard news stories. It's all fire related and we try to focus on things that the fire service can learn from various fire fighting experiences." Published 11 times a year.
WRITERS: "We have several correspondents that write freelance for us. We pay a flat rate of $35 for 2 double-spaced pages."
PHOTOGRAPHERS: Pays $7.50 per photo, usually purchased with accompanying article.
NOTES: Also publishes Atlantic Postcalls.

ATLANTIC FISHERMAN
1127 Barrington Street #107   **PHONE:** (902) 422-4990
Halifax, NS B3H 2P8   **FAX:** (902) 422-4728

CONTACT: John MacIntyre, Editor **DESCRIPTION:** Published by Graphic Advocate. Circulation 5,000. Published monthly.
NOTES: Please send a query letter to the attention of the editor for all freelance inquiries.

ATLANTIC FORESTRY JOURNAL
2099 Gottingen Street
Halifax, NS B3K 3B2

NOTES: NO LONGER PUBLISHED

ATLANTIC LIFESTYLE BUSINESS MAGAZINE
197 Water Street, Box 2356 Station C   **PHONE:** (709) 726-9300
St. John's, NF A1C 6E7   **FAX:** (709) 726-3013

CONTACT: Adrian Smith **DESCRIPTION:** Published by Communications Ten Limited. Circulation 25,000. A bi-monthly business publication. Issues covered include culture, lifestyle, and business in Atlantic Canada.
WRITERS: Contact Edwina Hutton. 70% freelance written. Byline given. Hires writers on assignment but doesn't pay expenses. Average article length is 2,000-2,500 words. Pays 15¢ per word or $650 for cover story. A kill fee is offered if an article is cancelled. Send resumé and business card to be kept on file for possible assignment. Guidelines available.
PHOTOGRAPHERS: Contact Lisa McKay. Purchases stock images and hires writers on assignment. Uses 35mm colour transparencies and 8x10 b&w. Captions preferred. Model releases not necessary. "Prices vary according to assignment." Credit line is given. Send resumé and business card to be kept on file for possible future assignments. Photo guidelines are available.
NOTES: Purchases one-time rights. Returns unsolicited materials with a SASE. Does not consider previously published work or simultaneous submissions. For a sample copy send 8.5x11" SASE with $1.38 postage.

ATLANTIC POSTCALLS
34 Spring Street   **PHONE:** (902) 667-5102
Amherst, NS B4H 1R9   **FAX:** (902) 667-0419

CONTACT: Doug Harkness, Editor **DESCRIPTION:** Published by Cumberland Publishing Ltd. Publication focuses on horses.
NOTES: Also publishes Atlantic Firefighter.

THE ATLANTIC REVIEW
Box 3370
Fredericton, NB E3B 5A2

NOTES: NO LONGER PUBLISHED

ATLANTIC SALMON JOURNAL

Box 429
St. Andrews, NB E0G 2X0

PHONE: (506) 529-4581
FAX: (506) 529-4985

CONTACT: Harry Bruce, Editor   **DESCRIPTION:** Published by Atlantic Salmon Federation. Circulation 21,000. "Atlantic salmon angling and conservation is the focus. Also feature adventures from Iceland to Quebec." Feature stories include the conservation and management of Atlantic Salmon, fly fishing for Atlantic salmon and angling techniques. Published quarterly. Established in 1952.
WRITERS: "We use an established source of freelancers who are experts in sportfishing. Send query letter with a written outline, a sample portfolio, and subject list." Text/photo packages are negotiable and purchased as a unit. Unsolicited submissions are returned if accompanied by SASE. Previously published work and simultaneous submissions will be considered. Captions and model releases are necessary.
PHOTOGRAPHERS: "Freelance photographers should send something to indicate that they have experience in photographing people sportfishing. Most photos are supplied with stories. Will consider pictorial spread of Atlantic salmon fishing scenes or of Atlantic salmon rivers." Buys 80 photos annually, uses approximately 20 per issue. 15% are assigned to freelancers, 85% are purchased as part of text/photo package. Some photos are purchased from stock and others are provided free by members. Pays $25 for b&w, $50 for colour, and up to $300 for colour cover. Buys first North American serial rights.

ATLANTIC TRANSPORTATION JOURNAL

6029 Cunard Street
Halifax, NS B3K 1E5

PHONE: (902) 420-0437
FAX: (902) 423-8212

CONTACT: Ken Partridge, Editor   **DESCRIPTION:** Published by Bilby Holdings Ltd. Circulation 26,500. Quarterly tabloid covering the Transport sector throughout Canada's Atlantic region. Topics include: government policy, regulation, technology innovations, new products, safety concerns, year-end performance results, annual meetings, take-overs etc. Includes air, rail, road and water transport. Established in 1989.
WRITERS: 30% freelance written. Purchases 100 non-fiction articles per year and pays 20-30¢ per word for articles averaging 500 words. Writers are hired on assignment and expenses are paid. A byline is given but no kill fee is paid if assignment cancelled. Prefers to be contacted by query letter or send resumé and business card to be kept on file. Writers' guidelines are available. "Likes Canadian spellings, suggestions, text/photo packages, local flavour, material on all modes of air/sea/truck/train travel. Dislikes American spellings, no photo opportunities, lack of quotes, repeated calls to revise submitted material."
PHOTOGRAPHERS: Purchases from stock. Buys approximately 24 photos annually. 90% assigned to in-house photographers, 3% to freelance and 3% included in text/photo packages. Colour formats used: 5x7 colour prints. b&w formats used: 5x7 matte prints. Captions are preferred and model releases are not necessary. Pays $20 per photo/text package. To contact journal send query letter. Photo guidelines are not available.
NOTES: Sample copies of this publication are available free upon request. Purchases one-time rights. Returns unsolicited materials with a SASE. Considers previously published work and simultaneous submissions.

ATLANTIC TRUCKING
920 Yonge Street 6 Fl.
Toronto, ON M4W 3C7

PHONE: (416) 961-1028
FAX: (416) 924-4408

CONTACT: Lori Knowles   **DESCRIPTION:** Published by Naylor Communications. Circulation 5,000. Contains news and trends of trucking in Atlantic Canada. Published quarterly. Established in 1986.
WRITERS: 50% freelance written. Writers are hired on assignment and negotiated expenses are paid while on assignment. Byline given. Average article length 1,500-2,000 words. Fees are negotiable. A 33% kill fee is offered if an article is cancelled. "No unsolicited material please. Send query with resumé and business card and a SASE for guidelines and sample copy."
PHOTOGRAPHERS: 50% assigned to in-house photographers, 25% assigned to freelance photographers and 25% purchased from stock. Colour formats used: 35mm transparencies, 2¼x2¼ transparencies, 4x5 transparencies, 5x7 colour prints, and 8x10 colour prints. b&w formats used: 5x7 prints, 8x10 prints, glossy and matte. Model releases are not necessary but captions are required. Fees negotiable. Credit line is given. New photographers should send query letter, subject list, brochure, flyers or tear sheet and resumé and business card. Photographer's guidelines are not available.
NOTES: For a sample copy send 9x12" SASE with appropriate postage. Purchases one-time rights. Doesn't return unsolicited materials with a SASE. Considers previously published work and simultaneous submissions.

ATLANTIS: A Women's Studies Journal
166 Bedford Highway
Halifax, NS B3M 2J6

NOTES: Couldn't locate. Phone number is not in service (902) 443-4450, Ext. 319.

AUTOCAD USER
1011 Upper Middle Road East #1235
Oakville, ON L6H 5Z9

PHONE: (905) 475-4231
FAX: (905) 845-5521

CONTACT: Bob Erickson   **DESCRIPTION:** Published by Swan Erickson Publishing Inc. Circulation 15,000. Read by users of autocad products across Canada.
WRITERS: "We sometimes purchase articles that are autocad specific."
PHOTOGRAPHERS: "We never purchase photography."

L'AUTOMOBILE
3300 Côte Vertu #410
St. Laurent, PQ H4R 2B7

PHONE: (514) 339-1399
FAX: (514) 339-1396

CONTACT: Marc Beauchamp   **DESCRIPTION:** Published by Southam. Circulation 11,000. Serves Quebec's automotive industry. Published 6 times a year in French. Established in 1939.

AUTOPINION
1775 Courtwood Crescent   **PHONE:** (613) 226-7631
Ottawa, ON   K2C 3J2   **FAX:** (613) 225-7383

CONTACT: David Steventon, Editor   **DESCRIPTION:** Published by Canadian Automobile Association. Circulation 56,000. Guide for car buyers, both new and used. Includes profiles on cars, and what is new in the industry. Published annually. Established in 1987. **WRITERS:** Purchases approximately 6 non-fiction 1,000 word articles per year. Pays 25¢ per word. No kill fee paid upon cancellation. Byline given. Writers are not hired on assignment. 80% freelance written. Writers' guidelines are available. Contact with a query letter. "As a car buyers guide we would consider topics relating to the car buying experience, and technical copy that is consumer oriented." **PHOTOGRAPHERS:** 80% of photos in text\photo package. 5% assigned in-house. Only purchases a few photos per year. Credit line is given. Uses 35mm transparencies. Model releases are required but captions are not necessary. Fees are negotiable. Photo guidelines are not available. "This annual is a car buyer's guide. Photos are related to new models and technical features." **NOTES:** For a sample copy send 9x12" SASE with appropriate postage. Purchases exclusive rights. Considers previously published work and simultaneous submissions. Returns unsolicited materials with a SASE.

AUTOROUTE
366 Adelaide Street West 6 Fl.   **PHONE:** (416) 599-9900
Toronto, ON   M5V 1R9   **FAX:** (416) 599-9700

CONTACT: John Terauds   **DESCRIPTION:** Published by Morris Marketing and Media Services Inc. Circulation 400,000. Quarterly magazine featuring a unique editorial mix of North American travel (by car), automotive styles and trends, motorsport and automotive do-it-yourself. Published 4 times a year in English and French. Established in 1989. **WRITERS:** 75% freelance written. Buys 40 articles per year. Byline given. Hires writers on assignment. Average article is 1,000 words. Pays 50¢ a word. "Columns are pre-assigned. Features open to freelancers are *Fun Drives* (day trips from a city) and *Motorsport Photo Essay.*" 50% kill fee is paid if assigned article is cancelled. Writers please contact with query, resumé and business card. "Photos are especially appreciated with articles. Want articles geared to magazine's theme of 'practical' motoring." Writers' guidelines are available. **PHOTOGRAPHERS:** Purchases approximately 24 photos annually. Most are included in text/photo packages. Some are purchased from stock. Model releases and captions are preferred. Pay is negotiated. Credit line is given. Contact by sending a resumé, business card, brochure, flyer or tear sheets. Each issue includes a photo feature *Hot Shot* which is a "hot" picture of a vehicle in motion." **NOTES:** Sample copy available, please enclose 10x12" SASE. Purchases one-time rights. Unsolicited materials will be returned with SASE. Considers previously published work and simultaneous submissions.

AVENIR
3715 Lacombe #200   **PHONE:** (514) 341-7916
Montreal, PQ   H3T 1M3   **FAX:** (514) 341-2644

CONTACT: see below   **DESCRIPTION:** Published by Les Editions du Mont. Royal Inc. Circulation 25,000. French consumer magazine with a focus on the human resource industry including management and professional development. Published every two months. Established in 1984.

WRITERS: 70% freelance written. Pays per article and depends on length of submission. Hires writers on assignment and pays expenses. Guidelines available. Contact Mr. Michel Guénard.

PHOTOGRAPHERS: Purchases stock images. Hires photographers on assignment and purchases approximately 20 photos annually. 80% assigned to freelance photographers and 20% included in text/photo packages. Colour formats used: 35mm transparencies and 4x5 transparencies. Uses 5x7 b&w prints. Photo guidelines are available. New photographers should send query letter, subject list, and resumé and business card to be kept on file. Contact Mr. Michel Guénard.

NOTES: Sample copies of this publication are available for $3.25. Returns unsolicited materials with a SASE. Considers previously published work. Contact by sending query letter, a fax, completed articles on spec or send your resumé and business card to be kept on file.

AVIATION TODAY
34 Lakeshore Road East
Port Credit, ON L5G 1C8

NOTES: NO LONGER PUBLISHED

AWARD MAGAZINE
4180 Lougheed Hwy #401   **PHONE:** (604) 299-7311
Burnaby, BC V5C 6A7   **FAX:** (604) 299-9188

CONTACT: Marisa Paterson, Editor   **DESCRIPTION:** Published by Canada Wide Magazines; Peter Legge. Circulation 7,500. Architecture, interior design, and construction trade magazine. Distributed in western Canada and Ontario. "We are read by architects, interior designers, landscape designers, developers and general contractors. Anyone involved in the building and design industry. Articles cover design trends. Project stories where we look at what's new in architecture across the country." The cover story is always on a firm and the inside features focus on trends. Regular columns include: Architects abroad; Spec Desk; Legal issues; and a Forum in which professionals are invited to answer reader's questions. Published 5 times a year. Established in 1986.

WRITERS: Hires freelance writers on assignment to do feature stories. Stories are generally 1,200 to 1,500 words. Pay is 30¢ a word. The editor would like query letters with ideas for articles. Resumés and samples will be kept on file. Pays negotiated expenses while on assignment. Purchases first North American serial rights. Will not consider previously published work, "It has to be original" or simultaneous submissions. Writers' guidelines are available with SASE.

PHOTOGRAPHERS: Hires photographers on assignment generally only for cover story. Photos in the magazine are usually supplied by people in the industry. Cover shots run $500 and are not purchased from stock. Photographers interested in being considered for assignment should send resumé, brochure or tear sheet samples; and business card to Lisa Forde, Art Director. Information is kept on file. Since articles are done on firms throughout western Canada and Ontario, photographers throughout the country are used. "We've had covers out of Toronto, Edmonton, Calgary and Vancouver." Photo guidelines are not available.

NOTES: Samples of the magazine are available upon request. Also publishes BC Business, BC Pharmacist, BC Home and Pacific Golf.

AZURE

2 Silver Avenue
Toronto, ON M6R 3A2

PHONE: (416) 588-2588
FAX: (416) 588-2357

CONTACT: Nelda Rodger, Editor   **DESCRIPTION:** Published by Azure Publishing. Circulation 12,000. Design, art and architecture magazine covering Canada and abroad. Reports on the forces that drive design, from new aesthetics and technological innovations to social issues. Published 6 times a year in English and French. Established in 1985.
WRITERS: "We do purchase writing, maybe 3 features and 2 shorter pieces. Freelancers should sumbit a resumé or submit an outline for a piece. We are a critical magazine but we are not academic. We are more casual and our readership are not just professional designers so the writing style should be appropriate."
PHOTOGRAPHERS: "Usually photos accompany the article. We use black and white and colour, all formats. Photographers should send a resumé or if they are particularly interested in shooting a project let us know about it."
NOTES: Sample copies of this publication are available for $6.25 or check newsstands and libraries. Purchases first Canadian serial rights. Considers previously published work if it was not published in Canada.

BABY AND CHILD CARE ENCYCLOPEDIA

37 Hanna Avenue #1
Toronto, ON M6K 1X1

PHONE: (416) 537-2604
FAX: (416) 538-1794

CONTACT: Shirley Ohannessian   **DESCRIPTION:** Published by Family Communications Inc. Reference publication for parents and care givers. Published annually. Established in 1990.
NOTES: This publication does not purchase freelance material. Also publishes Today's Bride, You, Expecting, Best Wishes and Baby and Child Care Encyclopedia.

BAKERS JOURNAL

106 Lakeshore Road East, #209
Port Credit, ON L5G 1E3

PHONE: (416) 271-1366
FAX: (416) 271-6373

CONTACT: Carol Horseman, Editor   **DESCRIPTION:** Published by NCC Publishing. Circulation 6,500. A trade publication aimed at the retail baker. Each issue has a theme. Published ten times a year. Established in 1938.
NOTES: Some freelance work may be accepted if it is aimed to the trade, not the public. Contact the editor with a query letter.

LE BANQUIER

Commerce Court West
199 Bay Street #3000
Toronto, ON M5L 1G2

PHONE: (416) 362-6092
FAX: (416) 362-7705

CONTACT: Jacques Hébert, Editor   **DESCRIPTION:** French language publication issued 6 times a year. English version is the Canadian Banker. Established in 1974.

BAR CODE QUARTERLY
777 Bay Street
Toronto, ON M5W 1A7

PHONE: (416) 596-5709
FAX: (416) 593-3193

CONTACT: Rob Robertson, Editor   **DESCRIPTION:** Published quarterly.
WRITERS: "Writing is purchased. Contact the editor by phone, fax or a query letter."
PHOTOGRAPHERS: "We hire photographers on assignment and purchase individual photos from time to time."

BARLEY COUNTRY
2116-27 Avenue NE #237
Calgary, AB T2E 7A6

PHONE: (403) 291-9111
FAX: (403) 291-0190

CONTACT: Stan Blade, Editor   **DESCRIPTION:** Published by Alberta Barley Commission. Circulation 43,500. Information specifically for barley farmers in Alberta. Articles cover research, demo plots, and even recipies. Published quarterly. Established in 1992.
WRITERS: "Articles are written by Barley Commission funded researchers, chemical companies or are staff written. We generally don't pay for the articles .. but would consider submissions if sent."
PHOTOGRAPHERS: All photos are included with text/photo packages or are taken by staff. No payment given.

LA BARRIQUE
5165 Sherbrooke Street West #414
Montreal, PQ H4A 1T6

PHONE: (514) 481-5892
FAX: (514) 481-9699

CONTACT: Nicole Barrette-Ryan   **DESCRIPTION:** Published by Kylix Media. Circulation 7,700. French publication issued 7 times a year. Established in 1972.
NOTES: This publication accepts freelance work occasionally.

BATH AND KITCHEN MARKETER: NO LONGER PUBLISHED

BC AGRI DIGEST
RR2
Chase, BC V0E 1M0

PHONE: (604) 679-5362
FAX: (604) 679-5362

CONTACT: Fran Kay   **DESCRIPTION:** Published by BC Interior Agri Publications. Circulation 10,000. Agricultural publication with production and marketing articles, mostly distilled from seminars. Published 6 times a year. Established in 1985.
WRITERS: Occasionally purchases articles, approximately 6-10 per year. Hires writers on assignment and pays expenses. Offers a 50% kill fee upon cancellation. Pays $150 per 700 word article. Average article is 500-700 words. "Regular features are almost always written by staff. Purchased articles are almost entirely profiles." Writers' guidelines are not available. Query by phone or fax. "We already have as many profile writers as we need at present, though would still be interested in suggestions from distant areas (Vancouver & Gulf Islands, Peace River, Kootenays, Northern Interior). Generally, content is 'extension' type material, written by staff."

PHOTOGRAPHERS: Purchases stock images and hires photographers on assignment. Purchases approximately 40 photos annually, 6-8 per issue. 100% assigned to freelance photographers; 50% from stock and 50% from text packages. Colour formats used: 35mm transparencies, 2¼x2¼ transparencies, 4x5 transparencies, 5x7 colour prints, 8x10 colour prints. b&w formats used: 5x7 prints, 8x10 prints, glossy, matte. Prefers transparencies. Pays $5 for photos, $25 for cover. Captions are preferred and a credit line is given. Photo guidelines are not available. "Call us. It will probably save you a lot of time. We are always on the look-out for good cover photos and inside ones with an obvious visual story. This is a multi-commodity agricultural paper specific to British Columbia."
NOTES: Sample copies of this publication are available free upon request. Purchases one-time rights. Returns unsolicited materials with a SASE. Prefers not to receive previously published work and simultaneous submissions but will consider them.

THE BC BROKER
Box 3311
Vancouver, BC   V6B 3Y3

PHONE: (604) 874-1001
FAX: (604) 874-3922

CONTACT: Patrick Durrant   **DESCRIPTION:** Published by Arbutus Publications Ltd. Published 6 times a year. Established in 1949.
NOTES: This publication does not use freelance material.

BC BUSINESS
4180 Lougheed Hwy #401
Burnaby, BC   V5C 6A7

PHONE: (604) 299-7311
FAX: (604) 299-9188

CONTACT: Bonnie Irving, Editor   **DESCRIPTION:** Published by Canada Wide
Magazines; Peter Legge.

THE BC BUSINESS EXAMINER
112 - 2465 Beta Avenue
Burnaby, BC   V5C 5N1

NOTES: Couldn't locate. Phone number is not in service (604) 291-1320.

BC DISCOVERY
400 The Station 601 W Cordova Street
Vancouver, BC   V6B 1G1

NOTES: Couldn't locate. Phone number is not in service (604) 688-8464.

BC HOME
4180 Lougheed Hwy #401
Burnaby, BC   V5C 6A7

PHONE: (604) 299-7311
FAX: (604) 299-9188

CONTACT: Ann Collette, Editor   **DESCRIPTION:** Published by Canada Wide Magazines. Circulation 100,000 through lower mainland and Victoria area. "Our focus is primarily home and garden. That includes stories related to renovation, architecture, elements of interior design, BC artisans, and all elements of gardening. In addition we also have a regular food column that features a personality or restaurateur and includes recipes." Published 6 times a year. Established in 1992.

WRITERS: "Our stories are definitely focused on the BC market. We are looking for BC people, BC residences, and products that are available to people here. Our stories are on an assignment basis. We don't accept unsolicited manuscripts. If someone is interested in writing for us and has a story idea I am more than happy to entertain those ideas with a query letter or phone call. Our average pay rate is about 30¢ a word. It varies according to the complexity of the story and the writer's experience. People must remember that we are totally BC focused. If it has a BC spin on it and involves BC artisans, home owners, architects or designers we will entertain those things. How-to articles are not something we have done a lot of but is an element that will be part and parcel of this magazine as it evolves." Writers' guidelines are available.

PHOTOGRAPHERS: "We hire freelance photographers to shoot our colour photos. People can contact us directly or our Art Director, Cathy Mullaly."

NOTES: Sample copies of this publication are available free upon request. Also publishes Award Magazine, BC Business, BC Pharmacist and Pacific Golf.

BC HOTELMAN see Inn Focus

BC MEDICAL JOURNAL
115-1665 West Broadway
Vancouver, BC   V6J 5A4

PHONE: (604) 736-5551
FAX: (604) 733-7317

CONTACT: Claudette Reed Upton   **DESCRIPTION:** Published by BC Medical Association. Circulation 7,800. Published monthly. Established in 1959.

WRITERS: "We publish very little work by non-physicians. This is a medical journal whose target audience is British Columbia doctors, so everything we publish must be of direct interest to the medical profession."

PHOTOGRAPHERS: 100% included in text/photo package. Model releases are required. Contact Jerry Wong.

NOTES: A limited number of sample copies of this publication are available free upon request.

BC ORCHARDIST
7602 Hudson Road
Salmon Arm, BC   V1E 4N6

PHONE: (604) 832-7703
FAX: (604) 433-0632

CONTACT: Jim Hayward, Editor   **DESCRIPTION:** Published by Jim Hayward. Circulation 2,300. Mainly a technical journal serving tree fruit growers and grape growers of the Okanagan Valley in BC. Published monthly. Established in 1959.

WRITERS: "We use some local freelance writers. Most of our copy and information comes from the ministry of Agriculture. We do very occassionally buy articles from freelance writers. We use articles that interview growers and discuss their problems and local political issues. For example the ALR is the big issue here." Unsolicited manuscripts are welcomed and returned with SASE. "We don't pay by the word but will negotiate according to the amount of work that goes into it. We are a small publication without a lot to spend."

PHOTOGRAPHERS: Does not buy photos. "We take our own."

NOTES: "The local point-of-view is critical."

BC OUTDOORS
1132 Hamilton Street, #202
Vancouver, BC   V6B 2S2

PHONE: (604) 687-1581
FAX: (604) 687-1925

CONTACT: Karl Bruhn, Editor   **DESCRIPTION:** Published by Rex Armstead. Circulation 42,000. Focuses on fishing (saltwater and freshwater), hunting, camping in British Columbia. Readers are very knowledgable outdoors people. "96% of our readers fish and 72% hunt." Published 8 times a year.
WRITERS: Majority freelance written. "Some of the writers we use are regulars, some are new freelancers. Purchase 8 to 12 articles per year from new writers. Gives byline. Writers on assignment can negotiate expenses as a special agreement. For example if we know a writer has to do a lot of long distance phoning or some traveling we will negotiate reasonable expenses." Pays 27¢ a published word. Most articles are 1,500 to 2,000 words. Purchases one-time rights. Prefers text/photo packages. There is no extra payment for photos when they are included in the text/photo package. Accepts unsolicited material. Guidelines available. A free sample copy of the magazine is available if you send a large SASE. Americans must use IRCs or Canadian postage.
PHOTOGRAPHERS: Usually writers supply photos along with their articles. "If we have a hole in a story and need a photo we do maintain an archive of photos so we can browse through it and pick something up. In that case it is worthwhile for people to send in their material for us to look at, however we do keep it on file for a long time. We use 35mm and larger format slides. We accept duplicates if they are good quality. We are tightly focused on fishing and hunting. Cover shots are real action fishing shots or really nice pictures of wildlife. We don't use bloody hunting shots." Five covers are fishing related, three are wildlife. Photo guidelines are available. Purchases one-time rights. Pays $250 for a cover shot.
NOTES: "We plan for an entire year in September. We line up all our articles and send out assignments to people who have submitted querys. From time to time we receive an exceptional unsolicited article in mid-year. If we happen to have a hole (which doesn't happen very often) we may use the article right away. More likely we call the writer and ask to hold the article until our planning session in September. If you are completely unknown to us, it may be more worthwhile to send a complete article so we can see your writing style and a query letter as well with other ideas. Remember we focus only on BC."

BC PHARMACIST
150-3751 Shell Road
Richmond, BC   V6X 2W2

PHONE: (604) 279-2053
FAX: (604) 279-2065

CONTACT: Judy Schlachter, Editor   **DESCRIPTION:** A publication of the British Columbia Pharmacy Association. Published bi-monthly.
WRITERS: "We very rarely purchase material. If we do it is very clinical oriented or we need someone who has done some original research on a pharmacy issue. Write a query letter to the editor."
PHOTOGRAPHERS: "We rarely purchase photography. It depends on the issue." A photographer may send a resume to be kept on file.
NOTES: Also publishes Award Magazine, BC Business, BC Pharmacist and Pacific Golf. Contact the editor for a copy of the magazine.

THE BC PROFESSIONAL ENGINEER
6400 Roberts Street #210
Burnaby, BC V5G 4C9

PHONE: (604) 929-6733
FAX: (604) 929-6753

CONTACT: Wayne Gibson, Editor   **DESCRIPTION:** Published by The Association of BC Professional Engineers and Geoscientists . Circulation 17,000. A trade publication issued 10 times a year. Established in 1949.
NOTES: "We don't accept freelance material."

BC SIMMENTAL NEWS
1860-232 Avenue RR9
Langley, BC V3A 6H5

PHONE: (604) 533-1054

CONTACT: Mary Watt, Editor   **DESCRIPTION:** Circulation 4,000. A quarterly publication for BC Simmental breeders.
WRITERS: "We have a very low budget. Anything we may be interested in would be breed related and on animal husbandry or something like that." Call the editor for more information. Writers' guidelines are available.
PHOTOGRAPHERS: "I do purchase photography but it is very specific; local events I can't get myself." Call the editor if you may be interested.

BC SPORTS FISHING
909 Jackson Crescent
New Westminster, BC V3L 4S1

CONTACT: Rikk Taylor, Editor
NOTES: Do not contact with photos or articles. Editor is not interested.

BC WINE TRAILS
Box 1077
Summerland, BC V0H 1Z0

PHONE: (604) 494-7733
FAX: (604) 494-7733

CONTACT: Dave Gamble, Editor\Publisher   **DESCRIPTION:** Circulation 15,000. A news magazine that takes its readers into the vineyards, cellars and tasting room of BC's wine industry. Distributed east to Manitoba. Published quarterly. Established in 1991.
WRITERS: "Because of infrequent publishing dates we do all work in-house. We do have columnists. We almost have more material than we can use."
NOTES: Also publishes Wine Regions of Ontario which is an annual.

BC WOMAN
704 Clarkson Street
New Westminster, BC V3M 1E2

PHONE: (604) 540-8448
FAX: (604) 524-0041

CONTACT: Anne Brennan, Editor   **DESCRIPTION:** Published by BC Woman to Woman Magazine. Circulation 28,000. Published monthly. Established in 1986.

BEAUTIFUL BRITISH COLUMBIA

929 Ellery Street
Victoria, BC V9A 7B4

PHONE: (604) 384-5456
FAX: (604) 384-2812

CONTACT: Bryan McGill, Editor-in-Chief   **DESCRIPTION:** Circulation 211,000. Published quarterly.
NOTES: "Thanks for the offer for us to be listed in *Canadian Markets for Writers and Photographers*, however we have a large network of writers and photographers within B.C. that more than enough meets our needs. We are not generally looking for submissions beyond B.C.'s borders."

THE BEAVER: Exploring Canada's History

478-167 Lombard Avenue
Winnipeg, MB R3B 0T6

PHONE: (204) 786-7048
FAX: (204) 774-8624

CONTACT: Christopher Dafoe, Editor   **DESCRIPTION:** Published by Canada's National History Society. Circulation 40,000+. Features well-researched factual articles on Canada's history, its life and culture. Published 6 times a year. Established in 1920. The Beaver has received numberous awards for writing and design and is noted for its historical accuracy.
WRITERS: "Sometimes we commission an article but most of the time articles are unsolicited." Although many of its contributors are historians, scholars and experts, the articles are generally aimed at a lay audience. Contact the editor by mail with a query letter, bio and previous work." Payment is negotiated and made upon acceptance. Average lenth of articles is 3,000 to 4,000 words. Writers' guidelines are available.
PHOTOGRAPHERS: "Some black & white and colour photos are purchased."
NOTES: For a sample copy send 9x12" SASE with appropriate postage.

BEEF IN BC

10145 East Trans Canada Hwy
Kamloops, BC V2C 2J3

PHONE: (604) 573-3611
FAX: (604) 573-5155

CONTACT: A.L. Leach   **DESCRIPTION:** Published by BC Cattlemen's Association. Contains information on beef animals, vet columns, brand inspection, and association news. Published 7 times a year.
WRITERS: "We currently have a few freelance writers. We assign some articles and are open to queries. An assigned article is $250, unassigned is $150. Send a resumé with samples, what they could write about and the area they live in (BC only)."
PHOTOGRAPHERS: "We pay $10 a photo for colour or black and white. We are always looking for a good front page photo on the beef industry. The photos inside usually go along with the articles."
NOTES: Sample copies of this publication are available free based upon availability. Considers previously published work.

LE BEL AGE

5148 boul. St. Laurent
Montreal, PQ H2T 1R8

PHONE: (514) 273-9773
FAX: (514) 273-9034

CONTACT: Lucie Desaulniers, Editor   **DESCRIPTION:** Published by Senior Publications Inc. Circulation 116,000. French senior publication issued 10 times a year.

WRITERS: "Most of our work is done by freelancers. We assign the articles. Lengths and rates are negotiated separately. Contact by mail with a query letter with samples of work."

PHOTOGRAPHERS: "Colour photography is assigned. Contact us by mail."

NOTES: Also publishes Sante, Good Times, and Son Hi-Fi Video.

BENEFITS AND PENSION MONITOR
245 Fairview Mall Drive #308
North York, ON M2J 4T1

PHONE: (416) 494-1066
FAX: (416) 946-8931

CONTACT: Mary Dispalatro, Editor   **DESCRIPTION:** Published by Powershift Communications Inc. Circulation 15,500. "The publication deals with benefits management and pension investment. We explore everything from technology, human resources, health, dental and other employee benefits. On the flip side we also look at pension investment issues; asset allocation, derivative use and anything that touches on investment on the plan sponsor side. Our primary audience is the plan sponsor. We also cater to money managers, benefits consultants, and insurance companies." Published 6 times a year.

WRITERS: "We do occasionally purchase freelance work although not often. Perhaps two articles per year. If you have an idea just give me a call. We don't have guidelines set out on paper."

PHOTOGRAPHERS: Have never hired a photographer. Use material supplied from catalogues.

BENEFITS CANADA
777 Bay Street
Toronto, ON M5W 1A7

PHONE: (416) 596-5958
FAX: (416) 596-5071

CONTACT: Paul Williams   **DESCRIPTION:** Published by Maclean Hunter Publishing. Circulation 13,000. Published eleven times a year. Established in 1977.

BEST WISHES
37 Hanna Avenue #1
Toronto, ON M6K 1X1

PHONE: (416) 537-2604
FAX: (416) 538-1794

CONTACT: Shirley Ohannessian   **DESCRIPTION:** Published by Family Communications Inc. Circulation 171,000. Consumer magazine focusing on post-natal care. Articles include: once the baby is born; 1st 6 months of life; post-natal blues; etc. Established in 1949.

WRITERS: "All articles are written by doctors and nurses."

NOTES: No freelance material is purchased for this publication. Also publishes Today's Bride, You, Expecting and Baby and Child Care Encyclopedia.

BINGO CALLER NEWS
19607 - 88 Avenue
Langley, BC V3A 6Y3

PHONE: (604) 888-7477
FAX: (604) 888-6495

CONTACT: Egon Neilson   **DESCRIPTION:** Published by 10,000. Publication aimed at the gaming industry and fundraising through lotteries, casinos, bingos etc. Published 24 times a year.

BINGO NEWS AND GAMING HIGHLIGHTS
Box 106, 10171 Saskatchewan Drive **PHONE:** (403) 433-9740
Edmonton, AB T6E 4R5 **FAX:** (403) 433-9842

CONTACT: Lorraine Kramer, Editor **DESCRIPTION:** Published by Bingo Hi-Lites Ltd. Circulation 25,000. A bingo and gambling magazine with stories on bingo, gambling, tips on gambling and gaming news from the western provinces and other parts of Canada. Published monthly. Established in 1984.
WRITERS: This publication purchases work very infrequently. May be interested in issues surrounding gaming from Alberta or other provinces. Query by mail or phone.
NOTES: Sample copies of this publication are available free, based on availability.

BLUE LINE MAGAZINE
12A-4981 #254 Hwy 7 East **PHONE:** (905) 640-3048
Markham, ON L3R 1N1 **FAX:** (905) 640-7547

CONTACT: Morely S. Lymburner, Editor **DESCRIPTION:** Published by Blue Line Magazine Inc., Morley S. Lymburner, Publisher. Circulation 10,000. A law enforcement publication issued monthly to those involved and interested in law enforcement in Canada. Reports on law changes and any novel ideas and programs started up by law enforcement. Established in 1988.
WRITERS: Very rarely purchases material. "I have paid for stories in the past because people have sent me a story and tempted me with it. They were well-written and to the point and actually of interest to my readers. I will negotiate payment but prefer people to be upfront about what they want for the article."
NOTES: Editor's note: It appears this publication gets a lot of material sent to them for free use. If you are submitting an article and expect payment you must state this on a cover letter or sheet.

BOAT GUIDE
447 Speers Rd. #4 **PHONE:** (905) 842-6591
Oakville, ON L6K 3S7 **FAX:** (905) 842-6843

CONTACT: Lizanne Madigan, Editor **DESCRIPTION:** Published by Formula Publications. Circulation 60,000 winter issue and 50,000 for summer issue. The winter issue is called the Boat Buyer's Guide. Both issues contain boat tests and lifestyle articles.
WRITERS: "We purchase approximately half a dozen to a dozen articles per issue. We have front of the book items which are about 300 words and then we can have our larger features which can go up to about 2,000 words. Guidelines and pay rates vary as material is readily available from the manufacturers and it's a matter of putting it together and in other situations it takes a lot of research and interviewing." Contact by phone initially but all serious inquiries are preferred written, either by fax or mail.
PHOTOGRAPHERS: Purchases mostly colour transparencies for this publication.
NOTES: Also publishes Boating Business.

BOATING BUSINESS
447 Speers Road #4
Oakville, ON L6K 3S7

PHONE: (905) 842-6591
FAX: (905) 842-6843

CONTACT: Lizanne Madigan   DESCRIPTION: Published by Formula Publications.
Circulation 5,000. Contains recreational boating industry news. Published bi-monthly.
WRITERS: "We purchases approximately half a dozen to a dozen articles per issue."
Hires writers on assignment and doesn't pay expenses. Articles average from 300-600
words. Guidelines and pay rates vary depending on the complexity of the assignment. Contact
by phone initially but all serious inquiries are preferred written, either by fax or mail.
PHOTOGRAPHERS: Purchases mostly black and white photos.
NOTES: Also publishes Boat Guide.

BOATING NEWS
1252 Burrard Street #201
Vancouver, BC V6Z 1Z1

PHONE: (604) 684-1643
FAX: none

CONTACT: George Railton, Editor   DESCRIPTION: Published by Tyrell Publishing.
Circulation 12,500. Covers sail and power boating and local events. Published 11 times
a year. Established in 1970.
WRITERS: "We don't purchase features, perhaps some local interest news items. We
have some freelancers already on track. Query the editor by phone."
PHOTOGRAPHERS: "We purchase photography from one source in Vancouver and
the photos are local and current which is what we need."

BODYSHOP
1450 Don Mills Road
Don Mills, ON M3B 2X7

PHONE: (416) 445-6641
FAX: (416) 442-2213

CONTACT: Brian Harper   DESCRIPTION: Published by Southam. Circulation 12,500.
Focuses on autobody repair and refinishing. Includes new product information. Published
6 times a year. Readers own and work in body shops. Established in 1970.

BOOKS IN CANADA
130 Spadina Avenue #603
Toronto, ON M5V 2L4

PHONE: (416) 601-9880
FAX: (416) 601-9883

CONTACT: Paul Stuewe, Editor   DESCRIPTION: Published by Canadian Review
of Books Ltd. Circulation 10,000. National magazine about the world of books and related
cultural fields. Carries author profiles, book reviews and news related to publishing in
Canada. Published nine times a year. Established in 1971.
WRITERS: "We very rarely employ freelancers and do not want freelance inquiries."

BORDER CROSSINGS
393 Portage Avenue, Suite 300
Winnipeg, MB R3B 3H6

PHONE: (204) 942-5778
FAX: (204) 949-0793

CONTACT: Meeka Walsh, Editor   DESCRIPTION: Circulation 3,800. An
interdisciplinary arts magazine covering a range of arts activities. Features book reviews,

artists' profiles, and interviews. Articles include architecture, photography, film, theatre, dance, poetry, and painting. Established in 1977.

WRITERS: "Most work is done on commission. Send a query letter to the editor. We recommend that the magazine be used as your guideline. Writers should be familiar with the magazine before they even send a query letter."

PHOTOGRAPHERS: "We purchase art photography and pay fees for everything we use. We use both black and white and colour. Look at several copies of the magazine before writing." Contact the editor.

NOTES: Copies are available at most independent book stores and art galleries across Canada.

BORDER/LINES

The Orient Bldg.
183 Bathurst Street, #301
Toronto, ON M5T 2R7

PHONE: (416) 504-5249
FAX: (416) 504-8781

CONTACT: Julie Jenkinson, Editor **DESCRIPTION:** A quarterly magazine exploring all aspects of culture. Articles include: reviews, arts, science, and communications.

BOREALIS: NO LONGER PUBLISHED

THE BOTTOM LINE

75 Clegg Road
Markham, ON L6G 1A1

PHONE: (905) 415-5803
FAX: (905) 479-3758

CONTACT: Michael Lewis **DESCRIPTION:** Published by Butterworths Canada. Circulation 38,000. Published monthly. Established in 1985.

WRITERS: 65% freelance written. Roughly 200 articles purchased per year. Writers hired on assignment (expenses paid) and byline given. A kill fee is offered if an article is cancelled. Average article is 850 words paying 25-30¢ per word. Contact with a query letter. Writers' guidelines are available. "Generally if the ideas don't include the word "accountant" we're not interested. Readers welcome discussion of technical financial issues and information systems news."

PHOTOGRAPHERS: Purchases stock images and hires photographers on assignment. Purchases approximately 25 photos annually, 2 per issue. 65% assigned to in-house photographers, 25% to freelance photographers, 5% purchased from stock and 5% included in text/photo package. Uses 5x7 colour prints and b&w 5x7 prints. Fees are negotiable. Model releases are not necessary, captions are preferred and a credit line is given. New photographers should send query letter and sample portfolio. Photo guidelines are available. "Accounting subjects are tough to illustrate - looking for imaginative, self-starting photographer."

NOTES: Purchases first North American serial rights. Does not consider previously published work or simultaneous submissions. Returns unsolicited materials with a SASE.

THE BOUNTY INFANTCARE GUIDE

746 Warden Avenue #2
Scarborough, ON M1L 4A2

NOTES: NO LONGER PUBLISHED

THE BOUNTY PREGNANCY GUIDE
746 Warden Avenue #2
Scarborough, ON M1L 4A2

NOTES: NO LONGER PUBLISHED

BOUT DE PAPIER
45 Rideau Street #301
Ottawa, ON K1N 5WB

NOTES: Could not locate.

BOW VALLEY THIS WEEK
Box 129, 233 Bear Street
Banff, AB T0L 0C0

PHONE: (403) 762-2453
FAX: (403) 762-5274

CONTACT: David Rooney, Editor   **DESCRIPTION:** Circulation 11,000. The arts
and entertainment guide for the Bow Valley. Published weekly.
WRITERS: "We do purchase writing, per month about four. Our standard rate is $30
per article upon publication of a 300-750 word article. Generally we assign but if a writer
comes forward with an idea we think is suitable for our publication then I will purchase
it. Contact me by fax, telephone or mail. Write a query letter with a SASE if there is a
manuscript included. We look for articles that have to do with arts and entertainment in
the Rocky Mountain region. The tighter the focus on the Banff Canmore corridor between
Calgary and Revelstoke the better. We publish poetry from time to time and essays. What
I am concerned about is the quality of writing and that it meets our requirements in terms
of this region."
PHOTOGRAPHERS: "We do purchase photos occasionally with articles. If someone
has a terrific stand alone we may purchase it as well. We pay $15 for photos upon publication.
NOTES: Purchases first North American serial rights. Considers previously published
work. Sample copies of this publication are available for $1. A supplement to the Banff
Crag and Canyon and Canmore Leader.

BOWBENDER MAGAZINE
237-8 Avenue SE #600
Calgary, AB T2G 5C3

PHONE: (403) 264-3270
FAX: (403) 264-3276

CONTACT: Tim Ottmann, Editor/Publisher   **DESCRIPTION:** Published by OT
Communications. A bi-monthly national archery magazine with technical information and
hunting stories. Established in 1984.
WRITERS: "We do purchase some work, mostly hunting stories. People submit to me
all the time and if I like it I call them. I prefer articles on spec. Our length is 1,500 and
the pay rate is negotiable. It has to be a Canadian hunting story." Contact the editor by
phone, fax or mail.
PHOTOGRAPHERS: "Most writers provide 35mm transparencies with the articles. If
a photographer is interested in stocking me with a minimum of 500 slides and are interested
in the Canadian market and they have a library I may be interested. I have a number of
people working with me from the photography world so I am not pressed. I like to use

many images from one or two sources opposed to 1 or 2 images from many sources."
Contact the editor by phone, fax or mail.
NOTES: Sample copies of this publication are available for $2.50 with SASE.

BRANDON SUN TV BOOK
501 Rosser Avenue
Brandon, MB R7A 0K4

PHONE: (204) 727-2451
FAX: (204) 725-0976

DESCRIPTION: Circulation 18,000. Weekly publication. Established in 1977.
NOTES: Doesn't purchase freelance material.

BREEDER & FEEDER see Ontario Beef

BRIARPATCH
2138 McIntyre Street
Regina, SK S4P 2R7

PHONE: (306) 525-2949
FAX: (306) 565-3430

CONTACT: George Martin Manz, Managing Editor **DESCRIPTION:** Published by
Briarpatch Inc. Circulation 2,100. We are a left-wing political magazine for political
activists involved in labour, social justice, women's, environmental and international
movements. Articles cover issues concerning Saskatchewan and Canada. Articles include:
the environment; agriculture; Aboriginal and women's rights, and labour. Published 10
times a year. Established in 1973.
WRITERS: "We are not financially able to pay writers. We do provide 3-5 free copies
of the magazine to authors we publish." Articles average 600 to 1200 words. Byline is
given. "We like short, punchy articles that are well-researched and well-written. We want
the facts with quotes from a few people rather than just the writer's opinion. Hard copy
necessary plus Word Perfect disk if possible."
PHOTOGRAPHERS: "We publish about 20 photos per issue but do not pay." Use colour
prints but prefer b&w prints. "We are a political magazine covering issues in Canada and
the Third World. Our supporters give us photos or lend them to us to publish. We cannot
afford to pay our photographers but are happy to publish up-and-coming photographers
who want their photos published. We can provide you with free copies of the magazine
in return."
NOTES: Sample copy available, enclose 9x12 SASE. Buys one-time rights. Unsolicited
materials will be returned with SASE. Considers previously published work and simultaneous
submissions. Guidelines are not available.

BRICK: A LITERARY JOURNAL
Box 537, Station Q
Toronto, ON M4T 2M5

NOTES: Couldn't locate. Phone number is not in service (519) 666-0283.

BRIDGES: NO LONGER PUBLISHED

BRITISH COLUMBIA REPORT
535 Thurlow Street #600
Vancouver, BC V6E 3L2

PHONE: (604) 682-8202
FAX: (604) 682-0963

CONTACT: Terry O'Neill, Editor-in-Chief **DESCRIPTION:** Published by British Columbia Report Magazine. Circulation 28,000 paid subscription. A weekly regional news magazine. Established in 1989.
WRITERS: "We purchase 5 stories a week. All of them are assigned. Contact the executive editor, Steve Lequire by mail with a proposal. We want to see regional news from outside the lower mainland. Our standard pay rate is $50 per 300 word column. An average article may run 2-3 columns." Writer's guidelines are not available.
PHOTOGRAPHERS: "We purchase both black & white and colour, but mostly black & white. Some photos come with the articles. We also assign some work." Contact the photo editor, Nick Procaylo with a query letter. Photo guidelines are not available.
NOTES: "Since we are dealing with news there is little reprint. If we buy it is purchased for the chain." Available on newsstands and in the library.

BROADCAST TECHNOLOGY
Box 420
Bolton, ON L7E 5T3

PHONE: (905) 857-6076
FAX: (905) 857-8045

CONTACT: Doug Loney **DESCRIPTION:** Circulation under 10,000. Trade magazine covering the broadcast industry, including television and radio. Published ten times a year.
NOTES: "We use only contributors who are involved in the broadcast industry."

BROADCAST WEEK
444 Front Street West
Toronto, ON M5V 2S9

PHONE: (416) 585-5045
FAX: (416) 585-5461

CONTACT: Trevor Cole **DESCRIPTION:** Published by The Globe and Mail. Circulation over 200,000. Television guide inserted in each Saturday edition of the Globe and Mail. Contains reviews, articles and profiles about television and the wide spectrum it entails.
WRITERS: 90% freelance written. Purchases 100 to 150 articles per year. Byline is given. Average article is 500 words. Pays 40¢ per word. "We want stories on television performers, writers and producers written exclusively for Broadcast Week."

BROADCASTER
1450 Don Mills Road
Don Mills, ON M3B 2X7

PHONE: (416) 445-6641
FAX: (416) 442-2213

CONTACT: John Bugaliskis, Editor **DESCRIPTION:** Published by Southam . Circulation 8,000. Reaches broadcasters in TV and radio and covers engineering and management. Published ten times a year. Established in 1942.
WRITERS: "We do purchase on occasion although we don't have a huge freelance budget. Articles are about 1,500 words and pay $250." Contact the editor with a query letter.
PHOTOGRAPHERS: "We don't purchase much photography."

BRUCE COUNTY MARKETPLACE

910 Queen Street Box 523
Kincardine, ON N2Z 2Y9

PHONE: (519) 396-9142
FAX: (519) 396-3555

CONTACT: Charles Whipp, Editor **DESCRIPTION:** Circulation 13,000. An upbeat community publication issued monthly to each resident in the area. Features news about people and happenings in the area. Established in 1989.
WRITERS: Have a pool of 22 writers that are consistently used. Freelancers should contact the editor with a query letter including portfolio of previously published material.
PHOTOGRAPHERS: Usually done in-house.

BRUCE TRAIL NEWS

11 Oriole Crescent
Guelph, ON N1G 1J5

PHONE: (519) 763-9357
FAX: (519) 836-0324

CONTACT: Scott Black, Editor **DESCRIPTION:** Published by New Paradigm Communications; Bruce Trail Association. Circulation 10,000. Magazine caters to hikers belonging to the Bruce Trail Association. Contains news, features on camping and outdoor life. Deals with issues regarding the Niagara escarpment and trail use. Looks at environmental and natural concerns of the area; the history of the communities along the trail. "The association is dedicated to the preservation and the conservation of Niagara escarpment. We are a 25 year old association which represents 8,500 members." Published quarterly. Established in 1963.
WRITERS: "We do purchase but we don't have a big budget for writers. We usually pay $100 for a feature, $25 for a book review. We are open to ideas, please send in a query letter. Usually we generate ideas and solicit writers but it would be great for writers to come up with ideas and submit them. It would be nice if they had photos with their stories or contact names for photos." Contact by phone or with a query letter.
PHOTOGRAPHERS: "We pay $100 for a colour cover photo and $25 for inside photos. The magazine is black & white so we can work with colour slides; prints are fine. Usually photos are of the region. They could be scenics, pictures of the area anywhere from Niagara to Tobermory. We would be interested in photos from any of the communities in the area." Contact by phone or with a query letter with description of your photos or non-returnable samples.

THE BRUNSWICK BUSINESS JOURNAL

599 Main Street #203
Moncton, NB E1C 1C8

PHONE: (506) 857-9696
FAX: (506) 859-7395
EMAIL abjpubl@nbnet.nb.ca

CONTACT: Ron Levesque, Editor **DESCRIPTION:** Published by ABJ Publishing Inc. Circulation 5,000+. BBJ is a tabloid sized monthly newspaper that focuses mainly on positive business news stories in New Brunswick. Established in 1984.
WRITERS: 90% freelance written. Byline is given. Purchases about 100 articles per year. Does not hire writers on assignment. Pays 15¢ per word (after relationship is established - usually 3 published stories) for articles averaging 800 words. A kill fee is not paid if an article is cancelled. "Some columns are paid for, others accepted in return for promotion (usually tag at bottom of column)." Writers' guidelines are available. Contact with a query letter, resumé and business card or email. "I like writers with initiative, who can come up with their own story ideas. Don't send complete stories. Prefer to be contacted by email or fax. Will only accept stories with link to New Brunswick. We also publish Atlantic Business Report for the Atlantic Canada market. Same guidelines as BBJ."

PHOTOGRAPHERS: 50% assigned to free-lance photographers and 50% included with text packages. Purchases approximately 3-4 photos per issue. Accepts 5x7 and 8x10 color prints and 8x10 b&w prints. Model releases are not necessary but captions are required. Pays $15 for photos, $35 for color cover plus processing expenses with receipt. No credit line is given. Please provide resumé and business card. "We only purchase photo/text packages. Would consider queries from freelance photographers located in our region." Photo guidelines are not available.
NOTES: For a sample copy send 9x12" SASE with 88¢ postage. Purchases first North American serial rights. Returns unsolicited materials with a SASE. Does not consider previously published work or simultaneous submissions.

BUILDCORE PRODUCT SOURCE
280 Yorkland Blvd.   **PHONE:** (416) 494-4990
North York, ON M2J 4Z6   **FAX:** (416) 756-2767

CONTACT: Nigel Heseltine, Editor   **DESCRIPTION:** Published by Daily Commercial News. Circulation 8,500. An anually published directory. Established in 1974.
WRITERS: "We don't publish any editorial articles."
PHOTOGRAPHERS: Most photography supplied from the companies listed. Prefers 2¼x2¼ transparencies for the few photos they may require.

BUILDING AND CONSTRUCTION TRADES TODAY
c\o 29 Bernard Avenue   **PHONE:** (416) 944-1217
Toronto, ON M5R 1R3   Editor (416) 532-1315
                           FAX: (416) 944-0133
CONTACT: Laura Kosterski, Editor   **DESCRIPTION:** Published by Heisey Publishing. Circulation 4,200. Published 8 times a year for trades contractors, trades people and general contractors in the greater Toronto area. Contains methods, management and news stories in a tabloid format. Established in 1990.
WRITERS: "We purchase 50+ articles per year. We pay $25 plus or minus. We want articles about big and small contractors, workers and projects. We want to do articles on government regulations and safety."
PHOTOGRAPHERS: "We have a need for freelance photography. We like photos of trades contractors and trades people in action on job sites. Mostly black and white. I will pay $15-25 for a good black and white photo. I need very detailed captions."
NOTES: Also publishes Georgian Bay Today.

BUILDING MAGAZINE
113 Davenport Road   **PHONE:** (416) 966-9944
Toronto, ON M5R 1H8   **FAX:** (416) 966-9946

CONTACT: John Fennell, Editor   **DESCRIPTION:** Published by Crailer Communications. Published 6 times a year. Established in 1951.

BUILDING MANAGEMENT AND DESIGN
136 Coleridge Avenue   PHONE: (416) 424-2152
Toronto, ON M4C 4H6   FAX: (416) 424-2624

CONTACT: Cindy Woods, Editor   DESCRIPTION: Published by Cinwood Communications. Circulation 14,000. Provides pertinent information to building managers and those who supply products and services to the industry. Provides educational and training support. Contents include building design, maintenance and management considerations. Published 6 times a year. Established in 1986.
NOTES: Formerly Building Property Owner and Manager

BUILDING PROPERTY OWNER AND MANAGER see Building Management and Design

LE BULLETIN DES AGRICULTEURS
75 Port Royal East #200   PHONE: (514) 382-4350
Montreal, PQ H3L 3T1   FAX: (514) 382-4356

CONTACT: Marc-Alain Soucy, Editor   DESCRIPTION: Published by Maclean Hunter. Circulation 33,000. French language publication issued 12 times a year for agricultural producers and farmers. "The magazine contains three sections: Economic including marketing and management; a technical section and rural life." Established in 1918.
WRITERS: "We do hire freelancers. We pay $70 a page (250 words). We are open to suggestions from French writers. Call me and explain the idea. If it is interesting and if it fits our magazine we may try it. We purchase 10 articles a month." Guidelines are available.
PHOTOGRAPHERS: "For photography we ask freelancers to take the photos and we pay a fee. We usually prefer colour photos, sometimes we use black and white. We pay $20 for a published picture and we pay the processing fee. Most of the photography is profile photography."
NOTES: Sample copies of this publication are available free upon request. Rights are negotiated.

BUMPS
2499 Yonge St. 2nd Flr.   PHONE: (416) 487-9575
Toronto, ON M4P 2H6   FAX: (416) 487-9680

CONTACT: Glenn Griffin, Editor   DESCRIPTION: Consumer publication containing articles related to growing flowering plants. Articles are primarily "plant profiles", with information on different varieties, how to make them flourish, and where to buy.
WRITERS: Contact this publication by sending a query letter. Send 9x12" SASE with appropriate postage for a sample copy. Byline given. Pay negotiable.
PHOTOGRAPHERS: 100% assigned to in-house photographers.

THE BUSINESS & PROFESSIONAL WOMAN
95 Leeward Glenway, Unit 121   PHONE: (416) 424-1393
Don Mills, ON M3C 2Z6   FAX: (416) 467-8262

CONTACT: Valerie Dunn, Editor   DESCRIPTION: Published by Val Publications Ltd. Circulation 3,600. Focuses on working women. Covers personal development, women's issues and anything that affects working women. Published quarterly in English and French. Established in 1934.

WRITERS: "We do purchase work. Payment is minimal. We don't need travel articles, we already have travel writers. We don't have specific needs at the moment, just anything that relates to our goals. It's best if people send something they think would be of interest to the readership. I would rather have a completed story, about 800 words (up to 1500 words). We have a very small staff so don't be worried if you don't hear from us right away, please be patient." Writers' guidelines are available. "Ours is a small publication especially for working women many of who are members of the Canadian Federation of Business and Professional Women's Clubs. Articles in a good, journalistic style on womens issues, lifestyles, health, humour are welcome. Please no profiles on successful women, we are deluged with items of "her successful business." Accompanying photos are welcome and are paid for at $10 each. Also supply author photo."

PHOTOGRAPHERS: "We rarely purchase photos."

NOTES: "We are looking for cartoons and are interested in them, although we don't pay a lot." Sample copy available. Send SASE. Unsolicited materials will be returned with SASE. Considers previously published work and simultaneous submissions. Also publishes Hi-Rise.

THE BUSINESS ADVOCATE
244 Pall Mall Street, Box 3295   **PHONE:** (519) 432-7551
London, ON   N6A 5P6   **FAX:** (519) 432-8063

CONTACT: John Redmond, Editor   **DESCRIPTION:** Published by London Chamber of Commerce.   Circulation 11,000.   Published monthly for the London Chamber of Commerce. Established in 1987.

WRITERS: "We haven't as of yet had to purchase any material."
PHOTOGRAPHERS: "We don't purchase photographs."

BUSINESS COMPUTER NEWS
1300 Don Mills Road
North York, ON   M3B 3M8

NOTES: NO LONGER PUBLISHED

BUSINESS EXAMINER
1824 Store Street   **PHONE:** (604) 381-3926
Victoria, BC   V8T 4R4   **FAX:** (604) 381-5606

CONTACT: Bjorn Stavrum, Editor   **DESCRIPTION:** Published by Island Publishers. Two editions published monthly. Established in 1984.

BUSINESS IN VANCOUVER

1155 West Pender Street #500　　　**PHONE:** (604) 688-2398
Vancouver, BC　V6E 2P4　　　　　**FAX:** (604) 688-1963

CONTACT: Maurice Bridge, Editor　**DESCRIPTION:** Published by BIV Publications Ltd. Circulation 11,000. A business newspaper for the greater Vancouver area. Published weekly. Established in 1989.
WRITERS: "We do occasionally purchase work. We have regular contributers and columnists and buy their work weekly. As far as sporadic freelance, maybe a dozen times a year. The best way to contact me is by phone or fax. I assign all articles." Writers' guidelines are not available.
PHOTOGRAPHERS: "We don't purchase photography."
NOTES: Sample copies of this publication are available for $1.85 with SASE.

BUSINESS INSIGHTS: NO LONGER PUBLISHED

BUSINESS PEOPLE MAGAZINE

232 Henderson Highway　　　　　**PHONE:** (204) 982-4002
Winnipeg, MB　R2L 1L9　　　　　**FAX:** (204) 982-4001

CONTACT: Al Davies, Editor　　**DESCRIPTION:** Published by McCain-Davies Communications Ltd. Publishing has been temporarily suspended. There are plans to resumé publishing. Subject matter is people in business, mostly in Manitoba. Established in 1984.
NOTES: This publication is not accepting freelance material at this time.

BUSINESS QUARTERLY

Western Business School,　　　　**PHONE:** (519) 661-3309
University of Western Ontario　　**FAX:** (519) 661-3838
London, ON　N6A 3K7

CONTACT: Angela Smith, Editor　**DESCRIPTION:** Published by Western Business School, The University of Western Ontario. Circulation 9,000. A national management magazine for executives. Published quarterly. Established in 1933.
WRITERS: "We don't purchase writing, however since we don't have writers on staff we depend upon submissions."
PHOTOGRAPHERS: "Photography is used but not purchased."
NOTES: Freelancers could writed, fax or call the editor for more information.

THE BUSINESS TIMES

231 Dundas Street #203　　　　　**PHONE:** (519) 679-4901
London, ON　N6A 1H1　　　　　　**FAX:** (519) 434-7842

CONTACT: David Helwig, Editor　**DESCRIPTION:** Published by Blackburn Magazine Group Inc. Circulation 10,000. Published every 4 weeks, 13 times per year. ".aimed at the owners, executives and employees of London businesses, with an emphasis on the useful information they need. We focus on marketing and strategy, trends and ideas. Our goal is to give every reader a $10,000 idea in every issue." Established in 1993.

WRITERS: 40% freelance written. "We are interested in articles about the following sectors: retail, financial, media, entrepreneurship, manufacturing, construction, business and law, services, technology and transportation. We are also hungry for ideas for our regular features. Articles must have local angle, must uncover timely news, trends and developments." Articles range from 75 to 600 words. Follow CP style book. "We insist on written queries from writers." New writers should send samples of their work. Payment negotiable. Writers' guidelines are available.

PHOTOGRAPHERS: Hires photographers on assignment. Purchases 12 photos annually. Uses 2¼x2¼ transparencies, 5x7 colour prints and 5x7 b&w prints. Model releases, captions are not necessary. Pays $25 for b&w; $50 colour inside; $100 colour cover. "We assign all photography. Prefer natural poses of personalities to go with major news stories."

NOTES: Also publishes London Magazine, London Guidebook and Cover Story.

BUSINEST
73 St Germain East, Box 410　　　　　**PHONE:** (418) 723-4800
Rimouski, PQ G5L 7C4　　　　　　　**FAX:** (418) 722-4078

CONTACT: Jean-Claude Leclerc　　**DESCRIPTION:** Published by Claude Bellavance. French language publication. Issued monthly. Established in 1986.

BUTTER FAT
Box 9100
Vancouver, BC V6B 4G4

NOTES: NO LONGER PUBLISHED

C MAGAZINE
Box 5, Station B　　　　　　　　　**PHONE:** (416) 539-9495
Toronto, ON M5T 2T2　　　　　　　**FAX:** (416) 539-9903

CONTACT: Joyce Mason, Editor　　**DESCRIPTION:** Circulation 3,000. A quarterly magazine of local and international contemporary visual art and criticism.

WRITERS: "We purchase most of our articles from freelancers, 85%. Rarely do we solicit. Write the editor a letter of proposal. Reviews are maximum 500 words and pay $100-$150. Feature lengths vary and so do pay rates. It's best to get the guidelines." Writers' guidelines are available.

PHOTOGRAPHERS: "No photography is purchased."

NOTES: Sample copies of this publication are available for $10.25 including shipping.

CA MAGAZINE
277 Wellington Street West　　　　　**PHONE:** (416) 977-3222
Toronto, ON M5V 3H2　　　　　　　**FAX:** (416) 204-3409

CONTACT: Ruby Andrew　　**DESCRIPTION:** Published by Canadian Institute of Chartered Accountants. Circulation 65,000. "The magazine is the flagship publication of the Institute of Chartered Accounts. It informs chartered accountants about developments affecting their profession." Published 10 times a year in English and French editions." Established in 1911.

WRITERS: "We purchase work in a very limited capacity. By and large the magazine is contributed to by members who are chartered accountants. Pay rates vary according to the length and complexity of the article and the writer's expertise. We only occasionally give freelance assignments to writers. We are a very specialized journal and the opportunities here are infrequent. Please send a query letter first." Writers' guidelines and a sample copy are available by mail. "We hold the copyright for the material we publish."
PHOTOGRAPHERS: "We purchase 2 or 3 photos per issue. We commission the photographs to go with particular pieces in the magazine." Contact our art director, Bernadette Gillen (416) 204-3259.

CABLE COMMUNICATIONS MAGAZINE
57 Peachwood Court   **PHONE:** (519) 744-4111
Kitchener, ON   N2B 1S7   **FAX:** (519 744-1261

CONTACT: Udo Salewsky, Editor   **DESCRIPTION:** Published by Ter-Sat Media Publications Ltd. Circulation 7,200. "A technical and management oriented magazine for the cable TV industry in Canada and the world. We provide analytical coverage of cable television news, views, issues and developments in Canada, US and world-wide." Published bi-monthly. Established in 1934.
WRITERS: "We do not cover non-fiction or items of that nature. We need very knowledgeable people who are well-versed in cable television industry affairs; technical, regulatory, business and management and all that is associated with it. From years of experience the only way we get this is to look for knowledgeable contributors on our own from and in the industry."

CABLECASTER
1450 Don Mills Road   **PHONE:** (416) 445-6641
Don Mills, ON   M3B 2X7   **FAX:** (416) 442-2213

CONTACT: Steve Pawlett   **DESCRIPTION:** Published by Southam. Circulation 5,000. "We reach the engineers, management and staff of the cable television system across Canada. We keep them informed on technology, management and marketing practices." Published 8 times a year. Established in 1989.
WRITERS: "We do purchase on occasion although we don't have a huge freelance budget. Articles are about 1,500 words and pay $250." Contact the editor with a query letter.
PHOTOGRAPHERS: "We don't purchase much photography."

CAD SYSTEMS
395 Matheson Blvd East   **PHONE:** (905) 890-1846
Mississauga, ON   L4Z 2H2   **FAX:** (905) 890-5769

CONTACT: Graham Pitcher   **DESCRIPTION:** Published by Kerrwil Publications Ltd. Circulation 17,900. Publication for the CAD/CAM system users. Published 6 times a year.
NOTES: Also publishes Formula, CAD Systems, Canadian Yachting, Electrical Business, Electrical Bluebook, Energy Manager, Lighting Magazine, Manufacturing & Process Automation and La Monde.

CAMERA CANADA
31858 Hopedale Ave   **PHONE:** (604)524-5037
Clearbrook, BC V2T 2G7

CONTACT: Marilyn McEwen, Editor   **DESCRIPTION:** Published by National Association for Photographic Art (NAPA). Circulation 4,500. Articles focus on basic camera handling techniques for new photographers, creative techniques, darkroom and lighting tips, reports on new photographic processes, personal experiences, interviews with prominent Canadian photographers, essays on the art of photography and historical developments in Canadian photography, and essays on improving the quality of readers' photographs. Published bi-annually.
WRITERS: Freelance written. No payment is given. Contributors receive two copies of the issue in which their material is published. For the types of articles used, see description above. Query first and send SASE.
PHOTOGRAPHERS: The magazine does not pay. Its purpose is to showcase the work of NAPA members. All contributors receive two copies of the issue in which their material is published. Requires one-time reproduction rights, copyright reverts to the photographer after six months. Sections open for submission. *Portfolios*: all portfolios must have a well-defined and consistent theme, style or technique. Send a maximum of 20 mounted slides or 20 unmounted, glossy 8x10 prints. *Gallery*: individual photos may be submitted (any subject) with details of where and why you took the photograph, as well as technical information. *Covers:* Usually the cover photo is selected from the Portfolio published in the same issue.

CAMPING CANADA
2585 Skymark Avenue, #306   **PHONE:** (905) 624-8218
Mississauga, ON L4W 4L5   **FAX:** (905) 624-6764

CONTACT: Diane Batten, Editor   **DESCRIPTION:** Published by Camping Canada Ltd. Circulation 40,000. Articles on routes and travel in general and information on the latest recreational vehicles including RV's and trailers. Published 7 times a year. Established in 1971.
WRITERS: "We do have regular writers and a large portion is freelance by assignment. I prefer people to query first before they submit, with a sample of their work. Article length is anywhere from 1,200-1,500 words. Pay rates vary depending on the writer and the subject matter. We are looking for travel pieces and personal RV related experience. Everything has to have an RV slant to it." Guidelines are not available.
PHOTOGRAPHERS: "We don't purchase photos individually. They come as part of an arrangement we make with the writer. A lot of our writers are photographers as well. Colour is preferred.
NOTES: May take previously published work depending on where it has been published. Prefers single submissions. Sample copies are given to those who are on assignment. Also publishes Power Boating Canada, Canadian RV Dealer.

CAMPUS CANADA
287 MacPherson Avenue   **PHONE:** (416) 928-2909
Toronto, ON M4V 1A4   **FAX:** (416) 928-1357

CONTACT: Sarah Moore   **DESCRIPTION:** Published by Canadian Controlled Media Communications. Circulation 125,000. Student lifestyle magazine featuring sports, entertainment, campus issues, and travel. Published 4 times a year. Established in 1983.

WRITERS: 20% freelance written. Gives a byline. Hires on assignment. Prefers to be contacted with a query letter with samples of work. Average article length is 800 words with payment of 10¢ a word. "Keep in mind the magazine is national. Stories must appeal to students right across the country. Stories should appeal to 18-25 year olds in general, students in particular."

PHOTOGRAPHERS: "Does not purchase from stock. Hires on assignment. Purchases 4-5 photos per issue. 50% of photos are included with text/photo packages. Uses all colour and b&w formats. Model releases and captions are preferred. Credit lines are given. Pay ranges from $30 for b&w to $500 for a colour cover. "We do have a circle of freelance photographers and we don't usually use people we are not familiar with." Photographers contact Margaret Kataska with a sample portfolio or brochure, flyers or tear sheets.

NOTES: Sample copies of this publication are available free upon request. Purchases one-time rights or first North American serial rights. Considers previously published work and simultaneous submissions.

CAMPUS REEL

900A Don Mills Road #1000
Don Mills, ON M3C 1V6

PHONE: (416) 445-4020
FAX: (416) 445-2894

CONTACT: Kim Greene, Editor   **DESCRIPTION:** Published by Sandra Stewart. Circulation 271,000. "Campus Reel consists of movie previews that are inserted into campus newspapers across Canada. Inserts are usually 8 pages long. Published quarterly. Established in 1992.

WRITERS: Doesn't usually purchase material.

NOTES: Also publishes Tribute Magazine, En Primeur Jeunesse, Kids Tribute, and En Primeur.

CANADA AND THE WORLD

Box 22099 Westmount Postal Outlet
Waterloo, ON N2L 6J7

NOTES: NO LONGER PUBLISHED

CANADA LUTHERAN

1512 St. James Street
Winnipeg, MB R3H 0L2

PHONE: (204) 786-6707
FAX: (204) 783-7548

CONTACT: Rev. Kenn Ward, Editor   **DESCRIPTION:** Published by Evangelical Lutheran Church in Canada. Circulation 23,000. "The official publication of the Evangelical Lutheran Church of Canada. Primarily geared for the lay people of the church. Provides a range of news stories primarily related to our denomination but the wider ecumenical scene as well." Issued 11 times a year. Established in 1986.

WRITERS: "We don't look for material from writers. We get a lot from the ecumenical partners and news agencies we belong to. We hire writers for our columns rather than solicit material. Our feature stories can range from general human interest with a Christian slant to inspirational stories to factual stories of interest to a Christian reader. Freelancers can submit an article with a SASE or send a query letter. Article lengths range 700-2,000 words. Payment varies from $60-$125 and we pay upon publication.

PHOTOGRAPHERS: "We publish black and white photos with articles. We also purchase individual photos, probably 4 or 5 per issue. Our rates vary according to the size and quality.

For cover photos we pay from $125-$200. Interior material is $25-$100 depending on what we use it for. Write a query letter to Darrell Dyck and he will indicate the kinds of things he is looking for. We do not have many good Canadian sources for photography. We tend to use European and American material although we prefer to use Canadian. It often is relational material showing people at work or in various professions, or in church settings of certain kinds. We would like to know the quality of a photographer's work and then ask them to do a shot. We prefer to keep stock photos on file for at least a year. Our turn-around time is so tight that an edited article may be approved, sent to the art director, a photo selected, scanned in and placed in a finished layout within a day or two. Obviously being able to turn to existing on-file stock means that whoever has the right image on file here when we need it - gets the sale. Remember - you are competing with stock libraries of high-quality images available on CD-ROM at low cost, accessible in less time than it takes to scan your image in and make tonal and colour-corrections!"
NOTES: Purchases one-time rights. Considers previously published work. Does not consider simultaneous submissions. Sample copies of this publication are available free upon request.

CANADA NEWS
Box 3044, 380 Vansickle Road #600
St. Catherines, ON L2R 7E3

NOTES: Couldn't locate. Phone number is not in service (905) 984-3147.

CANADA ON LOCATION
366 Adelaide Street West #500   **PHONE:** (416) 408-2300
Toronto, ON   M5V 1R9   **FAX:** (416) 408-0870

CONTACT: Mary Maddever, Editor   **DESCRIPTION:** Published by Brunico Communications Inc. Broadcast publication issued twice annually. Established in 1991.
WRITERS: "We usually assign articles to writers. We are so specialized that it is not appropriate for freelancers to send us material. It's not like the consumer market."
PHOTOGRAPHERS: Does not purchase.
NOTES: Also publishes Playback, Playback International and Canada on Location.

CANADA POULTRYMAN
Suite 105B, 9547 - 152 Street   **PHONE:** (604) 585-3131
Surrey, BC V3R 5Y5   **FAX:** (604) 585-1504

CONTACT: Tony Greaves, Editor   **DESCRIPTION:** Circulation 8,400. Canada's only poultry trade publication that goes to all the producers. Articles are technical in nature. Published monthly in English(90%) and French(10%). Established in 1912.
WRITERS: 90% assigned to in-house writers. Contact this publication by sending a query letter or a one-page fax without a cover letter. "Occasionally I have a need for a writer in a specific province and then I might contact people who could fill that need. That may be two times per year. I presently do not have contacts in Nova Scotia or Prince Edward Island."
PHOTOGRAPHERS: 100% assigned to in-house photographers.
NOTES: "People write us and send us articles about 'fluffy, little yellow chicks' and that is not what we need. Articles are more technical in nature about the poultry trade. I usually have my own contacts within the industry that can do the articles in the vein that I want them."

CANADA QUILTS

Box 39 Station A
Hamilton, ON L8N 3A2

PHONE: (905) 523-5828
FAX: (905) 523-7222

CONTACT: Deborrah Sherman, Editor   **DESCRIPTION:** Circulation 3,200-3,500. Contains features of Canadian quilt makers as well as events, reviews and patterns. Published 5 times a year.
WRITERS: "Often quilters will send in stories. We don't pay much. Some material is instructional and some is just news. For guild news I pay very little because it is promoting the guild. When an article is instructional I will pay more. If it is one small pattern maybe $25 and if it is a whole bigger pattern with an article and instructions it might go up to $100. It really varies. I am interested in material on historical\antique quilts with a bit of research behind them. When it comes to patterns I look for originality. I don't like the old standby American patterns. I try to encourage the creation of new Canadian patterns to happen."
PHOTOGRAPHERS: "We have never purchased photography. I use colour pictures of work that people send me. I prefer pictures of people in black and white."

CANADA'S FURNITURE MAGAZINE

312 Dolomite Drive, #217
Downsview, ON M3J 2N2

NOTES: Couldn't locate. Phone number is not in service (416) 667-6909.

CANADIAN

199 Avenue Road, 3rd Floor
Toronto, ON M5R 2J3

PHONE: (416) 962-9184
FAX: (416) 962-2380

CONTACT: Kathleen Hurd, Managing Editor   **DESCRIPTION:** Published by Synergism. Circulation 71,000. Inflight magazine for Canadian Airlines International. Full colour magazine focusing on business and travel. Published monthly in English and French. Established in 1987.
NOTES: "We are suddenly so totally overwhelmed with people sending work to us that we have a very limited use for freelance material now. That includes both writing and photography. If someone is to contact me I don't want a resumé, I want a fax of a specific query written in as few words as possible."

CANADIAN AGGRATES AND ROADBUILDING CONTRACTOR

4999 St. Catherines Street West #215
Westmount, PQ H3Z 1T3

PHONE: (514) 487-9868
FAX: (514) 487-9276

CONTACT: Robert L. Consedine, Editor   **DESCRIPTION:** Circulation 7,800. An engineering construction trade publication for aggregate producers and roadbuilders. Contains information on latest equipment and company profiles. Published 8 times a year. Established in 1987.

THE CANADIAN AIRCRAFT OPERATOR

4141 Dixie Road Box 149   **PHONE:** (905) 625-9660
Mississauga, ON L4W 1V5   **FAX:** (905) 625-9604

CONTACT: Edward Belitsky, Editor   **DESCRIPTION:** Published by Arthurs Marketing. Circulation 16,000. Published monthly for small airlines and aircraft owners. Established in 1964.
NOTES: This publication does not accept freelance work.

CANADIAN ARABIAN NEWS

4445 Calgary Trail #801 Terrace Plaza   **PHONE:** (403) 436-4244
Edmonton, AB T6H 5R7   **FAX:** (403) 436-4244

CONTACT: Peggy Arthurs, Editor   **DESCRIPTION:** Circulation 2,000. A national publication geared to arabian owners and enthusiasts. Published 6 times a year. Established in 1960.
NOTES: "We don't have a budget for freelance material."

THE CANADIAN ARCHITECT

1450 Don Mills Road   **PHONE:** (416) 445-6641
Don Mills, ON M3B 2X7   **FAX:** (416) 442-2077

CONTACT: Bronwen Ledger, Managing Editor   **DESCRIPTION:** Published by Southam. Circulation 10,000. "A professional journal for Canadian architects." Includes articles on design, technology, news, and business. Published monthly. Established in 1955.
WRITERS: "We do purchase material from architects or engineers."
PHOTOGRAPHERS: "We do purchase colour photography on assignment. We need specialist architectural photographers only. Send a query letter."
NOTES: Sample copies of this publication are available for $4.

CANADIAN ART

6 Church Street, 2nd Floor   **PHONE:** (416) 368-8854
Toronto, ON M5E 1M1   **FAX:** (416) 594-3375

CONTACT: Sarah Milroy, Editor   **DESCRIPTION:** Published by Canadian Art Foundation. Circulation 20,000. Features Canadian contemporary art including profiles of artists and their work. Previews of upcoming shows, reviews of art exhibitions and books are also published. Also features artist, dealer and collector profiles. Published quarterly.
WRITERS: "We rarely use unsolicited material. We have contributing editors that we work with, who refer writers to us." To contact please send in samples of work.
PHOTOGRAPHERS: "We do use photographers but they are usually referred to us." Send in samples of work when contacting the publication.
NOTES: As the office is small, please do NOT contact by phone.

CANADIAN AUTHOR

275 Slater Street, Suite 500
London, ON K1P 5H9

PHONE: no direct calls
FAX: (519) 473-4450

CONTACT: Welwyn Wilton Katz, Editor   **DESCRIPTION:** Published by Canadian Authors Association. Canada's national writer's magazine. Founded in 1919 as *The Bookman*, incorporating, since 1968 *Canadian Poetry*. Includes book reviews, information on the business of writing, articles on the "writing life," legal issues, markets for work, fiction and poetry.
WRITERS: Replies to your submissions will be faster if you address them to the appropriate editor. Fiction Editor, Veronica Ross; Poetry Editor, Sheila Martindale; Markets Editor, Bill Marles. If you want a reply you must send SASE. If you fax a submission or query and would like a reply, follow up with a note and SASE.
PHOTOGRAPHERS: All photography is supplied by authors or publishers.

CANADIAN AUTO REVIEW

1450 Don Mills Road
Don Mills, ON M3B 2X7

NOTES: NO LONGER PUBLISHED

CANADIAN AUTO WORLD

1200 Markham Road, Suite 220
Scarboro, ON M1H 3C3

PHONE: (403) 438-7777

CONTACT: Mike Goetz, Editor   **DESCRIPTION:** Published by World of Wheels Publishing. Circulation 5,000. Trade publication for the automobile industry. Articles deal with issues related to the making and selling of cars. Published once per month.
WRITERS: Approach this publication by either a phone call, fax, or letter. Pay negotiable. Byline given. "Do not submit large articles without talking to me first. Chances are it won't get read. Make sure the story you are pitching is related to our publication."
PHOTOGRAPHERS: 99% assigned to in-house photographers. Approach this publication by either a phone call, fax or letter. Pay negotiable. Occasionally purchases stock images. Submit colour prints with SASE.
NOTES: Returns unsolicited materials with SASE. Send 9x12" SASE with appropriate postage for a sample copy. Purchases all rights.

CANADIAN AUTOMOTIVE FLEET

152 Parliament Street
Toronto, ON M5A 2Z1

PHONE: (416) 864-1700
FAX: (416) 864-1498

CONTACT: Kevin Sheehy, Managing Editor   **DESCRIPTION:** Published by Bobit Publishing Canada Ltd. Circulation 12,000. A trade magazine that goes out to fleet managers across Canada. Published bi-monthly. Established in 1984.
WRITERS: "We very rarely purchase articles. You can contact us by letter or fax."
PHOTOGRAPHERS: Never purchases photography.

CANADIAN AUTOMOTIVE TECHNICIAN (CAT)
1450 Don Mills Road   **PHONE:** (416) 445-6641
Don Mills, ON M3B 2X7   **FAX:** (416) 442-2213

CONTACT: Gary Kenez, Editor   **DESCRIPTION:** Published by Southam Business Communications. Circulation 26,000. "Our focus is Canadian automotive service with technical articles on how to fix the latest technology and how to service vehicles from a professional point of view." Published monthy.
WRITERS: "I do purchase work. I am looking for articles on service, legislative articles, environmental articles, issues in the industry, and technical articles. The pay rate varies from nothing to $200-$300 for an article of 800-1,500 words."
PHOTOGRAPHERS: "We usually purchase photography in conjunction with the articles, mostly colour."
NOTES: This is part of Service Station and Garage Management.

CANADIAN AYRSHIRE REVIEW
Box 188   **PHONE:** (514) 398-7970
Ste. Anne de Bellevue, PQ H9X 3V9   **FAX:** (514) 398-7972

CONTACT: Patrice Prevost   **DESCRIPTION:** Published by Ayrshire Breeders' Association of Canada. Circulation 1,500. This magazine focuses on one breed of dairy cows and on the promotion of that breed. It is aimed at very specific readers and is a reference tool for Ayrshire breeders. Published monthly in English and French. Established in 1920.
WRITERS: "We don't really use outside sources. The review that we print is very very specific to one breed. All of our sources are insiders knowledgeable about that breed."
PHOTOGRAPHERS: Purchases photos. Must be specifically about ayrshires. The photographers must be knowledgeable about the breed.

CANADIAN BANKER
199 Bay Street #3000 Commerce Court   **PHONE:** (416) 362-6092
West, Box 348   **FAX:** (416) 362-5658
Toronto, ON M5L 1G2

CONTACT: Simon Hally, Editor   **DESCRIPTION:** Circulation 34,000. Focuses on issues within the banking industry and all chartered banks in Canada. Aims to provide those in the Canadian banking industry with up-to-date information and trends. Published bi-monthly. Established in 1893.
WRITERS: "Occasionally purchases articles. Phone the editor to discuss what they have in mind or send an outline of what they would like to do."
NOTES: French edition called Le Banquier.

THE CANADIAN BAPTIST
195 The West Mall #414   **PHONE:** (416) 622-8600
Etobicoke, ON M9C 5K1   **FAX:** (416) 622-0780

CONTACT: Larry Matthews, Editor   **DESCRIPTION:** Published by Canadian Baptist Editorial Board. Circulation 12,000. Religious publication published 10 times a year. Established in 1854.

WRITERS: 95% freelance written. Purchases 50 articles per year. Byline is given. Hires writers on assignment, expenses are negotiated. Articles range from 700 to 2,000 words. Pay rate is 5¢ to 10¢ a word. Kill fees are negotiated. Contact with a query letter.
PHOTOGRAPHERS: Stock photography is purchased. Approximately 10 photos per year. Most (90%) photos are included in text/photo packages. Model releases and captions are preferred. Credit line must be negotiated. Payment is negotiated. Uses colour or b&w prints 4x6 or larger. "Almost always a photo is either submitted by a writer who has been given an assignment or is assigned to someone we have used before. Photographers contact Charis Tobias, Art Director.
NOTES: Sample copy is available. Enclose large SASE with $1.83 postage. Previously published work is occasionally considered. Will not consider simultaneous submissions unless by prior arrangement. Guidelines are not available.

CANADIAN BAR REVIEW
Box 4400 Ludlow Hall
Fredericton, NB E3B 5A3

PHONE: (506) 453-4708
FAX: (506) 453-4604

CONTACT: Professor Edward Veitch, Editor **DESCRIPTION:** Circulation 56,000. Publication for judges and practicing lawyers. Published quarterly in English and French. Established in 1923.
WRITERS: Does not purchase freelance work.

CANADIAN BIOTECH NEWS SERVICE
Box 7131, Station J
Ottawa, ON K2J 3L3

NOTES: Could not locate.

CANADIAN BOATING
5805 Whittle Road, #208
Mississauga, ON L4Z 2J1

NOTES: Could not locate.

CANADIAN BUSINESS
777 Bay Street 5 Fl.
Toronto, ON M5W 1A7

PHONE: (416) 596-5100
FAX: (416) 596-5152

CONTACT: Arthur Johnson, Editor **DESCRIPTION:** Published by CB Media Ltd. Circulation 83,000. For business managers and owners and those involved in Canadian business. Targeted to companies that make 20 million dollars and more. Published monthly. Established in 1928.
WRITERS: "We have regular freelancers. New freelancers should send a story idea in by fax or mail. Lengths and pay rates vary." Writers' guidelines are available.
PHOTOGRAPHERS: "We have regular freelance photographers. We review portfolios the first and second Thursday of the month. Photographers drop off their portfolio and pick it up later. Most work is on assignment."
NOTES: A sample back issue of this publication is available free upon request.

CANADIAN BUSINESS LIFE
1 St. John's Road #501   PHONE: (416) 766-5744
Toronto, ON M6P 4C7   FAX: (416) 766-1970

CONTACT: Orest Tkaczuk, Editor   DESCRIPTION: Published by Paul Tuz, Better Business Bureau of Metropolitan Toronto. Circulation 48,000. "Our magazine is geared to small and medium sized businesses. We give tips on everything from hiring right the first time to home office equipment etc." Covers mainly small businesses and the issues affecting them. Published quarterly. Established in 1980.
WRITERS: "We purchase 3 or 4 articles per year. Contact by mail with a story idea, outline and some background information on the angle. If you are doing a business story it has to be about a member of the Better Business Bureau." Guidelines are available.
PHOTOGRAPHERS: "We do purchase some photography, mostly assigned to the photographer we use now. We prefer photos that come with the article."
NOTES: Sample copies of this publication are available free upon request, depending upon availability. Does not consider previously published work. Considers simultaneous submissions.

CANADIAN CERAMICS QUARTERLY
2175 Sheppard Avenue East, #310   PHONE: (416) 491-2886
Willowdale, ON M2J 1W8   FAX: (416) 491-1670

CONTACT: Dr. Mike Sayer, Editor   DESCRIPTION: Published by Canadian Ceramic Society. A membership publication for industrial ceramics. Published quarterly. Established in 1928.
NOTES: This publication is produced strictly by volunteers.

CANADIAN CHEMICAL NEWS
130 Slater Street, #550   PHONE: (613) 232-6252
Ottawa, ON K1P 6E2   FAX: (613) 232-5862

CONTACT: Nola Haddadian, Editor   DESCRIPTION: Published by Chemcam Publishers Ltd. Circulation 6,000. "A news and tactical magazine for the chemical profession." Published ten times a year. Established in 1949.
WRITERS: "We very occasionally purchase work, mabye once or twice a year. Contact me by phone and I will follow up."
PHOTOGRAPHERS: Uses in-house photographer.

CANADIAN CHURCHMAN see The Anglican Journal

CANADIAN CLINICAL LABORATORY
245 Fairview Mall Drive #500
Willowdale, ON M2J 4T1

NOTES: NO LONGER PUBLISHED

CANADIAN COIN BOX MAGAZINE

222 Argyle Avenue   **PHONE:** (519) 582-2513
Delhi, ON   N4B 2Y2   **FAX:** (519) 582-2513

CONTACT: Sandra L. Anderson, Editor **DESCRIPTION:** Published by NCC Publishing. Circulation 1,200. Published specifically for those in the coin-operated amusement business; video games, juke boxes etc. Published ten times a year. Established in 1946.

CANADIAN COIN NEWS

103 Lakeshore Road #202   **PHONE:** (905) 646-7744
St Catharines, ON L2N 2T6   **FAX:** (905) 646-0995

CONTACT: Bret Evans, Editor   **DESCRIPTION:** Published by Trajan Publishing. Circulation 15,000. Publication for Canadian coin collectors. Published bi-weekly. Established in 1962.
WRITERS: 90% freelance written. Purchases approximately 200 photos annually. Byline given on non-fiction work. Doesn't hire writers on assignment. Average article length 1,000 words. Pays $75 for articles. "All regular features and columns are done by contributors on long-term arrangements." Contact with a telephone call or fax. "Call, I can usually make a decision on the spot, or decide if I need more information. With more OCR programs it is more important than ever that copy be clean and dark."
PHOTOGRAPHERS: This publication uses photography but doesn't purchase it. Photo guidelines are not available.
NOTES: Sample copies of this publication are available free upon request. Purchases first North American serial rights. Does not return unsolicited materials. Considers previously published work if disclosed and simultaneous submissions if declared.

CANADIAN COLLECTIBLES RETAILER see Collectibles Canada

CANADIAN COMPUTER RESELLER

777 Bay Street   **PHONE:** (416) 596-2640
Toronto, ON M5W 1A7   **FAX:** (416) 593-3166

CONTACT: Paul Edwards, News Editor **DESCRIPTION:** Published by Maclean Hunter. Circulation 12,000. Trade magazine for computer resellers, integrators, consultants and manufacturers. Published twice a month.
WRITERS: "We use some articles on spec, but most are assigned." Contact the editor by phone or send in query and resumé. "We want articles that show a solid understanding of the channel through which goods move; a good understanding of technology; the ability to write and good industry contacts. We want them to tell us something new." Articles range from 900-2,400 words with pay rates from $600-800. Writers' guidelines are not available.
PHOTOGRAPHERS: "We buy colour photos to illustrate our articles. We prefer slides."
NOTES: Article examples are free upon request.

CANADIAN CONSULTING ENGINEER
1450 Don Mills Road   **PHONE:** (416) 445-6641
Don Mills, ON M3B 2X7   **FAX:** (416) 442-2214

CONTACT: Sophie Kneisel, Editor   **DESCRIPTION:** Published by Southam Business
Communications. Circulation 8,900. Magazine for Canadian consulting engineers and
architects in private practice. Published bi-monthly. Established in 1959.
WRITERS: "We don't purchase much. It depends on the budget and what themes we
are covering. We cover everything from the environment to building controls." Call the
editor to query.
PHOTOGRAPHERS: "We very rarely purchase photography."

CANADIAN CONSUMER
Box 9300
Ottawa, ON K1G 3T9

NOTES: NO LONGER PUBLISHED

CANADIAN CURLING NEWS see The Curling News

CANADIAN CYCLIST
3575 St Laurent #310
Montreal, PQ H2X 2T7

DESCRIPTION: Couldn't locate. Phone number is not in service (514) 847-0242.

CANADIAN DAIRY
3269 Bloor Street West #205   **PHONE:** (416) 239-8423
Toronto, ON M8X 1E2

CONTACT: Iain Macnab, Editor   **DESCRIPTION:** Circulation 2,000+. Published
5 times a year for the dairy processing industry in Canada.
WRITERS: "We don't purchase freelance work, it's all done internally. If someone comes
up with a great idea we may look at it, we don't have a closed mind. We don't do it frequently
because we are small and we have limited space. If someone has an excellent dairy processing
story, and they have the talent to do it the likelihood of us coming to an arrangement for
them to do the story on our behalf is good."
PHOTOGRAPHERS: "Most photography is supplied by our clients."
NOTES: Formerly Modern Dairy.

CANADIAN DATASYSTEMS: NO LONGER PUBLISHED

CANADIAN DEFENSE REVIEW
132 Adrian Crescent
Markham, ON L3P 7B3

PHONE: (905) 472-2801
FAX: (905) 472-3091

CONTACT: Nick Stephens, Managing Editor   **DESCRIPTION:** Published by Synergistic Publications. Circulation 6,500. A military focused publication issued quarterly.
WRITERS: "We purchase at least one one-page story per issue. Lengths and payment depends on the project. We do takes things on spec sometimes. A lot of people who write are experts in the field and some are non-paid. We would pay for an article if we have a specific theme in mind and we need a feature on a particular topic." Contact the editor with a query letter and samples of work in this field.
PHOTOGRAPHERS: "We may require black and white and colour. If we have a major feature we like to have the illustrating photos with the article."

CANADIAN DENTAL MANAGEMENT: NO LONGER PUBLISHED

CANADIAN DIMENSION
228 Notre Dame Avenue #401
Winnipeg, MB R3B 1N7

PHONE: (204) 957-1519
FAX: (204) 943-4617

CONTACT: Michelle Torres   **DESCRIPTION:** Published by Dimension Publications Inc. Circulation 3,000. "An independent newsmagazine written for, by and about progressive Canadians. Since its inception in 1963, it has earned a reputation for provocative and informative articles on local, national and international affairs. Our contributors and readers are environmentalists, trade unionsists, feminists .. committed people who are active in their communities." Published bi-monthly. Established in 1963.
WRITERS: 100% freelance written. "Most articles are written for free. Relatively few are purchased." Gives a byline. Average article length is 2,100 words. Payment is negotiated. Guidelines available and phone inquiries welcome. Writers' guidelines are available.
PHOTOGRAPHERS: Photography is purchased. Uses b&w 5x7 prints. Model releases are preferred by not necessary. Captions are preferred. Pays $25 for b&w photos. Gives a credit line. Contact editor by sending a query letter.
NOTES: Buys one-time rights. Returns unsolicited materials if SASE is included. Considers previously published work and simultaneous submissions.

CANADIAN DIRECT MARKETING NEWS
1200 Markham Road #301
Scarborough, ON M1H 3C3

PHONE: (416) 439-4083
FAX: (416) 439-4086

CONTACT: Stephen Beatty   **DESCRIPTION:** Published by CDMN Publishing. Circulation 7,000. Published monthly. Established in 1988.

CANADIAN DOCTOR
9040 Leslie Street, #7
Richmond Hill, ON L4B 1G3

NOTES: Could not locate. Phone number is not in service (416) 773-9354.

CANADIAN ELECTRONICS
135 Spy Court
Markham, ON   L3R 5H6

PHONE: (905) 477-3222
FAX: (905) 477-4320

CONTACT: Peter Thorne, Editor   **DESCRIPTION:** Published by Action Communications Inc. Circulation 21,800. "A tabloid trade magazine that goes to all electronic design engineers in Canada." Published 7 times a year. Established in 1986.
NOTES: "Our budget has been zeroed out in the last two years so we are not accepting material." A merger of Electronic Times and Electronic Engineering. Also publishes Design Product News and Woodworking.

CANADIAN ETHNIC STUDIES
University of Calgary, Canadian Ethnic
Studies Unit
Calgary, AB   T2N 1N4

PHONE: (403) 220-7257
Email: morel@acs.ucalgary.ca.
FAX: (403) 282-8606

CONTACT: Mary Anne Morel   **DESCRIPTION:** Circulation 1,000. The study of ethnicity, immigration, and the history of ethnic groups in Canada. Includes books reviews, opinions, and some creative writing. Published three times a year. Established in 1969.
WRITERS: "We are a scholarly journal. We receive submissions from academics. We do not use many freelance articles, having little space nor a mandate for general works. Our journal is refereed, and we have a board of directors. We receive 120-150 submissions yearly, and publish less than 40. Occasionally we accept book reviews that are unsolicited, if they are ethnically oriented. Byline given; no payment."

CANADIAN FACILITY MANAGEMENT AND DESIGN
62 Olsen Drive
Don Mills, ON   M3A 3J3

PHONE: (416) 447-3417
FAX: (416) 447-4410

CONTACT: Victor von Buchstab, Editor   **DESCRIPTION:** Published by CFM Communications Inc. Circulation 6,100. This publication covers facility management, design, ergonomics, and office space. Published six times a year and distributed across Canada.
NOTES: This magazine does not accept freelance work.

CANADIAN FAMILY PHYSICIAN
2630 Skymark Avenue
Mississauga, ON L4W 5A4

PHONE: (905) 629-0900
FAX: (905) 629-0893

CONTACT: Primrose Ketchum, Editor   **DESCRIPTION:** Published by The College of Family Physicians of Canada. Circulation 31,700. Published monthly. Established in 1954.
NOTES: Editor's note: This publication is not interested in receiving information from freelancers. "We already have hundreds more people than we can ever use."

CANADIAN FICTION MAGAZINE
Box 1061
Kingston, ON   K7L 4Y5

PHONE: (613) 548-8429
FAX: (613) 548-1556

CONTACT: Geoffrey Hancock, Editor   **DESCRIPTION:** Published by Quarry Press. Circulation 1,200. Publishes Canadian fiction including translations from languages spoken in Canada. Buys book reviews, interviews, and some graphics. Published quarterly.
WRITERS: "We are open to all Canadian writers with new and innovative fiction. Please read the magazine before you submit just to get a general idea of the publication. Articles are no more than 5000 words, paying $10 per page with a byline. We never hire writers on assignment. Contact us by mail with a manuscript. Please enclose a SASE to ensure a response in 8-12 weeks." Previously published work is not considered.
PHOTOGRAPHERS: Photography is not purchased.
NOTES: A sample copy may be in your local bookstore or send the $10 cover fee to the publication.

THE CANADIAN FIREFIGHTER
Box 95, Station D   **PHONE:** (416) 233-2516
Etobicoke, ON   M9A 4X1   **FAX:** (416) 233-2051

CONTACT: Lorne Campbell, Editor   **DESCRIPTION:** Published by Canadian Firefighter Publications. Circulation 12,000. Published for Canada's firefighters. Includes professional, event and training information. Read worldwide. Published 6 times a year in English and French. Established in 1977.
WRITERS: Does not purchase articles from freelancers. Written by firefighters.
PHOTOGRAPHERS: Purchases some photography, contact the editor with a query.

CANADIAN FLIGHT
Box 563, Station B   **PHONE:** (613) 565-0881
Ottawa, ON   K1P 5P7   **FAX:** (613) 236-8646

CONTACT: Doris Ohlmann, Managing Editor **DESCRIPTION:** Published by Canadian Flight Publishing. Circulation 50,000. "For Canadian general aviation pilots, ultralight pilots and home builders of air craft. Articles are about aviation, flying, maintaining aircraft, places to fly, safety, health issues related to pilots, book reviews, etc." Published quarterly. Established in 1955.
WRITERS: Uses freelance articles but does not pay. Gives a byline and complementary copies as payment. Uses fiction, non-fiction, poetry and fillers. Average articles 500 to 750 words. "Articles should be double-spaced, typed, no errors. On disk is wonderful. Would like to see well-written articles and photos with a new twist.
PHOTOGRAPHERS: Uses photos, does not pay. Formats include 4x6 colour prints, glossy or matte 4x6 and 5x7 b&w's. Captions are required. Credit line is given. "Mostly use photos submitted with article or with short captions for fillers. Payment is a credit line and complementary copies."
NOTES: Sample copies are available free upon request. One-time rights. Considers previously published work if published in a US publication. Will consider simultaneous submissions.

CANADIAN FLORIST, GREENHOUSE & NURSERY
1090 Aerowood Drive, Unit 1   **PHONE:** (905) 625-2730
Mississauga, ON   L4W 1Y5   **FAX:** (905) 625-1355

CONTACT: Peter Heywood, Editor   **DESCRIPTION:** Circulation 3,700. A gardening magazine geared to the trade industry in Canada. Contains features on gardening, greenhouses and nurseries. Published monthly. Established in 1905.

CANADIAN FOOTWEAR JOURNAL
1 Pacifique St
Ste.-Anne-de-Bellevue, PQ H9X 1C5

PHONE: (514) 457-2423
FAX: (514) 457-2577

CONTACT: Barbara McLeish, Managing Editor **DESCRIPTION:** Published by McLeish Communications Inc. Circulation 10,000. Specialized magazine for those in the footwear business. Published 8 times a year. Established in 1988.

CANADIAN FOREST INDUSTRIES
1 rue Pacifique
Ste.-Anne-de-Bellevue, PQ H9X 1C5

PHONE: (514) 457-2211 or (514) 339-1399
FAX: (514) 457-2558

CONTACT: Scott Jamieson, Editor **DESCRIPTION:** Published by JCFT Forest Communications Ltd. Circulation 13,000. Serves the logging and forest management industry. Hands on articles and field stories featuring new equipment and technology and environmentally sensitive techniques. Published 8 times a year. Established 1905.
WRITERS: 15% freelance written. Purchases 10 articles a year. Hires on assignment and pays expenses. Average article length 1,500-2,000 pays $500 (plus expenses). Kill fee is paid if assigned article is cancelled. "Writers should contact the editor with an idea by phone, letter or fax with a brief description of what they have in mind."
PHOTOGRAPHERS: "We purchase photos maybe once or twice a year with an article. If it is cover material it would probably be colour. Payment would be negotiated."
NOTES: Sample copies of this publication are available for $15.00. Purchases exclusive in Canada rights. Returns unsolicited materials with SASE. Does not consider simultaneous submissions (if sent elsewhere in Canada) or previously published work (in Canada).

THE CANADIAN FORUM
251 Laurier Avenue West, #804
Ottawa, ON K1P 5J6

PHONE: (613) 230-3078
FAX: (613) 233-1458

CONTACT: Duncan Cameron, Editor **DESCRIPTION:** Published by Canadian Forum. Circulation 10,000. "We are the oldest magazine of political record in the country. We have a dual purpose of covering both politics and culture." Articles include: politics; national and international affairs; economics; travel; the environment; film and literature. Published 10 times a year. Established in 1920.
WRITERS: "We have always operated on a shoe string so cover stories receive $250, secondary features $100, columns $75 and $50 for each book review. We give bylines. We also publish poetry, $75 and short stories at $100. The best way to contact us is to fax us a proposal or mail it to us. We do take things on spec, which is the way we prefer it to work. We return material with a SASE." Guidelines are available.
PHOTOGRAPHERS: "We do purchase preferably black and white photos. The best suggestion is to send a brief portfolio of work. Generally we pay $50 for a photo. The type of photography we are looking for depends on the article we are illustrating."
NOTES: "Most of our work is commissioned but we do accept freelance material." Sample copies are free upon availability. Purchases first North American serial rights. Very rarely accepts previously published work.

CANADIAN FRUITGROWER
222 Argyle Avenue
Delhi, ON N4B 2Y2

PHONE: (519) 582-2513
FAX: (519) 582-4040

CONTACT: Blair Adams, Editor   **DESCRIPTION:** Published by NCC Publishing.
Circulation 3,000. Published 9 times a year. Established in 1929.

CANADIAN FUNERAL DIRECTOR
174 Harwood Avenue South #206
Ajax, ON L1S 2H7

PHONE: (905) 427-6121
FAX: (905) 427-1660

CONTACT: Scott Hillier, Editor   **DESCRIPTION:** Published by Halket Publishing.
A monthly trade journal for the Canadian funeral industry. Established in 1923.
NOTES: This publication never purchases freelance material.

CANADIAN FUNERAL NEWS
237-8 Avenue SE #600
Calgary, AB T2G 5C3

PHONE: (403) 264-3270
FAX: (403) 264-3276

CONTACT: Natika Sunstrum, Editor   **DESCRIPTION:** Published by OT Communications.
Circulation 1,300. A national educational publication for funeral directors on management
and business. Published monthly. Established in 1975.
WRITERS: "We purchase an article maybe once a year. It is very rare."
PHOTOGRAPHERS: "We don't purchase much photography."
NOTES: Sample copies of this publication are available free upon request. Also publishes
Bowbender.

CANADIAN GARDENING
130 Spy Court
Markham, ON L3R 5H6

PHONE: (905) 475-8440
FAX: (905) 475-9246

CONTACT: Liz Primeau, Editor   **DESCRIPTION:** Published by Camar Publications.
Circulation 130,000. A consumer magazine for avid home gardeners. Focuses on Canadian
gardens from coast to coast. Articles cover design, garden "profiles", vegetables, fruits,
flowers, container gardens and organic or natural gardening. Published 7 times a year.
Established in 1990.
WRITERS: "Most of our articles are assigned. Freelancers can send a story on speculation
or an outline. Articles are 200-1,200 words. Pay ranges from $50-$700. Writers should
be aware of what has been published in previous issues. They should know that we are
interested in information-packed articles that are practical, up-to-date, and specific to the
topic. We are got going to run a general article on perennial gardening. We are a special
interest publication. We are always looking for writers and photographers especially in
the prairies and the east." Guidelines are available.
PHOTOGRAPHERS: "Most of our photography is done on assignment. We use freelance
photographers across the country. We are always looking for writers and photographers
especially in the prairies and the east. 90% of the photos are colour. We also use stock
photography for some plant profiles. Payment ranges from $50-$700. Credit line is given.
Photographers could send in a portfolio to the editor or Marcello Biagioni, the Art Director."
Guidelines are available.

NOTES: Sample copies of this publication are available free upon request for freelancers. Purchases first North American serial rights. Rarely considers previously published work. "We do occasionally run excerpts or adaptations of a book." Returns unsolicited materials with a SASE but be patient. "We discourage people from sending articles on spec."

CANADIAN GEOGRAPHIC
39 McArthur Avenue   **PHONE:** (613) 745-4629
Vanier, ON K1L 8L7   **FAX:** (613) 744-0947

CONTACT: Ian Darragh   **DESCRIPTION:** Published by Royal Canadian Geographical Society. Circulation 241,000. Consumer magazine focusing on natural history, the outdoors, the environment and people inhabiting Canada. Published 6 times a year. Established in 1930.
WRITERS: Writers contact Michael Clugston. 90% freelance written. Buys 36 articles per year. Byline is given. Hires writers on assignment, expenses paid while on assignment. Average article is 3500 words. Pay $1.00 per word. Kill fee is negotiated if assigned article does not run. Guidelines available. "We are looking for stories on the earth sciences. Generally, we have enough wildlife articles.
PHOTOGRAPHERS: Photography is purchased from stock and photographers hired on assignment. 60% assigned. 40% from stock. Uses colour, 35mm, 2¼x2¼ and 4x5 transparencies. Model releases are not necessary. Captions are required. Payment ranges from $75 for b&w to $600 for colour cover. Credit line is given. Contact with a query letter and include resumé and business card, brochure, flyer or tear sheets. Photographers contact Margaret Williamson. Guidelines are available. "We are looking for photos for pictorials on particular themes that suit our subject matter. Also looking for spectacular stand-alone photos for a new department called *Final Frame*. Contact our photo editor for details.
NOTES: Buys first North American serial rights. Will not consider previously published work. Will consider simultaneous submissions.

CANADIAN GLOBAL CARGOES
Box 41132
Ottawa, ON K1G 5K9

NOTES: Could not locate. Phone number is not in service (514) 630-4500.

CANADIAN GROCER
777 Bay Street   **PHONE:** (416) 596-5773
Toronto, ON M5W 1A7   **FAX:** (416) 593-3162

CONTACT: Simone Collier, Managing Editor   **DESCRIPTION:** Published by Maclean Hunter. Circulation 19,000. Trade magazine for Canadian grocery and food retailing industry. Published monthly. Established 1886.
WRITERS: 50% freelance written. Purchases 18 features and many news shorts per year. Gives a byline. Writers are hired on assignment and expenses (within reason) are paid. Article length varies from 100 (pay $25) to 1,800 words which pays up to $550. Writers' guidelines are available. Query over the phone. "Our writers all know and understand the issues and problems facing the grocery trade. We rely heavily on Canadian statistics for all articles. The Canadian grocery trade is vastly different from the American trade and it XXXX me off when people think they are the same. Writers should study back issues

for our writing style - we are relatively light and breezy but we still demand quality writing which includes following rules of English grammar."
PHOTOGRAPHERS: Colour and black and white photos are submitted with articles.
NOTES: Sample copies of this publication are available for $5 with a SASE. Purchases one-time rights or first Canadian rights. Will return unsolicited materials if SASE is enclosed. Will consider previously published work. Will not consider simultaneous submissions if they are being sent to the competition.

CANADIAN GUERNSEY JOURNAL
368 Woolwich Street
Guelph, ON N1H 3W6

PHONE: (519) 836-2141
FAX: none

CONTACT: V.M. MacDonald, Editor **DESCRIPTION:** Published by Canadian Guernsey Association. Circulation 500. An agricultural magazine devoted to Guernsey (dairy) cattle and related agricultural topics. Published 6 times a year.
NOTES: This publication does not accept freelance work.

CANADIAN GUIDER
50 Merton Street
Toronto, ON M4S 1A3

PHONE: (416) 487-5281
FAX: (416) 487-5570

CONTACT: Sharon Pruner, Editor **DESCRIPTION:** Circulation 50,000. National publication for the Girl Guides of Canada organization. Written mainly for leaders. Includes program and leadership tips, camping, outdoor activities, skills, etc. Published 5 times a year. Established in 1932.
WRITERS: "We normally use volunteer writers and very rarely purchase. We are not actively in pursuit of writing at the moment. We do not use poetry or fiction."
PHOTOGRAPHERS: Photographers are hired on assignment (50%). Purchase approximately 40 photos annually. Uses all formats in colour and b&w. Model releases are preferred. Captions are not necessary. Credit lines are given. Payment is negotiated. Contact us with a query letter.
NOTES: Sample copies of this publication are available for $1.50. Normally purchases all rights. Will not consider previously published work or simultaneous submissions. Guidelines are not available.

CANADIAN HEAVY EQUIPMENT GUIDE
1625 Ingleton Avenue
Burnaby, BC V5C 4L8

PHONE: (604) 291-9900
FAX: (604) 291-1906

CONTACT: Len Webster, Editor **DESCRIPTION:** Published by Engelbert Baum. Circulation 31,700. Industrial trade publication for new products and services. Published 9 times a year. Established in 1986.
WRITERS: 50% freelance written. Byline given. Does not pay. Tear sheets provided.
PHOTOGRAPHERS: 100% assigned to in-house photographers.

CANADIAN HEREFORD DIGEST

5160 Skyline Way NE   **PHONE:** (403) 274-1734
Calgary, AB T2E 6V1   **FAX:** (403) 275-4999

CONTACT: Kurt Gilmore, Editor **DESCRIPTION:** Published by Kurt Gilmore. Circulation 4,500. Agricultural publication for ranchers and farmers. Focuses on the hereford breeding industry. Published monthly in English(95%) and French(5%). Established in 1956.
WRITERS: 90% assigned to in-house writers. Returns unsolicited materials with SASE. Byline given.
PHOTOGRAPHERS: 95% assigned to in-house photographers. Contact this publication by sending a query letter.
NOTES: Send $4.00 & 9x12" SASE with appropriate postage for a sample copy.

CANADIAN HISTORICAL REVIEW

University of Toronto Press
5201 Dufferin Street
Downsview, ON M3H 5T8

NOTES: Could not locate. Phone number is not in service (416) 677-7781.

CANADIAN HOME ECONOMICS JOURNAL

151 Slater Street, Suite 901   **PHONE:** (613) 238-8817
Ottawa, ON K1P 5H3   **FAX:** (613) 238-1677

CONTACT: Estelle Reddin **DESCRIPTION:** Published by Canadian Home Economics Association. An academic professional journal primarily focusing on the profession of home economics and related fields. Distributed to 2,400 members. "The CHEJ publishes articles from home economists and others who share their interest in promoting the well-being of individuals and families." Published quarterly. Established in 1950.
WRITERS: Articles address current issues for families and home economists; contribute to knowledge and understanding; encourage thought and reflection on the part of the reader; present subject matter that is accurate, up-to-date and supported by good references and logical reasoning. Articles vary from 500-3,500 words. No payment is given. Contact with query letter and "please read and follow the author's guide outlined in the journal."
PHOTOGRAPHERS: All photography is supplied with articles. Credit line is not given. Model releases are required. Captions are preferred. Does not pay.
NOTES: Asks for exclusive rights. Unsolicited materials will be returned with SASE. Does not consider previously published work or simultaneous submissions. This publication never purchases freelance material. Sample copy free upon request.

CANADIAN HOMESTYLE MAGAZINE

598 Stillwater Court   **PHONE:** (905) 681-7932
Burlington, ON L7T 4G7   **FAX:** (905) 681-2141

CONTACT: Laurie O'Halloran **DESCRIPTION:** Circulation 7,500. A trade publication geared to housewares' buyers and retailers, covering trends and new product updates. Published 7 times a year. Established in 1989.
WRITERS: "We purchase between 12-15 articles per year. We hire writers on assignment and give a byline. Our average article length is 2,000 words at 45¢ a word. Our columns

are freelanced out to the same people on a regular basis. Contact me with a written resumé and samples of work. I would prefer someone in the retail industry - retail oriented writers. "
PHOTOGRAPHERS: "We never purchase any photography. "

CANADIAN HORSEMAN

Box 670, 225 Industrial Parkway South   **PHONE:** (905) 727-0107
Aurora, ON L4G 4J9   **FAX:** (905) 841-1530

CONTACT: Lee Benson   **DESCRIPTION:** Circulation 10,000. Well researched articles on horse care and farm management. Published 6 times a year. Established in 1983.
WRITERS: 20% freelance written. Byline is given. Pays 15¢ a word. "Some training articles accepted with preference given to western technique." Guidelines are available. Contact with a query letter.
PHOTOGRAPHERS: Only purchases photos as part of text/photo submission. Pays $15 for b&w; $25 for colour inside and $100 for colour cover.
NOTES: Purchases first North American serial rights. Unsolicited material will be returned with SASE. Considers previously published work. Will not consider simultaneous submissions. Also publishes Canadian Thoroughbred, Corinthian Horse Sport and Horse Power.

CANADIAN HOTEL & RESTAURANT

23 Lesmill Road #101   **PHONE:** (416) 447-0888
Don Mills, ON N3E 3P6   **FAX:** (416) 447-5333

CONTACT: Rosanna Caira, Editor   **DESCRIPTION:** Published by Kostuch Publications. Circulation 21,000. Published 5 times a year and geared for restaurant and hotel operators. It zeros in on new products for the industry.
NOTES: No freelance work is purchased for this publication. Also publishes Foodservice and Hospitality and Hotelier.

CANADIAN HOUSE AND HOME

511 King Street West, Suite 120   **PHONE:** (416) 593-0204
Toronto, ON M5V 2Z4   **FAX:** (416) 591-1630

CONTACT: Cobi Ladner, Editor   **DESCRIPTION:** Published by Lynda Reeves. Circulation 130,000. A design and decorating magazine focusing on home decor, design, renovation and home entertainment in Canada. Includes travel and food features as well as product shots of artisans and crafts-people. Published 10 times a year. Established in 1982.
WRITERS: "The majority is freelance written. We have blurbs in the artisan and entrepreneur section which are 200-300 words. Full page articles are 900 words at approximately $1 a word. Freelancers should send a query letter with photos, what they would like to write about and samples of published writing. The photos don't have to be professionally done, something to show us the design."
PHOTOGRAPHERS: "We hire on assignment. Send a query letter, bio and samples of work."
NOTES: Purchases first North American serial rights. Considers simultaneous submissions, but "please let us know." This magazine is available on newsstands, check out several issues before making a submission.

CANADIAN INDUSTRIAL EQUIPMENT NEWS

1450 Don Mills Road   **PHONE:** (416) 445-6641
Don Mills, ON M3B 2X7   **FAX:** (416) 442-2214

CONTACT: Olga Markovich, Editor **DESCRIPTION:** Published by Southam Magazine Group. Circulation 24,000. "A new-product tabloid which runs descriptions of new products that manufacturers use." Published monthly. Established in 1940.
WRITERS: "Mostly written in-house and with press releases. We don't use any outside writers."
PHOTOGRAPHERS: "We don't use any outside photographers."

CANADIAN INSURANCE

111 Peter Street, Suite 202   **PHONE:** (416) 599-0772
Toronto, ON M5V 2H1   **FAX:** (416) 599-0867

CONTACT: Sally Praskey, Editor   **DESCRIPTION:** Published by Stone and Lox Ltd. Circulation 11,000. A national magazine serving the property and casualty insurance industry. Published monthly. Established in 1905.
WRITERS: "We just aren't in the market for any writers and photographers right now. We have a few people that we use regularly." Contact only with a mailed query letter.

CANADIAN INTERIORS

113 Davenport Road   **PHONE:** (416) 966-9944
Toronto, ON M5R 1H8   **FAX:** (416) 966-9946

CONTACT: Sheri Craig, Editor   **DESCRIPTION:** Published by Crailer Communications. Circulation under 10,500. National trade magazine for interior designers, architects and the design community. Main features include Canadian interior design projects, and interior design products. Published 6 times a year. Established in 1964.
WRITERS: 10% freelance written. Byline is given. Average article 1,000 words. Payment is negotiated. Contact with query letter, send resumé, business card and samples.
PHOTOGRAPHERS: Very occasionally purchases photos, most are supplied by the trade or with articles. Uses all formats colour, glossy b&ws. Credit lines are given. Contact with brochure, flyer or tear sheets.

CANADIAN JERSEY BREEDER

350 Speedvale Avenue West, Unit 9   **PHONE:** (519) 821-9150
Guelph, ON N1H 7M7   **FAX:** (519) 821-2723

CONTACT: Betty Clements, Editor   **DESCRIPTION:** Published by The Jersey Cattle Association of Canada. Circulation 1,800. A dairy cattle publication issued ten times a year. Features articles on dairy type (conformation), genetics, and production issues. Established in 1945.
WRITERS: Hires writers on assignment. Pays expenses while on assignment. Pays from $50 to $100 per article. Send resumé, business card and samples.
PHOTOGRAPHERS: Purchases from stock. Purchases 150 photos annually. 50% of photos purchased from freelancers. "We work with commercial livestock photographers." Uses 5x7 colour prints and glossy b&w. Captions are preferred. Credit line must be negotiated. Payment negotiated. "Photos of Jersey cattle for Jersey farms."

NOTES: Sample copy free upon request. Considers previously published and simultaneous submissions.

CANADIAN JEWELLER

1448 Lawrence Avenue East #302
Toronto, ON M4A 2V6

PHONE: (416) 755-5199
FAX: (416) 755-9123

CONTACT: Carol Besler   **DESCRIPTION:** Published by Style Communications Inc. Circulation 6,500. Published 6 times a year. Established in 1879.
WRITERS: Purchases articles. Gives a byline. Average article length is 800 words. Pays 25¢ a word. Writers can make contact with a query letter, fax or phone. Unsolicited articles will be considered. Send resumé and samples to be kept on file for possible assignment. "A good writer is a good writer, and turns in a good story no matter what the fee. That's the way to win the undying loyalty of an editor, who just wants help on producing a good publication."
PHOTOGRAPHERS: Hires photographers on assignment. Pay is negotiated. Credit lines are given. Uses all colour formats. Make contact by sending a sample portfolio.
NOTES: Purchases first North American serial rights.

CANADIAN JEWISH OUTLOOK

6184 Ash Street, Suite 3
Vancouver, BC V5Z 3G9

PHONE: (604) 324-5101
FAX: (604) 325-2470

CONTACT: Henry Rosenthal   **DESCRIPTION:** Published by Canadian Jewish Outlook Society. Circulation 2,000. Outlook provides a Jewish secular, humanist perspective on political and cultural issues. It features original articles, poems, stories and reviews by writers from Canada, the United States, Israel, Germany and Eastern Europe. Contributions are translated from Yiddish and Hebrew.
WRITERS: 80 % assigned to in-house photographers. Returns unsolicited materials with SASE. Does not pay. Byline given.
PHOTOGRAPHERS: 100 % assigned to in-house photographers.
NOTES: Send $4.00 & 9x12" SASE with appropriate postage for a sample copy. "We are happy to have contributions that suit our editorial content as long as you realize we do not pay."

CANADIAN JOURNAL OF EDUCATION

1 Stewart Street, Suite 205
Ottawa, ON K1N 6H7

PHONE: (613) 230-3532
FAX: (613) 230-2746

CONTACT: Tim Howard   **DESCRIPTION:** Published by Canadian Society for the Study of Education. Circulation 1,200. Focuses on educational psychology, curriculum studies, sociology, administration, and comparative education. Articles are in English and in French. Published quarterly.
WRITERS: "We sometimes have guest editors and they may solicit articles on a certain theme but we don't pay for them. We mostly publish research articles which are peer reviewed."
PHOTOGRAPHERS: "We rarely use photos."

CANADIAN JOURNAL OF HOSPITAL PHARMACY

1145 Hunt Club Road, #350
Ottawa, ON K1V 0Y3

PHONE: (613) 736-9733
FAX: (613) 736-5660

CONTACT: Mr. Scott Walker, Editor **DESCRIPTION:** Published by Canadian Society of Hospital Pharmacists. Circulation 3,500. "The objectives are to publish original research, clinical reviews, case reports and topical discussions on pharmacy practice and to report the activities of the Canadian Society of Hospital Pharmacists." Published bi-monthly.
NOTES: "We do not purchase work. We are strictly a peer-reviewed article journal."

CANADIAN JOURNAL OF MEDICAL TECHNOLOGY

Box 2830
Hamilton, ON L8N 3N8

PHONE: (905) 528-8642
FAX: (905) 528-4968

CONTACT: Kurt Davis, Business Editor   **DESCRIPTION:** Published by Candian Society of Labratory Technologists. Circulation 22,500. Contains medical features, profiles and news in the industry. Published quarterly. Established in 1937.
WRITERS: "We occasionally purchase articles, no more than 1 per issue. Articles are 800-1,200 words with a pay rate of about $250. Contact me with a story idea or an outline. It's only pre-approved manuscripts that are accepted. We have a few freelancers who have done stories on health-related issues that relate to the lab. They should have a national perspective to them. If there is something unique and innovative then I will consider it. It's a matter of appealing to a rather diverse readership. Some of our members also write for us. We have a management series, an internet series, and a find a job series. We prefer to recieve the article on diskette, IBM Wordperect 5.1 or on any other wordprocessing."
Guidelines are only available for the scientific section, not the general interest section.
PHOTOGRAPHERS: "We purchase photography if it is relevant to the story. We run both colour and black and white."
NOTES: Purchases one-time rights. Does not consider previously published work. For a potential author a sample copy is free upon request.

CANADIAN JOURNAL OF SOCIOLOGY

Department of Sociology, University of
Alberta, 5-21 Tory Bldg.
Edmonton, AB T6G 2H4

PHONE: (403) 492-7196

CONTACT: Susan McDaniel, Editor   **DESCRIPTION:** Each bilingual issue contains information on Canadian society as well as book reviews, and a forum for commentary and debate. Published quarterly.
WRITERS: "Those who wish to submit can write to the editor for more information. Our guidelines are on the last page of the journal." Writers' guidelines are available with a SASE.
NOTES: Sample copies of this publication are available for $20.

CANADIAN JOURNAL OF WOMEN AND THE LAW
Box 450 Station A   **PHONE:** (613) 562-5800 ext. 3473
575 King Edward Avenue   **FAX:** (613) 562-5129
Ottawa, ON K1N 6N5

CONTACT: Martha Jackman, Co-Editor   **DESCRIPTION:** Circulation 1,500. Provides in-depth analysis of legal issues of concern to women. Published twice a year in English and French. Established in 1986.
WRITERS: This publication does accept work but doesn't pay. Contact the editor with a query letter.

CANADIAN JOURNAL OF WOMEN'S HEALTH CARE
8102 Trans Canada Highway   **PHONE:** (514) 333-5350
St. Laurent, PQ H4S 1Z4   **FAX:** (514) 333-5146

CONTACT: Terry O'Shaughnessy, Managing Editor   **DESCRIPTION:** Published by Rodar Publishing. Circulation 17,000. Aimed at physicians who treat women. Contains clinical and psychological information. Published six times a year.
WRITERS: Less than 10% freelance written. Contact with query letter. Fees negotiable. Guidelines available.
PHOTOGRAPHERS: 95% assigned to in-house photographers.
NOTES: "We are a 'pure view' journal so all the articles are written by doctors, nurses, psychologists, or social workers. All articles are read by two physicians to make sure the content is correct." Returns unsolicited materials (from those in the health care field) with SASE.

CANADIAN LAWYER
240 Edward Street   **PHONE:** (905) 841-6480
Aurora, ON L4G 3S9   **FAX:** (905) 841-5078

CONTACT: Catherine Kentridge, Executive Editor   **DESCRIPTION:** Circulation 29,000. Publication is aimed at members of the legal profession, legal suppliers and consultants as well as anyone interested in the practice of law. Articles include: trends and developments; law firm mergers and expansions; investigative pieces on cases and events; and social issues from a legal perspective. Published 10 times a year.

THE CANADIAN LEADER
Box 5112 Station F   **PHONE:** (613) 224-5131
Ottawa, ON K2C 3H4   **FAX:** (613) 224-3571

CONTACT: G.A. Johnson, Executive Editor   **DESCRIPTION:** Published by Boy Scouts of Canada. Circulation 45,000. The official magazine of the Boy Scouts of Canada. Published 10 times a year. Established in 1970.
NOTES: "On an exceptionally rare basis would we purchase writing or photography. We are almost completely volunteer written. 30-40% is written in-house by staff and the balance of it is material submitted to us, both copy and photography by leaders across the country. They can contact us by phone, fax or letter."

CANADIAN LIBRARY JOURNAL see Feliciter

CANADIAN LITERATURE

University of British Columbia
#223-2029 West Mall
Vancouver, BC V6T 1W5

PHONE: (604) 822-2780
FAX: (604) 822-9452

CONTACT: W.H. New, Editor   **DESCRIPTION:** Published by Canadian Literature. Circulation 1,500. The journal considers essays, interviews, etc. on all aspects of Canadian writing. It publishes poems by Canadian writers only. It does NOT publish fiction.
WRITERS: 90% freelance written. Purchases 20 articles per year. Byline is given. Prefers articles from 3,000 to 6,000 words. Pays $5 a page for articles; $10 a poem. "Look at previous issues for samples of the kind of work we publish."
NOTES: Samples are available for $18.05. Publishes one-time rights. Unsolicited material (2 copies please) are returned with SASE. Does not consider previously published material or simultaneous submissions.

CANADIAN LIVING

25 Sheppard Avenue West #100
North York, ON   M2N 6S7

PHONE: (416) 733-7600
FAX: (416) 733-3398

CONTACT: Bonnie Baker Cowan, Editor   **DESCRIPTION:** Circulation 600,000. Monthly magazine aimed at Canadian women. Articles on food, beauty, fashion, health, fitness, decorating, crafts, and contemporary living. Established in 1975.
WRITERS: "We use freelance writers on a regular basis. We purchase mostly non-fiction and we give a by-line. *Oh Canada* is a regular column for freelancers. A freelance writer should contact us with a query letter and outline. Request our writers' guidelines, they change all the time." Article lengths and pay rates vary.
PHOTOGRAPHERS: "We use freelance photographers on a regular basis. We usually use colour transparencies, 2x3. The art director will assign a photographer to a specific story. A freelance photographer should contact our Art Director, Martha Weaver. She will look at a portfolio and then take it from there."

CANADIAN MACHINERY & METALWORKING

777 Bay Street
Toronto, ON M5W 1A7

PHONE: (416) 596-5720
FAX: (416) 593-5881

CONTACT: Mike Overment, Editor   **DESCRIPTION:** Published by Maclean Hunter. Circulation 18,000. Aimed at Canada's metalworking industry. Features new methods, developments, products and technologies. Published 8 times a year. Established in 1905.
WRITERS: "We purchases articles on occasion, perhaps one per issue. We purchase short pieces if they are applicable. We always provide a byline. We normally give freelancers assignments. Articles average 1,000 words and our rate is around 30¢ per word." Contact by phone or by mail.
PHOTOGRAPHERS: "We very rarely purchase photographs, maybe once a year where we have specifically asked a photographer to got out and take shots." Contact by phone or by mail.

CANADIAN MANAGER MAGAZINE
2175 Sheppard Avenue East, #310
Willowdale, ON M2J 1W8

PHONE: (416) 493-0155
FAX: (416) 491-1670

CONTACT: Ruth Max, Editor **DESCRIPTION:** Published by Canadian Institute of Management. Circulation 6-7,000. "The Canadian Manager focuses on managers in middle to senior positions. Each issue provides articles on managment situations or systems faced by managers every day. Recent issues have included articles on teambuilding, marketing, performance appraisals, meetings and much, much more." Published quarterly. Established in 1942.
WRITERS: "The Canadian Institute of Managament, publisher of The Canadian Manager Magazine, is a non-profit organization. Therefore no payment is given for articles. If writers wish to submit articles they can. If we do use an article we will send the writer 6 copies of the issue. Articles average 1,200 to 1,400 words and should relate to the management field. Each article should include a b&w photo (of the author) and a brief bio." Writers' guidelines are available.
PHOTOGRAPHERS: "Most people who submit articles send black and white photos."
NOTES: Sample copies of this publication are available free upon request. Unsolicited submissions are returned with SASE.

CANADIAN MEDICAL ASSOCIATION JOURNAL
1867 Alta Vista Drive
Ottawa, ON K1G 0G8

PHONE: (613) 731-9331
FAX: (613) 523-0937

CONTACT: Patrick Sullivan, Editor **DESCRIPTION:** Circulation 50,000. Journal for physicians and those in the medical profession. Contains information about new technology and advances in the medical profession. Published twice monthly. Established in 1911.
WRITERS: 25-30% freelance written. Purchases 150-200 articles per year. Byline is given. Articles average from 1,200 to 2,000 words. Pays 40-50¢ per word.
PHOTOGRAPHERS: Seldom buys - uses Canapress.
NOTES: 20-50% freelance written. Pays $200-$900 for articles. Phone inquiries welcome.

THE CANADIAN MESSENGER
661 Greenwood Avenue
Toronto, ON M4J 4B3

PHONE: (416) 466-1195
FAX: none

CONTACT: Rev. F.J. Power **DESCRIPTION:** Published by The Apostleship of Prayer. Circulation 17,000. A religious Roman Catholic magazine. It's spiritual and rather specialized in things that pertain to the Apostleship of Prayer. The articles are not general in nature. Published 11 times a year. Established in 1891.
WRITERS: "We get many unsolicited articles but they have to be of the particular nature that fits in with our objective. We publish articles that help people with their daily christian living, so its not just information. We do not publish poetry. We already have contributors that write our columns. We pay 4¢ a word for not more than 1,500 words. We like articles 800-1,100 words. We prefer a completed article as the author wants it."
PHOTOGRAPHERS: "We don't buy photography, we use a US clip service and we have our own library of photographs."
NOTES: Buys first North American rights. Very seldom considers something that was previously published. For a sample copy send $1 to the publisher and a SASE 9x12" envelope.

CANADIAN MINING JOURNAL
1450 Don Mills Road
Don Mills, ON M3B 2X7

PHONE: (416) 442-2094
FAX: (416) 442-2272

CONTACT: Craig Coulter, Editor **DESCRIPTION:** Published by Southam. Circulation 8,000. Published bi-monthly. Established in 1879.

CANADIAN MODERN LANGUAGE REVIEW
237 Hellems Avenue
Welland, ON L3B 3B8

PHONE: (905) 734-3640
FAX: (905) 734-3640

CONTACT: Sally Rehorick, Viviane Edwards, Editors **DESCRIPTION:** Circulation 2,100. We publish linguistic and pedagogical articles, book reviews, current advertisements and other material of interest to teachers of French, German, Italian, Russian, Spanish, Ukrainian, and English as a second language and other modern languages at all levels of instruction. Established in 1944.
WRITERS: "Anyone is welcome to send in an article but contributors are not paid. Simultaneous submissions are considered." See "Guide to Authors" section in publication or contact editors for guidelines.
PHOTOGRAPHERS: Photography is never purchased.

CANADIAN MONEYSAVER
Box 370
Bath, ON K0H 1G0

PHONE: (613) 352-7448
FAX: (613) 352-7448

CONTACT: Dale Ennis **DESCRIPTION:** Circulation 30,600. A personal finance magazine offering topics on personal finance, investment techniques, retirement planning, small business practice and consumer purchases. Published 11 times a year. Established in 1981.
WRITERS: "We very occasionally purchase articles."
PHOTOGRAPHERS: "We never purchase photography."

THE CANADIAN MUSIC EDUCATOR
16 Royaleigh Avenue
Etobicoke, ON M9P 2J5

PHONE: (416) 244-3745
FAX: (416) 235-1833

CONTACT: Dr. Brian Roberts, Editor **DESCRIPTION:** Published by Canadian Music Educators Association. Circulation 2,500. Contains association news, reviews, workshops etc. Published 7 times a year in English and French.
NOTES: This publication never purchases freelance work.

CANADIAN MUSIC TRADE
67 Mowat Avenue #350
Toronto, ON M6K 3E3

PHONE: (416) 533-8303
FAX: (416) 533-1630

CONTACT: Shauna Kennedy, Editor **DESCRIPTION:** Published by Norris-Whitney Communications Inc. Circulation 3,400. A national trade magazine for music and instrument retailers. Published 6 times a year. Established in 1979.

WRITERS: "I do purchase work, however I do have stringent guidelines that writers have to fall within. They must be musically and technically literate with a recording or engineering degree. I prefer writers to send me copies of their published work." Writers' guidelines are not available.
PHOTOGRAPHERS: "We rarely purchase photography. We have photographers we send out on assignments." Contact the editor by mail.
NOTES: Contact this address for sample copy information: 23 Hannover Drive Unit 7, St. Catharines, ON L2W 1A3. Also publishes Canadian Musician.

CANADIAN MUSICIAN
67 Mowat Avenue #350   **PHONE:** (416) 533-8303
Toronto, ON   M6K 3E3   **FAX:** (416) 533-1630

CONTACT: Shauna Kennedy, Editor   **DESCRIPTION:** Published by Norris-Whitney Communications Inc. Circulation 27,000. "A national magazine written by and for amateur, semi-professional and professional musicians." Consumer magazine with a focus on practical information of interest to Canadian musicians. Published 6 times a year. Established in 1979.
WRITERS: "I do purchase work, however I do have stringent guidelines that writers have to fall within. They must be musically and technically literate with a recording or engineering degree. I prefer writers to send me copies of their published work." Writers' guidelines are not available.
PHOTOGRAPHERS: "We rarely purchase photography. We have photographers we send out on assignment." Contact the editor by mail.
NOTES: Contact this address for sample copy information: 23 Hannover Drive Unit 7, St. Catharines, ON L2W 1A3. Also publishes Canadian Music Trade.

CANADIAN NOTES AND QUERIES
Box 367 Station F
Toronto, ON   M4Y 2L8

NOTES: Could not locate.

THE CANADIAN NURSE
50 The Driveway   **PHONE:** (613) 237-2133
Ottawa, ON   K2P 1E2   **FAX:** (613) 237-3520

CONTACT: Heather Broughton, Editor-in-Chief   **DESCRIPTION:** Published by Canadian Nurses Association. Circulation 109,900. Published 11 times a year in English and French. Established in 1908.
WRITERS: "We don't purchase many articles. We do sidebars and columns to complement features, about 6 per year all together. Freelancers can send a query letter if they have a specific story to pitch. A query letter with 5 or 6 different story ideas would be good. We look for things heath-related. The best thing is for a writer to get a copy to take a look at all the different departments. Lengths vary and so do the pay rates."
PHOTOGRAPHERS: "We purchase maybe 40-50 photographs per year. Mostly colour but some black and white. A photographer can contact us with a letter and we would make an appointment to view their portfolio. Our pay rates are $200 or so. It depends, we may pay more for covers shot in-studio."

NOTES: Purchases first North American serial rights. Sample copies of this publication are available free upon request.

CANADIAN OCCUPATIONAL SAFETY

Royal Life Building, #209
277 Lakeshore Road East
Oakville, ON L6J 6J3

PHONE: (905) 842-2884
FAX: (905) 842-8226

CONTACT: Jackie Roth, Editor   **DESCRIPTION:** Published by Clifford/Elliot. Circulation 11,500. Published bi-monthly. Established in 1962.

CANADIAN PACKAGING

777 Bay Street
Toronto, ON M5W 1A7

PHONE: (416) 596-5746
FAX: (416) 596-5810

CONTACT: Douglas Faulkner, Editor   **DESCRIPTION:** Published by Maclean Hunter. Circulation 12,200. Published eleven times a year. Established in 1948.

CANADIAN PEACE REPORT: NO LONGER PUBLISHED

CANADIAN PHARMACEUTICAL JOURNAL

20 Camelot Drive Unit 600
Nepean, ON K2G 5X8

PHONE: (613) 727-1364

CONTACT: Andrew Reinbolt, Editor   **DESCRIPTION:** Circulation 12,900. Publication for pharmacy owners and pharmacists. Covers a variety of heath issues. Published monthly. Established in 1868.
WRITERS: Pays $100-$1000 for articles. Guidelines available.
PHOTOGRAPHERS: Accepted.

CANADIAN PLASTICS

1450 Don Mills Road
Don Mills, ON M3B 2X7

PHONE: (416) 445-6641
FAX: (416) 442-2213

CONTACT: Michael Shelley, Editor   **DESCRIPTION:** Published by Southam Business Communications. Circulation 10,000. A trade magazine on the plastics industry in Canada. Published eight times a year. Established in 1943.
WRITERS: "I tend to seek my own freelancers I don't use unsolicited copy."
PHOTOGRAPHERS: "I have my own photographers, if I assign a photographic project."
NOTES: This publication is not interested in receiving queries.

CANADIAN POETRY: STUDIES, DOCUMENTS, REVIEWS

University of Western Ontario Department   **PHONE:** (519) 661-3403
of English   **FAX:** (519) 661-3640
London, ON N6A 3K7

CONTACT: David Bentley, Editor   **DESCRIPTION:** Published by Canadian Poetry Press. Circulation 400. Journal devoted to the study of poetry. Articles also include reviews, and articles. Published twice a year. Established 1977.
NOTES: Does not purchase articles.

CANADIAN POOL & SPA MARKETING

270 Esno Park Drive, Unit 12   **PHONE:** (905) 513-0090
Markham, ON L3R 1H3   **FAX:** (905) 513-1377

CONTACT: David Barnsley   **DESCRIPTION:** Published by Hubbard Marketing & Publishing Ltd. Circulation 8,000. Industry profiles, news, new products, trade show reviews and financial and marketing advice for the pool and spa trade.
WRITERS: 30% freelance written. Purchase 15 articles a year. Gives a byline. Hires writers on assignment and pays expenses while on assignment. Average article 1,200 words. Pays 15¢ per word on publication. Kill fee is paid if assigned article cancelled. Would like to see "technical articles on pool and spa equipment; retail and marketing advice for small business owners; profiles of commercial waterparks."
PHOTOGRAPHERS: Purchases photos; 70% of photos are purchased as part of text/photo pkg. Uses all formats colour and b&w. Model releases are required. Captions are not necessary. Pays $50 for b&w; $50 for colour inside; $100 for colour cover. Pays on publication. "Vertical shots are preferred of underground, above ground pools, saunas, spas and backyard patio settings and landscaped areas around the pool."
NOTES: Buys first time rights only.

CANADIAN PRINTER

777 Bay Street   **PHONE:** (416) 596-5781
Toronto, ON M5W 1A7 **FAX:** (416) 596-5965

CONTACT: Nick Hancock, Editor   **DESCRIPTION:** Published by Susan Leggset. Circulation 11,500. Published for Canada's printing companies with the latest information on new technology and issues affecting the business. Delivers a comprehensive industry overview to Canada's graphic arts professionals. Published 10 times a year. Established in 1893.
WRITERS: 10% freelance written. Buys 8-10 articles per year. Byline given. Hires writers on assignment and pays expenses while on assignment. Article length 1,500 to 2,000 words. Pays 30¢ per word. 50% kill fee paid if assigned article is cancelled. Mail or fax queries.
NOTES: Buys one-time rights. Sample is free upon rquest. Unsolicited materials will not be returned. Photo guidelines are not available.

CANADIAN PROCESS EQUIPMENT & CONTROL NEWS
343 Eglinton Avenue East PHONE: (416) 481-6483
Toronto, ON M4P 1L7 FAX: (416) 481-6436

CONTACT: Vincent Sharp **DESCRIPTION:** Circulation 23,100. Published for the chemical process industry and other mechanical industries utilizing chemical engineering. Published six times a year. Established in 1972.
NOTES: Does not purchase material from freelancers.

CANADIAN PROPERTY MANAGEMENT
33 Fraser Avenue, #208 PHONE: (416) 588-6220
Toronto, ON M6K 3J9 FAX: (416) 588-5217

CONTACT: Kim Morningstar, Editor **DESCRIPTION:** Published by RK Communications. Circulation 14,500. Published seven times a year. Established in 1986.

CANADIAN PUBLIC ADMINISTRATION JOURNAL
150 Egligton Avenue East #305 PHONE: (416) 932-3666
Toronto, ON M4P 1E8 FAX: (416) 932-3667

CONTACT: Paul Thomas, Editor **DESCRIPTION:** Published by Institute of Public Administration of Canada. Circulation 4,200. A refereed bilingual scholarly publication committed to the examination of the structures and outcome of public policy in all spheres of government. Published 4 times a year. Established in 1958.

CANADIAN PUBLIC POLICY\ANALYSE DE POLITIQUES
University of Guelph, PHONE: (519) 824-4120 ext. 3330
MacKinnon Bldg. Room 039 FAX: (519) 837-9953
Guelph, ON N1G 2W1

CONTACT: Nancy Olewiler, Editor **DESCRIPTION:** Published by Canadian Public Policy. Circulation 2,000. A quarterly bilingual journal about economic and social policy developments affecting all Canadians.
WRITERS: "We publish work about public policy. Contributors are **charged** a $10 per page fee. We need 5 copies of the paper which should not normally exceed 5,500 words, and a 100 word summary abstract." Send to Nancy Olewiler at Simon Fraser University, Dept. of Economics, Burnaby, BC V5A 1S6.
PHOTOGRAPHERS: Does not purchase photographs.
NOTES: A sample copy of the publication is free upon request.

CANADIAN PURCHASING JOURNAL
245 Fairview Mall Drive #308 PHONE: (416) 494-2960
North York, ON M2J 4T1 FAX: (416) 494-2536

CONTACT: Bill Roebuck, Editor **DESCRIPTION:** Published by Powershift Communications. Published 6 times a year. Established in 1993.
NOTES: Also publishes Fleet Management Journal and Benefits and Pension Monitor.

CANADIAN QUARTER HORSE JOURNAL see The Rider

CANADIAN RAILWAY MODELLER
28103-1453 Henderson Highway   PHONE: (204) 668-0168
Winnipeg, MB R2G 4E9   FAX: (204) 668-0168

CONTACT: Morgan Turney, Editor   DESCRIPTION: Published by North Kildonan
Publishers. Circulation 4,000. "A Canadian content magazine for those who like to model
Canadian railways. It contains articles on how to build locomotives and pieces of rolling
stock and basic structures that one would find in a railway set. We also publish historical
information on Canadian railways. We include video and book reviews." Publishes information
connected to the historical significance of railways in Canada's development. Contains
new product details, book reviews, and articles on how to model railway items. Published
bi-monthly. Established in 1989.
WRITERS: "We don't usually purchase. Most of our writing is submitted by model
railroaders. We pay them a fee for their aritcles. Once in awhile a professional writer submits
an article, occasionally we take one. Contact me by mail with the idea."
PHOTOGRAPHERS: "We don't purchase photography."

CANADIAN REALTOR NEWS
320 Queen Street #2100   PHONE: (613) 237-7111
Ottawa, ON K1R 5A3   FAX: (613) 234-2567

CONTACT: Jim McCarthy, Editor DESCRIPTION: Published by Canadian Real Estate
Association. Published monthly. Established in 1946.

CANADIAN RENTAL SERVICE
145 Thames Road West   PHONE: (519) 235-2400
Exeter, ON N0M 1S3   FAX: (519) 235-0798

CONTACT: Peter Darbishire, Managing Editor   DESCRIPTION: Published by AIS
Communications. Circulation 3,500. A trade publication for construction, tool and equipment
rentals. Published eight times a year. Established in 1977.
WRITERS: 5% freelance written. Purchases 6 articles per year. Byline is given. Average
article is 800 words, pay is negotiated. "CRS is a trade magazine for the tool and equipment
as well as party rental trade. We would only consider a freelance contribution if it is specific
to the industry's needs."
PHOTOGRAPHERS: "We purchase freelance work very infrequently. Generally speaking
with all of our publications we don't do much with unsolicited material. We tend to keep
a stable of freelancers handy. If there's a hole or if we need something done in a certain
area we either put it into our travel plans or hire on assignment. We may work easily 12
months ahead on some things as far as getting photos and then getting stories later and
so on. Generally our stories are not time-sensitive. Contact us by mail or fax if you have
a suggestion. I am not in a position where I am really clamoring for photos or stories."
NOTES: Also publishes Agri Book Magazine, Glass Canada and Water Well.

CANADIAN RESOURCES REVIEW
1777 Victoria Avenue #1000   **PHONE:** (306) 584-1000
Regina, SK S4P 4K5

CONTACT: Tom Steve, Editor   **DESCRIPTION:** Published by Charleton Communications
Ltd. A quarterly for the oil, forestry, gas and mining industry.
WRITERS: "We may purchase one or two articles per issue. Freelancers should contact
the editor with a story idea. Payment varies."
PHOTOGRAPHERS: "We don't purchase photography."
NOTES: Sample copies of this publication are available free upon request. Also publishes
Prairie Landscape, DC Magazine and Landmark.

CANADIAN RETAILER
250 The Esplanade #201   **PHONE:** (416) 867-1042
Toronto, ON M5A 1J2   **FAX:** (416) 867-1115

CONTACT: Andrea Kuch, Editor   **DESCRIPTION:** Published by August Communications.
Circulation 11,000. A national trade magazine for the Retail Council of Canada. Published
6 times a year. Established in 1990.
WRITERS: "Some freelance work is purchased. There are no standard lengths and rates
are negotiable. Contact the editor with a query letter. We do take pitched articles from
time to time."
PHOTOGRAPHERS: "We occasionally purchase photography." Contact the editor with
a letter of inquiry.
NOTES: Sample copies available for serious potential writers. Also publishes Association
and University Manager.

CANADIAN RODEO NEWS
2116-27th Avenue NE   **PHONE:** (403) 250-7292
#223 Stockmans Centre   **FAX:** (403) 250-6926
Calgary, AB T2E 7A6

CONTACT: P. Kirby Meston, Editor   **DESCRIPTION:** Circulation 4,000. Consumer
magazine about the professional rodeo in Canada. Features contestants, stock, committees,
historical and promotional stories. Readers are rodeo fans and contestants. Published monthly.
Established in 1964.
WRITERS: 60% freelance written. Buys 84 articles annually. Gives a byline. Average
length 1,000-1,200 words. Pays $50 for ½ page articles. "Articles must pertain to professional
rodeos in Canada, contestants, stock, committees, personnel, etc. Call to discuss ideas
first to see if it is something we could use. Our readers are all educated rodeo people and
terminology must be correct - ie. if you don't know much about rodeo, don't try to tell
them how it feels to ride a bull. Contact me before you writer. We do not accept chuckwagon
racing articles."
PHOTOGRAPHERS: Purchases 70 photos annually. 80% from freelancers. Model releases
are not necessary. Captions are preferred "participants must be identified." Uses colour
prints and glossy or b&w prints (all sizes). Pays $10 for b&w; $10 for inside colour; $15
for colour cover; $60 for photo/text package. "Photos must pertain to CPRA professional
rodeos in Canada. Must be relatively current."
NOTES: Sample copy is free upon request. Unsolicited materials are returned with SASE.
Previously published work and simultaneous submissions are considered.

CANADIAN ROOFING CONTRACTOR

1735 Bayly Street, Suite 7A　　　　**PHONE:** (905) 831-4711
Pickering, ON　L1W 3G7　　　　　**FAX:** (905) 831-4725

CONTACT: Tanja Nowotny, Editor　**DESCRIPTION:** Published by Perks Publications Inc. Circulation 4,500. "A trade publication for roofing contractors, architects, spec writers, and engineers. The main editorial thrust is new products and new product profiles. We also do project and service profiles as well as news." Published quarterly. Established in 1984.
NOTES: This publication is completely done in-house.

CANADIAN RV DEALER

2585 Skymark Avenue, #306　　　　**PHONE:** (905) 624-8218
Mississauga, ON　L4W 4L5　　　　**FAX:** (905) 624-6764

CONTACT: Norm Rosen, Editor　　**DESCRIPTION:** Published by Camping Canada Ltd. Industry publication for those in the recreational vehicle business. Published bi-monthly. Established in 1975.
WRITERS: "We do have regular writers and a large portion is freelance by assignment. I prefer people to query first before they submit, with a sample of their work. Article length is anywhere from 1,200-1,500 words. Pay rates vary depending on the writer and the subject matter. We are looking for travel pieces and personal RV related experience. Everything has to have an RV slant to it." Guidelines are not available.
PHOTOGRAPHERS: "We don't purchase photos individually. They come as part of an arrangement we make with the writer. A lot of our writers are photographers as well." Colour is preferred.
NOTES: May take previously published work depending on where it has been published. Prefers single submissions. Sample copies are given to those who are on assignment. Also publishes Power Boating Canada and Camping Canada.

CANADIAN SAILINGS

4634 St. Catherine Street West
Montreal, PQ　H3Z 1S3

NOTES: Could not locate. These phone numbers were not in service (514) 943-0373 or (514) 937-4639.

CANADIAN SECURITY

46 Crockford Blvd.　　　　　**PHONE:** (416) 755-4343
Scarborough, ON　M1R 3C3　　　**FAX:** (416) 755-7487

CONTACT: Robert Robinson, Editor　**DESCRIPTION:** Published by Security Publishing Ltd. Circulation 11,000. Published seven times a year. Established in 1979.

CANADIAN SELECT HOMES
25 Sheppard Avenue West #100
North York, ON M2N 6S7

PHONE: (416) 733-7600
FAX: (416) 218-3632

CONTACT: Barbara Dixon, Editor **DESCRIPTION:** Published by Telemedia. Circulation 174,400. A renovating and home decorating magazine. Published 8 times a year.
WRITERS: "We purchase some material. We want to see Canadian renovating and decorating. We are primarily interested in Canadian homes and homeowners and anything connected to the home. Writers should send a query letter." Writers' guidelines are available.
PHOTOGRAPHERS: "We have a lot of photographers we use on a regular assignment basis. Potential freelancers should send a query letter with samples of their work."
NOTES: Formerly called Canadian Select Homes and Food. Available on newsstands. Purchases first North American serial rights. Considers previously published work.

CANADIAN SHAREOWNER
1090 University Avenue West, #204
Windsor, ON N9A 5S4

PHONE: (519) 252-9965
FAX: (519) 252-9570

CONTACT: John Bart, Editor **DESCRIPTION:** Circulation 8,000. Features articles on topics including financial and tax planning. Published 6 times a year. Established in 1987.

CANADIAN SHIPPER
777 Bay Street
Toronto, ON M5W 1A7

PHONE: (416) 596-5708
FAX: (416) 596-5881

CONTACT: Robert Robertson, Editor **DESCRIPTION:** Circulation 5,000. "An association magazine for the Canadian Industrial Transportation League which are the foremost transportation buyers in Canada. It presents news and information for buyers of transportation services." Published 5 times a year. Established in 1983.
WRITERS: "Writing is purchased. Contact the editor by phone, fax or a query letter."
PHOTOGRAPHERS: "We purchase on assignment. From time to time we may purchase stock photos."

CANADIAN SPORTFISHING
937 Centre Road #2020
Waterdown, ON L0R 2H0

PHONE: (905) 689-1112
FAX: (905) 689-2065

CONTACT: Kerry Knudsen, Editor **DESCRIPTION:** Published by Canadian Sportfishing. Circulation 45,000. Published 6 times a year. Established in 1988.
WRITERS: 40% freelance written. Purchases 25 articles per year. Byline is given. Writers are hired on assignment and expenses are paid. Average article is 1,800 words. Pay rate is 20¢ a word. "Features include; How-to's, location, species spotlight, anecdotes. Send query by mail or fax. Send completed articles on spec. "I like clean copy, nice angles, good quotes, real information. I hate arrogant writers, stupid cliches, padded stories and laziness."
PHOTOGRAPHERS: Photos are purchased from stock. Photographers are hired on assignment. Approximately 100 photos are used annually. 50% of photos are provided by freelancers. Uses 35mm & 2¼x2¼ transparencies. Model releases and captions are required. Pays $5-250 for inside colour; $200-500 for colour covers. Credit lines must

be negotiated. Contact the editor with a query letter and include subject list and brochure, flyer or tear sheets. "I need a photo page titled "How can you take a picture like this?" I love clear, underwater shots; well lit subjects from front to back and big fish. I hate dead fish, staged photos and photographic dishonesty."

CANADIAN SPORTSCARD COLLECTOR

103 Lakeshore Road #202   **PHONE:** (905) 646-7744
St. Catherines, ON L2N 2T6   **FAX:** (905) 646-0995

CONTACT: Jeffrey Morris, Editor   **DESCRIPTION:** Published by Trajan Publishing Corp. Circulation 25,000. "Canada's sportscard collectibles magazine and price guide. We focus on sports collectibles, cards and memorabilia as well as Canadian sports nostalgia." Published monthly. Established in 1990.
WRITERS: "We get a lot of submissions from writers. We purchase about 20 per year; non-fiction with a given byline. We hire writers on assignment. We have a stable of writers across the country and if something is going in Calgary we will call our Calgary contact. We won't usually send somebody. We have short articles and long features anywhere from 500-2,500 depending on the subject matter. Our pay rate fluctuates and varies. Usually writers work on spec, after an article is published we pay for it. If it doesn't run we don't pay for it. If we have assigned an article and don't run it, we pay a kill fee. I get a lot of letters from people interested in writing. The best thing to do is send a sample of their work and follow-up with a phone call."
PHOTOGRAPHERS: "We rarely purchase from photographers. We have ourselves set up with a hockey photographer - most of our work is done in-house."

THE CANADIAN SPORTSMAN

Box 129, 25 Old Plank Road   **PHONE:** (519) 866-5558
Straffordville, ON N0J 1Y0   **FAX:** (519) 866-5596

CONTACT: Gary Foerster, Editor   **DESCRIPTION:** Circulation 5,000. Features weekly news about harness racing in Canada.
WRITERS: "Our writers are very specialized and I have a network of writers I normally use, so I am not really in the market at this time."
PHOTOGRAPHERS: "I have a list of photographers I regularly use."
NOTES: Interested freelancers can contact this publication by letter.

CANADIAN STAMP NEWS

103 Lakeshore Road, #202   **PHONE:** (905) 646-7744
St Catharines, ON L2N 2T6   **FAX:** (905) 646-0995

CONTACT: Ellen Rodger, Editor   **DESCRIPTION:** Published by Trajan Publishing. Circulation 9,500. A magazine for stamp hobbyists. Published twice a month.

CANADIAN TELECOM
36 Toronto Street #1160   **PHONE:** (416) 359-2918
Toronto, ON M5C 2C5   **FAX:** (416) 359-9909

CONTACT: John Burry, Editor   **DESCRIPTION:** Published by A&B&Y Group. Circulation 6,000. A national telecommunications industry magazine. Published 5 times a year with one directory issue.
WRITERS: "We purchase 3-4 articles per issue. Length and payment varies. Freelancers should phone me. All of our stories are hi-tech telecommunications stories. A writer would have to have some telecommunications or data background. Some articles are assigned and some are pitched to us. If someone has a good story we certainly can have a discussion." Query with a letter. Writers' guidelines are not available.
PHOTOGRAPHERS: "Our stories are high-tech and photographs are problematic."
NOTES: Sample copies of this publication are available free on request, based upon availability.

CANADIAN TELEPHONE CARD COLLECTOR
103 Lakeshore Road #202   **PHONE:** (905) 646-7744
St. Catharines, ON L2N 2T6   **FAX:** (905) 646-0995

CONTACT: Bret Evans, Editor   **DESCRIPTION:** Published by Trajan Publishing. Provides information on the collection of pre-paid telephone cards from around the world. A tabloid published 4 times a year.
WRITERS: "I purchase very little but we are always interested in adding to the core. Anyone wishing to write must be able to offer us some specialized knowledge about these collections. We commission 5-6 articles per year mostly from the USA because of their market knowledge. I would rather use Canadians."

CANADIAN TEXTILE JOURNAL
1 Pacifique   **PHONE:** (514) 457-2347
Ste. Anne de Bellevue, PQ H9X 1C5   **FAX:** (514) 457-2147

CONTACT: Gillian Crosby, Editor   **DESCRIPTION:** Circulation under 3,500+. Trade review for the Canadian textile industry. Publishes profiles, technical articles and features related to the textile industry. Articles are of interest to both manufacturers and suppliers. Published 7 times a year. Established in 1883.
WRITERS: 10% freelance written. Purchases 10-15 articles per year. Gives a byline. Hires on assignment. Average length of articles 1000 words. Payment negotiable. Make contact by sending query letter. "Any newsworthy item or new "angle" on the textile industry." Pays $50-$300 for articles. Phone inquiries welcome.
PHOTOGRAPHERS: Does not purchase photography.
NOTES: Purchases all rights. Returns unsolicited materials with SASE. Will not consider previously published work. Will consider simultaneous submissions.

CANADIAN THOROUGHBRED
Box 670, 225 Industrial Parkway South   **PHONE:** (905) 727-0107
Aurora, ON L4G 4J9   **FAX:** (905) 841-1530

CONTACT: Lee Benson   **DESCRIPTION:** Circulation 10,000. Focuses on racing and breeding of thoroughbreds. Knowledgeable industry experts report on races, breeding

techniques and news about owners, trainers and horses. Published monthly. Established in 1969.
WRITERS: 20% freelance written. Byline is given. Pays 15¢ a word. Guidelines are available. Contact with a query letter. "No poetry or sappy fiction! We like to see tight, concise reporting on issues and well researched articles with up-to-date information. Quotes from recognized names or experts are helpful."
PHOTOGRAPHERS: 69% assigned to freelance photographers. Also purchases photos as part of text/photo submission. Uses all formats colour and b&w. Pays $15 for b&w; $25 for colour inside and $75-125 for colour cover. "I want to see bright, in focus and sharp photos only. No arty shots, dark or badly exposed photos."
NOTES: Purchases first North American serial rights. Unsolicited material will be returned with SASE. Considers previously published work. Will not consider simultaneous submissions. Also publishes Corinthian Horse Sport and Horse Power.

CANADIAN TOBACCO GROWER
222 Argyle Avenue   **PHONE:** (519) 582-2510
Delhi, ON   N4B 2Y2   **FAX:** (519) 582-4040

CONTACT: Marlene Opdecam, Editor   **DESCRIPTION:** Published by NCC Publishing. Circulation 2,500. Published 4 times a year. Established in 1952.

CANADIAN TRANSPORTATION LOGISTICS
1450 Don Mills Road   **PHONE:** (416) 442-2888
Don Mills, ON   M3B 2X7   **FAX:** (416) 442-2214

CONTACT: Bonnie Toews, Editor   **DESCRIPTION:** Published by Southam. Circulation 16,000. Publication about the various modes of transportation within Canada including information on cargo and freight. Published monthly. Established in 1898.
WRITERS: 10% freelance written. Average length 750-1,500 words. Pays $250 for a 750 word article. "Columns are not freelanced. Writers have to request editorial calendars for possible stories they can work on. We are a very specialized magazine in logistics." Contact by sending query letter with samples and resumé. These will be kept on file. "Writers must do homework and know what the magazine publishes. Coming up with an idea that's been played to death wastes everyone's time and energy. Verify! Verify! Verify! Write in clear crisp English with good anecdotes and easy comparisons the most technical reader or the novice can understand and apply. Think "how-to" in structuring stories. Readers want to know how to do their jobs more effectively and trends affecting changes in their job processes."
PHOTOGRAPHERS: Occasionally buys photos. "Most photos are donated by suppliers to the industry." Uses transparencies and colour prints and 5x7 glossy b&w. Pay for b&w negotiated; for colour ranges from $250 to $500 for a colour cover.

THE CANADIAN TRAPPER MAGAZINE
1132 - 98 St., Box 430   **PHONE:** (306)445-4401
North Battleford, SK   S9A 2Y5   **FAX:** (306)445-1977

CONTACT: Becky McIntosh McDonald, Editor   **DESCRIPTION:** Published by Rod McDonald. Circulation 7,000. Magazine focusing on the multi-billion dollar trapping industry. Articles feature what's happening in the trapping world. National articles about changes in standards; local articles about trapping tips and techniques, clear-cutting problems, how to maintain species and a line.

WRITERS: Contact this publication by sending a query letter. Byline given. Pay negotiable.
PHOTOGRAPHERS: 90% in-house freelance written. Contact this publication by sending a query letter. Do not contact this publication unless you have photographs of live fur-bearing animals such as lynx, wolves, coyotes, bobcats, or fox.
NOTES: "I have yet to find a freelance writer that has the type of skills and knowledge of the industry that I am looking for. I don't want animal rights propaganda."

CANADIAN TRAVEL PRESS

310 Dupont Street   **PHONE:** (416) 968-7252
Toronto, ON M5R 1V9   **FAX:** (416) 968-2377

CONTACT: Robert Mowat, Editor   **DESCRIPTION:** Published by Baxter Publishing Co. Circulation 12,700. Published weekly. Established in 1968.
NOTES: This publication never purchases freelance work. Also publishes Canadian Defence Quarterly.

CANADIAN TRAVELLER

5200 Miller Road #115   **PHONE:** (604) 276-0818
Richmond, BC V7B 1K5   **FAX:** (604) 276-0843

CONTACT: Doreen Ormiston   **DESCRIPTION:** Circulation 15,000. Published monthly. Established in 1983.
WRITERS: Articles are purchased. 5% freelance written. Purchase 10 articles per year. Byline is given. Average article is 1400 words, payment is negotiable.
PHOTOGRAPHERS: Uses colour photography inside and on cover. Pay is negotiable. Formats preferred 35mm and larger transparencies. Model releases and captions are preferred. Uses approximately 100 photos annually. "Love to see: architectural shots done at unusual angles, people shots in travel locations. Hate seeing: cliche sunset beach shots, tropical shots, passive people shots." Photographers contact John Frazer.
NOTES: Sample copies please enclose 9x12" SASE with first class postage. Returns unsolicited work with SASE. Considers previously published work and simultaneous submissions.

CANADIAN TREASURER

8 King Street East #1010   **PHONE:** (416) 367-8500
Toronto, ON M5C 1B5   **FAX:** (416) 367-3240

CONTACT: Bruce McDougall, Managing Editor   **DESCRIPTION:** Published by Treasury Management Association of Canada. Circulation 3,500. A bi-monthly publication which covers treasury issues. Established in 1985.

CANADIAN UNDERWRITER

1450 Don Mills Road   **PHONE:** (416) 445-6641
Don Mills, ON M3B 2X7   **FAX:** (416) 442-2213

CONTACT: Larry Welsh   **DESCRIPTION:** Published by Southam Magazine Group. Circulation 6,200. Published monthly. Established in 1934.

CANADIAN VENDING
222 Argle Avenue   **PHONE:** (519) 582-2513
Delhi, ON   N4B 2Y2   **FAX:** (519) 582-4040

CONTACT: Dan Wilkins   **DESCRIPTION:** Published by NCC Publishing. Circulation 1,400. Publication geared to those who operate and service vending equipment and machines. Published bi-monthly. Established in 1953.

CANADIAN VET SUPPLIES
505 South Street, Suite 205
Cowansville, PQ   J2K 2X9

NOTES: Could not locate. Phone number is not in service (514) 263-5339.

THE CANADIAN VETERINARY JOURNAL
339 Booth Street   **PHONE:** (613) 236-1162
Ottawa, ON K1R 7K1   **FAX:** (613) 236-9681

CONTACT: Dr. Doug Hare, Editor   **DESCRIPTION:** Published by Canadian Veterinary Medical Association. Circulation 5,000. Published monthly in English and French and distributed to veterinarians across Canada and overseas. Established in 1960.
NOTES: This publication does not purchase freelance material.

CANADIAN VOCATIONAL JOURNAL
Box 3435, Station D   **PHONE:** (613) 596-2515
Ottawa, ON K1P 6L4   **FAX:** (613) 596-2515

CONTACT: Bob Louks, Editor   **DESCRIPTION:** Published by Canadian Vocational Association. Circulation 1,000 . Published quarterly.
NOTES: "Being a non-profit association most of the work is done by the membership."

CANADIAN WATER WELL
145 Thames Road West   **PHONE:** (519) 235-2400
Exeter, ON N0M 1S3   **FAX:** (519) 235-0798

CONTACT: Peter Darbishire, Editor   **DESCRIPTION:** Published by Peter Phillips. Circulation 3,900. Published quarterly.

CANADIAN WELDER AND FABRICATOR
3500 Dufferin Street, #103
Downsview, ON M3K 1N2

NOTES: Could not locate. Phone numbers are no longer in service. (416) 633-2020 or (204) 775-0201.

CANADIAN WEST
Box 3399
Langley, BC   V3A 4R7

NOTES: NO LONGER PUBLISHED

CANADIAN WOMAN STUDIES
212 Founders College, York University   **PHONE:** (416) 736-5356
4700 Keele Street
North York, ON   M3J 1P3

CONTACT: Luciana Ricciutelli, Editor   **DESCRIPTION:** Published by Inana Publications and Education Inc. Circulation 6,000. A bilingual thematic feminist quarterly making current research and writing on a wide variety of feminist topics accessible to the largest possible community of women. Established in 1978.
WRITERS: "All work is donated. Contact the editor with a letter of intent."
PHOTOGRAPHERS: "Sometimes we receive photo essays relating to our theme but we are a non-profit charity so we are unable to pay."
NOTES: Phone the office for a list of themes or ask to be put on our mailing list for calls for papers. All large libraries carry copies of this publication.

CANADIAN WOOD PROCESSING
7575 Trans Canada Highway #500   **PHONE:** (514) 333-1116
St. Laurent, PQ   H4T 1V6   **FAX:** (514) 631-8858

CONTACT: Keith Fredericks   **DESCRIPTION:** Published 6 times a year. Established in 1900.

CANADIAN WOOD PRODUCTS
1 rue Pacifique   **PHONE:** (514) 457-2211
Ste. Anne de Bellevue, PQ   H9X 1C5   **FAX:** (514) 457-2558

CONTACT: Scott Jamieson, Editor   **DESCRIPTION:** Published by JCFT Forest Communications. Circulation 6,400. An industrial and technical magazine for solid wood products in Canada. Features columns by industry professionals, company profiles and special features on developing technology and first-ever installations. Published 6 times a year. Established in 1991.
WRITERS: "On rare occasions we purchase work. Our articles are 1,500 words maximum and the pay rate is $500 per article plus expenses. Writers should contact the editor with an idea by phone, letter or fax with a brief description of what they have in mind."
PHOTOGRAPHERS: "We purchase photos maybe once or twice a year with an article. If it is cover material it would probably be colour. Payment would be negotiated."
NOTES: Purchases exclusive Canadian rights. Sample copies of this publication are available for $5.00. Will not consider simultaneous submissions if in Canada. Will not consider material published previously in Canada.

CANADIAN WORKSHOP
130 Spy Court
Markham, ON L3R 5H6

PHONE: (905) 475-8440
FAX: (905) 475-9246

CONTACT: Hugh McBride **DESCRIPTION:** Published by Camar Publications Ltd. Circulation 115,000. A magazine for hobby woodworkers as well as those interested in do-it-yourself home renovation and repair. Published monthly. Established in 1977.
WRITERS: "We purchase freelance articles almost exclusively on home renovation and repair. We are interested in original woodworking designs. Writers should contact us expressing an interest in writing for the magazine. Include samples or portfolio pieces that might pertain, particularly samples of service journalism. We probably purchase 15 features and 10 short features per year. A byline is always given. We normally hire writers on assignment. A kill fee is likely paid if the assignment is cancelled, which is a rare occurance. I am not very interested in queries. I am more interested in people proving that they are good service writers, if not on home renovation than on some other subject. If I like what I see, I will assign an article. Features are around 1,500 words and pay approximately $600. $300 for short features 700-800 words in length. I am very interested in new service writers in Ontario."
PHOTOGRAPHERS: "We purchase quite a bit of photography and have a stable of contributing photographers. We purchase probably 30 individual photographs per issue. We prefer colour 35mm transparencies. Captions are not necessary. We never use unsolicited submissions. All photography is done under the close guidance of our art director." Payment is negotiable. A credit line is always given. Contact our art director, Marcello Biagioni.
NOTES: Also publishes Photo Life, Canadian Gardening, Craft Supplies, Snow Goer and Water Goer.

CANADIAN WRITER'S JOURNAL
Box 6618 Depot 1
Victoria, BC V8P 5N7

PHONE: (604) 477-8807
FAX: none

CONTACT: Gordon Smart, Editor **DESCRIPTION:** Published by Gordon M. Smart publications. Circulation 300. Contains articles on the "how-to's" of writing, including helpful tips on getting ideas and focusing them, marketing your work and keeping a positive attitude. Published quarterly.
WRITERS: 75% freelance written. Accepts mostly how-to articles from all levels of writers. Contact this publication by sending a query letter. Returns unsolicited materials with SASE. Pays $5 per item; negotiable. Considers simultaneous submissions unless to a competing publication. Byline given. Purchases first North American serial rights. Send $5 & 9x12" SASE with appropriate postage for a sample copy.
NOTES: "We don't want articles with common topics that are overworked or are found in all the writers' books. Articles should focus on something the writer has done personally to improve their writing.
"We run two contests a year as well; a short fiction contest and a poetry contest. The short fiction deadline is October 15; the poetry contest deadline is June 30. We pay an honorarium for each of the winners."

CANADIAN YACHTING
395 Matheson Blvd East
Mississauga, ON L4Z 2H2

PHONE: (905) 890-1846
FAX: (905) 890-5769

CONTACT: Graham Jones, Editor   **DESCRIPTION:** Published by Cam MacDonald. Circulation 15,800. Covers all aspects of Canadian sailing from Victoria to St.John's, including racing, cruising, keelboats and dinghies. Published 6 times a year. Established in 1977.
WRITERS: 75% freelance written. Hires on assignment, and pays expenses while on assignment. Purchases fiction and non-fiction. Average article length 1,800 words. Pays 25¢ per word. Byline is given.
PHOTOGRAPHERS: Hires photographers on assignment. Uses approximately 15 photos per issue. Does not purchase from stock. Prefers 35mm transparencies, 5x7 colour prints and 5x7 b&w prints. Model releases not necessary. Captions preferred. Pays $20-40 for b&w; $35-50 for inside colour; $200 for colour cover. Credit line is given. Make contact by sending query letter.
NOTES: Sample is available, please enclose large SASE. Unsolicited materials are returned with SASE. Previously published work is considered. Simultaneous submissions are not considered. Also publishes Formula, CAD Systems, Electrical Business, Electrical Bluebook, Energy Manager, Lighting Magazine, Manufacturing & Process Automation and La Monde.

CANINE REVIEW
SS2, Site 4, Comp 22 Beaton Road
Kamloops, BC V2C 6C3

PHONE: (604) 828-1978
FAX: (604) 828-0052

CONTACT: Helen W. Lee, Editor   **DESCRIPTION:** Circulation 1,500. Publication geared to dog-lovers with an interest in local and national dog shows and other canine issues. Published 10 times a year. Established in 1978.
WRITERS: 98% assigned to in-house writers. "Writers are paid with an advertising trade. If they just want to be published we do not pay." Byline given. Sample copies not available.
PHOTOGRAPHERS: 100% assigned to in-house photographers.

CANOLA GUIDE
Box 6600
Winnipeg, MB R3C 3A7

PHONE: (204) 944-5767
FAX: (204) 942-8463

CONTACT: Ray Wytinck, Editor   **DESCRIPTION:** Published by Farm Business Communications. Circulation 23,000. A national farm publication for crop producers. Published 9 times a year.
WRITERS: "We run 5-10% freelance. Generally I assign articles if I think its something our people can't get to or if it is geographically easier. Very rarely would I take an article without any prior arrangement." Contact the editor by phone. "I am always open to ideas."
PHOTOGRAPHERS: "On the odd occasion we will purchase cover colour photos. All our covers are farm based." Send me a portfolio or call me.
NOTES: Sample copies of this publication are available free upon request. Purchases one-time rights.

CAPE BRETON'S MAGAZINE
Wreck Cove
Cape Breton, NS B0C 1H0

PHONE: (902) 539-3817
FAX: (902) 539-9117

CONTACT: Ronald Caplan, Editor **DESCRIPTION:** Published by Cape Breton Magazine Ltd. Circulation 7,500. Covers the history, natural history, folklore, photography and the traditions of Cape Breton. Published three times a year in English, French, Gaelic and MicMak. Established in 1972.
WRITERS: "We really don't purchase very much. Contact me with a query letter. We don't have a standard pay rate but we would certainly try not to hurt anybody."
PHOTOGRAPHERS: Photography not purchased.

CARGO EXPRESS
310 Dupont Street
Toronto, ON M5R 1V9

NOTES: NO LONGER PUBLISHED

CARGUIDE/LE MAGAZINE CARGUIDE
447 Speers Rd #4
Oakville, ON L6K 3S7

PHONE: (905) 842-6591
FAX: (905) 842-6843

CONTACT: Alan McPhee, Editor **DESCRIPTION:** Published by Formula Publications. Circulation English 85,000 French 35,000. "An automotive general interest magazine. It's not a buff or performance magazine. You can find information such as road tests, technical articles, stories about touring; any kind of information people can use to help them make rational decisions in the marketplace." Buyer's guide published 6 times a year. Established in 1972.
WRITERS: "We purchase about 10 articles per issue. It's all non-fiction assignment with a byline. We purchase first time rights. There is no average article length, a contribution can be anything from 400-2,000 words. We don't pay by the word, we pay according to the project and how complicated it is and how much research is involved. Writers should spend some time reading the publication first so that they understand the kinds of things that we are doing. If they feel they can make a contribution they can give us a call."
PHOTOGRAPHERS: "We sometimes hire on assignment. If it is a special concern or subject we use one of the various stock libraries. We purchase anywhere from 20-30 photos per issue. We prefer slides, its all four colour. Depending on the purpose of the photograph, for cover shots for example, we would want 2¼ square at least. Our pay rate depends on what the subject is and what is involved in getting the shot." Contact by telephone. "Look at the magazine and do some research."
NOTES: The publication is available at newsstands.

CARLETON ARTS REVIEW
Carleton University
Ottawa, ON K1S 5B6

NOTES: Could not locate.

CARP NEWS

27 Queen Street East #702
Toronto, ON M5C 2M6

PHONE: (416) 363-5562
FAX: (416) 363-7394

CONTACT: David Tafler, Editor **DESCRIPTION:** Published by Canadian Association of Retired Persons. Circulation 100,000. Seniors' publication issued 6 times a year. Established in 1985.
WRITERS: Occasionally buys articles. "Pay rates vary as we are a non-profit based organization. The range is about 30¢ a word, although this is under review."
PHOTOGRAPHERS: "We have a regular photographer."
NOTES: Contact the editor for current guidelines.

CATHOLIC INSIGHT

Box 625 Adelaide Station,
36 Adelaide Street East
Toronto, ON M5C 2J9

PHONE: (416) 368-0250
FAX: (416) 368-8575

CONTACT: Alphonse De Valk, Editor **DESCRIPTION:** Circulation 3,000. Provides comprehensive and incisive analysis and comment of the political, cultural and religious issues facing Catholics in Canada. Informs and comments on spiritual life, and family issues from a Catholic perspective. Established in 1993. Issued 10 times a year.
WRITERS: "A good deal of assigned writing goes to a stable of regular writers. A query letter with bio and samples of work is the best way to approach us."
PHOTOGRAPHERS: "We don't purchase photography."
NOTES: Sample copies of this publication are available free upon request.

CATTLEMEN

Box 6600 201 Portage Avenue
Winnipeg, MB R3C 3A7

PHONE: (204) 944-5753
FAX: (204) 942-8463

CONTACT: Gren Winslow, Editor **DESCRIPTION:** Published by Farm Business Communications. Circulation 34,000. "A national monthly publication targeted at Canadian beef cattle producers. Includes information on health, feed, reproduction and new ranching methods." Published monthly. Established in 1938.
WRITERS: "We purchase 2-5 stories per month. We have a stable of freelancers. Contact me directly by fax or phone with suggestions for stories. The pay rate ranges from $100-$200. We take anything from 800-1,200 words. We look for practical items that are of use to working cattle producers."
PHOTOGRAPHERS: "We rarely purchase photos unless they come with the stories. We prefer colour prints or slides." Contact the editor.
NOTES: Sample copies of this publication are available free upon request. Purchases first time rights. Rarely considers previously published work; it must have been published outside the audience area. Does not consider simultaneous submissions.

CAUT BULLETIN
2675 Queensview Drive
Ottawa, ON K2B 8K2

PHONE: (613) 820-2270
FAX: (613) 820-2417

CONTACT: Liza Duhaime, Managing Editor   **DESCRIPTION:** Published by Canadian Association of University Teachers. Circulation 34,000. A bilingual bulletin published ten times a year. Focuses on the issues of higher education. Established in 1953.
WRITERS: Occasionally purchases non-fiction articles. Byline is given. Writers are hired on assignment. 50 % kill fee if assigned article is cancelled. Average articles run 800 words. Pays 40¢ per word. Interested writers should send in resumé, subject area, business card and samples. These will be kept on file for possible assignment.
PHOTOGRAPHERS: Purchases from stock and hires on assignment. Uses b&w. Pay range is $30-50 for b&w photo. Credit line is given. "We are open to receiving queries from photographers across Canada with a selection of their work, but we don't purchase much." Send brochure, flyer, or tear sheets and a price list.
NOTES: "We purchase political cartoons more than anything else. We pay $50." Sample copies of this publication are available free upon request. Unsolicited materials are returned with SASE. Previously published work is considered. Simultaneous submissions are not considered. Guidelines are not available.

CCL (CANADIAN CHILDREN'S LITERATURE)
Department of English
University of Guelph
Guelph, ON N1G 2W1

PHONE: (519) 824-4120
FAX: (519) 837-1315

CONTACT: Gay Christofides, Administrator   **DESCRIPTION:** Published by Canadian Children's Press. Circulation 1,000. "A bilingual journal of criticism and review covering Canadian books for children and young adults." Published quarterly. Established in 1975.
WRITERS: "All submissions are from academics or writers who understand that we are a scholarly journal and that no payment will be made for work submitted. Includes librarians, teachers, generally people who have expertise in a particular area of children's literature from some point of view. We have some freelance writers doing reviewing for us. If someone can show us that they have expertise in an area than we will consider them. We use approximately 12 non-fiction articles per year and we give the writer a byline. We do not hire writers on assignment. Our average article length is 5,000 words. We accept: critical articles on children's literature, preferably with some reference to Canadian material or illustration; in-depth reviews of current Canadian children's books (a review form is available upon request); interviews with Canadian writers for children and young adults with emphasis on their literary work. Talk to the editor before doing any interviews. Send completed articles on spec. Proposals for articles are welcomed and should be accompanied by a resumé. We have call for papers regularly in the journal so people should keep their eye on the journal to see what it is we're looking for. Reviewers may write for our reviewer information sheets and review form, which will be kept on file. Please state area of interest and qualifications - illustration, poetry, science, history etc. If they can attach previously published material so that we can get some idea of the quality of their work, that would help. If they are of interest to us we will keep them on file and when a book comes in on that subject we would ask them if they would be interested in reviewing that book and send it to them. If its successful then we may ask them again. Articles must be of a high scholarly standard. All articles are submitted to peer reviewers. For English articles contact Mary Rubio, for French articles contact Daniel Chouinard. Guidelines are available.
NOTES: Acquires one-time rights and a permission form, as a few American publishers regularly reprint the reviews. CCL negotiates for the writers and sends them less 20 %

what they are paid for re-publication. Returns unsolicited materials with a SASE. Does not considers previously published work or simultaneous submissions. A sample copy of CCL is available for $10.

CEDA CURRENT ANNUAL
395 Matheson Blvd East
Mississauga, ON L4Z 2H2

NOTES: NO LONGER PUBLISHED

CENTRAL NOVA BUSINESS NEWS
228 Main Street   **PHONE:** (902) 895-7948
Bible Hill, NS B2N 4H2   **FAX:** (902) 893-1427

CONTACT: Karen Fulton, Editor   **DESCRIPTION:** Published by Truro and District Chamber of Commerce. A local business publication issued monthly.
NOTES: Rarely buys freelance material. Also publishes The Light and Truro Magazine.

CENTRE MAGAZINE
1450 Don Mills Road   **PHONE:** (416) 445-6641
Don Mills, ON M3B 2X7   **FAX:** (416) 442-2213

CONTACT: Elena Opasini, Editor   **DESCRIPTION:** Published by Southam Business Communications. Circulation 15,000. A business publication which caters to the hardware trade, and home improvement retail industry. Published 8 times a year. Established in 1977.
WRITERS: "I do purchase freelance however I have several freelance writers that write for me so I am not open to queries at this time."
PHOTOGRAPHERS: "I occasionally purchase from a small group of local photographers. I don't have any opportunities to use outside photographers."

CENTURY HOME
12 Mill Street South   **PHONE:** (905) 885-2449
Port Hope, ON L1A 2S5   **FAX:** (905) 885-5355

CONTACT: Tom Cruikshank, Editor   **DESCRIPTION:** Published by Bluestone House Inc. Circulation 50,000. A shelter publication. It features traditional homes and contemporary information. It focuses on traditional homes and decor. Articles include new home products, furnishings, antiques, gardens, country inns and art. Published 8 times a year.
WRITERS: "We're sometimes open to freelancers. It is mostly staff written, probably 85%. Contact with a query letter. The number of articles differs depending on the economic world and the number of pages in an issue. We have a number of freelancers we work with but we are willing to look at query letters. If we think it is a good idea we might act on it. Articles are 1,500-2,000 words with a negotiable pay rate. We usually purchase outright. We may use previously published work, it would depend upon how fresh it was, how topical and where it was published. We don't really consider simultaneous submissions. It would be wise for writers to analyze the magazine before they send in their query letters." Guidelines are not available.

PHOTOGRAPHERS: "We purchase photography to a limited degree. Most of it is staff driven. We only purchase visuals that go with text. We give credit lines when requested and if necessary. Normally photographers send us a short bio, resumé or a description of their firm."

CHAMPION
1600 James Naismith Drive #204
Ottawa, ON K1B 5N4

NOTES: NO LONGER PUBLISHED

CHARLAIS BANNER
3016-19 Street N.E. #205   **PHONE:** (403) 291-1420
Calgary, AB T2E 6Y9   **FAX:** (403) 291-0081

CONTACT: Rob Peck, Managing Editor   **DESCRIPTION:** Published by Parkland. Circulation 2,800. Canadian Charlais Association and subscriber publication for the Charlais cattle industry. Articles include advertising-related items, sales summaries, and letters to the editor. Published monthly. Established in 1966.
WRITERS: 2% freelance written. Contact this publication by sending a query letter. Byline given.
PHOTOGRAPHERS: 100% assigned to in-house photographers.

CHATELAINE
777 Bay Street, 8th Floor   **PHONE:** (416) 596-5425
Toronto, ON M5W 1A7   **FAX:** (416) 593-3197

CONTACT: Ivor Shapiro, Managing Editor   **DESCRIPTION:** Published by MacLean Hunter. Circulation 900,000. Monthly magazine for Canadian women. Articles on parenting, health, beauty, politics and travel. Published in both English and French versions. Established in 1928.
WRITERS: "Most of our magazine is freelance written. Purchases non-fiction columns (house centre, parents and kids) and features. We do hire writers on assignment with a 3-4 month lead time, and pay expenses up to a certain limit. Our articles are 1,500-2,500 words. To contact please send a query letter. Call for the article requirements (writers' guidelines) before doing anything.
PHOTOGRAPHERS: "We purchase maybe 35% from stock and the rest is assignment. The numbers of photos we purchase per year depends on how big the issue is. In the summer months we don't have that many pages and in the winter/spring months there is more, from 50-300. We prefer colour transparencies. Captions are not required because we write our own. We give a credit line to all contributors. Our rate for one page is $175 and $50 for additional photos. Contact Karen Watkins, Art Director by dropping off portfolio at reception. Let her know that it is coming. Once she looks at it (a day or two) come and pick it up. Karen will get in touch with photographers she is interested in. Or send us one or two samples in the mail." No guidelines are available.
NOTES: For a copy of Chatelaine please send SASE and the newstand price of one issue. Purchases first North American publication rights and electronic rights as well. Returns unsolicited materials with a SASE. Doesn't usually purchase previously published material, prefers fresh stuff. Simultaneous submissions are fine.

LE CHEF DU SERVICE ALIMENTAIRE
252 Route 171   **PHONE:** (418) 831-5317
St. Eitienne-de-Lauzon, PQ G6J 1S2   **FAX:** (418) 831-5172

CONTACT: Maurice LeBlanc, Editor **DESCRIPTION:** Published by Maurice LeBlanc. Circulation 16,700. Food service publication published 6 times a year in French. Established in 1982.

CHICKADEE
179 John Street #500   **PHONE:** (416) 971-5275
Toronto, ON M5T 3G5   **FAX:** (416) 971-5294

CONTACT: Lizann Flatt, Editor **DESCRIPTION:** Published by Owl Communications. Circulation 110,000. "Chickadee is 32 pages of science and nature for children aged 3-8. We have a lot of animals, crafts, fiction and poetry." Chickadee helps children discover the world around them, with a focus on appreciating nature and the environment. The mix of stories, activities, photographs and illustrations is designed for beginning readers. Published 10 times a year. Established in 1979.

WRITERS: "We purchase 20-25 pieces per year including articles, poetry, puzzles and crafts. Stories are up to 900 words and pays $250 per story. Photo stories pay $100-150. Poetry runs from 5-50 lines and pays $3 per line. Bylines are given. Writers' guidelines are available with a business size SASE. We buy all rights for fiction and for poetry we buy one-time rights. We don't usually buy previously published work; simultaneous submissions are OK." Contact editor preferably by sending completed manuscript. "My advice is to read back issues, that's really important, and get our writers' guidelines. We don't usually publish religious material or talking animal stories. Think about what interests a 5 year old child. Most of our fiction is based on something that would happen to a child; the childs' experience not an adult perspective."

PHOTOGRAPHERS: "We purchase around 10 photos per issue. We get photos from stock agencies and freelancers as well. We prefer colour, very rarely black and white unless we were doing some sort of historical piece. Transparencies are preferred. Model releases are necessary and captions may be required depending on the story. I may need to know what that animal is, what its Latin name is and things like that. Fees vary depending on where the photo is going to appear. We accept photos for our covers. Freelancers can send submissions on any relevant topic, if we like the submission we may flag it. Generally per issue we put out a call to agencies and known freelancers; we do accept photographers stock work. We purchase one-time rights if its an agency and for freelancers mostly one-time and if we use it again we will pay a step-up fee. We also have licensed French editions that need to have access - they translate our material a year later. We accept previously published photos. A byline is given. Photo guidelines are available to photographers with a business size SASE. Freelancers can contact us by sending us a sample of their work on slides. We are always looking for animals and real kids engaged in something (a trail ride, that sort of thing). We have also done close-up studies of a sprouting pumpkin or dandelion."

NOTES: "We use a lot of commissioned freelance artwork". If you want a copy of the magazine send a SASE 8.5x11". Also publishes Owl Magazine.

CHRISTIAN INFO NEWS
#200, 20316-56 Avenue
Langley, BC   V3A 3Y7

PHONE: (604) 534-1444
FAX: (604) 534-2970

CONTACT: Flyn Ritchie, Editor   **DESCRIPTION:** Published by Allan Stanchi. Circulation 28,000. Christian, non-sectarian, lifestyle publication issued monthly. Articles feature book and music reviews, personality profiles and current events in the Christian community. Established in 1982.
WRITERS: Contact this publication by sending a query letter. Follow-up with a phone call. Returns unsolicited materials with SASE. Byline given. Pay negotiable.
PHOTOGRAPHERS: 90% assigned to in-house photographers. Do not send photos in the mail. Contact this publication by sending a query letter. Follow-up with a phone call. Hires photographers on assignment. Reasonable expenses are paid.
NOTES: "We are very much focused on the southwestern B.C. geographic area. Articles from this area will receive first consideration."

CHRISTIAN WEEK
Box 725
Winnipeg, MB   R3C 2K3

PHONE: (204) 943-1147
FAX: (204) 947-5632

CONTACT: Harold Jantz, Editor   **DESCRIPTION:** Published by Christianweek. Religious publication issued twice monthly. A current event paper directed toward the evangelical christian market. It covers everything from theology to book reviews to politics.
WRITERS: "We purchase a limited number of articles. Since ours is an evangelical Christian newspaper we want writers who share our point of view. That's one determining factor in deciding who we have writing for us. We do have a number of freelance writers we call upon from time to time." Rates work up to $100 for a 1,000 word piece. Does assign work to writers. Send queries if you are interested in doing work for this publication.
PHOTOGRAPHERS: "We use a limited amount of photos. We do in fact have photographers in various parts of the country we call upon." Contact editor with a query letter.

CHURCH MAGAZINE
4040 Creditview Road #11 Box 1800
Mississauga, ON   L5C 3Y8

PHONE: (905) 569-1800
FAX: (905) 569-1818

CONTACT: Eleanor Parkinson, Editor   **DESCRIPTION:** Published by Momentum Media Management. Circulation 12,000. A church business and technology magazine covering the business side of running a church in Canada. Contains goods and services information as well as computer applications for the church whether accounting, music or bible related. Published 6 times a year. Established in 1993.
WRITERS: "Has in the past exchanged articles for exposure in the magazine. Call or write with a query."
PHOTOGRAPHERS: "All photos are supplied or taken in-house."

CIM BULLETIN
3400 de Maisonneuve Blvd. West, #1210   **PHONE:** (514) 939-2710
Montreal, PQ H3Z 3B8   **FAX:** (514) 939-2714

CONTACT: P. Gantz, Editor   **DESCRIPTION:** Published by Canadian Institute of Mining, Metallurgy and Petroleum. Circulation 10,000. Published 10 times a year and distributed across Canada. Established in 1898.

CineACTION!
40 Alexander Street, #705   **PHONE:** (416) 964-3534
Toronto, ON M4Y 1B5   **FAX:** none

CONTACT: Robin Wood, Editor (one of seven)   **DESCRIPTION:** Circulation 2,000. "The full title is CineACTION: Radical films, film criticism and theory. We try to approach films from the viewpoint of the various progressive and radical movements in the country. Feminism, socialism, gay rights, race issues." This film magazine features independent productions. Published three times a year.
WRITERS: Contributors get one year's complementary subscription to the magazine. "Freelancers should know what the magazine is by reading a few issues, so they know what they are doing.. and then send us some work."
PHOTOGRAPHERS: Does not purchase photography.

CIO CANADA
501 Oakdale Road   **PHONE:** (416) 746-7360
North York, ON M3N 1W7   **FAX:** (416) 746-1421

CONTACT: David Carey, Managing Editor   **DESCRIPTION:** Published by Laurentian Technomedia Inc. Circulation 6,600. Focuses on information technology for executives. Published 7 times a year. Established in 1993.
WRITERS: "CIO is pretty much completely written by freelancers. We purchase about 30 articles. The average length would be 1,500-2,000 words and the rate is typically around 70¢ per word. Contact by fax or telephone is probably most expedient (416) 694-6932.
PHOTOGRAPHERS: "We use extensive photography, strictly freelance. We do probably 20-30 photo shoots. We prefer colour but this depends on the article. Model releases are required. The majority of of photos are industry figures mentioned in the articles. Fees vary according to the use. It might be a photograph for inside, anything from 3 inch square to full page, or it might be a full cover shot. That would vary up to $700. We give credit lines." Contact Virginia Hutton.
NOTES: Also publishes Computerworld, Info Canada, Network World, and Reseller World.

CITY AND COUNTRY HOME
777 Bay Street 8Fl
Toronto, ON M5W 1A7

NOTES: NO LONGER PUBLISHED

CITY MAGAZINE
Box 26083
Winnipeg, MB R3C 4K9

PHONE: (204) 489-8145
FAX: (204) 788-0109

CONTACT: Rob Ferguson **DESCRIPTION:** Quarterly magazine covers urban politics, city planning, public art, architecture, and urban culture. Articles also include: urban design; community design, suburbia, housing, prostitution and slum clearance.
WRITERS: "We don't pay writers so we are not really in the market, everything is a volunteer effort."

CITY PARENT
467 Speers Road
Oakville, ON L6K 3S4

PHONE: (905) 815-0017
FAX: (905) 815-0511

CONTACT: Liz Campbell, Associate Editor **DESCRIPTION:** Published by Metroland Printing, Publishing and Distributing. Circulation 155,000 and growing as editions are added. "A free newspaper for parents and children in Ontario, available at libraries, banks and stores. Launching to Quebec and the West." A monthly parenting magazine with children's activities, book reviews, new products and services, and safety and health information. Circulated mostly in the Metro Toronto area.
WRITERS: "We use nothing but freelancers. We are always interested in Canadian freelancers. Send ideas along, we are always willing to listen. Article lengths vary. We do feature pieces which are quite long, others are quite short. Our pay rate varies anywhere from $50 to $150 depending on the length of stories. We try and pay as much as we can for things; we try to be fair to our writers. A query letter is best because then I can get an idea of a writer's style. Samples are a great help. We do take previously published work provided the piece belongs to the writer and not the publication and only if it's a very special piece. I appreciate very clean copy; we don't have time to edit spelling and grammar. If you are a professional writer with some experience we are always interested. We like to promote Canadian writers as much as possible. We are interested in anything to do with parenting issues, children and their growth and any unique, exciting activities for kids. It has to be generic so that we can use it through the network (across Canada). Local writers are welcome to make suggestions as well. We try to maintain an upbeat perspective; I don't want to know about some dreadful thing that has happened to some kid."
PHOTOGRAPHERS: "We do occasionally use freelancers but they are right here and we know them and have used them before. For the most part we have two in-house photographers that do most of our work. We are interested in receiving text/photo packages." Colour photos are best.
NOTES: Considers simultaneous submissions. Also publishes Today's Seniors.

CITYSCOPE
304 - 1324 - 11th AVE SW
Calgary, AB T3C 0M6

PHONE: (403) 228-7020
FAX: (403) 228-7193

CONTACT: Karen Riva **DESCRIPTION:** Published by Randy Goertzen. Circulation 61,000. "Cityscope is an arts, entertainment and lifestyle publication for the city of Calgary. It is also the listings guide for this city's Rep and first fun ART film house, the Plaza. Issued 6 times a year. Established in 1977.
WRITERS: Articles are purchased. 70% freelance written. Purchases 36-40 articles per year. Gives a byline. Average length of articles 500-1,500 words. Pays 20¢ a word. Kill fee of 25% for assigned articles. "I love to get query letters, especially with well thought

out and targeted story ideas. I look for unusual, unpublicized material. I would rather run a story on a small theatre company than on a big budget high profile production because I believe Cityscope's mandate should be to keep its readers informed of all kinds of events and people, not just those who are already popular with the mainstream media. I really like stories that deal with trends and with the sublime and unusual."

PHOTOGRAPHERS: Hires on assignment. Does not purchase from stock. 85% is done in-house, 15% assigned to freelancers. Uses all colour and b&w formats. Model releases are preferred. Captions not necessary. Credit lines are given. Fees are negotiated. "Right now we have a staff photographer but there are times when we may need an extra lens. It is a good idea to make yourself known to us and to make it clear as to the rates you charge." Contact the editor and bring in a portfolio.

NOTES: "In my last issue, four out of the six articles were assigned based on query letters. I usually go through my portfolio and if that person has expertise in an area I want written about then I give them a call. I will often invite them to meet me and show me their portfolio or some of their work. We are very Calgary-focused so I would usually choose someone who lives here."

CLASSICAL MUSIC MAGAZINE

121 Lakeshore Road East, #207
Mississauga, ON L5G 1E5

PHONE: (905) 271-0339
FAX: (905) 271-9748

CONTACT: Rick MacMillan, Editor   **DESCRIPTION:** Published by Music Magazine. Circulation 7,000. Classical music includes national news stories of the music scene; reviews of new recordings and books on classical music; feature articles on composers, musicians and historical articles. Published 4 times a year. Established in 1978.
WRITERS: "Almost all of it is freelance. Features are 1,700 words. Pay rate is $300 per feature. Mail in proposals first. I want to see critical and analytical articles." Writers' guidelines are available.
PHOTOGRAPHERS: "Photography should be included with article submissions, both colour and black and white."
NOTES: Sample copies of this publication are available for $5 and include writers' guidelines.

CLIK

20 Lower Spadina Ave
Toronto, ON M5V 2Z1

NOTES: Could not locate. Phone number is not in service (416) 203-2545.

CLIN D'OEIL

7 Bates Road
Outremont, PQ H2V 1A6

PHONE: (514) 270-1100
FAX: (514) 270-6900

CONTACT: Dominique Bertrand, Editorial Director   **DESCRIPTION:** Published by Publicor. Circulation 73,800. French magazine published monthly.
NOTES: Also publishes Femme Plus, Clin d'oeil, Les Idees De Ma Maison, Decoration Chez-soi, Renovation Bricolage, Plans de Maisons Quebec and En Route.

CMA MAGAZINE

120 King Street West Box 176
Hamilton, ON L8N 3C3

PHONE: (905) 525-4100
FAX: (905) 525-4533

CONTACT: Kevin Graham, Associate Publisher   **DESCRIPTION:** Published by the Society of Management Accountants of Canada. Circulation 75,000. "The focus of the magazine is primarily on accounting and management practice." Published 10 times a year. Established in 1926.
WRITERS: "We occasionally purchase freelance work. I have a couple of freelancer writers I tend to use. Freelancers should send in information on their background, their interests. If I have an assignment I go through my files. We develop an annual editorial plan for our features and we try to work from that plan by soliciting articles. Articles mostly come from people in consulting, industry and government positions in management. Articles are 1,500-2,500 words. We look for something that is very practically focused on how to help Canadian business make better management decisions." Guidelines are available.
PHOTOGRAPHERS: "We purchase photography. We normally commission colour photographic work based on something for cover treatments." Contact the art director, Michael Heatherington. For photography all rights are purchased.
NOTES: Sample copies of this publication are available free based on availability.

CN WEST

10004-104th Avenue, 23rd Floor
Edmonton, AB T5J 0K2

PHONE: (403) 421-6757
FAX: (403) 421-6019

CONTACT: Donna Semeniuk   **DESCRIPTION:** CN WEST is an employee publication for CN Rail. Published bi-monthly.
WRITERS: "We occasionally use freelancers - maybe for 30 assigned articles per year. Our articles are generally one or two pages. Pay ranges from $300-$450. Contact us by fax with a query letter and samples of previous work. We never accept anything on spec. Most of the stories I use have very specific and current messages. When we identify a need for a freelancer I use our pool of writers from across western Canada."
PHOTOGRAPHERS: "We do use some photographers from our pool of freelancers."
NOTES: This publication currently has an established pool of both writers and photographers. For a sample copy send 9x12" SASE with appropriate postage.

COAST GUARD

Box 100
Shelburne, NS B0T 1W0

PHONE: (902) 875-3244
FAX: (902) 875-3454

CONTACT: Len Pace, Editor **DESCRIPTION:** Circulation 4,700. Weekly community newspaper covering fishing, local people and business in the area. Established in 1903.
NOTES: This publication rarely purchases freelance material.

COAST MOUNTAIN NEWS

Box 250
Hagensborg, BC V0T 1H0

PHONE: (604) 982-2696
FAX: (604) 982-2512

CONTACT: Angela Hall, Editor   **DESCRIPTION:** Published by Angela Hall. Circulation 1,200. Mainly covering local issues in northwestern B.C., such as bear sightings, fishing issues, park openings, sports events, and local political issues. Published 6 times a year.

WRITERS: 50% freelance written. Contact this publication by sending a query letter. Returns unsolicited materials with SASE. Pays $1.25 per line. Purchases one-time rights.
PHOTOGRAPHERS: 100% assigned to in-house photographers.
NOTES: "We are looking for local interest stories."

COATINGS
406 North Service Road East #1   **PHONE:** (905) 844-9773
Oakville, ON L6H 5R2   **FAX:** (905) 844-5672

CONTACT: G. Barry Kay, Editor   **DESCRIPTION:** Published by Kay Publishing. Circulation 8,000. Serves the coating and finishing industrial market of Canada. Includes case studies, who's who in the industry, what's new and new technology that may affect the industry. Published 6 times a year. Established in 1979.
WRITERS: "We have purchased in the past. We will hire a freelance writer and we have got the story ideas that we give them. We don't frequently use freelance writers."
PHOTOGRAPHERS: "We do purchase photographs but not for editorial. We purchase photographs for our covers."

COLLECTIBLES CANADA
103 Lakeshore Road #202   **PHONE:** (905) 646-7744
St. Catharines, ON L2N 2T6   **FAX:** (905) 646-0995

CONTACT: Bret Evans, Editor   **DESCRIPTION:** Circulation 20,000. Published 10 times a year. Established in 1981.
WRITERS: 30% freelance written. Purchases approximately 40 non-fiction articles per year and gives a byline. Average article length is 1,200 words. Pays $90 per article. Columns and features are "all done by special arrangement." Writers' guidelines are available. Contact by phone or fax. "We specifically deal with limited edition collectibles, plates, prints, dolls, figurines etc. We rarely cover one-of-a-kind art or collectibles that are not limited edition."
NOTES: *Collectibles Retailer* is a sister publication. Articles are published in both magazines for the same fee. Purchases first North American serial rights. Does not return unsolicited materials with a SASE. Considers previously published work and simultaneous submissions if disclosed. Sample copies of this publication are available free upon request.

COLLECTIBLES RETAILER see Collectibles Canada

COMDA KEY
3464 Kingston Road, #204   **PHONE:** (416) 261-1607
Scarborough, ON M1M 1R5   **FAX:** (416) 261-1679

CONTACT: Frank Stephen, Editor   **DESCRIPTION:** Published by Published by the Canadian Office Machine Dealers' Association. The publication is focused on office equipment, office supply, computer and local area network dealers." Published 5 times a year.
NOTES: This publication never purchases freelance work.

COMMERCE NEWS
10123 - 99 Street #600
Edmonton, AB T5J 3G9

PHONE: (403) 426-4620
FAX: (403) 424-7946

CONTACT: Gretchen Ziegler, Editor   **DESCRIPTION:** Published by Edmonton Chamber of Commerce. Circulation under 10,000. Publication covering the local business community as well as issues that affect business in Canada. Published 10 times a year. Established in 1973.
WRITERS: Less than 10% freelance written.

COMMERCIAL NEWS
1597 Bedford Highway #303
Bedford, NS B4A 1E7

NOTES: Couldn't locate. Phone number is not in service (902) 835-4302.

COMMUNICATING TOGETHER
Box 986
Thornhill, ON L3T 4A5

PHONE: (905) 766-1757

CONTACT: Shirley McNaughton   **DESCRIPTION:** Published by Sharing to Learn. Circulation under 1,000. Published quarterly. Focuses on communication skills for non-speaking people.
WRITERS: "We have not purchased in the last two years. The work is mostly volunteer."
PHOTOGRAPHERS: "Photography is mostly volunteer. The odd time we pay someone but we are a very small group so it is mostly volunteer."

COMMUNICATION
1133 Melville Street, 6th Floor
Vancouver, BC V6E 4E5

PHONE: (604) 681-3264
FAX: (604) 681-1523

CONTACT: Penny Noble, Editor   **DESCRIPTION:** Published by Chartered Accountants of BC. Circulation 7,000 members 1,000 students. Published 10 times a year for the membership of the Chartered Accountants of BC.
NOTES: "We don't solicit outside writers or photographers."

COMMUNITY ACTION
Box 448
Don Mills, ON M3C 2T2

PHONE: (416) 449-6766
FAX: (416) 444-5850

CONTACT: Leon Kumove, Editor   **DESCRIPTION:** Published by Community Action Publishing. Circulation 12,000. A national publication primarily aimed at those in social services. Published 22 times a year. Established in 1985.
WRITERS: "We occasionally purchase work. Most everything is done in house. We run little columns called '10 Tips' and if someone offers 10 tips in a field of interest to our readers we may use it. There is a stipend paid."
PHOTOGRAPHERS: No photography is purchased.

COMPANION

Box 535, Station F
Toronto, ON M4Y 2L8

PHONE: (416) 690-5611
FAX: (416) 690-3320

CONTACT: Betty McCrimmon, Managing Editor **DESCRIPTION:** Circulation 5,000. Monthly general-interest magazine focusing directly on the Roman Catholic family. Established in 1937.
WRITERS: "We purchase freelance work all the time, at least one or two a month. We like 600-1,200 words and we pay 6¢ a word. We don't have themes - we look for material that is Franciscan, ideal, Catholic and oriented to the family. We ask writers to send in a manuscript and we respond. We pay upon publication." Writers' guidelines are available.
PHOTOGRAPHERS: "We purchase colour or black & white with the articles, but black & white preferably."
NOTES: For a sample copy send 9x12" SASE with appropriate postage. Does not consider previously published work.

COMPASS: A JESUIT JOURNAL

10 St. Mary Street, #300
Toronto, ON M4Y 1P9

PHONE: (416) 921-0653
FAX: (416) 921-1864

CONTACT: Robert Chodos, Editor **DESCRIPTION:** Circulation 18,000. "This publication is ecumenical in spirit. It provides a forum for lively debate and an ethical perspective on social and religious questions." Articles are on contemporary religious and social issues. Published bi-monthly.
WRITERS: Articles range from 750-2,000 words. Pays from $150-$500. Guidelines available.

COMPLEAT MOTHER

RR2
Chelsey, ON N0G 1L0

PHONE: (519) 363-3778
FAX: none

CONTACT: Catherine Young, Editor **DESCRIPTION:** Circulation 15,000 in 14 countries, only in English. A magazine about pregnancy, birth and breastfeeding. "We are off the wall, on the cutting edge." Published quarterly. Established in 1985.
WRITERS: "We don't purchase material. Most of the material is written by our subscribers. We look for things that come from the gut. We take personal stories mainly."
PHOTOGRAPHERS: "We rarely purchase photos."

COMPUTER DEALER NEWS

2005 Sheppard Avenue East, 4th Floor
Willowdale, ON M2J 5B1

PHONE: (416) 497-9562
FAX: (416) 497-9427

CONTACT: Jim Buchok **DESCRIPTION:** Published by Plesman Publications Ltd. Circulation 13,108. A business publication for computer resellers and management information technologists. Published bi-weekly. Established in 1985.
WRITERS: "We are 15-20% freelance written. Contact me by phone or mail with samples of work and a query letter. We will also look at articles on spec. Our pay rate is 40¢ a word for 750-1,000 words. We look for news that impacts computer resellers." Writers' guidelines are not available.
PHOTOGRAPHERS: "I haven't purchased photography for a long time but it is possible. I may buy if they come with the story." Photo guidelines are not available.

NOTES: Sample copies of this publication are available free upon request. Also publishes Computing Canada.

THE COMPUTER PAPER

3661 West 4th Avenue, #8
Vancouver, BC V6R 1P2

PHONE: (604) 733-5596
FAX: (604) 732-4280

CONTACT: David Tanaka   **DESCRIPTION:** Circulation 355,000. Computer trade publication directed at end-users. Articles are end-user oriented and focus on IBMs and compatibles, and on Macintosh computers. Includes news features, events and product reviews. Published monthly. Established 1988.
WRITERS: Articles are purchased from freelancers. Byline is given. Writers are hired on assignment. Average article is 1,500 words. Payment is negotiated. Guidelines available. Prefer queries by fax. "The ideal contact is one page detailing the writer's idea for a worthwhile article/review."
NOTES: Previously published work is considered. Unsolicited materials are not returned. Sample copy is available. Enclose a large SASE.

THE COMPUTER POST

68 Higgins Avenue 3 Fl.
Winnipeg, MB R3B 0A5

PHONE: (204) 947-9766
FAX: (204) 947-9767

CONTACT: Sylvia Douglas, Editor   **DESCRIPTION:** Circulation 10,000. "A computer tabloid split between business and technology for the prairies." Published monthly. Established in 1990.
WRITERS: "We very rarely purchase material, although we have a wealth of people trying."

COMPUTERS IN EDUCATION

1300 Don Mills Road
Don Mills, ON M3B 3M8

NOTES: NO LONGER PUBLISHED

COMPUTERWORLD CANADA

501 Oakdale Road
North York, ON M3N 1W7

PHONE: (416) 746-7360
FAX: (416) 746-1421

CONTACT: John Pickett, Editor-in-Chief   **DESCRIPTION:** Published by Laurentian Technomedia Inc. Circulation 40,000. Computerworld serves computer professionals. Published semi-monthly. Established in 1984.
WRITERS: "This is a technical publication and we know most of the people who contribute. Most of them are industry people rather than freelancers. We do use freelance work. Our articles are technical in nature, often reviews of consumer products, software and hardware. There is a fairly specific technical background requirement because we serve a technical audience. Rates are substantially lower than CIO. Probably more like 30¢ a word for 400-1,000 words on those rare occasions when we do purchase freelance."
PHOTOGRAPHERS: "We don't use much freelance photography."

COMPUTING CANADA
2005 Sheppard Avenue East, 4th Floor
Willowdale, ON M2J 5B1

PHONE: (416) 497-9562
FAX: (416) 497-9427

CONTACT: Jim Buchok   **DESCRIPTION:** Published by Plesman Publications Ltd. Circulation 35,800. Publication serving computer professionals and users. Published twice monthly. Established in 1974.
WRITERS: "We are 15-20% freelance written. Contact me by phone or mail with samples of work and a query letter. We will also look at articles on spec. Our pay rate is 40¢ a word for 750-1,000 words. We look for news that affects computer resellers." Writers' guidelines are not available.
PHOTOGRAPHERS: "I haven't purchased photography for a long time but it is possible if they come with the story." Photo guidelines are not available.
NOTES: Sample copies of this publication are available free upon request. Also publishes Computer Dealer News.

COMPUTING NOW
10 Gateway Blvd. #490
North York, ON M3C 3T4

PHONE: (416) 696-5488
FAX: (416) 696-7395

CONTACT: Margaret Williamson, Assistant Editor   **DESCRIPTION:** Published by Moorshead Magazines. Circulation 15,000. "A magazine for your PC user, whether it be consumer, SOHO (small office/home office) user or someone in a corporate environment. We have feature articles, hardware and software reviews, game reports and internet and compuserve issues. We also have industry features on what is currently happening in the industry." Published monthly. Established in 1983.
WRITERS: "We purchase over 100 freelance articles per year. Half is assignment and half freelance. I accept query letters. Some of our articles are assigned to freelancers. Usually if someone has an interesting topic they will write to me and say I want to write this article because it will pertain to your magazine this way .. then we may accept it. We give bylines. The reviews are anywhere from 900-1,000, for features 1,200-1,600 words. We pay 17¢ per word. I like to have a disk in either Wordperfect 5.1 or 6.1 or MS word. Accompanying photography as well. Before sending unsolicited manuscripts send a query to me (Margaret Williamson) or give me a call or fax." Guidelines are available with a SASE.
PHOTOGRAPHERS: "We purchase maybe 100 per year. Our photos usually go along with an article. We don't use stand-alone photographs. We pay $20 for screen shots or photos.
NOTES: Purchases first North American serial rights. Doesn't return unsolicited material due to volume of mail. Do not normally use previously published work or simultaneous submissons. Also publishes Government Purchasing Guide and Pets Magazine.

THE CONDOMINIUM MAGAZINE
33 Fraser Avenue #208
Toronto, ON M6K 3J9

PHONE: (416) 588-6220
FAX: (416) 588-5217

CONTACT: Kim Morningstar, Editor   **DESCRIPTION:** Published by R.K. Communications Inc. Circulation 2,500. A national publication providing condominium (multi-unit residential buildings) boards of directors and property managers with the latest information on industry news, legislation, building science, management issues, products and services. Published monthly.

WRITERS: Articles can be submitted but are not purchased. A byline is given. Average article length is 1,200 words. Writers' guidelines are available. "Writers must be familiar if not well-versed in the business of property management or building science. Case summaries from lawyers pertaining to condominium law are also welcomed."

PHOTOGRAPHERS: Photos may occasionally be purchased. All formats are used. Payment is negotiable. Credit line is given. Captions are preferred. Contact by sending a query letter, with resumé and business card and a subject list. Photo guidelines are not available.

NOTES: Sample copy available. Send 9x11" SASE with $1.20 postage. Also publishes Canadian Property Management.

THE CONDOMINIUM MANAGER

1 Eva Road #409   **PHONE:** (416) 626-7895
Etobicoke, ON M9C 4Z5   **FAX:** (416) 620-5392

CONTACT: Denis Oloranshaw, Editor   **DESCRIPTION:** Published by Association of Condominium Managers of Ontario. Circulation 3,700. Published quarterly. Established in 1979.

NOTES: This publication does not accept freelance work.

CONGRES MENSUEL

Editorial Dept. Box 365   **PHONE:** (514) 274-0004
Montreal, PQ H2Y 3H1   **FAX:** (514) 274-5884

CONTACT: Guy J. Jonkman, Chief Editor   **DESCRIPTION:** Published by Publicom Inc. Circulation 5,500. For French speaking meeting planners in eastern Canada. Published 10 times a year in French. Established in 1986.

WRITERS: "We do most of our articles in-house. Sometimes we use a freelancer when we don't want to travel. We then call someone in the area and ask them to report for us. This is very rare."

PHOTOGRAPHERS: "We have very few photos. The ones we publish are provided by hotels and the tourism industry."

NOTES: Also publishes Excursions en Autocar.

CONSTRUCTION ALBERTA NEWS

10536 - 106 Street   **PHONE:** (403) 424-1146
Edmonton, AB T5H 2X6   **FAX:** (403) 425-5886

CONTACT: Don Coates, Editor   **DESCRIPTION:** Circulation 4,000. "We publish tender information for the province of Alberta and the Northwest Territories." Published twice a week. Established in 1983.

WRITERS: "We have a supplement once a year and interview various MD's and counties. This would be the only time we would use a freelancer. Contact me by phone. I do have a long list of freelancers."

PHOTOGRAPHERS: No photography is purchased.

CONSTRUCTION SIGHTLINES
124 West 8th Street
North Vancouver, BC V7M 3H2

NOTES: Could not locate. Phone number is not in service (604) 985-8711.

CONSTRUIRE
4970 Place de la Savane #200   **PHONE:** (514) 739-2381
Montreal, PQ H4P 1Z6   **FAX:** (514) 341-1216

CONTACT: Marie Christine Tremblay, Editor   **DESCRIPTION:** Published by Yvon Giroux, Association de la construction du Quebec. Circulation 9,400. French language publication. Issued 6 times a year. Established in 1986.

CONTACT
350 Sparks Street #402
Ottawa, ON K1R 7S8

NOTES: Could not locate.

CONTEMPORARY VERSE 2
Box 3062   **PHONE:** (204) 949-1365
Winnipeg, MB R3C 4E5   **FAX:** none

CONTACT: Editorial Collective   **DESCRIPTION:** Circulation 700. A feminist literary journal. Publishes poetry, prose poetry, short fiction, essays, and reviews. Published four times a year. Established in 1975.
WRITERS: Submissions welcome, but query first. Guidelines available.

CONTENT
RR #2
Mountain, ON K0E 1S0

NOTES: NO LONGER PUBLISHED

CONTINUITE
82 Grande-Allée W   **PHONE:** (418) 647-4525
Québec, PQ G1R 2G6   **FAX:** (418) 647-6483

CONTACT: Micheline Piché, Editor   **DESCRIPTION:** French language publication. A publication aimed at preserving Quebec's heritage and historic buildings. Published quarterly. Established in 1982.

CONTRACT MAGAZINE see Insight

CONVENTIONS & MEETINGS CANADA

5762 Highway 7, Suite 207   **PHONE:** (905) 471-1550
Markham, ON   L3P 1A8   **FAX:** (905) 471-1552

CONTACT: James Nuttall   **DESCRIPTION:** A hotel directory listing all the properties in Canada. Published annually.
NOTES: This publication does all work in-house.

LE COOPERATEUR AGRICOLE

9001 boul. de l'Acadie Bureau 200   **PHONE:** (514) 384-6450
Montreal, PQ   H4N 3H7   **FAX:** (514) 858-2025

CONTACT: Patrick Dupuis, Editor   **DESCRIPTION:** Published by La Coopérative Fédérée de Québec. Circulation 24,900. Published 9 times a year in French. Established in 1972.

COOPERATEUR FORESTIER

520 des Méandres   **PHONE:** (418) 877-4583
Quebec, PQ   G2E 5N4   **FAX:** (418) 877-6449

CONTACT: Alain Castonguay, Editor-in-chief   **DESCRIPTION:** Circulation 17,000. French language. Published 10 times a year. Established in 1987.

COPA CONVERSATION

1243 Islington Avenue #911   **PHONE:** (416) 239-2737
Toronto, ON   M8X 1Y9   **FAX:** (416) 239-1553

CONTACT: Darrell Townson, Editor   **DESCRIPTION:** Published by Canadian Office Products Association. Circulation 5,700. Trade magazine for the office products industry with articles on the issues affecting the business. Published 4 times a year in English and French.
NOTES: Has purchased freelance work before. Contact the publication with a query letter.

CORINTHIAN HORSE SPORT

Box 670, 225 Industrial Parkway South   **PHONE:** (905) 727-0107
Aurora, ON   L4G 4J9   **FAX:** (905) 841-1530

CONTACT: Lee Benson   **DESCRIPTION:** Circulation 10,000. Focuses on Canadian equestrian competition (driving, dressage, jumper, hunter, hunting). Also includes general information articles on health, nutrition, riding technique, and coaching; management and occasional personality profiles. Published monthly. Established in 1969.
WRITERS: 20% freelance written. Byline is given. Pays 15¢ a word. Guidelines are available. Contact with a query letter. "No poetry or sappy fiction! We like to see tight, concise reporting on issues and well researched articles with up-to-date information. Quotes from recognized names or experts are helpful."
PHOTOGRAPHERS: 69% assigned to freelance photographers. Also purchases photos as part of text/photo submission. Uses all formats colour and b&w. Pays $15 for b&w; $25 for colour inside and $75-125 for colour cover. "I want to see bright, in focus and sharp photos only. No arty shots, dark or badly exposed photos."

NOTES: Purchases first North American serial rights. Unsolicited material will be returned with SASE. Considers previously published work. Will not consider simultaneous submissions. Also publishes Canadian Thoroughbred and Horse Power.

CORN-SOY GUIDE
Box 6600   **PHONE:** (204) 944-5760
Winnipeg, MB R3C 3A7   **FAX:** (204) 942-8463

CONTACT: Dave Wreford, Editor   **DESCRIPTION:** Published by Farm Business Communications. "We publish material related to the production and management side of commercial agriculture." Published quarterly.
WRITERS: "We purchase material the odd time. Freelancers can contact me by phone or by mail with an outline of their proposal. Our publications are semi-technical journals and we find very few freelance people who are interested, and who can supply us with the kind of material we need."
PHOTOGRAPHERS: "Done in-house."
NOTES: Sample copies of this publication are available free upon request for freelancers who have a real interest in commercial agriculture topics. Also publishes Corn-Soy Guide, Crops Guide, Canola Guide and Cattleman.

CORPORATE FLEET MANAGEMENT see Modern Purchasing

COSMETICS
227 Front Street East #100   **PHONE:** (416) 865-9362
Toronto, ON M5A 1E8   **FAX:** (416) 865-1933

CONTACT: Ronald A. Wood, Editor   **DESCRIPTION:** Published by Maclean Hunter Publishing Ltd. Circulation 13,000. Magazine for the cosmetic and fragrance industry of Canada, including manufacturers and retailers. Published 6 times a year. Established 1972.
WRITERS: 60% freelance written, approximately 75 articles purchased per year. Byline is given. Pays approximately $100 for 400 word articles. Queries are welcome by mail or phone. "We have a part-time freelancer who receives almost all assignments needed to be written. Other non-staff articles are written by columnists and correspondents assigned to regular columns and features."
PHOTOGRAPHERS: Purchases stock photography and hires on assignment. Purchases 40-50 photos per issue. 50% assigned; 25% purchased from stock; 25% included in text/photo pkgs. Uses all formats of colour and all formats of b&w. Model releases are preferred. Captions are required. Pays $15-25 for b&w; $20-30 for inside colour; $250 for colour cover. Credit lines are given. "The Editorial staff takes most news photos; product photos supplied by manufacturers. One main feature is assigned by the Editor to a photographer (mainly in Toronto or Montreal) for each issue. Freelancers have an opportunity to be published on the cover - high fashion photos required featuring excellent, real life cosmetics on females and top grooming for males."
NOTES: Copies of the magazine are available for free. Send 10x13" SASE with $2.50 CND postage.

COTTAGE LIFE

111 Queen Street East #408
Toronto, ON M5C 1S2

PHONE: (416) 360-6880
FAX: (416) 360-6814

CONTACT: Ann Vanderhoof, Editor   **DESCRIPTION:** Published by Quarto Communications. Circulation 70,000. Magazine for water-based cottagers primarily in Ontario. "Strong service slant, combining useful "how-to" journalism with coverage of the people, trends, and issues in cottage country. Regular columns are devoted to boating, fishing, watersports and more. Published 6 times a year. Established in 1988.
WRITERS: "We are 80-85% freelance written. Queries should be in writing and should include a succinct outline (one page) - explain your angle and why it is timely and appropriate for the magazine, potential sources and expected length. New writers should include samples of published work. Our articles range from a short of 100 words at $50 to a 3,500 word feature paying $2,200. Although most of our readers are based in Ontario, we welcome stories about cottagers and cottaging in other parts of Canada and the northern US as well." Contact the editor by letter and request the writers' guidelines.
PHOTOGRAPHERS: "All of our photography is commissioned by the art department. We look at portfolios and are open to story ideas from photographers (we will assign a writer). "Contact Steve Manley." Very comprehensive photo guidelines are available.
NOTES: Purchases first North American serial rights. Very rarely considers previously published work. "The magazine does not publish poetry or fiction."Sample copies of this publication are available for $6.25. Include a SASE for writers' guidelines.

COTTAGE MAGAZINE

4611 William Head Road
Victoria, BC V9B 5T7

PHONE: (604) 478-9209
FAX: (604) 478-1184

CONTACT: Peter Chettleburgh, Editor/Publisher   **DESCRIPTION:** Published by Harrison House Publishers. A bi-monthly glossy magazine for cottage owners and potential cottage and cabin owners in BC and Alberta. "Feature articles include entertaining profiles on individuals and companies as well as in-depth analysis of political issues that could effect the owners of recreational property in western Canada. The emphasis is on practical information that will help cottage owners outfit and enjoy their vacation homes."
WRITERS: "We purchase mostly feature material. Three features, a couple of columns and 6 news items per issue. Freelancers can contact us by phone, fax or mail. I prefer to see samples of previously published work. I look for anything relating to cottages in western Canada. We pay per article and it ranges from about $150 for a column to $500 for a feature." Bylines are given.
PHOTOGRAPHERS: "I am always looking for colour cover photography; cottage scenes appropriate to the publication. You pretty well have to look at a copy to get an understanding of our needs. I prefer colour transparencies for the cover and colour or glossy b&w prints for inside." Pays $300 for the cover. Inside photos negotiable. Contact by phone, letter or fax.
NOTES: Guidelines are available. May possibly consider previously published work. Also publishes Northern Aquaculture. Purchases first North American serial rights. For a sample copy send a $1.40 SASE 9x12". envelope.

COULICOU
300 Arran Street
Saint-Lambert, PQ J4R 1K5

PHONE: (514) 875-0327
FAX: (514) 672-5448

CONTACT: Yves Boillon **DESCRIPTION:** Published by Les Editions Héritage Inc. Circulation 35,000. French language publication for children age 8 and younger. Each issues contains a story or article on animals, and games which can be done both individually or with the assistance of an adult. Published 10 times a year. Established in 1984.
NOTES: Also publishes Hibou Magazine.

COUNTRY
RR1
Holstein, ON N0G 2A0

PHONE: (519) 334-3246
FAX: (519) 334-3366

CONTACT: Jim Baine, Editor **DESCRIPTION:** Circulation 20,000. Country music magazine focuses on stories, events, and personalities from a Canadian perspective. Published bi-monthly. Established in 1989.
WRITERS: "We have purchased work from freelancers in the past. Right now we are not looking for any new contributors."
PHOTOGRAPHERS: "We don't purchase photography."
NOTES: Editor's note: This publication is not interested in hearing from freelancers at this time.

COUNTRY CONNECTION
Box 100
Boulter, ON K0L 1G0

PHONE: (613) 332-3651
FAX: (613) 332-5183

CONTACT: Gus Zylstra, Editor **DESCRIPTION:** Published by Pine Cone Publishing. "A magazine for country folk and those that wish they were." A general interest regional magazine for central and eastern Ontario. It explores the natural environment, heritage arts and culture. Includes fiction and non-fiction. The main subscriber base comes from the tourists, residents and cottagers. Published twice a year, summer and winter.
WRITERS: "I am interested in articles from across Canada if it is a fiction piece about living in the country. We don't take historical pieces from outside of Ontario and we don't take travel pieces from outside of Ontario. We look for lifestyle, how-to articles and art and culture material between 1,000-1,500 words. I will accept more fiction pieces if they are 800-1,000 words. Anything over that takes up too much space. We pay 10¢ a word." Stories should be submitted on PC format discs in either ASCII, text only, or Word Perfect and must be accompanied by a double spaced hardcopy. Include the file name and word count. Writers' guidelines are available.
PHOTOGRAPHERS: "I do a lot of my own photography. I like people to submit photography with their stories. One of the weaknesses I find is a story without support pieces. An article with a photo tends to get looked at faster. I pay between $10-$50 for photos depending on use. We use both colour and black and white.

COUNTRY ESTATE
178 Main Street
Unionville, ON L3R 2G9

NOTES: NO LONGER PUBLISHED

COUNTRY GUIDE
Box 6600
Winnipeg, MB R3C 3A7

PHONE: (204) 944-5760
FAX: (204) 942-8463

CONTACT: Dave Wreford, Editor   **DESCRIPTION:** Published by Farm Business Communications. Circulation 75,000. "We publish material related to the production and management side of commercial agriculture; commercial livestock and crop production." Published 11 times a year. Established in 1882.
WRITERS: "We purchase material the odd time. Freelancers can contact me by phone or by mail with an outline of their proposed article. Our publications are semi-technical journals and we find very few freelance people who can supply us with the kind of material we want."
PHOTOGRAPHERS: "We don't really purchase photography. Most is done in-house."
NOTES: Sample copies of this publication are available free upon request for freelancers who have a real interest in commercial agriculture topics. Also publishes Corn-Soy Guide, Crops Guide, Canola Guide and Cattleman.

COUNTRY LIFE IN BRITISH COLUMBIA
3308 King George Highway
Surrey, BC V4P 1A8

PHONE: (604) 536-7622
FAX: (604) 536-5677

CONTACT: Malcolm Young, Editor   **DESCRIPTION:** Published monthly.

THE COUNTRY SIDE
RR1
Terra Cotta, ON L0P 1N0

NOTES: NO LONGER PUBLISHED

COUP D'OEIL
620 Industriel Blvd.
St.-Jean-sur-Richelieu, PQ J3B 7X4

PHONE: (514) 856-7821
FAX: (514) 359-0836

CONTACT: Martine Breton, Editor   **DESCRIPTION:** Published by Publédition. Circulation 3,000. Magazine aimed at the optical trade. Published 6 times a year. Established in 1982.
WRITERS: 100% staff written.
PHOTOGRAPHERS: Photography is purchased from stock (50%). Photographers hired on assignment (50%). All formats colour and b&w are used. Pay is negotiable, ranged up to $200 for colour cover. Credit line must be negotiated. Contact with query letter, include list of relevant subjects.
NOTES: Most work is done in-house. Sample copy is free upon request. Normally purchases one-time rights. Unsolicited materials will not be returned. Previously published and simultaneous submissions are considered.

COUP DE POUCE
2001 University Street #900
Montreal, PQ H3A 2A6

PHONE: (514) 499-0561
FAX: (514) 499-1844

CONTACT: Michéle Cyr   **DESCRIPTION:** Published by Les Editions Télémédia.
Circulation 146,600. French language women's magazine. Published 13 times a year.
Established in 1984.
WRITERS: 50-100% freelance written. Pays $50-$100 for articles.

COUP DE POUCE EXTRA CUISINE
2001 University Street #900
Montreal, PQ H3A 2A6

PHONE: (514) 499-0561
FAX: (514) 499-1844

CONTACT: Michéle Cyr   **DESCRIPTION:** Published by Les Editions Télémédia.
French language publication. Issued quarterly. Established in 1985.

COURRIER HIPPIQUE
4545 Pierre-de-Coubertin Box 1000
Station M
Montreal, PQ H1V 3R2

PHONE: (514) 252-3053
FAX: (514) 252-3165

CONTACT: Jocelyn Lortie, Artistic Director   **DESCRIPTION:** Circulation 7,000.
French language publication focusing on horse riding and driving. Mainly distributed in
Quebec. Published 6 times a year. Established in 1983.
WRITERS: Purchases a few articles. "It all depends on the type of article and how specialized
it is." Contact and query by phone. "A writer must be familiar with horses of course. We
are looking for somebody who can tell stories about horses. I have good veterinarians who
can write articles but if there is someone who has a different story, something in particular
that would appeal; a story that we don't see very often, or a problem that has been solved,
I'd be willing to talk about it."
PHOTOGRAPHERS: "We purchase very few photos. Usually they are included with
the articles. We use colour or black & white."

COVER STORY
231 Dundas Street #203
London, ON N6A 1H1

PHONE: (519) 679-4901
FAX: (519) 434-7842

NOTES: Also publishes London Magazine, London Guidebook and The Business Times.

COVERSTORY
17533-106 Avenue
Edmonton, AB T5S 1E7

NOTES: NO LONGER PUBLISHED

CRAFTNEWS
35 McCaul Street Chalmers Bldg.   **PHONE:** (416) 977-3551
Toronto, ON M5T 1V7   **FAX:** (416) 977-3552

CONTACT: Anne McPherson, Editor   **DESCRIPTION:** Published by Ontario Crafts Council. Quarterly magazine dedicated to craftspeople. Publishes features on people and their work. Established in 1976.
NOTES: No budget is available for freelance material.

CRAFTSPLUS
130 Spy Court   **PHONE:** (905) 475-8440
Markham, ON L3R 5H6   **FAX:** (905) 475-9560

CONTACT: Erina Kelly   **DESCRIPTION:** Published by Camar Publications. Circulation 100,000 with 400,000 readership. A national craft and needlework magazine with home decor and gift-giving projects in sewing, stencilling, knitting and national news. Published 8 times a year.
WRITERS: "We purchase mostly freelance work, 95% freelance. Write in for guidelines and take it from there."
PHOTOGRAPHERS: "We have our own photographers."
NOTES: Rights are negotiated. Does not consider previously published work. Sample copies of this publication are available free upon request and on newsstand across Canada.

CRESCENDO
101 Thorncliffe Park Drive
Toronto, ON M4H 1M2

NOTES: Could not be located. Phone number is not in service (905) 421-1020.

CROC
5800 St-Denis #605   **PHONE:** (514) 990-2762
Montreal, PQ H2S 3L5   **FAX:** (514) 272-6310

CONTACT: Jacques Hurtubise **DESCRIPTION:** Published by Zizinosaure. Circulation 41,000. French publication issued monthly. Established in 1979.

CROISSANCE PERSONNELLE
860 Montée Meunier #106   **PHONE:** (514) 565-9256
Bellefeuille, PQ J0R 1A0   **FAX:** (514) 565-2797

CONTACT: Jean-Serge Turcot, Managing Editor   **DESCRIPTION:** Published by Francois Charron. Circulation 30,000. French language publication issued 10 times a year. Established in 1994.
WRITERS: 70% freelance written. Buys 100 articles annually. Hires on assignment, pays expenses while on assignment. Byline must be negotiated. Also uses fillers. "Pays $40 per sheet." Writers' guidelines are available. "Our articles vary between subjects like: well-being, alternatives, medicines, health care, skin care, spirituality, human potential, music, books, society, cooking and dreams." Kill fee of 50% is given if assigned article cancelled. Query over the phone. "We want to pass on a positive message and inform the

reader about the trends and paradigms in personal growth. To explain that all information in the market are only tools to help discover one's innerself and potential. Interviews with people having a vision or experience that could benefit the reader is an asset."
PHOTOGRAPHERS: Buys from stock and hires on assignment. Buys 100 photos annually. Uses all colour formats. Model releases and captions are not necessary. Pays $40 to $100 for inside photos. Credit line must be negotiated. Contact with subject list and sample portfolio. Photographers contact Francois Charron. "A good photographer is creative, imaginative, sees farther than the camera, what disturbs the eye, varies the shots, is fast and efficient, relates things with the topic, can mind-meld with our vision." Photo guidelines are available.
NOTES: Sample free upon request. Buys one-time rights. Considers previously published work and simultaneous submissions. Unsolicited materials will be returned with SASE.

CROPS GUIDE
Box 6600
Winnipeg, MB R3C 3A7

PHONE: (204) 944-5760
FAX: (204) 942-8463

CONTACT: Dave Wreford, Editor　　**DESCRIPTION:** Published by Farm Business Communications. "We publish material related to the production and management side of commercial agriculture." Published quarterly.
WRITERS: "We purchase material the odd time. Freelancers can contact me by phone or by mail with an outline of their proposal. Our publications are semi-technical journals. We find very few freelancers interested in supplying us with the material we want."
PHOTOGRAPHERS: "We don't really purchase photography. Most is done in-house."
NOTES: Sample copies of this publication are available free upon request for freelancers who have a real interest in commercial agriculture topics. Also publishes Corn-Soy Guide, Crops Guide, Canola Guide and Cattleman.

THE CURLING NEWS
401 Richmond Street West, Ste. 102
Toronto, ON M5V 1X3

PHONE: (416) 596-2389

CONTACT: George Karrys　　**DESCRIPTION:** Published by Brian Cooke. Circulation 50,000. TCN is Canada's only, national monthly curling magazine, covering each and every elite or novice aspect of the sport. Editorial includes major in-depth features, news reports, analysis, human interest and 5 or 6 departments. Published 7 times per year.
WRITERS: 40-50% freelance written. Buys 30+ articles annually. Byline is always given. Hires writers on assignment, expenses are not paid. Average article 1500 to 1000 words. Pays $75 per story. Kill fee is not paid. Phone or write. Queries are welcome. Send samples, resumé and business card. "No one need be a curling expert to do a job for us. We are the pros, and can easily add stuff to your curling story. The key is to focus on the players, as they are real people, with real full-time jobs and bills to pay. Curling is a very unique sport and can provide a wealth of writing opportunity to those willing to give it a shot."
PHOTOGRAPHERS: Photographers are hired on assignment. 70% assigned to freelancers. Uses 30 photos per issue. Uses colour; medium and large format transparencies and prints. "No 35mm's please." Payment is negotiated. Credit line is always given. Mail or phone with queries. Send subject lists, sample portfolio or other samples such as brochures, tear sheets or flyers. "Great curling photos are tough - very tough. If you're good, we want to hear from you!!"

NOTES: Sample copies available for $3.50. Purchases all rights. Returns unsolicited materials with SASE. Considers previously published work and simultaneous submissions. Guidelines are not available.

CV PHOTO
4060 Boulevard Saint-Laurent #301
Montreal, PQ H2W 1Y9

DESCRIPTION: Published by Productions Ciel Variable. Published quarterly, each issue contains several portfolios with accompanying texts. Contains English and French material.

CYCLE CANADA
86 Parliament Street, Suite 3B
Toronto, ON M5A 2Y6

PHONE: (416) 362-7966
FAX: (416) 362-3950

CONTACT: Bruce Reeve, Editor   **DESCRIPTION:** Published by Turbo Presse Inc. Circulation 28,000. A national magazine for Canadian motorcycle enthusiasts, including maintenance advice, evaluations and all aspects of motorcycles. Published 10 times a year. Established in 1971.
WRITERS: "We purchase about 20 articles per year. We take some items on spec, we also assign. Contact with a query letter and samples of work. Contributors need to be familiar with motorcycling and they need to be familiar with the magazine. I am not interested in people coming in cold. We accept short and long pieces and pay anywhere from $50-$600."
PHOTOGRAPHERS: "Generally our photos are assigned but we may buy something someone has already. We prefer to work from colour transparencies but can use black and white. Rates vary from $50-$400." Contact with a query letter.
NOTES: Copies on newsstands across Canada.

DAILY COMMERCIAL NEWS AND CONSTRUCTION RECORD
280 Yorkland Blvd.
North York, ON M2J 4Z6

PHONE: (416) 494-4990
FAX: (416) 756-2767

CONTACT: Al Zabas, Editor   **DESCRIPTION:** Published by Daily Commercial News, Southam. Circulation 5,400. Contains news stories pertaining to the construction industry, general and sub-contractors, design professionals, architects, and engineers. Carries legal, export and lien information. Published daily and distributed throughout Ontario. Established in 1927.
WRITERS: "We purchase 50-60 articles per year. We generally pay 25/30¢ per word up to $500. Call me or send a query letter." Byline is given. Writers are hired on assignment. Average article is 800 words.
PHOTOGRAPHERS: 85% assigned to freelance photographers. Does not purchase from stock. Model releases are not necessary. Captions are preferred. "We purchase construction photos and on-site photos. We use both black & white and colour. Pays $100 for colour cover; $50 for first inside photo (b&w or colour) and $30 for each additional photo in a series. "Contact by phone or query letter with samples of work or portfolio."
NOTES: Sample copies of this publication are available free upon request.

DAIRY CONTACT

Box 549
Onoway, AB T0E 1V0

PHONE: (403) 967-2929
FAX: (403) 467-2930

CONTACT: Dr. Allen Parr, Editor   **DESCRIPTION:** Circulation 4,000. A publication for dairy farmers in western Canada. Published monthly. Established in 1976.
WRITERS: "We occasionally purchase work, maybe 3-4 articles per year. Contact the editor by phone. Length and payment varies. We are looking for material on new farming products or dairy producer profiles. Writers must have some dairy knowledge."
PHOTOGRAPHERS: "We purchase photos that are taken at dairy shows. We use both black and white and colour."
NOTES: Sample copies of this publication are available free upon request with 9x12" SASE.

DAIRY GUIDE

Box 6600
Winnipeg, MB R3C 3A7

PHONE: (204) 944-5767
FAX: (204) 942-8463

CONTACT: Dave Wilkins, Editor   **DESCRIPTION:** Published by Farm Business Publications. Circulation 17,000. Published quarterly. Established in 1970.

DANCE CONNECTION

815 - 1st Street S.W. #603
Calgary, AB T2P 1N3

PHONE: (403) 237-7327
FAX: (403) 237-7327

CONTACT: Heather Elton, Editor   **DESCRIPTION:** Published by Clear Running Water Presentations Society. Circulation 5,000. Features contemporary issues relating to dance. Published five times a year.
WRITERS: 80% freelance written. Buys 30 articles per year. Buys non-fiction, fiction, poetry and fillers. Hires writers on assignment. Does not pay expenses. Articles range from 800 to 2,500 words. Pays 10¢ per word. Features 1800-3500 words pay $150-350; reviews 800 words pay $75; multiple reviews/festival 1100-1600 words pays $150 and book reviews 800 words pay $75. Kill fee is not paid. Contact the editor with a query letter, fax or phone call. Guidelines available. "We ask writers to be bold, entertaining, and always meaningful, with a point of view backed by solid research and sound logic. Be progressive in your approach to contemporary dance and amaze us with new information. We don't often do profiles; instead we are looking for information on a technique, a history, a new product, trend or other phenomenon. Our attention to culture-specific dance and interdisciplinary performance makes us one of the few alternative dance magazines in North America. Present your material with wit, style and an unwavering attention to its relevance to every kind of dance enthusiast."
PHOTOGRAPHERS: Occasionally hires photographers on assignment. "Usually we receive photos free of charge from dance company publicists." Captions are preferred. Pays $250 per shoot. Contact the editor by sending a brochure, flyer, tear sheets or a sample portfolio. "Our photographers do not approach the form purely as documentarian. Rather, they create a unique artistic expression, one that is true to the work itself but which creates its own narrative, explores the psychological or philosophical elements of the movement and operates effectively on a number of levels."
NOTES: Buys one-time rights. Unsolicited materials will be returned with SASE. Considers previously published work and simultaneous submissions. Sample copy is free upon request.

DANCE IN CANADA
35 McCaul Street, Suite 324c
Toronto, ON M5T 1Z7

NOTES: Could not locate. Phone number not in service (416) 595-0165.

DC MAGAZINE
Box 50536   **PHONE:** (416) 633-5360
North York, ON M3J 1L5   **FAX:** (416) 633-5717

CONTACT: Patrick Matishak, Editor   **DESCRIPTION:** Published by Charleton
Communications Inc. Circulation 23,000. A publication for the beauty trade. Contains
technical, fashion, new product and event news from across Canada. Published monthly.
WRITERS: Articles are rarely purchased. To contact, send a fax or a letter. "I like seeing
stuff that is from personal experience and a little avant garde and leading edge. I don't
like seeing submissions that are not well thought out and which include spelling errors.
Standard length is no more than 750 words. We may possibly hire someone on assignment."
PHOTOGRAPHERS: "We never purchase photographs. We get photos sent to us
internationally on a regular basis which we can use if credit is given."
NOTES: For a sample copy send a $3 cover price. Also publishes Landmark, Prairie
Landscape and Canadian Resources Review.

LES DEBROUILLARDS
3995 Ste.-Catherine E   **PHONE:** (514) 522-1304
Montreal, PQ H1W 2G7   **FAX:** (514) 522-1761

CONTACT: Maryse Bérubé, Editor   **DESCRIPTION:** Published by Les Publications
BLD. Circulation 29,000. French language publication. A children's science magazine
published 10 times a year.
WRITERS: "We have regular freelance writers and we always use the same ones. Contact
us by letter with a resumé. All articles should be science related." Guidelines are not available.
PHOTOGRAPHERS: "We very rarely purchase photography." Contact with a letter and
resumé.
NOTES: Sample copies of this publication are available free upon request.

DECORATING CENTRE
7895 Tranmere Drive, Unit 5
Mississauga, ON L5S 1V9

NOTES: NO LONGER PUBLISHED

DECORATION CHEZ SOI
7 Bates Road   **PHONE:** (514) 270-1100
Outremont, PQ H2V 1A6   **FAX:** (514) 270-6900

CONTACT: Pierre Deschenes, Editorial Director   **DESCRIPTION:** Published by Publicor.
Circulation 64,200. French language publication. Issued 10 times a year. Established in
1977.

DECORMAG
5148 Saint-Laurent Blvd.　　　　　**PHONE:** (514) 273-9773
Montreal, PQ H2T 1R8　　　　　　**FAX:** (514) 273-9034

CONTACT: André Vilder　**DESCRIPTION:** Published by Les Editions du Feu Vert. Circulation 57,700. French language publication. Issued 10 times a year. Established in 1972.

DEL CONDOMINIUM LIFE
4800 Dufferin Street　　　　　　**PHONE:** (416) 661-3151
Downsview, ON M3H 5S9　　　　　**FAX:** (416) 661-8653

CONTACT: Patricia MacKellar, Editor　**DESCRIPTION:** Circulation 25,000. For residents of luxury condominiums. This publication aims to inform, entertain and enlighten its readers. Published quarterly. Established in 1986.

DENTAL PRACTICE MANAGEMENT
1450 Don Mills Road　　　　　　**PHONE:** (416) 445-6641
Don Mills, ON M3B 2X7　　　　　**FAX:** (416) 442-2214

CONTACT: Janet Bonellie, Editor　**DESCRIPTION:** Published by Southam. Circulation 16,000. "This publication goes to all the dental practices in Canada. Articles have a business slant providing information on the administration of dental practices. Published quarterly. Established in 1985.
NOTES: "We do not purchase much. Most of the material is staff-written or contributed free by people who work in the profession."

DENTIST'S GUIDE
1120 Birchmount Road #200　　　　**PHONE:** (416) 750-8900
Scarborough, ON M1K 5G4　　　　　**FAX:** (416) 751-8126

CONTACT: Heather Howie, Editor　**DESCRIPTION:** Published by Thomson Health Care. Circulation 16,000. Published quarterly. Established in 1993.

DESCANT
Box 314, Station P　　　　　　　**PHONE:** (416) 593-2557
Toronto, ON M5S 2S8　　　　　　**FAX:** none

CONTACT: Tracy Jenkins, Managing Editor　**DESCRIPTION:** Published by Descant Arts & Letters Foundation. Circulation 1,200. "We are a literary quarterly and we publish work by both established and emerging writers and artists. We include fiction, poetry, essays, drama and visuals. 75% of the work is Canadian."
WRITERS: We pay $100 per contributor, regardless of length." Guidelines are available with a SASE.
PHOTOGRAPHERS: "We do purchase photography and we treat it like any other contribution and give a $100 payment. Mostly black and white for internal images. We do occasionally use a colour photograph for the cover. Send us samples of work. We'll look at almost any format except slides. We are interested in art photography and what

we have published has been quite varied. We don't publish a lot of photography but we usually have one visual element per issue."

NOTES: "People who have taken a look at the magazine are more successful in their submissions. Send for a copy by enclosing $7 plus shipping."

DESIGN ENGINEERING
777 Bay Street
Toronto, ON M5W 1A7

PHONE: (416) 596-5819
FAX: (416) 596-5881

CONTACT: Steve Purwitsky, Editor   **DESCRIPTION:** Published by Maclean Hunter. Circulation 18,400. A broad-based magazine catering to the design engineer in all forms of design from CAD\CAM, to mechanical and electronic. Features business and technical information for product and system designers. Includes innovations in the industry and career information. Published 8 times a year. Established in 1955.
WRITERS: "We purchase 5 or 6 articles per year, usually on assignment. We give a byline. Articles are 1,500 words with a negotiable payment. Because of the small amount I purchase I have a few writers I usually call upon." Phone inquiries welcome. Guidelines are not available.
PHOTOGRAPHERS: Does not purchase photography.
NOTES: All North American rights are purchased. May accept something previously published depending on the project concerned. Does not consider simultaneous submissions.

DESIGN PRODUCT NEWS
135 Spy Court
Markham, ON L3R 5H6

PHONE: (905) 477-3222
FAX: (905) 477-4320

CONTACT: Michael Edwards, Editor   **DESCRIPTION:** Published by Action Communications. Circulation 18,900. Published bi-monthly. Established in 1973.
NOTES: "Our budget has been zeroed out in the last two years so we are not accepting material." Also publishes Canadian Electronics and Woodworking.

DESIGNS
85 St-Paul W
Montreal, PQ H2Y 3V4

NOTES: Could not locate. Phone number not in service (514) 842-4436.

DESTINATIONS
444 Front Street West
Toronto, ON M5V 2S9

NOTES: NO LONGER PUBLISHED

DETAIL
4316 St-Laurent Blvd. #400   **PHONE:** (514) 842-5873
Montreal, PQ H2W 1Z3   **FAX:** (514) 842-2422

CONTACT: Bruno Gautier   **DESCRIPTION:** Published by August Communications Ltd. Circulation 15,000. French publication geared to Quebec's retail industry. Covers all aspects of the industry including hardware, beauty, food and beverage, furniture, sports and more. Deals with distribution, merchandising and other practical information. Published 5 times a year. Established in 1993.

DIABETES DIALOGUE
15 Toronto Street #1001   **PHONE:** (416) 363-3373
Toronto, ON M5C 2E3   **FAX:** (416) 363-3393

CONTACT: Cynthia Lank, Cindy Campbell, Editors   **DESCRIPTION:** Published by Canadian Diabetes Association. Circulation 55,000. Goes out to members of the Association. "Articles deal with everything from lifestyle, fitness health type things to research features and anything that would be of interest to people with diabetes." Published quarterly.
WRITERS: "We do purchase some writing. We don't have a very large freelance budget. Most of the work is done for free. Our average length is around 500 words. We have columns written by nutritionists, doctors, and pharmacists. We have a feature called *The Way We Are*; an extraordinary story about a person with diabetes. A query letter with a proposal is the best idea. We have an editorial board which reviews stories and proposals."
PHOTOGRAPHERS: "We do occasionally purchase photography although our budget isn't very big. We use both colour and black and white and the format depends on what we are looking for. Writing (a query letter) would be the best thing but we don't have a lot of work for photographers."
NOTES: A sample copy is available free upon request.

DIGEST BUSINESS AND LAW JOURNAL
826 Erin Street   **PHONE:** (204) 775-8918
Winnipeg, MB R3G 2W4   **FAX:** (204) 788-4322

CONTACT: Walter Bowden   **DESCRIPTION:** Published weekly. Established in 1972.
WRITERS: "We don't purchase writing."
PHOTOGRAPHERS: "At times we purchase photos for the front cover. Otherwise we have a photographer we use."
NOTES: This publication is not open to inquiries.

DIMENSIONS IN HEALTH SERVICE see Leadership in Health Services

DIOCESAN TIMES
5732 College Street
Halifax, NS B3H 1X3

NOTES: Could not locate.

DIRECT ACCESS see Computer World

DIRECTION INFORMATIQUE
2005 Sheppard Avenue East 4 Fl.   **PHONE:** (416) 497-9562
Willowdale, ON M2J 5B1   **FAX:** (416) 497-9427

CONTACT: Patrice-Guy Martin, Editor   **DESCRIPTION:** Published by Paul Plesman. Circulation 17,500. Published monthly in English and French. Established in 1988.

DOCTOR'S REVIEW
400 McGill Street, 3rd Fl.   **PHONE:** (514) 397-8833
Montreal, PQ H2Y 2G1   **FAX:** (514) 397-0228

CONTACT: Madeline Partous   **DESCRIPTION:** Published by Parkhurst Publishing. Circulation 38,000. A travel and leisure magazine for Canadian physicians. Published monthly. Established in 1983.
WRITERS: "We do purchase some material, 40% freelance written. Byline is given. Send us a complete manuscript 1,200-1,500 words. Articles must be practical, we are moving away from exotic travel. Feature conference destinations from around the world. Pays $275, reprint fees are $150-200. Available for freelance: humour; travel; leisure; sports (participatory only); car reviews. "I never accept queries from writers whose style I don't know. Until I get to know you, send full manuscript on spec. Previous published examples are a plus, but not enough .. they've been edited already. Also, patience is required. It takes at least a month to respond!"
PHOTOGRAPHERS: "We use colour photography and we prefer it accompanies the article. We do have a few regular photographers but we are always in need, you never know what we may need. We do like to receive lists of available destinations from travel photographers. We'll call photographers when we need specific locations. Formats used: 35mm, 4x5 transparencies and 5x7 and 8x10 colour prints. We pay $25/30 per inside photo. $300/400 colour cover. Credit line is given.
NOTES: Sample copies of this publication are available for $6. Purchases one-time rights. Prefer writers don't write for other medical magazines.

DOGS IN CANADA
89 Skyway Avenue Suite 200   **PHONE:** (416) 675-5511
Etobicoke, ON M9W 6R4   **FAX:** (416) 675-6506

CONTACT: Allan Reznik, Editor   **DESCRIPTION:** Published by Apex Publishers. Circulation 21,000. A trade magazine aimed at breeders and exhibitors of purebred dogs and a small section on purebred cats, in the dogs annual. Published monthly.

DRUG MERCHANDISING
777 Bay Street
Toronto, ON M5W 1A7

NOTES: NO LONGER PUBLISHED

EARTHKEEPER MAGAZINE
Box 1649
Guelph, ON N1H 6R7

NOTES: NO LONGER PUBLISHED

EASTERN WOODS & WATERS MAGAZINE
Box 428
Dartmouth, NS B2Y 3Y5

NOTES: Could not locate. Phone number is out of service (902) 468-2682.

ECHEC+
Box 640 Station C   **PHONE:** (514) 252-3034
Montreal, PQ H2L 4L5   **FAX:** (514) 251-8038

CONTACT: Michel Berubé, Editor   **DESCRIPTION:** Circulation 2,000. A french language publication which specializes in the game of Chess. Distributed to members. Articles are purely technical. "We occasionally have historical information but it's mainly on the technique of Chess." Includes analysis, strategy and news articles from around the world. Published bimonthly. Established in 1973.
WRITERS: "We accept articles, maybe 20-25 per year. Articles are two to two and a half magazine pages. Pay rate depends on who is writing; Grand Masters from outside Canada or Masters and International Masters." Contact by mail.
PHOTOGRAPHERS: "We purchase photography. Prefer black and white PMT's and if it is already digitized that's better. We pay $25 for a photograph including the colour front cover." Contact by mail.

L'ECHO DU TRANSPORT
7493 Trans-Canada Hwy #103   **PHONE:** (514) 337-9043
St-Laurent, PQ H4T 1T3   **FAX:** (514) 337-1862

CONTACT: Jean-Roch Savard, Editor   **DESCRIPTION:** Published by Les Editions Bomart Lteé. Circulation 18,900. French language publication. Issued 10 times a year. Established in 1977.
NOTES: Also publishes L'expediteur.

ECLAIRAGE PLUS
1500 boul. Jules-Poitras #200   **PHONE:** (514) 745-5720
Ville Saint-Laurent, PQ H4N 1X7   **FAX:** (514) 339-2267

CONTACT: Guy Choiniére   **DESCRIPTION:** French language publication. Focuses on lighting. Published quarterly. Established in 1989.

EDGES: NEW PLANETARY PATTERNS

577 Kingston Road #1
Toronto, ON M4E 1R3

PHONE: (416) 691-2316
FAX: (416) 691-2491

CONTACT: Brian Stanfield **DESCRIPTION:** Published by Canadian Institute of Cultural Affairs. Circulation 74,500. Features articles in the arena of consultation, facilitation, training, and creating a culture of participation. For example citizen involvement and methods used in social change. Published once a year with 2 newsletters. Established in 1988.
WRITERS: "There may be some freelance work for the April issue. Articles must really be honed to the topic."
PHOTOGRAPHERS: "We publish photos but we are unable to pay for them."
NOTES: Sample copies of this publication are available for $2.

EDMONTON COMMERCE AND INDUSTRY

215 Inglewood Bldg, 11802-124 Street
Edmonton, AB T5L 0M3

PHONE: (403) 454-5540
FAX: (403) 453-2553

CONTACT: D. Homersham **DESCRIPTION:** Circulation 5,000. A business tabloid newspaper covering the business sectors of Edmonton, Calgary and Vancouver. Published monthly. Established in 1971.
WRITERS: "We very seldom purchase material. Freelancers can initially approach us by phone."
PHOTOGRAPHERS: "Photography is done in-house."

EDMONTON DOWNTOWNER

10179-105 Street #800
Edmonton, AB T5J 3N1

PHONE: (403) 429-1610
FAX: (403) 421-7677

CONTACT: Colin Smith, Editor **DESCRIPTION:** Published by Lorne Silverstein. Circulation 30,000. A community paper published monthly. Established in 1990.
WRITERS: "We purchase 2-3 articles per issue. The focus is broad. The best thing to do is to send or fax me a letter of inquiry or resumé and follow up with a phone call. We pay 5¢ a word for articles up to 800 words."
PHOTOGRAPHERS: "Photography is done in-house."
NOTES: Also publishes a sister publication called Edmonton Southsider and the same information applies. Also publishes Edmonton Senior and Edmonton Woman.

EDMONTON SENIOR

10179-105 Street #800
Edmonton, AB T5J 3N1

PHONE: (403) 429-1610
FAX: (403) 421-7677

CONTACT: Colin Smith, Editor **DESCRIPTION:** Published by Lorne Silverstein. Circulation 30,000. Senior Citizens publication issued 10 times a year. Established in 1990.
WRITERS: "We purchase 2-3 articles per issue. The focus is broad. The best thing to do is to send or fax me a letter of inquiry or resumé and follow up with a phone call. We pay 5¢ a word for articles up to 800 words."
PHOTOGRAPHERS: "Photography is done in-house."
NOTES: Also publishes Edmonton Woman, and Edmonton Downtowner and Southsider.

EDMONTON WOMAN
10179-105 Street #800
Edmonton, AB T5J 3N1

PHONE: (403) 424-1221
FAX: (403) 421-7677

CONTACT: Laurie Roswell, Editor **DESCRIPTION:** Published by Lorne Silverstein. Circulation 30,000. Published 10 times a year. Established in 1993.
WRITERS: "We purchase about 3-4 articles per issue. We pay $25 for 250-300 words. Writers can call the editor or mail in a query letter. We have an automotive section, women in business, nutrition, health, and fitness sections."
PHOTOGRAPHERS: Photography is done in-house.
NOTES: Sample copies of this publication are available city-wide in a variety of stores. Sample copies of this publication are available free upon request.

EDUCATION FORUM
60 Mobile Drive
Toronto, ON M4A 2P3

PHONE: (416) 751-8300
FAX: (416) 751-3394

CONTACT: Renata Brandon, Editor **DESCRIPTION:** Published by Ontario Secondary Teachers' Federation. Circulation 40,000. Ontario high school teacher's magazine covers news, adventure, views, and personal experience. Published 3 times a year. Established in 1921.

EDUCATION TODAY
439 University Avenue, 18th Floor
Toronto, ON M5G 1Y8

PHONE: (416) 340-2540
FAX: (416) 340-7571

CONTACT: Heather Roseveare Dion, Editor **DESCRIPTION:** Published by Ontario Public School Boards Association. Circulation 4,000. Magazine for educators, about issues and trends in Ontario's education system. Deals with issues like waste management in schools and education in other countries. Published 5 times a year.
WRITERS: "We assign articles to freelance writers. A standard pay rate is given. Articles are about 3 magazine pages. A byline is given. We prefer to get resumés with samples of writing and we look at that. We usually call people up from the periodical writer's directory or people we have used and know about and occasionally we do use people who send in resumés. We don't accept previously published work or simultaneous submissions." Guidelines are not available.
PHOTOGRAPHERS: "We purchase some work for the cover."
NOTES: Sample copies are available free upon request.

EIC ELECTRONIQUE INDUSTRIELLE & COMMERCIALE
8735 Lucien Plante
Montreal, PQ H2M 2M7

PHONE: (514) 383-7700
FAX: (514) 383-7691

CONTACT: Pierre Tremblay, Editor **DESCRIPTION:** Published by Serpro Int Inc. Circulation 9,000+. An industrial electronics publication issued 5 times a year in French. Established in 1980.
WRITERS: "We have not purchased any freelance material in the last 15 years."
PHOTOGRAPHERS: "We don't purchase photography."

ELAN
1620 Pine Avenue West
Montreal, PQ H3G 1B4

NOTES: NO LONGER PUBLISHED

ELCIC SUNDAY BULLETINS
14-5 Lake Crest Road
Winnipeg, MB R3T 4M3

NOTES: Could not locate. Phone number is not in service (204) 474-1543.

ELECTRICAL BUSINESS
395 Matheson Blvd. East   **PHONE:** (905) 890-1846
Mississauga, ON L4Z 2H2   **FAX:** (905) 890-5769

CONTACT: Robert Burford Mason, Editor   **DESCRIPTION:** Published by Kerrwil Publications Ltd. Circulation 20,000. Business publication covering the electrical industry. Published monthly. Established in 1964.
PHOTOGRAPHERS: 10% freelance written. Byline is given. "See copy of publication for freelance possibilities." Payment is negotiated. "We need authoritative articles about the electrical industries - manufacture and supply, distribution, utilities, application stories. We do NOT need historical material, speculative material, or anything which is not supported by personal knowledge, industry insight, or intelligent research and analysis. I am always interested in talking about story ideas."
NOTES: Unsolicited materials will be returned with SASE. Does not consider previously published work and simultaneous submissions. Sample copy is available. Enclose large 8x10 SASE with 88¢ postage. Also publishes Formula, CAD Systems, Canadian Yachting, Electrical Bluebook, Energy Manager, Lighting Magazine, Manufacturing & Process Automation and La Monde.

ELECTRICAL EQUIPMENT NEWS
1450 Don Mills Road   **PHONE:** (416) 445-6641
Don Mills, ON M3B 2X7   **FAX:** (416) 442-2214

CONTACT: Olga Markovich, Editor   **DESCRIPTION:** Published by Southam. Circulation 24,000. Published monthly. Established in 1956.
WRITERS: "We don't use any outside writers or photographers."
NOTES: A supplement to Canadian Industrial Equipment News.

ELECTRICAL SYSTEMS ENGINEER see Electrical Business Magazine

ELECTRICITY TODAY
345 Kingston Road #101   **PHONE:** (905) 509-4448
Pickering, ON L1V 1A1 or L1W 3X8   **FAX:** (905) 509-4451

CONTACT: Randolph Hurst, Editor   **DESCRIPTION:** Published by Canadian Electricity Forum. Circulation 14,000. Published ten times a year.

ELECTRONIC COMPOSITION & IMAGING
2240 Midland Avenue #201   **PHONE:** (416) 299-6007
Willowdale, ON M4T 2B6   **FAX:** (416) 299-6674

CONTACT: Scott Olson, Editor   **DESCRIPTION:** Published by Youngblood Publications. Publication covering pre-press production and electronic publishing. Published 6 times a year. Established in 1987.
NOTES: Also publishes PrintAction.

ELECTRONIC ENGINEERING see Canadian Electronics

ELECTRONIC LINK
885 Don Mills Road #324   **PHONE:** (416) 510-0909
Don Mills, ON M3C 1V9   **FAX:** (416) 510-0913

CONTACT: Joanna Pachner   **DESCRIPTION:** Circulation 12,000. Published by Applied Arts Inc. A how-to magazine of digital creativity, *Electronic Link* covers computer-based visual communications through profiles, step-by-step features and practical advice from experts. Reports on technology and areas of endeavour. A computer publication with the latest information on digital technology. Published quarterly. Established in 1994.
PHOTOGRAPHERS: Please send sample of work. Contact Georges Haroutian.
NOTES: Sample copies of this publication are available free upon request. Purchases North American one-time rights. Returns unsolicited materials with a SASE. Considers previously published work but not simultaneous submissions.

ELECTRONIC PRODUCTS AND TECHNOLOGY
1200 Aerowood Drive, Unit 27   **PHONE:** (905) 624-8100
Mississauga, ON L4W 2S7   **FAX:** (905) 624-1760

CONTACT: E. David Kerfoot, Editor   **DESCRIPTION:** Published by Lakeview Publications. Circulation 23,300. A trade magazine that goes to electronic design engineers across Canada. Published 7 times a year. Established in 1979.
WRITERS: "We infrequently purchase articles. Most of the material is contributed by advertisers."
PHOTOGRAPHERS: "We have never purchased photography."

ELECTRONICS & TECHNOLOGY TODAY
1300 Don Mills Road
Don Mills, ON M3B 3M8

NOTES: NO LONGER PUBLISHED

ELECTRONICS TIMES see Canadian Electronics

ELLE QUEBEC
2001 rue University #900
Montreal, PQ H3A 2A6

PHONE: (514) 499-0561
FAX: (514) 499-1844

CONTACT: Martine Demange, Editor **DESCRIPTION:** Published by Les Publications Télémédia-Hachette Inc. Circulation 36,400. French women's monthly magazine. Established in 1989.

ELLIPSE
FLSH, CP10 University of Sherbrooke
Sherbrooke, PQ J1K 2R1

PHONE: (819) 821-7277
FAX: (819) 821-7285

CONTACT: Monique Grandmangin, Editor **DESCRIPTION:** Circulation 750. Dedicated to Canadian poetry in translation, two poets are featured in each issue, one who published in French and one in English. "In every issue there is a Quebecois poet's poems translated into English and an English poet's work translated into French. They are paired. We also may have a thematic issue." Published twice a year.
WRITERS: "We contact people and ask to translate their poems. We do have people submitting ideas for issues and we examine them in our editorial board. People should write us and tell us what they have in mind and we will answer." Writers' guidelines are available.
PHOTOGRAPHERS: "We may use black & white photographs of the poets themselves."
NOTES: Sample copies of this publication are available for $6.

EMERGENCY PREPAREDNESS CANADA
122 Bank Street
Ottawa, ON K1A 0W6

PHONE: (613) 991-7040
FAX: (613) 998-9589

CONTACT: Ann-Marie Demers **DESCRIPTION:** Published by Canada Communications Group. Circulation 2,500. Published quarterly in English and French. Established in 1961.
WRITERS: "We use a firm of writers, editors and translators." Does not accept queries or submissions.
PHOTOGRAPHERS: Photography is purchased from stock. Uses 35mm transparencies, 5x7 and 8x10 colour prints; 5x7, 8x10 glossy b&w prints. Credit line is given. "We purchase many of our photos from Canapress and newspapers. Prices vary from $10 to $200. "We need photos that will reproduce well either in b&w or colour. We have very few colour photos in the Digest, and we can't always know in advance whether a shot will be printed in b&w or colour. Hard-to-find shots: with human interest (showing emotions, stress) and everyday-life scenes (showing ordinary people, alone or interacting with others)."
NOTES: Unsolicited materials will be returned with SASE. Previously published work is considered. Simultaneous submissions are not considered. Purchases one-time rights. Sample copy can be purchased for $6.00 from Canada Communications Group.

EN PRIMEUR
900A Don Mills Road #1000
Don Mills, ON M3C 1V6

PHONE: (416) 445-0544
FAX: (416) 445-2894

DESCRIPTION: Published by Sandra Stewart. Circulation 52,800. A general interst magazine with an emphasis on film and previews of upcoming films. Published quarterly in French. Established in 1989.

WRITERS: "We have a small base of freelancers which we draw from. We very rarely take submissions. People are welome to query us."
PHOTOGRAPHERS: "We never purchase photography."
NOTES: Also publishes Tribute Magazine, En Primeur Jeunesse, Kids Tribute, and Campus Reel.

EN PRIMEUR JEUNESSE
900A Don Mills Road #1000
Don Mills, ON   M3C 1V6

PHONE: (416) 445-4020
FAX: (416) 445-2894

DESCRIPTION: Published by Sandra Stewart. Circulation 50,000. A general interest magazine for kids with an emphasis on film and a preview of the upcoming films for kids. Published quarterly. Established in 1989.
WRITERS: "We have a small base of freelancers which we draw from. We very rarely take submissions. People are welome to query us."
PHOTOGRAPHERS: "We never purchase photography."
NOTES: This is the French version of Kids Tribute. Also publishes Tribute Magazine, Campus Reel, Kids Tribute, and En Primeur.

EN ROUTE
7 Bates Road
Outremont, PQ   H2V 1A6

PHONE: (514) 270-1100
FAX: (514) 270-6900

CONTACT: Lise Ravary, Editorial Director   **DESCRIPTION:** Published by Publicor.
NOTES: Also publishes Femme Plus, Clin d'oeil, Les Idees De Ma Maison, Decoration Chez-soi, Renovation Bricolage, Plans de Maisons Quebec and En Route.

EN VILLE
8270 Avenue Mountain Sights #201
Montreal, PQ   H4P 2B7

NOTES: Could not locate. Phone number is not in service (514) 731-9471.

ENERGY MANAGER
395 Matheson Blvd East
Mississauga, ON   L4Z 2H2

PHONE: (905) 890-1846
FAX: (905) 890-5769

CONTACT: Bryan Rogers, Editor   **DESCRIPTION:** Published by Kerwill Publications Ltd. Circulation 12,000. "For building owners, managers, facilities, engineers and architects. Contains articles on energy efficient products and technology in the commercial and industrial area, not residential." Published 6 times a year. Established in 1994.
NOTES: "We are a brand-new publication and do not purchase freelance material as yet. We don't have a budget for freelance material. We are not looking to buy material for the next year or so." Also publishes Formula, CAD Systems, Canadian Yachting, Electrical Business, Electrical Bluebook, Lighting Magazine, Manufacturing & Process Automation and La Monde.

ENGINEERING DIGEST
5080 Timberlea Blvd. Suite 8
Mississauga, ON L4W 5C1

NOTES: Could not locate. Phone number is not in service (416) 602-0814.

ENGINEERING DIMENSIONS
25 Sheppard Avenue West #1000   **PHONE:** (416) 224-1100
North York, ON M2N 6S9

CONTACT: Connie Mucklestone, Managing Editor   **DESCRIPTION:** Published by Association of Professional Engineers of Ontario. Circulation 59,800. Published bi-monthly. Established in 1980.

ENGLISH RIDER
491 Book Road   **PHONE:** (905) 648-2035
Ancaster, ON L9G 3L1   **FAX:** (905) 648-6977

CONTACT: Barry Finn   **DESCRIPTION:** Circulation 10,000. English horse publication containing all of the national news. Published bi-monthly. Established in 1970.
WRITERS: 15% freelance written. Purchases 40 articles per year. Byline given. Hires writers on assignment. Pays $15 per typed double spaced page. Articles are 1,000-2,000 words. Columnists write for ad-exchange or volunteer. "We prefer articles on news topics, current information on shows, breeds, and health issues. We generally do not publish lengthly feature stories." Contact with a query letter or by phone.
PHOTOGRAPHERS: Purchases 6 photos annually. Majority assigned to in-house photographers with 20% in text\photo submissions. Uses 5x7 and 8x10 colour prints and 5x7, 8x10 glossy black & white. Payment negotiated. Query by letter.
NOTES: Purchases one-time rights. Considers previously published work. Considers simultaneous submissions. Sample copies of this publication are available free upon request.

enROUTE MAGAZINE
33 Fraser Avenue #113   **PHONE:** (416) 538-0152
Toronto, ON M6K 1Y7   **FAX:** (416) 538-0373

DESCRIPTION: Published by Spafax Canada Inc. Circulation 125,000. Bilingual magazine with an emphasis on travel. Articles include; business, technology, lifestyle stories, and profiles of unusual Canadians. Published monthly and distributed on all Air Canada flights. Established in 1973.

LES ENSEIGNANTS
1316 Domaine de Moulin   **PHONE:** (418) 872-6966
L'Ancienne-Lorette, PQ G2E 4N1   **FAX:** (418) 872-6966

CONTACT: Jean-Louis Jobin, Editor   **DESCRIPTION:** French language publication issued 10 times a year. Established in 1970.

ENTREPRENDRE

1600 St-Martin Blvd. E Tower B #630
Laval, PQ H7G 4S7

PHONE: (514) 669-8373
FAX: (514) 669-9078

CONTACT: Edmond Bourque   **DESCRIPTION:** Published by The Centre of Entrepreneurship. Circulation 50,000. "A magazine for the decision-makes, owners and managers of large, medium and small business and for managers of government affairs." Inside you can find business, economics and profiles of success. Published 6 times a year in French and English. Established in 1987.
WRITERS: "We do purchase work. Contact us by mail including a resumé with your experience in business and economic affairs. We have 10 criteria and writers should request them."
PHOTOGRAPHERS: "We do purchase photography sometimes, mainly colour. We look for mostly human interest."
NOTES: "Journalists and photographers are two important members of our team. They are important to the dynamics of the magazine." This is distributed on Via Rail, Air Canada, Royal Air and Canadian International Air.

ENVIRONMENTAL SCIENCE AND ENGINEERING

220 Industrial Parkway South #30
Aurora, ON L4G 3V6

PHONE: (905) 727-4666
FAX: (905) 841-7271

CONTACT: Tom Davey, Editor   **DESCRIPTION:** Circulation 19,200. Business publication with a highly specialized focus - ESZE. Published 6 times a year. Established in 1988.
WRITERS: "We don't use freelancers, all our articles are directly commissioned. We prefer not to be contacted by freelance writers."

EQUINOX

25 Sheppard Avenue West #100
North York, ON M2N 6S7

PHONE: (416) 733-7600
FAX: (416) 218-3633

CONTACT: Jim Cormier   **DESCRIPTION:** Published by Telemedia Inc. Circulation 160,000. Equinox is subtitled "Canada's Magazine of Discovery" and carries photo-heavy features on geography, science, nature and wildlife, arts & culture. *Nexus* is a digest section of short pieces on science, environment and technology. The magazine's editorial range is extensive and eclectic - with a special emphasis on biology, astronomy, the earth sciences, medicine, the arts, architecture, travel and adventure. While exploring the unfamiliar, Equinox also provides fresh insights into the familiar. Published 6 times a year. Established in 1981.
WRITERS: 95% freelance written. Purchases 35 to 50 articles a year. Byline is given. Writers are hired on assignment. Articles range from 1,500 to 4,000 words. Pays approximately $1 per word. A kill fee of 50% is given if an assigned article is cancelled. In addition to feature articles and *Nexus*, the magazine also includes book and CD-ROM reviews. Contact by sending a query letter. "We prefer WRITTEN queries. New writers have the best chance of breaking in through the *Nexus* section." Guidelines available.
PHOTOGRAPHERS: Stock photography is purchased (50%). Photographers are hired on assignment (50%). Formats used include: 35mm, 2¼ x 2¼ and 4x5 colour transparencies. Captions are required. Credit line is given. Pays $125 to $400 for inside colour and $500 for colour covers. Contact by sending a query letter. "Best to propose photo essays or story ideas rather than simply sending portfolio or resumé." Photo guidelines are available.

NOTES: Buys first North American serial rights. Unsolicited materials will be returned with SASE. Does not consider previously published work or simultaneous submissions. A sample copy is available for $5.

EQUIPMENT JOURNAL

150 Lakeshore Road West #36
Mississauga, ON L5H 3R2

PHONE: (905) 274-4883
FAX: (905) 274-4883

CONTACT: Matthew Wilson, News Editor   **DESCRIPTION:** Circulation 18,000. A national trade publication dealing with heavy construction equipment. "We include news releases of bulldozers, excavaters, front-wheel loaders. Our articles include news related to mining, construction and forestry industry." Published 50 times a year. Established in 1966.
WRITERS: "We don't purchase freelance work from writers."
PHOTOGRAPHERS: No photography is purchased.

ESPACES VERTS MAGAZINE

33 Champagne
Blainville, PQ J7C 2Z4

PHONE: (514) 435-1890
FAX: (514) 435-0424

CONTACT: Francois Bertrand, Editor-in-Chief **DESCRIPTION:** Published by Editions versicolores inc. Circulation 1,981. A trade magazine published 7 times a year in French. Established in 1988.

ESSAYS ON CANADIAN WRITING

2120 Queen Street East #200
Toronto, ON M4E 1E2

PHONE: (416) 694-3348
FAX: (416) 698-9906

CONTACT: Robert Lecker, Jack David, Co-Editors   **DESCRIPTION:** Published by ECW Press. Circulation 1,000. Concentrating on contemporary authors and current critical approaches, this publication is devoted to the criticism of Canadian writers and their work. Publishes bibliographies, interviews, poetry, criticism, and fiction book reviews. Published 3 times a year. Established in 1974.
NOTES: "Most of our articles are written by academics. We occasionally have theme issues. Query first with a letter. If we are interested we will ask for more."

L'ESSENTIAL

7 Bates Road
Outremont, PQ H2V 1A6

PHONE: (514) 270-1100
FAX: (514) 270-6900

CONTACT: Sylvie La Plant, Editorial Director   **DESCRIPTION:** Published by Publicor. Circulation 85,000. Published monthly in French. Established in 1988.

EXCHANGE
75 King Street S.　　　　　　　　　　PHONE: (519) 886-2831
Waterloo, ON　N2G 4E5　　　　　　　FAX: (519) 886-9383

CONTACT: Rick Campbell, Editor　DESCRIPTION: Published by Fairway Group
Magazines. Circulation 15,000. Regional publication for Waterloo area with stories about
local people and events. Published monthly. Established in 1983.
WRITERS: 60% freelance written. Buys 24 articles per year. Gives a byline. Hires on
assignment; pays expenses while on assignment. Articles 1,000-2,000 words. Pay varies:
major feature $800-1,200; feature $600; secondary feature $400; short articles (800-1,200
words) $225. Kill fee paid if assigned article cancelled. "We are a local, regional business
publication. We like to provide content on local businesses." Contact with query letter
or completed articles on spec, send resumé and business card (to be kept on file). Writers'
guidelines available.
PHOTOGRAPHERS: Hires photographers on assignment. Buys 150 photos annually.
Uses all colour formats. 5x7 or 8x10 matte b&w. Model releases required. Captions required.
Credit line is given. Pays $25-100 for b&w or colour inside. $200-400 for photo/text package.
Contact with query letter, brochure, flyer or tear sheets. "We are a local, regional publication
and look for local, regional business people in our photographs." Photo guidelines available.
NOTES: Buys one-time rights. Will not return unsolicited materials. Considers previously
published work and simultaneous submissions. For sample copy send 9x12" SASE with
$1.40 postage.

EXCURSIONS EN AUTOCAR
CP 365 Place d'Armes　　　　　　　PHONE: (514) 274-0004
Montreal, PQ　H2Y 3H1　　　　　　　FAX: (514) 274-5884

CONTACT: Guy J. Jonkman, Editor　DESCRIPTION: Published by Publicom Inc.
Circulation 6,400. French language publication for tour group organizers and planners.
Published monthly. Established in 1988.
WRITERS: "We do most of our articles in-house. Sometimes we use a freelancer when
we don't want to travel. We call them and ask them to report for us. This is very rare."
PHOTOGRAPHERS: "We use very few photos. Many photos are provided by hotels
and the tourism industry."
NOTES: Also publishes Congres Mensuel.

EXPECTING
37 Hanna Avenue #1　　　　　　　　PHONE: (416) 537-2604
Toronto, ON　M6K 1X1　　　　　　　FAX: (416) 538-1794

CONTACT: Shirley Ohannessian　DESCRIPTION: Published by Family Communications
Inc. Circulation 145,200. Consumer magazine focusing on pre-natal care. Articles include:
timely information for mothers-to-be, ie. breast feeding etc. Published twice a year.
Established in 1984.
WRITERS: "All articles are written by doctors and nurses."
NOTES: No freelance material is purchased for this publication. Also publishes Today's
Bride, You, Expecting and Baby and Child Care Encyclopedia.

L'EXPEDITEUR

7493 Transcanada Hwy #103
St-Laurent, PQ H4T 1T3

PHONE: (514) 337-9043
FAX: (514) 337-1862

CONTACT: Steve Bouchard, Editor **DESCRIPTION:** Published by Les Editions Bomart Lteé. Circulation 11,000. A logistics and transportation publication with most readership in Quebec. Published 10 times a year in French. Established in 1988.
WRITERS: "We do not purchase freelance writing, everything is on a volunteer basis."
PHOTOGRAPHERS: "We have a bank of two or three photographers that we normally use. Freelancers can send a resumé. Payment is negotiable."
NOTES: Also publishes L'Echo du Transport.

EYE WEEKLY

57 Spadina Avenue #207
Toronto, ON M5V 2J2

PHONE: (416) 971-8421
FAX: (416) 971-7786

CONTACT: Bill Reynolds **DESCRIPTION:** Published by Andrew V. Go. Circulation 100,000. Published weekly. Established in 1991.
WRITERS: 90% freelance written. Buys hundreds of articles annually "but regular contributors take up the lion's share." Byline is given. Articles range from 500-900 words. Pay ranges from $100-300. Regular features include *Rolling Eye* - short, satirical items about T.O. ($25-100) and *News & Views* - medium length news or op.ed. stories, could have a satirical bent ($125-200). 50% kill fee is paid "if it's our fault the story doesn't run: not if the writer deviates wildly from the assignment." Guidelines are not available. "Send query letter, with resumé and 3 to 5 examples of work (samples are very important). I look for writers who flourish in an independent, humour-filled environment, who have a strongly developed style and a unique POV."
PHOTOGRAPHERS: Photographs are purchased from stock (10%). Photographers are hired on assignment (10%). The majority of photos are submitted as part of a text/photo package (50%, or are staff taken, 30%). All colour formats and all b&w formats are used. Model releases are not necessary. Captions are not necessary. Pays $120 inside and $350 for cover. Credit line is given. Contact with a sample portfolio. Photographers contact Kevan Buss.
NOTES: Sample copy is available. Send 9x12" SASE with 88¢ postage; back issues are available for $2. Buys one time rights plus world wide web site placement. Unsolicited materials will be returned with SASE. May consider previously published work. Will not consider simultaneous submissions.

FABRIC CARE CANADA

Box 968
Oakville, ON L6J 5E8

PHONE: (905) 825-2415
FAX: (905) 825-2333

CONTACT: Marcia Todd, Editor **DESCRIPTION:** Published by CTJ-Inc. Circulation 7,000. A national publication for people engaged in the professional cleaning of clothes and linens; drycleaners, launderers, people who supply linens to restaurants, and institutional laundries. Publishes articles on drycleaning and laundering for laundry companies and suppliers. Published 6 times a year. Established in 1955.
WRITERS: "We seldom have a budget for it. Mostly staff written."
PHOTOGRAPHERS: "We have a staff photographer. I might be interested in getting some contact with freelance photographers. Once in awhile we have a cover that needs to be shot and it is not feasible to send our guy across the country. We need someone who

has had experience in shooting covers of trade publications. Contact with samples of work and a resumé. We never know where we may need someone."
NOTES: Sample copies of this publication are available for $7. Formerly Canadian Cleaner and Launderer.

FACEOFF

1465 St. James Street
Winnipeg, MB R3H 0W9

PHONE: (204) 949-6100
FAX: (204) 949-6122

CONTACT: David Rigby **DESCRIPTION:** Published by Canadian Publishers. Circulation 20,000. A monthly amateur hockey tabloid regarding all Manitoba amateur hockey. Contains coaching tips, player profiles, industry trends, local and equipment features. Published 6 times a year. Established in 1992.
WRITERS: "We freelance the whole thing, probably 8 stories per issue. Articles are around 500 words and pay $50. We hire writers on assignment. Contact in writing with samples. Writers should have a knowledge of amateur hockey and sports. There is a completely different slant you put on amateur sports." Guidelines are available.
PHOTOGRAPHERS: "We have purchased a little bit in the past. We run a four colour front cover and we use black and white inside. We pay $35 for the front cover and $15 for the inside. Prefers text/photo packages. Contact in writing with samples. Has to be Manitoba content."
NOTES: This publication does not run articles/photos unless they focus on Manitoba.

FAITH TODAY

175 Riviera Drive
Markham, ON L3R 5J6

PHONE: (905) 479-5885
FAX: (905)

CONTACT: Audrey Dorsch **DESCRIPTION:** Published by The Evangelical Fellowship of Canada. Circulation 18-20,000. A national evangelical news feature magazine issued 6 times a year. Established in 1983.
WRITERS: "We purchase 15-20 articles per issue from short news items to major features. Send an SASE for guidelines. Length and rates are negotiable. We want journalistic style rather than commentary or opinion pieces, well-researched with a balance of perspectives represented. Study the magazine; we get so much material that is not related to our publication."
PHOTOGRAPHERS: "We rarely purchase photos."
NOTES: Sample copies of this publication are available free upon request. Purchases first North American serial rights. Does not consider previously published work.

FAMILY PRACTICE

1120 Birchmount Road #200
Scarborough, ON M1K 5G4

PHONE: (416) 750-8900
FAX: (416) 751-8126

CONTACT: John Shaughnessy, Editor **DESCRIPTION:** Published by Thomson Healthcare Communications. Circulation 26,000. Focuses on medical practices and issues of interest to family physicians. Features and columns include: medical news; medical politics; medical legal issues; physician profile; clinical news; travel; humour; physician lifestyle. Published 32 times a year. Established in 1989.
WRITERS: 50% freelance written. Buys fiction, non-fiction and fillers. Hires writers on assignment and pays expenses while on assignment. Average articles are 750 worlds.

Pays 38¢ per word. Kill fee (50%) is given if assigned article is cancelled. Contact with a query letter, resumé and business card. Guidelines are not available.
PHOTOGRAPHERS: Purchases 100 photos annually. 25% from stock. 75% assigned to photographers. Uses colour prints. Model releases and captions are preferred, but are not necessary. Credit line is not given. Contact with a query letter. Photo guidelines are not available.
NOTES: Buys first Canadian rights. Unsolicited materials will be returned with SASE. Will not consider previously published work or simultaneous submissions.

FARM & COUNTRY

100 Broadview Avenue #402   **PHONE:** (416) 463-8080
Toronto, ON M4M 3H3   **FAX:** (416) 463-1075

CONTACT: John Muggeridge, Managing Editor   **DESCRIPTION:** Published by Agricultural Publishing Co. Circulation 52,000. Focus is on agriculture, business, technology, and science. Published 18 times a year. Established in 1935.
WRITERS: 25% freelance written. Purchases 250 articles a year. Writers are hired on assignment, and expenses are paid while on assignment. A byline is given. Average article length is 1,000 words. Average article pays $250, op ed articles $125. Contact the editor with a query letter, include resumé and business card. These will be kept of file for possible future assignments. The editor wants to see 'tight, concise, punchy, to-the-point' style. If it doesn't have a farm focused and $$ angle our readers aren't interested. Double spaced with good pics preferred."
PHOTOGRAPHERS: Stock photos are purchased and photographers are hired on assignment. Prefers 2¼x2¼ transparencies or 5x7 colour prints. Model releases are not necessary. Captions are required. Credit line is given. Inside pay negotiated. Colour cover $200. Contact by sending a sample portfolio. "I need vertical shots for the cover - lots of colour, action. No "calender" shots. Always ties in with lead article."
NOTES: Purchases one-time rights. Unsolicited materials will be returned with SASE. Considers previously published work (if a different market) and simultaneous submissions. A sample copy is available free upon request. Also publishes Pork Producers.

FARM FOCUS

Box 128   **PHONE:** (902) 742-7111
Yarmouth, NS B5A 4B1   **FAX:** (902) 742-2311

CONTACT: Heather Jones, Editor   **DESCRIPTION:** Published by Fundy Group Publications. Atlantic Canadian farming publication containing a wide range of agricultural information and news for the region. Published twice a month. Established in 1973.

THE FARM GATE

15 King Street   **PHONE:** (519) 669-5155
Elmira, ON N3B 2R1   **FAX:** (519) 669-5928

CONTACT: Bob Verdun, Editor   **DESCRIPTION:** Published by North Waterloo Publishing Ltd. Circulation 21,000. Contains information for farmers about innovations, equipment and agricultural methods. Published monthly. Established in 1977.
NOTES: The majority of this publication is produced in-house.

FARM LIGHT & POWER
2330 - 15 Avenue
Regina, SK S4P 1A2

PHONE: (306) 525-3305
FAX: (306) 757-1810

CONTACT: Pat Rediger   **DESCRIPTION:** Published by Farm Light & Power Publications Ltd. Circulation 166,000. Western Canadian publication informing farmers of new farming techniques, weather forecasts, sales and marketing, products and equipment and farm profitability. Published 10 times a year. Established in 1959.
WRITERS: 50-100% freelance written. Pays $100-$300 for articles. Phone inquiries welcome.
PHOTOGRAPHERS: Purchases photos b&w inside, colour cover (vertical).

FARMING TODAY
16 Hincks Street
St. Thomas, ON N5P 3W6

NOTES: Could not locate. Phone number is not in service (519) 633-8811.

FEATHER FANCIER
5 Lake Road
Forest, ON N0N 1J0

PHONE: (519) 899-2364
FAX: (519) 899-2364

CONTACT: Jim Gryner, Editor   **DESCRIPTION:** Circulation 2,700. An agricultural publication dealing with purebred birds; poultry, pigeon, waterfowl etc. Published monthly.
WRITERS: "All of our writers are volunteers. We don't purchase work."
PHOTOGRAPHERS: "We don't purchase photography."

FEATURE
2100 St. Catherine Street West 9 Fl.
Montreal, PQ H3H 2T3

PHONE: (514) 939-5024
FAX: (514) 939-1515

CONTACT: David Sherman, Managing Editor   **DESCRIPTION:** Published by Feature Publishing Ltd. Circulation 433,000. Published monthly. Established in 1990.
WRITERS: This publication does not purchases freelance writing.

FELICITER
200 Elgin Street #602
Ottawa, ON K2P 1L5

PHONE: (613) 232-9625 ext. 321
FAX: (613) 563-9895

CONTACT: Mary Moore, Editor   **DESCRIPTION:** Published by Canadian Library Association. Circulation 3,700. Published for the members of the Canadian Library Association. Published 10 times a year.
WRITERS: "All our articles are written by volunteers or staff." Average article length 800-2,400 words. Writer's guidelines are available.
PHOTOGRAPHERS: 95% assigned to in-house photographers. 5% volunteer done. "We rarely use photos."
NOTES: Considers previously published work. Considers simultaneous submissions. Sample copies of this publication are available free upon request.

FEMME PLUS
7 Bates Road
Outremont, PQ H2V 1A6

PHONE: (514) 270-1100
FAX: (514) 270-6900

CONTACT: Gennieve St. Germain, Editorial Director   **DESCRIPTION:** Published by Publicor. Circulation 70,700. French language publication focusing on issues of interest to women. Published monthly.
NOTES: Also publishes Filles D'Aujourd'hui, Clin d'oeil, Les Idees De Ma Maison, Decoration Chez-soi, Renovation Bricolage, Plans de Maisons Quebec and En Route.

THE FIDDLEHEAD
Campus House, University of New
Brunswick, Box 4400
Fredericton, NB E3B 5A3

PHONE: (506) 453-3501
FAX: (506) 453-4599

CONTACT: Don McKay, Editor **DESCRIPTION:** Circulation 900. Literary magazine publishes poetry, prose, book reviews, and art work. Published quarterly.
WRITERS: Accepts submissions of no more than 10 poems and fiction up to 3,000 words. Pays approximately $10 a page upon publication. Items must be literary in nature and complete upon submission. No solicited material requested.
PHOTOGRAPHERS: Occasionally purchases black and white photography, mainly from New Brunswick photographers. Pays $20 per photo.
NOTES: Purchases first North American Serial rights. Does not accept previously published work. For a sample copy send $7.

FIFTY-FIVE PLUS
RR1
Battersea, ON K0H 1H0

PHONE: (613) 353-2060
FAX: (613) 353-2060

CONTACT: Sharon Freeman, Editor   **DESCRIPTION:** Published by Limestone City Publications. Circulation 40,000. A regional publication for retirees in eastern Ontario. Addresses finances, health, people, columns, and travel. Published 6 times a year. Established in 1988.
WRITERS: "We purchase 4 articles per issue. Freelancers should request our writer's guidelines. We really like submissions specific to our readers."
PHOTOGRAPHERS: "We don't purchase photography very often."
NOTES: Sample copies of this publication are available free upon request. Does not consider previously published work.

FILLES D'AUJOURD'HUI
7 Bates Road
Outremont, PQ H2V 1A6

PHONE: (514) 270-1100
FAX: (514) 270-6900

CONTACT: Francine Trudeau, Editorial Director **DESCRIPTION:** Published by Publicor. Circulation 70,000. Women's monthly magazine, published in French. Established in 1980.
NOTES: Also publishes Femme Plus, Clin d'oeil, Les Idees De Ma Maison, Decoration Chez-soi, Renovation Bricolage, Plans de Maisons Quebec and En Route.

FINANCIAL POST MAGAZINE

333 King Street East, 3rd Floor   **PHONE:** (416) 350-6172
Toronto, ON M5A 4N2   **FAX:** (416) 350-6171

CONTACT: David Bailey, Editor   **DESCRIPTION:** Circulation 200,000. Magazine featuring a business oriented lifestyle. Also includes political, personal finance and general interest columns. Published monthly.
WRITERS: 70% freelance written. Buys 100 articles a year. Byline is given. Average article length is 3,000 words. Pays up to $1,500 per article. Kill fee is paid if assigned article is cancelled. "Material that is business oriented, but not too dry. Should be about people. Must be informative and entertaining as well."
PHOTOGRAPHERS: 100% freelance. Buys from stock and hires on assignment. Model releases are preferred. Captions are required. Credit line is given. Pays $1,000 for b&w, $1,500 for inside colour, $2,000 for colour cover. Make contact by sending query letter and sample portfolio. Photographers contact David Woodside.
NOTES: Unsolicited materials will be returned with SASE. Does not consider previously published work or simultaneous submissions.

FIRE FIGHTING IN CANADA

222 Argyle Avenue   **PHONE:** (519) 582-2513
Delhi, ON N4B 2Y2   **FAX:** (519) 582-4040

CONTACT: James Haley, Editor   **DESCRIPTION:** Published by NCC Publishing. Circulation 7,500. "A national magazine for officers of the Canadian fire service, which relates information in management and training as well as news of the fire service." Published 10 times a year. Established in 1957.
WRITERS: "In the past I have purchased approximately 10%. I normally buy technical material. Freelancers can contact me by phone or they can write me a proposal, however I prefer to talk to people. Usually we pay $125 for 800 words." Guidelines are not available.
PHOTOGRAPHERS: "We purchase both colour and black & white photos, both with articles and individually. I buy about a dozen photos a year. Most of my photos are submitted by a fire department." Send the photo or a proof on spec. "I like to see photos of emergency scenes, whether they are fire or rescue or accidents. If it is unusual or striking I would certainly consider it. I do use freelancers every once in awhile for my cover photographs. We pay $50 for colour cover photos." Guidelines are not available.
NOTES: Sample copies of this publication are available free upon request. Purchases first North American serial rights. Considers previously published work if it wasn't in a competing market.

FISH'N CANADA NEWS

385 Bloor Street West   **PHONE:** (416) 571-3223
Oshawa, ON L1J 6Z9   **FAX:** (416) 571-3328

CONTACT: Angelo Viola   **DESCRIPTION:** Outdoor fishing video magazine (75 minutes) for Canada's sportfishers. Published 4 times a year. Available on newsstands across Canada. Established in 1988.
WRITERS: This publication accepts material on spec.

FLARE
777 Bay Street
Toronto, ON M5W 1A7

PHONE: (416) 596-5462
FAX: (416) 596-5799

CONTACT: Bonnie Brooks, Editor   **DESCRIPTION:** Published by Maclean Hunter. Circulation 191,400. An editorial magazine on fashion, beauty and lifestyle. Articles include: health, sex, relationships, travel, recreation, and home decorating. Published monthly. Established in 1979.
WRITERS: "Read back issues of the magazine to make sure your idea fits our general editorial tone and audience. Briefly summarize your proposal in writing indicating theme, main points, research and approximate article length. Attach your resumé and tear sheets of previously published work." Contact: Liza Finlay, Managing Editor. Flare does not publish fiction. Does not publish unsolicited manuscripts. Writers' guidelines are available.
PHOTOGRAPHERS: Photography is done on assignment. Photo fees average $75-200 inside, $400 cover. Some expenses are covered.
NOTES: Copies are available on newsstands.

FLEET MANAGEMENT JOURNAL
235 Yorkland Blvd. 3rd Floor
North York, ON M2J 4Y8

PHONE: (416) 494-2960
FAX: (416) 491-2757

CONTACT: Tony Whitney, Editor   **DESCRIPTION:** Published by Powershift Communications.
NOTES: Also publishes Canadian Purchasing Journal and Benefits and Pension Monitor.

FLEUR DESIGN MAGAZINE
3170 rue Dubé
Québec, PQ G1M 3K4

PHONE: (418) 687-6008
FAX: (418) 628-0524

CONTACT: Caty Bérubé, Editor-in-Chief   **DESCRIPTION:** Published by Editions versicolores inc. Circulation 1,514. A trade magazine published 6 times a year in French. Established in 1985.

FLEURS, PLANTES ET JARDINS MAGAZINE
6538 de Lanaudiére
Montréal, PQ H2G 3A9

PHONE: (514) 495-1985
FAX: (418) 495-3819

CONTACT: Bertrand Dumont, Editor   **DESCRIPTION:** Published by Editions versicolores inc. Circulation 53,231. A French language consumer magazine focusing on gardening. Issued 8 times a year. Established in 1990.

FLOOR COVERING PLUS
1448 Lawrence Avenue East #302
Toronto, ON M4A 2V6

PHONE: (416) 755-5199
FAX: (416) 755-9123

CONTACT: Jill Sawyer, Editor   **DESCRIPTION:** Published by Style Communications Ltd. Circulation 7,000. Published 7 times a year. Established in 1955.
WRITERS: 40% freelance written. Buys approximately 15 articles a year. Byline is given. Writers are hired on assignment, travel expenses are paid. Articles range from 800 to 1,000

words. Pays 25¢ a word. Regular columns are staff written. Contact editor with query letter, resumé and samples. Guidelines are not available. "Writers with specific experience covering interior design and decor would be most welcome. Don't just send a resumé and clips. Follow up with a phone call. I'm happy to send copies of the magazine so writers can get an idea of our style."

PHOTOGRAPHERS: Photography is used but is not purchased. "I'm more likely to hire a cartoonist or illustrator."

NOTES: Buys one-time rights. Unsolicited materials will be returned with SASE. Will not consider previously published work or simultaneous submissions. Sample copy is available free upon request. Also publishes Canadian Jeweller, Footwear Forum, and Style.

FLOWER SHOP
22 Argyle Avenue
Delhi, ON   N4B 2Y2

NOTES: NO LONGER PUBLISHED

FOCUS ON WOMEN
1218 Langley Street, 3rd Floor   **PHONE:** (604) 388-7231
Victoria, BC   V8W 1W2   **FAX:** (604) 383-1140

CONTACT: Kerry Slavens, Editor   **DESCRIPTION:** Published by Campbell Communications. Circulation 30,000. Published monthly. Established in 1988.

WRITERS: 80% freelance written. Buys 50-100 articles per year. "Because we have an editorial plan for the next twelve months, we have decided to not accept queries at this time. However, we will look at articles on spec. If you follow the guidelines and study our magazine realistically, your chances of publication will increase." Submissions will be returned with a SASE. "We'd prefer to see a hard copy and if we decide to publish your work would like to obtain the copy on a 3.5" disk. We can read most programs, but Mac/Writenow is the software we are currently using. Stories are 1,000 to 1,500 words. Subject must be a Vancouver Island or Gulf Island woman. The bulk of our profiles are from Victoria. We like to hear about women who are dong really interesting things with their lives." Payment is $50 on publication. Fiction short stories are accepted, up to 2,500 words, shorter is better. Payment $50 on publication "You are encouraged to submit a photo to give us an idea of the visual aspect of the story, but we may re-do unless it is good quality b&w or colour print." Writers' guidelines are available upon request.

PHOTOGRAPHERS: Most photography is done in-house. Occasionally hires photographers on assignment. Uses 5x7 and 8x10 colour prints and all print b&w formats. Model releases and captions are preferred. Pays $10-25 per photo. Credit line is given. Send query letter with resumé and several samples of your work. Guidelines are not available.

NOTES: Buys first North American serial rights. Unsolicited materials will be returned with SASE. Considers simultaneous submissions. Previously published work is not considered. For sample copy send 9x12" SASE. Recent issues are free, back issues send $2 each.

FOOD AND DRINK
55 Lakeshore Blvd. East   **PHONE:** (416) 864-6748
Toronto, ON   M5E 1A4   **FAX:** (416) 365-5935

CONTACT: Lisa Cain, Editor   **DESCRIPTION:** Published by Liquor Control Board of Ontario. Circulation 330,000 for the holiday issue and spring/summer/fall 300,000.

A lifestyle and entertaining publication issued quarterly in English and French and distributed in Ontario. Established in 1988.

WRITERS: "We just had an RSP for writers and editors where we sent out a proposal and we've received responses back and will be putting a number of writers and editors on contract. Freelancers can still contact us for small pieces of work, however it is more likely we will use someone we have on contract."

PHOTOGRAPHERS: "Most of our work is assigned. We don't normally purchase stock photography. A photographer could send in some of their material for review."

FOOD IN CANADA

777 Bay Street	**PHONE:** (416) 596-5819
Toronto, ON M5W 1A7	**FAX:** (416) 593-3189

CONTACT: Catherine Wilson, Editor   **DESCRIPTION:** Published by Heather Oliver. Circulation 9,000. Food processing industry publication with articles on the business and issues affecting it. Published 9 times a year. Established in 1941.

WRITERS: "We do purchase freelance writing on assignment. Generally a couple features per issue plus some smaller news items. Contact the editor by phone. We pay 35¢ per word for 1,500 word features. We try to keep a national perspective." Guidelines are not available.

PHOTOGRAPHERS: "We don't purchase frequently. We are fortunate to get photos supplied free from various sources."

NOTES: Sample copies of this publication are available free upon request. Purchases First Canadian rights.

FOODSERVICE & HOSPITALITY

23 Lesmill Road #101	**PHONE:** (416) 447-0888
Don Mills, ON N3E 3P6	**FAX:** (416) 447-5333

CONTACT: Rosanna Caira, Editor   **DESCRIPTION:** Published by Kostuch Publications. Circulation 25,000. Trade publication for restaurant owners and managers across Canada including chain restaurants, independents and any foodservice operation. Contains trends, news, and issues affecting the business. Published monthly. Established in 1968.

WRITERS: "We hire writers on assignment. Contact us with a query letter with resumé and samples of work. We are looking for a lot of how-to articles and trend analysis geared to the Canadian industry as much as possible. We don't take case studies. We occasionally take articles on spec." Standard length is 1,500 words and the rate is 35¢ a word. Guidelines are available.

PHOTOGRAPHERS: "We purchase colour transparencies or slides, no negatives. We hire photographers on assignment all the time. Pay rates depend on the kind of photo and where it is being used. Most shots are of people or restaurant operations. Credit lines are given." Contact the art director, Linda Irvin.

NOTES: Purchases first North American serial rights. Considers previously published work, depending on where it was published. Sample copies of this publication are available free upon request. Also publishes Canadian Hotel and Restaurant, and Hotelier.

FOOTWEAR FORUM
1448 Lawrence Ave East #302
Toronto, ON   M4A 2V6

PHONE: (416) 755-5199
FAX: (416) 755-9123

CONTACT: Victoria Curran, Editor   **DESCRIPTION:** Published by Style
Communications Inc. Circulation 9,000. A trade magazine that is distributed to retailers,
manufacturers and importers across Canada. Covers the new fashions a year before they
come out in the retail stores. Includes merchandising and marketing tips and
employee/customer training. Published 7 times a year.
WRITERS: "We probably purchase two articles per issue and we hire writers on assignment.
We try to keep articles short, maximum 800 words. Pay rate is 25¢ and under. Contact
by letter with story ideas. Unless they come up with their own story ideas I tend to go
with three freelance writers whom I've groomed to know about the footwear industry."
Guidelines are not available.
PHOTOGRAPHERS: "We purchase photographs. It is usually done in conjunction with
the stories. I don't usually buy photos without a story. I will pay a freelancer who is doing
a profile $15 per published picture and the expense of film developing. I have one photo
feature per issue and I generally stick with an established photographer. I have a couple
photographers in Toronto who are very good with shoes and I tend to use them. I usually
view portfolios at the same time as our sister magazines. (Style, Canadian Jeweller and
Floor Covering Plus.)
NOTES: Also publishes Canadian Jeweller, Floor Covering Plus, and Style.

THE FORESTRY CHRONICLE
151 Slater Street, #606
Ottawa, ON K1P 5H3

PHONE: (613) 234-2242
FAX: (613) 234-6181

CONTACT: Vidar Nordin, Darwin Burgess, Co-Editors   **DESCRIPTION:** Published
by Canadian Institute of Forestry. Published bi-monthly for the Canadian Institute of Forestry.
WRITERS: This publication charges for publication. Writers pay $100 a page to be published.
All inquiries and manuscripts should be sent attention Mr. Vidar Nordin. Written guidelines
are available.
NOTES: A sample copy of this publication is free upon request.

FORET & CONSERVATION
175 Saint-Jean St 4 Fl.
Quebec, PQ G1R 1N4

PHONE: (418) 529-2542
FAX: (418) 529-3021

CONTACT: Serge Beaucher, Editor-in-Chief **DESCRIPTION:** Published by L'Association
forestiére quebécoise Inc. Published 6 times a year in French. Established in 1939.

FORMULA: THE INTERNATIONAL AUTOSPORT MAGAZINE
395 Matheson Blvd. East
Mississauga, ON L4Z 2H2

PHONE: (416) 890-1846
FAX: (416) 890-5769

CONTACT: M. Elston **DESCRIPTION:** Published by Kerrwil Publications Ltd. Features
all aspects of road racing including Formula One, Indy, IMSA, etc.
NOTES: Also publishes CAD Systems, Canadian Yachting, Electrical Business, Electrical
Bluebook, Energy Manager, Lighting Magazine, Manufacturing and Process Automation
and La Monde.

LA FOURNEE

1600 Henri-Bourassa W #404
Montreal, PQ H3M 3E2

PHONE: (514) 332-8376
FAX: (514) 332-2666

CONTACT: Gilles Veronneau **DESCRIPTION:** Published by Communications Vero Inc. Circulation 4,400. Publication for the bakery and pastry-making industry in Quebec. French language publication. Issued 4 times a year. Established in 1934.
WRITERS: "Most of our editorial comes from freelancers, 6 articles or pictures per issue. We have two or three regular contributors who we call upon for various assignments. Sometimes people will solicit us with ideas on topics related to the magazine and if we feel it's interesting we would negotiate a price or buy it. Most of our publications have editorial themes and stories are ordered ahead of time. The most expedient way to contact us is by phone with supporting documentation by fax. Most of the time people send me photocopies of articles on subjects that may be of interest to us. All of our publications are trade magazines. We don't want subjects that are too technical. Most of our assignments are action stories, job descriptions and on-sight reporting. We prefer to get diskettes, Mac or IBM in WordPerfect or Microsoft Word. Average stories are three type-written pages, double spaced. We have a standard rate of $40 per typewritten page, depending on the writer. If there are expenses involved we would give a higher rate to cover incidental costs." Guidelines are not available.
PHOTOGRAPHERS: "Most of the time we try to buy photography together with the article. If we have a three page text we will ask for at least one picture or more depending on the subject."
NOTES: "Usually we buy exclusive rights for one given issue. We would perhaps consider something that was previously published if it wasn't in a competitive magazine." Sample copies are available free upon request. Also publishes L'Hospitlite, La Revue Municipale and Le Mart.

FRAIS DU JOUR

252 route 171
St-Etienne de Lauzon, PQ G6J 1S2

PHONE: (418) 831-5317
FAX: (418) 831-5172

CONTACT: Maurice LeBlanc, Editor **DESCRIPTION:** Published by Le Chef du Service Alimentaire Inc. Circulation 12,400. Published 6 times a year in French. Established in 1992.

FRANC-VERT

690 Grande-Allée Est 4 Fl.
Québec, PQ G1R 2K5

PHONE: (418) 648-2104
FAX: (418) 648-0991

CONTACT: Louise Desautel, Editor **DESCRIPTION:** Published by l'union québécoise pour la conservation de la nature. Circulation 7,000. Natural science and environment magazine for Quebec. Published 6 times a year in French. Established in 1984.
WRITERS: "All of our articles are freelance. Look at the magazine before contacting us with a proposed idea." Guidelines are not available.
PHOTOGRAPHERS: "We purchase photographs. We pay $50 per colour photo, 35mm transparencies or larger formats. We are only looking for nature photos from Quebec." Contact by telephone. Guidelines are not available.

FURNITURE RETAILER
6420 Victoria Avenue, Unit 8
Montreal, PQ H3W 2S7

NOTES: Could not locate. Phone number is not in service (514) 731-3523.

FUSE MAGAZINE
401 Richmond Street West #454　　　　　**PHONE:** (416) 367-0159
Toronto, ON M5V 3A8　　　　　　　　**FAX:** (416) 360-0781

CONTACT: Suzanne Methot, Editorial Coordinator　　**DESCRIPTION:** Circulation 4,000. Focuses on all aspects of contemporary culture from production to media. "We are a multi-disciplinary arts magazine. We do articles about wider social issues such as the rise of the far right, and social analyses in terms of how it affects the art community. We publish reviews of non-mainstream film and video, books if they relate to race issues, art or current events that would affect the climate in which art is created. We tend to stay away from music." Published 5 times a year.
WRITERS: "We purchase most of our material from freelancers on spec. We take 50% unsolicited and the rest is assigned on spec. One-page reviews pay $75 and two-page reviews pay $130. Any other news items is 10¢ per word. The features are $700 for full length ranging from 4,500-6,000 words. Issue oriented columns on cultural events and practices are paid 10¢ a word. Contact us with a letter. We publish a lot of material from people who may not get published anywhere else or whose voice may not be considered mainstream. If we are interested, we will go with it. We definitely don't want fiction or poetry. We like a lot of analysis, some description of the work and the connection between the artistic world and the community, political or cultural issues in our reviews, articles and columns."
PHOTOGRAPHERS: "We very rarely purchase photography. We tend to do mostly black & white with a colour cover. We do have a 2-4 page section of the magazine called the Artist's Project which can encompass photography and art. Contact the production coordinator, Petra Chevrier."
NOTES: Buys first-time rights. A copy is available by subscription or on some Toronto newsstands. Writers' guidelines are available with a standard business SASE.

GAM ON YACHTING
250 The Esplande #202　　　　　　　　**PHONE:** (416) 368-1559
Toronto, ON M5A 1J2　　　　　　　　**FAX:** (416) 368-2831

CONTACT: Karen Larson, Editor　　**DESCRIPTION:** Circulation 20,000. Published for the racing and cruising sailor. Articles include upcoming events, harbour profiles, equipment and safety information, and book reviews. Published 8 times a year. Established in 1957.

GARRISON
5775 Yonge Street　　　　　　　　　　**PHONE:** (416) 733-4681 ext. 5501
North York, ON M2M 4J7　　　　　　**FAX:** (416) 733-5315

CONTACT: Capt. Robert H. Kennedy, Editor　　**DESCRIPTION:** An army publication issued 8 times a year. Established in 1991.

WRITERS: "I don't have an editorial budget. I have a lot of news so I really need a reason to run an article. If it is compelling and has an army hook I may be interested. I have an open mind and a big appetite but I don't have a budget."

GEO PLEIN AIR
1251 Rachel East   **PHONE:** (514) 521-8356
Montreal, PQ H2J 2J9   **FAX:** (514) 521-5711

CONTACT: Simon Kretz, Editor-in-Chief Pierre Hamel, Editor   **DESCRIPTION:** Published by Productions André Croteau Inc. Circulation 100,000. French language publication. An outdoor magazine focusing on trekking, cross-country skiing etc. in Quebec. Issued 6 times a year. Established in 1988.
WRITERS: "Over 50% of the articles are from freelancers. Sometimes we have an idea for a feature and we assign someone to it and other times someone will suggest a feature that is already written. We pay $50 per page (22 double-spaced lines). We don't want anything on motorized sports, we look at more of the traditional sports. If people travel around and have a good story to tell with a lot of research we may be interested. Look through the magazine and see what is in it."
PHOTOGRAPHERS: "We purchase a lot of photography. We look for sport and outdoor activities. We use material from Quebec mostly but we try to have at least one feature from outside Quebec. We do business with some of the agencies and we have a regular freelance photographer." Contact the editors by phone.
NOTES: This publication is available on newsstands.

GEORGIA STRAIGHT
2nd Floor, 1235 West Pender Street   **PHONE:** (604) 681-2000
Vancouver, BC V6E 2V6   **FAX:** (604) 681-0272

CONTACT: Charles Campbell, Managing Editor   **DESCRIPTION:** Published by Dan McLeod. Circulation 100,000. Contains local articles on arts, events, music, theatre, movies, food, sports, and news. Published weekly. Established in 1967. Published weekly.
WRITERS: 80% freelance written. Buys 2,000 articles per year. Byline is given. Hires writers on assignment, pays expenses while on assignment. Entertainment articles approximately 1,500 words. Cover story 4,000 words. Pays 35¢ per word. Guidelines are not available. Contact the editor with a query letter. "The *Georgia Straight* is a Vancouver news-and-entertainment weekly with a relentlessly local focus. If it isn't happening in Vancouver or making news in BC, we are not interested."
PHOTOGRAPHERS: Buys from stock. Hires on assignment. Buys 250 photos annually. 99% assigned and 1% stock. Uses 8x10 b&w photos. Captions are required. Credit line is given. Pays $35-125 b&w inside; $200 b&w cover. Contact the editor with a sample portfolio. "Almost all of our photos are assigned. Most illustrate our news-oriented cover features."

GEORGIAN BAY TODAY
c/o 29S Bernard Avenue   **PHONE:** (416) 944-1217 Editor's direct
Toronto, ON M5R 1R3   line (905) 457-9721
                                          FAX: (416) 944-0133
CONTACT: Andrea Stenberg, Editor   **DESCRIPTION:** Published by Heisey Publishing. Circulation 3,500-4,500. A tabloid linking recreationists, residents and tourists around the shore of Georgian Bay A seasonal publication issued quarterly. Established in 1988.

WRITERS: "We need stories about recreational activities and tourism. We can't pay much, $25 plus or minus. We have a problem getting good regional balance so it would be a pleasure to hear from writers in the Bruce Peninsula, the Manitoulin Island and at the top of the bay areas. We don't have enough dependable stringers so we would be happy to hear from people with article proposals."
PHOTOGRAPHERS: "We need regional photography in the worst way. I will pay $15-25 for mostly colour but I need a very detailed caption."
NOTES: Sample copies of this publication are available free upon request. Also publishes Building and Construction Trades Today.

GERMINATION
428 Yale Avenue
Riverview, NB E1B 2B5

NOTES: Could not locate. Phone number is not in service 506 386-1687.

GESTION
5255 Decelles Avenue
Montreal, PQ H3T 1V6

PHONE: (514) 340-6677
FAX: (514) 340-6382

CONTACT: Laurent Lapierre   **DESCRIPTION:** Published by Revue Internationale de Gestion. Circulation 6,000. French language publication. Issued quarterly. Established in 1976.
NOTES: This publication doesn't purchase freelance material.

GIFTS & TABLEWARES
1450 Don Mills Road
Don Mills, ON M3B 2X7

PHONE: (416) 445-6641
FAX: (416) 442-2213

CONTACT: Dawn Dickinson, Editor   **DESCRIPTION:** Published by Southam. Circulation 10,700. "We are a magazine directed to retailers. We cover the gift, decorative accessory, tableware and stationery markets in Canada." Provides retailers with product information and sales and display advice. Published 7 times a year. Established in 1976.
WRITERS: "We occasionally purchase material. I want writers with retail and giftware experience." Contact the editor with a query letter.

GLASS CANADA
145 Thames Road West Box 1060
Exeter, ON N0M 1S3

PHONE: (519) 235-2400
FAX: (519) 235-0798

CONTACT: Peter Darbishire, Managing Editor   **DESCRIPTION:** Published by AIS Communications. Circulation 6,500. Published 6 times a year for glazing contractors. Established in 1989.
WRITERS: "We purchase freelance work very infrequently. Generally speaking with all of our publications we don't do much with unsolicited material. We tend to keep a list of freelancers handy. If there's a hole or if we need something done in a certain area we either put it into our travel plans for the next 12 months or we may assign something. We may work easily 12 months ahead on some things as far as getting photos and then getting

stories later and so on. Generally our stories are not time-sensitive. Contact us by mail or fax with ideas or suggestions. I am not really clamoring for stories."
NOTES: Also publishes Agri Book Magazine, Canadian Rental Service, Glass Canada and Water Well.

GLOBAL BIODIVERSITY

Canadian Centre for Biodiversity
Canadian Museum of Nature
Box 3443 Station D
Ottawa, ON K1P 6P4

PHONE: (613) 991-0270
FAX: (613) 991-8819

CONTACT: Don E. McAllister, Editor   DESCRIPTION: Circulation 600. An international forum emphasizing Canadian issues, research and strategies with papers on plants, animals, ecosystems and the wide use of biodiversity. "We are a semi-scientific publication. Our target is people interested in conservation and environmental issues." Published quarterly. Established in 1991.
WRITERS: "Contact the editor with a query letter or by phone before doing an article. Our writers receive copies of the publication. Photos are supplied with the articles."
NOTES: Sample copies of this publication are available for $7.50.

GOLF ALBATROS

Box 115 Stn Cotes Des Neiges
Montreal, PQ H3S 2S4

PHONE: (514) 737-4050
FAX: (514) 737-1639

CONTACT: Marjorie Greau, Editor   DESCRIPTION: Circulation 30,000. French lanugage publication for golfers of all levels. Covers golf tips, techniques, equiptment and travel. Published twice a year. Established in 1984.
WRITERS: "We assign articles. Writers can query us and let us know what they have pertaining to golf and travel."
PHOTOGRAPHERS: "We don't purchase photography."
NOTES: Sold on newsstands in Quebec.

GOLF CANADA

24 Mercer Street #200
Toronto, ON M5V 1H3

PHONE: (416) 596-1555
FAX: (416) 596-1520

CONTACT: Paul Daulmage, Editor   DESCRIPTION: Published by Canadian Golf Press Inc. Published quarterly. Established in 1993.
WRITERS: "Some written work is accepted." Query the editor by phone or letter.

GOLF INTERNATIONAL

798 Arthur Sauve Box 91022
St. Eustache, PQ J7R 6V9

PHONE: (514) 974-7985
FAX: (514) 974-2212

CONTACT: Jacque Landry, Editor   DESCRIPTION: Circulation 26,800. French language publication. A consumer magazine focusing on golf. Mainly distributed in Quebec. Published 6 times a year. Established in 1992.

WRITERS: "We may purchase once in awhile. If writers have an article to suggest they can just call me. I prefer to talk to people first. We are looking for golf related topics, travelling, humour etc." Guidelines are not available.
PHOTOGRAPHERS: "We are pretty well covered for photography."
NOTES: Does not consider previously published work. A free sample is available upon request.

GOOD TIMES
5148 St. Laurent Blvd.   **PHONE:** (514) 273-9773
Montreal, PQ H2T 1R8   **FAX:** (514) 273-3408

CONTACT: Denise Crawford, Editor-in-Chief   **DESCRIPTION:** Published by Senior Publications Inc. Circulation 115,000. Focuses on retired Canadians and those planning retirement. Articles include: financial planning, health and fitness, personal rights, interpersonal relationships, celebrities, and leisure activities. Published 10 times a year.
WRITERS: "We are a retirement publication - articles are assigned to writers with solid experience in areas of interest to a mature readership - writers should be familiar with our format and focus. All articles are assigned." Byline is given. Article lengths vary. Payment to be negotiated. If an assigned article is cancelled a 50% kill fee is paid. "Query by letter ONLY, with SASE (no phone or fax queries). Our magazine is available on newsstands, in libraries, etc. Read several issues to be familiar with format and focus."
PHOTOGRAPHERS: Does not purchase photography.
NOTES: Unsolicited materials will be returned with SASE. Does not consider previously published work or simultaneous submissions. For sample copy please send large SASE and $3.50.

GOODLIFE MAGAZINE
1300 Yonge Street, Suite 500,
Toronto, ON M4T 1X3

NOTES: Could not locate. Phone number is not in service (416) 961-5002.

GOSPEL HERALD
4904 King Street   **PHONE:** (905) 563-7503
Beamsville, ON L0R 1B6   **FAX:** (905) 563-7503

CONTACT: Wayne Turner, Editor   **DESCRIPTION:** Published by Gospel Herald Foundation. Circulation 1,500. Monthly religious publication. Articles promote New Testament Christianity including teaching material for youth. Contains news and family life information. Established in 1936.
NOTES: All articles and photos are submitted on a gratis basis.

GOVERNMENT BUSINESS
4040 Creditview Road Unit #11 Box 1800   **PHONE:** (905) 569-1800
Mississauga, ON   L5C 3Y8   **FAX:** (905) 569-1818

CONTACT: Hugh Parkinson, Editor   **DESCRIPTION:** Circulation 22,000. "A business publication profiling the goods and services being used by municipal, provincial and federal government agencies across Canada." Published bi-monthly.
WRITERS: "We don't purchase articles very often. Contact me by phone first. If writers have a piece prepared that involves a government agency or application and they want to send it or fax it over that is fine. We are a non-political publication, we deal with government applications of goods and services. If an article profiles a particular department, agency or facility, that is good as most of our material is focused on the use of products in a particular situation. We also look at management ideas and productivity gains as well." Guidelines are not available.

GOVERNMENT PURCHASING GUIDE
10 Gateway Blvd. #490   **PHONE:** (416) 696-5488
North York, ON   M3C 3T4   **FAX:** (416) 696-7395

CONTACT: Margaret Williamson, Assistant Editor   **DESCRIPTION:** Published by Moorshead Magazines. Circulation 28,000. "A product guide for various levels of government; federal, provincial and municipal. It tells about new technology and products out there that would pertain to each of the offices."
WRITERS: "At this time we mainly deal with in-house writers, we really don't take any freelance material."
NOTES: Also publishes Computing Now and Pets Magazine.

GRAIL: AN ECUMENICAL JOURNAL
University of St. Jerome's College Press
Waterloo, ON   N2L 3G3

CONTACT: MW Higgins, Editor   **DESCRIPTION:** Circulation 1,500. Multidisciplinary journal inspired by Vatican II's urging for investigating of the human condition in modern scholarship. Published quarterly. Established in 1985.

GRAIN
Box 1154   **PHONE:** (306) 244-2828
Regina, SK   S4P 3B4   **FAX:** (306) 565-8554

CONTACT: Geoffrey Ursell, Editor   **DESCRIPTION:** Published by Saskatchewan Writer's Guild. Literary publication containing quality literary and visual art. Fiction, poetry, creative non-fiction, songs, and excerpts from produced plays accepted. Published quarterly.
WRITERS: Pays $30-$100 on publication. Guidelines available.

GRAINEWS

Box 6600 2500-201 Portage Avenue
Winnipeg, MB R3C 3A7

PHONE: (204) 944-5569
FAX: (204) 944-5416

CONTACT: Roger Olson, Editor   DESCRIPTION: Published by Palmer Anderson.
Circulation 60,000. Published 17 times a year. Company established 1975.
WRITERS: 20% freelance written. Buys 23-30 articles a year. Byline is given. Buys fiction
and non-fiction. Writers are hired on assignment. Average article length is 700 words.
Pays $100+ for articles. If an article is accepted and then not published a full kill fee is
paid. Contact the editor by phone, mail or fax a query. The editor is looking for: "how-to's
covering rural and farm subjects; historical agriculture - old times; humour, cartoons and
articles." Writers' guidelines are available.
PHOTOGRAPHERS: Photography is supplied with article.
NOTES: Buys one-time rights. Unsolicited materials will be returned with SASE. Considers
previously published work and will occasionally consider simultaneous submissions. Sample
copy is free upon request.

THE GRAPHIC EXCHANGE

65090-358 Danforth Avenue
Toronto, ON M4K 3Z2

PHONE: (416) 961-1325
FAX: (416) 961-0941

CONTACT: Dan Brill, Editor   DESCRIPTION: Published by Brill Communications.
Circulation 15,000. "A high-end graphic publication reporting on computer design and
electronic illustration. A trade news magazine for the pre-press industry." Published 8
times a year.
WRITERS: "We do purchase but we have a few regualr writers already."
PHOTOGRAPHERS: "We are not accepting freelance photography right now."

THE GRAPHIC MONTHLY

1606 Sedlescomb Drive, #8
Mississauga, ON L4X 1M6

PHONE: (905) 625-7070
FAX: (905) 625-4856

CONTACT: Alexander Donald, Editor   DESCRIPTION: Published by North Island
Publishing. National graphic arts magazine featuring new trends and how-to articles.
Published 6 times a year. Established in 1980.
NOTES: Also publishes Mississauga Business Times.

GREAT LAKES NAVIGATION

1434 St. Catherine Street West #512
Montreal, PQ H3G 1R4

PHONE: (514) 861-6715
FAX: (514) 861-0966

CONTACT: Megan Perkins, Editor   DESCRIPTION: Published by Canadian Marine
Publications Ltd. Published annually.
NOTES: This publication is not open to receiving freelance material. Also publishes Ports
Annual.

GREATER WINNIPEG BUSINESS
117 Hutchings Street
Winnipeg, MB   R2X 2V4

NOTES: Could not locate. Phone number is not in service (204) 633-5575.

GREENHOUSE CANADA
222 Argyle Avenue
Delhi, ON   N4B 2Y2

PHONE: (519) 582-2513
FAX: (519) 582-4040

CONTACT: Blair Adams, Editor   **DESCRIPTION:** Published by NCC Publishing. Circulation 4,000. Published for greenhouse operators across Canada. Published monthly. Established in 1980.

GREENMASTER
80 W Beaver Creek #18
Richmond Hill, ON   L4B 1H3

PHONE: (905) 771-7333
FAX: (905) 771-7336

CONTACT: Dennis Mellersh, Editor   **DESCRIPTION:** Published by Kenilworth Publishing Inc. Circulation 3,500. Published 6 times a year for the Canadian Golf Course Superintendants Association. Established in 1967.
NOTES: This publication does not often purchase freelance material. All decisions are made by the Association's editorial advisory board. Also publishes Municipal Monitor, Registered Nurse and Signs Canada.

GROCER TODAY
401 - 4180 Lougheed Highway
Burnaby, BC   V5C 6A7

PHONE: (604) 299-7311
FAX: (604) 299-9188

CONTACT: Marisa Paterson, Editor   **DESCRIPTION:** Published by Canada Wide Magazines Ltd. Circulation 11,500. Focuses on trends and controversial issues in the grocery industry. Includes corporate profiles, category features, new products and regional news. Serves readers in western Canada. Readers include food buyers and executives, independent retailers, wholesale grocers, food brokers and manufactures, and processors of food and beverage products.
WRITERS: Most stories are assigned - your ideas are welcomed. "If you have a story idea, please submit a brief but specific story outline. It is also helpful if you include published samples of your work. We prefer written outlines to phone calls." Rarely use unsolicited manuscripts. Stories range from 750 to 1,600 words. Pay ranges from $150 for a mini profile to $600 for corporate profiles. A kill fee is paid if an assigned story is not used. House style is based on CP guidelines and the Oxford English Dictionary. You will be expected to provide your story on disk (Mac MS Word 5.0 or ASCII) along with a hard copy. Writers Guidelines are available.
PHOTOGRAPHERS: Does purchase some photography, cover and for feature stories. Many photos are supplied with articles or by advertisers. Formats used include colour transparencies and prints and b&w prints.

GROUP TRAVEL/VOYAGE EN GROUPE
425 Harris Street
St. Laurent, PQ H4N 2G8

PHONE: (514) 744-3867
FAX: none

CONTACT: André Quesnel, Editor   **DESCRIPTION:** Published by Voyage en Groupe. Circulation 10,500. French language publication. Travel and tourism magazine published bi-monthly. Established in 1982.
NOTES: This publication does not accept freelance material.

THE GROWER
355 Elmira Road, #103
Guelph, ON N1K 1S5

PHONE: (519) 763-8728
FAX: (519) 763-6604

CONTACT: Blair Adams, Editor   **DESCRIPTION:** Published by Ontario Fruit & Vegetable Grower's Association. Circulation 9,000. "All articles are geared toward Canadian agriculture, in particular horticulture, and cover a variety of subjects ranging from new products to hard agricultural news and research." Published monthly. Established in 1878.
PHOTOGRAPHERS: Photography accepted.   Query with samples of work.

GROWTH SPURTS
Box 325 Station P
Toronto, ON M5S 2S8

PHONE: (416) 488-1047
FAX: (416) 978-7821

CONTACT: Ruth Bradley-St-Cyr, Editor   **DESCRIPTION:** Circulation 6,000. Parenting magazine written by parents and others with practical experience. Intimate, fresh "with a variety of voices not found in many other parenting magazines. Publishes non-fiction features, short fiction, poetry, reviews of Canadian books and other materials and a variety of regular columns. "Growth Spurts seeks to provide support and information for parents who choose "alternative" parenting styles such as midwifery, breastfeeding, naturopathic health care, discipline without violence, the family bed, home schooling etc. We are not interested in formula, disposable products, or gender-specific toys." Published quarterly. Established in 1988.
WRITERS: Uses freelance material extensively, however does not pay. Asks for one time-rights and will barter either subscription or ad space. Submissions on 3½ inch disk are required. "We are looking for personal expertise and experience, not 'journalistic' pieces." Writers' guidelines are available. "We strongly prefer Canadian contributors."
PHOTOGRAPHERS: Uses photography. Does not pay. Will barter photos for subscription or ad space. Credit lines are given. Contact by sending the editor a query letter.
NOTES: Buys first North American serial rights and reprint rights. Unsolicited materials will be returned with SASE. Considers previously published work and simultaneous submissions. "We are also on the lookout for new column ideas and regular columnists." Sample copy available for $3.95 and 9x12" SASE (88¢ postage).

LE GUIDE BOUNTY DE LA GROSSESSE
746 Warden Avenue #2
Scarborough, ON M1L 4A2

NOTES: NO LONGER PUBLISHED

LE GUIDE BOUNTY DES SOINS AU NOURRISSON
746 Warden Avenue #2
Scarborough, ON M1L 4A2

NOTES: NO LONGER PUBLISHED

GUIDE RESOURCES
4388 St. Denis #305
Montreal, PQ H2J 2L1

PHONE: (514) 847-0060
FAX: (514) 847-0062

CONTACT: Lucie Dumoulin, Managing Editor   **DESCRIPTION:** Published by SWAA Communications Inc. Circulation 16,000. French language publication. Issued 10 times a year. Established in 1985.

GUIDE VOYAGE
11 des Plaines St
St.-Etienne-de-Lauzon, PQ G6J 1L8

PHONE: (418) 836-0654
FAX: (418) 831-7195

CONTACT: Daniel Belanger, Editor   **DESCRIPTION:** Published by Guide Voyage Super Destinations Ltd. Circulation 100,000. Published twice yearly in English and French. Established in 1992.
WRITERS: All writing and photography is done in-house.
NOTES: This publication does not purchase freelance work at this time. Freelancers are welcome to contact by phone or letter.

HALLELUJAH
Box 25, 65 Front Street West #0116
Toronto, ON M5J 1E6

PHONE: (416) 778-8042

CONTACT: Bruce Arnold   **DESCRIPTION:** Published by D. Bruce Arnold Publications. Circulation 2,000. General interest Christian publication issued quarterly. Features news, music reviews and editorial comments of interest to Christians. Established in 1986.
NOTES: "Our budget doesn't allow for the purchase of freelance material."

HAMILTON BUSINESS REPORT
875 Main Street West
Hamilton, ON L8S 4R1

PHONE: (905) 522-6117
FAX: (905) 529-2242

CONTACT: Rachel Leaney   **DESCRIPTION:** Published by Town Publishing Inc. Circulation Published quarterly. Established in 1986.

HAMILTON THIS MONTH
875 Main Street West
Hamilton, ON L8S 4R1

PHONE: (905) 522-6117
FAX: (905) 529-2242

CONTACT: Elizabeth Kelly, Editor   **DESCRIPTION:** Published by Town Publishing Inc. Circulation 40,000. A local-interest magazine featuring events, fashion, restaurants and people in the news. Published 5 times a year. Established in 1984.

WRITERS: "We purchase 2-3 articles per issue. The length and pay rate depends on the type of article. Either send samples or a letter to the editor. We like to see general lifestyle and entertainment stories and opinion columns. We're not too big on sports or political articles although we have done a bit in the past."

PHOTOGRAPHERS: "We purchase two or three photos per issue from freelance photographers and 1 or 2 from stock agencies. Tranparencies are great - we can use almost any format. Our freelancers usually take pictures of people and our stock photos are chosen to go with a story line. Payment is negotiable - depends on what it is being used for. Contact the editor either by phone or mail."

NOTES: This publication is presently looking for freelance artists for their portfolio as they have exhausted what they currently have on file. Also publishes Report Business Quarterly.

HARROWSMITH COUNTRY LIFE
25 Sheppard Avenue West #100   **PHONE:** (416) 733-7600
North York, ON M2N 6S7   **FAX:** (416) 733-8272

CONTACT: Arlene Stacy, Editor   **DESCRIPTION:** Published by Telemedia. Circulation 128,300. "Harrowsmith is a national award-winning magazine. Articles cover: the environment; alternative energy; organic gardening; agriculture; architecture; small animal husbandry; and ecology." Published bi-monthly. Established in 1976.

HAZARDOUS MATERIALS MANAGEMENT
401 Richmond Street West #139   **PHONE:** (416) 348-9922
Toronto, ON M5V 1X3   **FAX:** (416) 348-9744

CONTACT: Todd C. Latham, Publisher   **DESCRIPTION:** Published by CHMM Inc. Circulation 18,700. "The magazine encompasses all disciplines of environmental engineering including air, water, soil, sludge and solid waste management, with regular features on new regulations, personal protection, water treatment, site remediation and waste minimization, recycling and disposal. Readers include corporate executives, compliance and safety officers, industrial plant managers and engineers, municipal, provincial and federal environment officials and working scientists." Published 6 times a year. Established in 1989.

WRITERS: Purchases 2 unsolicited articles per year. Byline is given. Writers are hired on assignment, expenses are not paid. Average article is 1,200 words. Query by phone or fax. Guidelines available. "Make sure you understand the magazine and its readers before even calling. We don't pay for weak research and don't have a lot of patience for amateurs. Material must be informative, lively and very relevant."

PHOTOGRAPHERS: 6-8 photos are purchased annually. Most photos are included in text/photo submissions. Model releases and captions are not necessary. Uses all formats colour and b&w. Credit line is given. Contact editor with sample portfolio. Pays $300 for colour covers. Looking for "high impact, very striking, theme-specific."

NOTES: Buys all rights. Unsolicited materials will be returned with SASE. Will not consider previously published work. For sample copies enclose $10 for one issue or $42.27 for a years subscription.

HEAD OFFICE AT HOME
20 Crown Steel Drive Unit 10
Markham, ON L3R 9X9

PHONE: (905) 477-4349
FAX: none

CONTACT: Elizabeth Harris, Editor   **DESCRIPTION:** Published by Abco Communications Ltd. Circulation 50,000. Published 6 times a year.
NOTES: "All our articles are freelanced out, generally to people who have been working with us for a long time."

HEALTH ADVOCATE: NO LONGER PUBLISHED

HEALTH NATURALLY
Box 580
Perry Sound, ON P2A 2X5

PHONE: (705) 342-1360
FAX: (705) 342-9552

CONTACT: Lorrie Imbert, Editor **DESCRIPTION:** Circulation 53,000. An alternative health publication. Contains articles on health care, herbs, and alternative healing. Published 6 times a year. Established in 1992.
WRITERS: "We don't often purchase articles. We have a number of writers who are well qualified in their field. Request the writers' guidelines before contacting with a query.
PHOTOGRAPHERS: "We occasionally purchase photos. We have a number of established photographers." Send a query letter. Guidelines are not available.

HEALTH WATCH
25 Sheppard Avenue West #100
Toronto, ON M2N 6S7

PHONE: (416) 733-7600
FAX: (416) 218-3633

CONTACT: Constance Droganes   **DESCRIPTION:** Published by Telemedia. Circulation 455,000. Consumer health magazine published quarterly. Established in 1989.

HEALTHCARE MANAGEMENT FORUM
350 Sparks Street #402
Ottawa, ON K1R 7S8

NOTES: Could not locate. Phone number is not in service (613) 742-8800.

HEALTHSHARING
14 Skey Lane
Toronto, ON M6J 3S4
NOTES: Could not locate. Phone number is not in service (416) 532-0812.

HEATING-PLUMBING AIR CONDITIONING
1370 Don Mills Road #300
Don Mills, ON M3B 3N7

PHONE: (416) 759-2500
FAX: (416) 759-6979

CONTACT: Bruce Cole, Editor   **DESCRIPTION:** Published by Cowgate Communications Inc. Circulation 16,300. Focuses on product information and feature articles including

application stories of interest to contractors involved in heating, plumbing, air conditioning, refrigeration and ventilation. Published 7 times a year. Established in 1927.
WRITERS: 25% freelance written. Buys 14 articles a year. Byline is given. Writers are hired on assignment, expenses are paid while on assignment. Average article length is 1,000 words. Pays 25¢ a word. A kill fee of 50% is paid for cancelled articles. Contact with query letter or send completed article on spec. Editor is looking for "anything of interest to mechanical contractors; easy-to-read writing style; technical affinity." Guidelines available and phone inquiries welcome.
PHOTOGRAPHERS: Buys from stock. All formats colour and b&w are used. Model releases and captions are preferred. Credit line is given. Contact the editor with a query and stock listing.
NOTES: Buys one-time rights. Unsolicited materials will be returned with SASE. Considers previously published work and simultaneous submissions. For sample copy enclose 9x12" SASE and $1.40 postage.

HECATE'S LOOM
Box 5206 Station B   **PHONE:** (604) 477-8488
Victoria, BC   V8R 6N4   **FAX:** (604) 721-1029

CONTACT: Attn: Yvonne   **DESCRIPTION:** Published by Hecate's Loom Publishing Collective. Circulation 1,500. A quarterly for all pagan and nature oriented religions in Canada. Publishes pieces about pagan, witches, goddess and earth-centered worshippers in English and French text. Established in 1986.
WRITERS: "We are entirely volunteer run. Those who wish to submit can call us to see if we are interested in what they have got or they can send unsolicited material although there won't be a quick response to it. We do welcome submissions or inquiries by phone, fax or mail. We look for news articles to do with pagan religions. We are very much readership run. We encourage our readers to write about the things they know. News, articles, and reviews. We presently have a two year backlog of poetry so I would discourage sending anymore. Anyone who contributes gets a copy of the publication."
PHOTOGRAPHERS: "We use colour photography for the cover and black and white inside. This is a volunteer effort."
NOTES: Sample copies of this publication are available for $3.95 including shipping.

HI-RISE
95 Leeward Glenway, #121   **PHONE:** (416) 424-1393
Don Mills, ON M3C 2Z6   **FAX:** (416) 467-8262

CONTACT: Valerie Dunn   **DESCRIPTION:** Circulation 25,000. A metro-Toronto publication for apartment and townhouse residents emphasizing positive lifestyles. Includes articles on people, health, things to do, politics, cooking, etc. Published monthly. Established in 1980.
WRITERS: "We do purchase work. Payment is minimal. We don't need travel articles, we already have travel writers. We don't have specific needs at the moment, just anything that relates to our goals. It's best if people send something they think would be of interest to the readership. I would rather have a completed story, about 400 words. We have a very small staff so don't be worried if you don't hear from us right away, please be patient."
PHOTOGRAPHERS: "We rarely purchase photos."
NOTES: "We are looking for cartoons and are interested in them, although we don't pay a lot." Also publishes The Business & Professional Woman.

HIBOU
300 Arran Street
St-Lambert, PQ J4R 1K5

PHONE: (514) 875-0327
FAX: (514) 672-5448

CONTACT: Yves Boillon   **DESCRIPTION:** Published by Les Editions Héritage Inc. Circulation 35,000. A magazine for children between the age of 8 and 13. Contains nature and animal articles, games and stories. Published 10 times a year in French. Established in 1980.
NOTES: Also publishes Coulicou Magazine.

THE HOCKEY NEWS
85 Scarsdale Road, #100
Toronto, ON M3B 2R2

PHONE: (416) 445-5702
FAX: (416) 445-0753

CONTACT: Steve Dryden, Editor-in-Chief   **DESCRIPTION:** Published by Transcontinental Publications Ltd. . Circulation 108,000. Features all levels of hockey, from minor, college and amateur to international professional teams. A weekly tabloid distributed around the world. Established in 1947.
WRITERS: "Does purchase some work but very rarely. We do assign stories, normally to our regular correspondents. Call first to see if there is any interest."
PHOTOGRAPHERS: "We do purchase photography, both colour and black & white, on a freelance basis. 99% is assignment. If someone would come to us with an outstanding photograph I am sure we would consider it. Payment ranges from $50 to a couple of hundred. We are looking for anything hockey related, Canadian or international." Contact by telephone to see if there is interest.
NOTES: Doesn't consider previously published work. For a sample copy please send the $2.95 cover price of the magazine. Also publishes Ontario Fisherman.

HOG MARKET PLACE QUARTERLY see Pork Producers

HOLSTEIN JOURNAL
9120 Leslie Street #105
Richmond Hill, ON L4B 3J9

PHONE: (905) 886-4222
FAX: (905) 886-0037

CONTACT: Bonnie Cooper, Editor   **DESCRIPTION:** Published by The Holstein Journal Group Inc. Circulation 10,600. "News and information related to the purebred Holstein breeding industry. Articles include herd stories; breeder profiles; show, sale and industry meeting reports; genetic and research information; production news; and other related industry reports." Published monthly in English and French. Established in 1938.
WRITERS: 10% freelance written. Purchases 10 articles per year. Byline is given. Hires writers on assignment. Articles range from 1,200-2,500 words. Pays $150 per page. Guidelines are not available. Full kill fee paid. Contact editor with phone query. "Writers should contact us in advance as our needs are very specific. Stories must be of interest and value to our readers, who are the middle to top level purebred Holstein breeders in Canada."
PHOTOGRAPHERS: Buys 5-6 photos per issue. Uses 5x7 and 8x10 colour prints and 5x7 and 8x10 glossy b&ws. Captions are required. Credit line is given. Pays $100 for colour cover. "Almost all of our photos are professionally taken by livestock photographers

who are trained specifically in this area. Pictures for our cover must have Holstein cattle in them."

HOME BUILDER MAGAZINE
Box 400, Victoria Station
Westmount, PQ H3Z 2V8

PHONE: (514) 489-4941
FAX: (514) 489-5505

CONTACT: Frank O'Brien, Editor   **DESCRIPTION:** Circulation 16,900. Published for the Canadian home building industry. Published bi-monthly. Established in 1988. **NOTES:** May purchase photos and articles on occasion.

HOME COMPUTING AND ENTERTAINMENT
2005 Sheppard Ave East, 4 Fl
Willowdale, ON M2J 5B1

PHONE: (416) 497-9562
FAX: (416) 497-9427

CONTACT: Rosalind Stefanac, Assistant Editor   **DESCRIPTION:** Published by Plesman Publications Ltd. Circulation 150,000. A consumer magazine dealing with audio, computers and home entertainment. Provides information on new technology to home users. Published 9 times a year. Established in 1993.
WRITERS: "We depend a lot on freelance work. Purchase a minimum of four articles per issue. A byline is given. We hire on assignment from our established pool of writers. Average length is 1,500 words paying between $800-$1,000 per article. Our regular features/columns include an educational software review section, a games review and a movie/video review. Contact us with a concrete idea on paper or call us with detailed information. We want to see anything new and innovative. We don't want anything re-hashed from other magazines or previous issues. We are always looking for unique ideas on consumer related products and applications."

HOME HEALTH CARE MERCHANDISING
26 Dorchester Avenue
Toronto, ON M8Z 4W3

NOTES: Could not locate.

HOME RENOVATOR MAGAZINE
822A Maitland Street, Suite 200
London, ON N6B 3L2

NOTES: Could not locate. Phone number is not in service (519) 432-6849.

HOMEMAKER'S MAGAZINE
25 Sheppard Avenue West #100
North York, ON M2N 6S7

PHONE: (416) 733-7600
FAX: (416) 733-8683

CONTACT: Sally Armstrong, Editor-in-Chief   **DESCRIPTION:** Published by Telemedia Communications. Circulation 1,300,000 English and 300,000 French for Madame au Foyer. "We consider ourselves the thinking woman's magazine. We usually carry features covering current issues. We also carry food, beauty, decor, fashion, and health features. Directed at women between 25 and 54 with children at home." Published 8 times a year. Established in 1965.

WRITERS: "We purchase material. The editor reviews unsolicited manuscripts. If there is something they feel can be used in the magazine they will get in touch with the writer. The editor prefers to have a proposal letter before the full manuscript is sent. Length (averages 2,500 words) and payment is negotiable with the editor and depends on the story." Guidelines are available. "We prefer to receive an outline first, together with samples of your published work. The outline should indicate how you intend to handle the suggested subject, and include some of the probable sources/authorities to be consulted in research. We would appreciate a SASE for our reply."

PHOTOGRAPHERS: "We don't accept freelance inquiries."

NOTES: Sample copies of this publication are available free upon request. Purchases first North American serial rights. Considers previously published work. Does not consider simultaneous submissions. Also publishes Madame au Foyer, the French version.

HOMES AND COTTAGES

#D-6557-Mississauga Road
Mississauga, ON L5N 1A6

PHONE: (905) 567-1440
FAX: (905) 567-1442

CONTACT: Janice Naisby, Editor   **DESCRIPTION:** Published by Steven J. Griffin. Circulation 54,000. Magazine contains home building information. Published 8 times a year. Established in 1987.

WRITERS: 80% freelance written. Average articles range from 1,200 to 1,500 words. Pays $600 per article. Kill fee paid if assigned article is cancelled. Please contact with query letter only. Guidelines are available.

PHOTOGRAPHERS: Photographers are hired on assignment. Uses all colour formats. Credit line is given. Payment negotiated. Please send query letter.

NOTES: Buys first North American serial rights. Unsolicited materials will be returned with SASE. Does not considers previously published work or simultaneous submissions. Sample copy is free, please send large SASE.

HOMES MAGAZINE

178 Main Street
Unionville, ON L3R 2G9

PHONE: (905) 479-4663
FAX: (905) 479-4482

CONTACT: Rise Levy, Editor   **DESCRIPTION:** Published by Michael Rosset. Home renovation and housing magazine. Published 8 times a year.

PHOTOGRAPHERS: Photography is done in-house.

HORIZON MAGAZINE

2857 Sherwood Heights Drive Unit #3
Oakville, ON L6J 7J9

PHONE: (905) 829-0403

CONTACT: Alan MacPherson, Editor   **DESCRIPTION:** Published by PJ Spratt and Associates Inc. A component of an education program published three times a year and distributed to elementary and secondary school teachers across Canada. Established in 1994.

WRITERS: "Writers are usually recruited to submit articles for publication. On occasion when I have had the need for freelancers I usually access them through our own independent sources. A resumé through the mail is fine. I am more interested in reading abstracts of what they have done in the past and whether or not they are applicable to the contents of this magazine. A maximum pay ceiling is set on articles 1,500-2,000 words."

PHOTOGRAPHERS: Black & white photos are purchased approximately 10 times per year.

HORSE ACTION
Box 1778
Vernon, BC V1T 8C3

PHONE: (604) 545-9896
FAX: (604) 545-9896

CONTACT: Dr. B.J. (Jan) White   **DESCRIPTION:** Published by Whitehouse Publishing Co. (1974) Ltd. Circulation 10,000. Gives wide coverage of current and coming events, news and information of all breeds and disciplines. Published monthly. Established in 1989.
WRITERS: 25% freelance written. Buys 50 articles per year. Gives a byline. Buys nonfiction. Hires writers on assignment. Articles range from 1000 to 1500 words. Pays $25 to $100 per article. Looks for "clarity and humour; good English, spelling, grammar and punctuation." Would like to see "profiles/interviews of International riders, coaches, places etc." Contact by sending completed articles on spec. Writers' guidelines are available. Please send SASE.
PHOTOGRAPHERS: Purchases from stock and hires on assignment. Buys 60 photos annually. Uses 5x7 and 8x10 colour prints and all formats b&w prints. Captions are preferred. Pay can be negotiated but averages $5-10 for inside b&w or colour and $40-100 for colour covers. Wants to see "unusual photos with clarity, definition and humour." Doesn't like "dark horses against a dark background." Photographers' guidelines are available. Please send SASE.
NOTES: Purchases one-time rights, first North American rights and occasionally exclusive rights. Unsolicited materials will be returned with SASE. Previously published work is considered. Simultaneous submissions are sometimes considered. Sample copy is available. Please send 9x11" SASE with $2 CDN postage.

HORSE POWER
Box 670, 225 Industrial Parkway South
Aurora, ON L4G 4J9

PHONE: (905) 727-0107
FAX: (905) 841-1530

CONTACT: Lee Benson   **DESCRIPTION:** Published by Horse Publications. Circulation 10,000. A magazine for young horse lovers. General, clearly explained instruction articles on horse care and riding, with an emphasis on safety. Some entertaining "fiction" accepted with preference given to actual events and people. Average age of readers is 12 years. Published 6 times a year. Established in 1988.
WRITERS: 20% freelance written. Byline is given. Pays 15¢ a word. Guidelines are available. Contact with a query letter. "No poetry or sappy fiction! We like to see tight, concise reporting on issues and well researched articles with up-to-date information. Quotes from recognized names or experts are helpful."
PHOTOGRAPHERS: 69% assigned to freelance photographers. Also purchases photos as part of text/photo submission. Uses all formats colour and b&w. Pays $15 for b&w; $25 for colour inside and $75-125 for colour cover. "I want to see bright, in focus and sharp photos only. No arty shots, dark or badly exposed photos."
NOTES: Purchases first North American serial rights. Unsolicited material will be returned with SASE. Considers previously published work. Will not consider simultaneous submissions. Also publishes Canadian Thoroughbred.

HORSE SPORT see Canadian Thoroughbred

HORSES ALL
4000-19th Street NE
Calgary, AB T2E 6P8

PHONE: (403) 250-6633
FAX: (403) 291-0502

CONTACT: Mickey Dumont, Editor **DESCRIPTION:** Published by Quarter Horse Association of Alberta and North Hill News; Dennis McCormack. Circulation 10,000. Monthly Equestrian magazine about horses and clubs. Official publication for 42 national and regional associations. Established in 1977.
WRITERS: We do accept work from freelancers. "Many of our submissions are from vets or club members who are not paid. We do hire the occasional freelancer to write some of the feature articles." Pays from $20-$100 for articles and $5 for photos. Articles are around 1,000 words. You can approach this magazine by sending a query letter with several ideas. The editor will respond by mail or phone. Rights are negotiated. Writers' guidelines are not available.
PHOTOGRAPHERS: Photos are not purchased. "Photos are usually supplied by our regular writers as part of text/photo package. We use mostly black & white prints. The cover and several inside shots are colour.

HOSPITAL NEWS
23 Apex Road
Toronto, ON M6A 2V6

PHONE: (416) 781-5516
FAX: (416) 781-5499

CONTACT: Donna Kell, Editor **DESCRIPTION:** Published by Auto Mart Magazine Ltd. Circulation 50,000. A health care publication targeted to those who work in and visit Ontario hospitals. Publication features news on programs, legislation, work environment and research. Published monthly. Established in 1987.
NOTES: "We do purchase work but we are small and we aren't looking for anybody to do freelance work."

HOSPITAL TRUSTEE see Leadership In Health Services

L'HOSPITALITE
1600 Henri-Bourassa Blvd W #404
Montreal, PQ H3M 3E2

PHONE: (514) 332-8376
FAX: (514) 332-2666

CONTACT: Gilles Verronneau **DESCRIPTION:** Published by Communications Vero Inc. Circulation 17,200. French language publication. A magazine focusing on restaurant and hotel owners, managers, caterers, and chefs. Published 6 times a year. Established in 1976.
WRITERS: "We have two or three regular contributors we call upon for various assignments. Sometimes people will solicit us with ideas on topics related to the magazine. If we feel it's interesting we will negotiate a price or buy it. Most of our publications have editorial themes and stories are ordered ahead of time. The most expedient way to contact us is by phone with supporting documentation by fax. Most of the time people send me photocopies of articles on subjects that may be of interest to us. All of our publications are trade magazines. We don't want material that is too technical. Most of our assignments are for action stories, job descriptions and on-sight reporting. We prefer articles on diskette,

Mac or IBM in WordPerfect or Microsoft Word. Usually most of the stories won't go beyond three type-written pages, double spaced. We have a standard rate of $40 per typewritten page, depending on the writer. If there are expenses involved we would give a higher rate to cover incidental costs." Guidelines are not available.

PHOTOGRAPHERS: "Most of the time we try to buy photography together with the article. If we have a three page text we will ask for at least one picture or more depending on the subject."

NOTES: "Usually we buy exclusive rights for one given issue. We would perhaps consider something that was previously published if it wasn't in a competitive magazine." Sample copies are available free upon request. Also publishes La Fournee, La Revue Municipale and Le Mart.

HOT WATER

2585 Skymark Avenue, #306   **PHONE:** (905) 624-8218
Mississauga, ON L4W 4L5   **FAX:** (905) 624-6764

CONTACT: Peter Tasler, Editorial Director   **DESCRIPTION:** Published by Camping Canada Ltd. Covers personal watercraft like Sea Doos and Jet Skis.

WRITERS: "We do accept freelance. A large portion is freelance by assignment. I prefer people to query first, with a sample of their work, before they submit. Article length is anywhere from 1,200-1,500 words. Pay rates vary depending on the writer and the subject matter. We are looking for travel pieces and personal RV related experience. Everything has to have an RV slant to it." Guidelines are not available.

PHOTOGRAPHERS: "We don't purchase photos individually. They come as part of an arrangement we make with the writer. A lot of our writers are photographers as well." Colour is preferred.

NOTES: May take previously published work depending on where it has been published. Prefers single submissions. Sample copies are given to those who are on assignment. Also publishes Camping Canada and Power Boating Canada.

HOTELIER

23 Lesmill Road #101   **PHONE:** (416) 447-0888
Don Mills, ON N3E 3P6   **FAX:** (416) 447-5333

CONTACT: Rosanna Caira, Editor   **DESCRIPTION:** Published by Kostuch Publications. Circulation 8,000. Goes to hotel professionals including owners, operators, executive chefs and executive housekeepers. Published 6 times a year.

WRITERS: "We do hire writers on assignment. Contact us with a query letter with resumé and samples of work. Standard length is 1,500 words, the rate is 35¢ a word. We are looking for a lot of how-to articles and trend analysis geared to Canadian industry as much as possible. We don't take case studies. We occasionally take articles on spec." Guidelines are available.

PHOTOGRAPHERS: "We purchase colour transparencies, no negatives. We hire photographers on assignment all the time. Pay rates depend on the kind of photo and where it is being used, it really ranges. Most shots are of people or restaurant operations. Credit lines are given." Contact the art director, Linda Irvin.

NOTES: Purchases first North American serial rights. Considers previously published work, depending on where it was published. Sample copies of this publication are available free upon request. Also publishes Foodservice and Hospitality and Canadian Hotel and Restaurant.

HUM-THE GOVERNMENT COMPUTER MAGAZINE

557 Cambridge Street South #202
Ottawa, ON K1S 4J4

PHONE: (613) 237-4862
FAX: (613) 237-4232

CONTACT: Tim Lougheed, Co-Editor   **DESCRIPTION:** Published by Hum Communications. Circulation 15,000. Aimed at decision makers and managers in information technology in the public sector (any level) across Canada. Describes the application and purposes of information technology. Written at an easily understood technical level. Published 11 times a year. Established in 1991.
WRITERS: "We publish between 10-20 articles per year. We do take articles on spec. We take things in excess of 2,000 words all the way down to a few paragraphs. Pays 20¢ a word. Contact the co-editor directly at 613-746-7227 or fax 613-746-4744 or INTERNET 73423.17@compuserve.com. We tend not to do product reviews or highly technical pieces. We are interested more in trends and what the implications are for the way business or policy processes take place. We emphasize the meaning of technology rather than describing it in lurid detail. Keep that in mind before reviewing a piece of software or hardware. There is always emphasis on government; whether it is an actual story about a government department or a regulation controlled by the government or some aspect that involves government. That is really the hook of the whole publication."
PHOTOGRAPHERS: "We do purchase photography."
NOTES: A sample copy is free upon request.

HUMAN RESOURCES PROFESSIONAL

2 Bloor Street West #1902
Toronto, ON M4W 3E2

PHONE: (416) 923-2324
FAX: (416) 923-7264

CONTACT: Joanne Eidinger, Editor   **DESCRIPTION:** Published by Human Resources Professionals Association of Ontario. Circulation 7,900. Magazine for the human resource professional. Publishes articles on any issue related to employment, employment law, recruiting, wrongful dismissal, employee motivation, re-engineering and training and development. Published monthly. Established in 1985.
WRITERS: "We purchase freelance work all the time, always on assignment. A minimum of two articles per issue and a maximum of three. Average length is 1,500 words paying 50¢ a word. Contact with a query, a proposal, and examples of your most recently published work. Before submitting anything call and ask for an editorial calendar and a copy of the magazine so that you have a sense of what our readership is all about. Do not send an unsolicited manuscript because 99.9% of the time we don't reply."
PHOTOGRAPHERS: "We assign photographers. Call and make an appointment to bring in your portfolio."
NOTES: Previously published work and simultaneous submissions are rarely accepted. Guidelines are only given after a query has been accepted.

HUMANIST IN CANADA

Canadian Humanist Publications
Box 3769 Station C
Ottawa, ON K1Y 4J8

PHONE: (613) 722-4652
FAX: (613) 749-8929

CONTACT: Joe Piercy   **DESCRIPTION:** Published by Canadian Humanist Publications. Circulation 1,500. Promotes critical thinking and rational investigation of contemporary issues. Published quarterly.

WRITERS: "We take submissions but we do not pay. Writers will receive copies of the magazine."
PHOTOGRAPHERS: "We do our own photography."

HURON CHURCH NEWS
220 Dundas Street 4 Floor
London, ON N6A 1H3

PHONE: (519) 434-6893
FAX: (519) 673-4151

CONTACT: The Rev. Kevin Dixon, Editor   **DESCRIPTION:** Published by Anglican Diocese of Huron. Circulation 25,000. Published monthly. Established in 1951.

HURONIA BUSINESS TIMES
24 Dunlop Street East 2 Fl
Barrie, ON L4M 1A3

PHONE: (705) 721-1450
FAX: (705) 721-1449

CONTACT: Eric Skelton, Editor   **DESCRIPTION:** Published by Huronia Business Times. Circulation 8,000. Published 10 times a year. Established in 1987.

ICAO JOURNAL
1000 Sherbrooke Street West #652
Montreal, PQ H3A 2R2

PHONE: (514) 285-8222
FAX: (514) 286-6376

CONTACT: Eric Macburnie, Editor   **DESCRIPTION:** Published by International Civil Aviation Organization. Published 10 times a year in English, French and Spanish. Established in 1947.
WRITERS: "We do not pay for articles, they are submitted by volunteers from the avaiation community."
PHOTOGRAPHERS: "I do use some stock photography or its done in-house. Shots are always on aviation; airports, airplanes etc."

LES IDEES DE MA MAISON
7 Bates Road
Outremont, PQ H2V 1A6

PHONE: (514) 270-1100
FAX: (514) 270-6900

CONTACT: Beatrix Marik, Editorial Director **DESCRIPTION:** Published by Publicor. Circulation 68,600. Published 10 times a year in French. Established in 1983.
NOTES: Also publishes Femme Plus, Filles d'aujourd'hui, Clin d'oeil, Les Idees De Ma Maison, Decoration Chez-soi, Renovation Bricolage, Plans de Maisons Quebec and En Route.

THE IDLER
255 Davenport Road
Toronto, ON M5R 1J9

NOTES: Could not locate. Phone number is not in service (416) 962-6001.

IMAGE DE LA MAURICIE

564 Blvd. des Prairies
Cap-de-la-Madeleime, PQ G8T 1K9

PHONE: (819) 378-2176
FAX: (819) 374-2263

CONTACT: Gilles Mercier, Editor **DESCRIPTION:** French language publication.
Issued monthly. Established in 1976.
NOTES: This publication does not purchase freelance material.

IMAGES

25 Sheppard Avenue West #100
North York, ON M2N 6S7

PHONE: (416) 733-7600
FAX: (416)

CONTACT: Kate Macdonald, Editor **DESCRIPTION:** Published by Telemedia Procom
Inc. Circulation 450,000. Fashion, beauty and lifestyle magazine for working women.
Published quarterly. Established in 1984.

IMPACT

880 Queen Street West
Toronto, ON M6J 1G3

PHONE: (416) 531-8040
FAX: (416) 531-2388

CONTACT: Mary Dickie, Editor **DESCRIPTION:** Published by Roll Magazines Inc.
Circulation 94,700. Music and pop culture magazine distributed mostly in Canada. Covers
Canadian independent artists as well as international artists. Includes interviews, reviews,
etc. Published monthly. Established in 1993.
WRITERS: 50% freelance written. Buys "dozens" of articles annually. Short pieces average
250 words; subfeatures 750 words; features 3,000 words. Pay is negotiable and ranges
from $50 to $500. A kill fee (50%) is given if assigned articles are cancelled. Looking
for "specific, original ideas that fit the magazine." Contact the editor with a query letter.
Guidelines are not available.
PHOTOGRAPHERS: Photographers are hired on assignment. Uses all formats colour
and b&w. Model releases are not necessary. Captions are preferred. Pays from $40 to
$300 depending on the photos and where they are used. Credit line is given. To make
contact send brochure, flyer or tear sheet samples of your work. Photographers contact
Robin Dickie.
NOTES: Buys first North American serial rights. Unsolicited materials will not be returned.
Previously published work is not considered. Simultaneous submissions are considered.
Sample copy available. Please send 9x12" SASE with $2 CDN postage.

L'IMPORTANT (LAVAL)

877 Rue Ste. Pierre
Terrebonne, PQ J6W 1E6

PHONE: (514) 964-7590
FAX: (514) 964-2327

CONTACT: Louise Bourbonnais, Editor **DESCRIPTION:** Published by Group Magazines.
French language publication. Issued quarterly. Established in 1991.
NOTES: Also publishes Influence.

IN TOUCH WITH WHAT'S HAPPENING see What's Happening Magazine

INDEPENDENT SENIOR

1268 West Pender Street
Vancouver, BC V6E 2S8

PHONE: (604) 688-2271
FAX: (604) 688-2038

CONTACT: Adrian Leonard, Editor   **DESCRIPTION:** Published by K.W. Publishing Ltd. Circulation 48,400. News publication for mature readers. Contains information on housing, politics, health and finances for Western Canada. Published 10 times a year.
WRITERS: "We very rarely purchase work. A freelancer can call by fax or contact us by mail. I do accept unsolicited material. I get a lot of stuff coming in and don't have enough space to publish all of it. Most of the material that I do accept is written by retired journalists or other seniors that want to try their hand at writing. I don't have a very big budget and often people will submit material at no charge to get their name in print. Pieces should be 600-800 words."
PHOTOGRAPHERS: "We occasionally purchase black & white photography. I accept query letters."
NOTES: For a sample copy send 9x12" SASE with appropriate postage.

INDUSTRIAL PROCESS PRODUCTS AND TECHNOLOGY

1011 Upper Middle Road East #1235
Oakville, ON L6H 5Z9

PHONE: (905) 475-4231
FAX: (905) 845-5521

CONTACT: Bob Erickson   **DESCRIPTION:** Published by Swan Erickson Publishing Inc. Circulation 23,400. "A product tabloid servicing the process industry; petrochemical, food and beverage, gas etc." Published 6 times a year. Established in 1987.
NOTES: "We never purchase anything for this publication." Also publishes Autocad User.

L'INFIRMIERE AUXILIAIRE

531 Sherbrooke Street East
Montreal, PQ H2L 1K2

PHONE: (514) 282-9511
FAX: (514) 282-0631

CONTACT: Madeleine Pelletier, Editor   **DESCRIPTION:** Published by Corporation Professionnelle de Infirmieres et Infirmiers Auxiliaires du Quebec. Circulation 21,000. Published 3 times a year in French. Established in 1974.

L'INFIRMIERE DE QUEBEC

4200 Dorchester Blvd. West
Montreal, PQ H3Z 1V4

PHONE: (514) 935-2501
FAX: (514) 935-1799

CONTACT: Guylaine Chabot, Editor   **DESCRIPTION:** Circulation 64,000. French language publication. Issued 6 times a year. Focuses on nurses and nursing issues in the province of Quebec. Established in 1920.
WRITERS: "We purchase about 15 articles per year. Usually we pay between $70 and $100 per standard page. We sometimes hire writers on assignment. Usually the articles I commission are about special events in the province of Quebec. Contact me by fax." Guidelines are available.
PHOTOGRAPHERS: "We purchase both colour and black & white, 20 per year. We hire on assignment and purchase individual photos. Contact me by fax. The photographs are usually of nursing or new technology." Guidelines are not available.
NOTES: Sample copies of this publication are available free upon request. Purchases one-time rights. Considers previously published work.

INFLIGHT

3300 Bloor Street West
#3120 Centre Tower
Toronto, ON M8X 2X3

PHONE: (416) 233-4348
FAX: (416) 233-9367

CONTACT: Susan Melnyk, Editor   **DESCRIPTION:** Published by Melaine Communications Group Inc. Circulation 75,000-100,000. Published twice yearly in two issues, one English, one French. Magazine for Canada 3000 Airlines Ltd. Established in 1990.
WRITERS: 100% freelance written. Byline is given. Buys non-fiction and fillers. Does not hire on assignment. Average article is 2,000 words. Pays $700 per article. "We have a number of regular writers we assign articles to. We concentrate on certain areas in each issue. Destinations must be related to cities where CANADA 3000 flies." Send completed articles on spec. "Articles cannot be written in first person. Articles must relate to destinations served by CANADA 3000. Articles cannot promote specific restaurants, tour guides, etc." Guidelines are not available.
PHOTOGRAPHERS: "We don't purchase a lot of photography. Usually the writers we work with has slides with them."
NOTES: Unsolicited materials will be returned with SASE. Does not consider previously published work or simultaneous submissions. Sample copy is available. Send 9x12" SASE with $3 postage.

INFLUENCE

877 St. Pierre
Terrebonne, PQ J6W 1E6

PHONE: (514) 964-7590
FAX: (514) 964-2327

CONTACT: Sophie Bertrand, Editor   **DESCRIPTION:** Published by Groupe Magazines. Fashion magazine published 3 times a year. Established in 1992.
PHOTOGRAPHERS: Photography is sometimes purchased.
NOTES: Also publishes L'Important.

INFO CANADA

501 Oakdale Road
North York, ON M3N 1W7

PHONE: (416) 746-7360
FAX: (416) 746-1421

CONTACT: John Pickett, Editor-in-Chief   **DESCRIPTION:** Published by Laurentian Technomedia Inc. Circulation 32,000. Focuses on information technology for business users. Published monthly. Established in 1976.
WRITERS: "We buy very little freelance. This is a technical publication and we know most of the people who contribute. Most of them are industry people rather than freelancers. We do take freelance work. Primarily it would be technical in nature, often reviews of consumer products, software and hardware. So there is a fairly specific technical background requirement, as we serve quite a specific technical audience. We don't use a lot of freelance input here. Rates are substantially lower than CIO. Probably more like 30¢ a word for 400-1,000 words on those rare occasions when we do purchase freelance."
PHOTOGRAPHERS: "We don't use much freelance photography."
NOTES: Also publishes CIO Canada, Computerworld, Network World and Reseller World.

INFO PRESSE COMMUNICATIONS
4316 St-Laurent Blvd. #200   **PHONE:** (514) 842-5873
Montreal, PQ H2W 1Z3   **FAX:** (514) 842-2422

CONTACT: Bruno Gautier, Editor   **DESCRIPTION:** Published by Les Editions Info Presse Inc. French language publication. Provides monthly coverage of media and publicity news in Quebec including television, magazine, advertising, radio etc. Established in 1986.

INFO-AFFAIRES
Box 399   **PHONE:** (506) 523-1123
Richibucto, NB E0A 2M0   **FAX:** (506) 523-1122

CONTACT: Gilles Belleau, Editor   **DESCRIPTION:** Published by Bell Productions Inc. French language publication. A tabloid issued monthly. Focuses on New Brunswick business news. Established in 1989.

INFOTECH
3480 St. Denis Street   **PHONE:** (514) 288-8875
Montreal, PQ H2X 3L3   **FAX:** (514) 288-6931

CONTACT: Alain Thibault, Editor   **DESCRIPTION:** Published by Trancontinental Publications & Voir Communications. Circulation 100,000. A tabloid published 6 times a year. Established in 1994.

INSIDE GUIDE see Acumen Magazine

INSITE
312 Dolomite Drive #217   **PHONE:** (416) 667-9609
Downsview, ON M3J 2N2   **FAX:** (416) 667-9715

CONTACT: Adele Weder, Editor   **DESCRIPTION:** Published by Manor Communications. Circulation 17,000. An architecture and design magazine published 6 times a year in French and English. "For a professional readership and is often written by architect or design critics."
WRITERS: "We occasionally purchase work. Writers should be specialists in architecture and design. We have a modest freelance budget for writers and photographers. Our article length tends to be on the shorter side, anywhere from 200-1,200 words depending on the kind of article. If you are not a specialist in this field it is probably not worth soliciting our magazine. You should have a strong knowledge of architecture and design or a strong interest in it. We publish reviews (like the Bata shoe museum for example) but writers should have a very strong angle in mind and that helps tremendously. Freelancers should have already written or studied design."
PHOTOGRAPHERS: "We have a modest freelance budget for writers and photographers. We showcase a lot of work, but it is on a pro bono basis. We work with photographers who have existing work, and who want to showcase it in our magazine. It is art photography

which is useful for our readers who are visual. Photographers may end up getting a commission because of the exposure. Its an ideal vehicle for showing existing work, but unfortunately we cannot pay. We give the photographer credit which is very important. We take both colour and black & white but we advise photographers to submit brochures or colour laser prints at first. This is beause we recieve so much material we can't guarantee the safe return of it unless we solicit it. I prefer seeing some documentary photographs like a laser print of their work or a cheap print of their work (the higher the quality the better). If they have some work on a brochure or a gallery invitation that is best. Then if it seems to be suitable for an upcoming issue I can contact them to arrange for their portfolio.
NOTES: Accepts previously published work on rare occasions. For a sample back issue send $5 to the publisher.

INTER-MECANIQUE DE BATIMENT
8175 Saint-Laurent Blvd.   **PHONE:** (514) 382-2668
Montreal, PQ H2P 2M1   **FAX:** (514) 954-8933

CONTACT: André Dupuis, Editor   **DESCRIPTION:** Published by Corp. of Master Pipe Mechanics of Quebec. Circulation 5,500. French language publication. Issued 10 times a year. Established in 1985.

INTERCHANGE MAGAZINE (Winnipeg) see The Paper

INTERCULTURE
Intercultural Institute of Montreal,   **PHONE:** (514) 288-7229
4917 rue St-Urbain   **FAX:** (514) 844-6800
Montreal, PQ H2T 2W1

CONTACT: Robert Vachon   **DESCRIPTION:** Circulation 1,000. Focuses on contemporary cultures, explores issues raised by cultures and identifies and facilitates communication among scholars. Issued 4 times a year.
WRITERS: "We have an international network of collaborators. Most of our articles come from this network."

INTEREST
7th Floor, 1 Place Ville Marie   **PHONE:** (514) 874-8282
Montreal, PQ H3C 3A9   **FAX:** (514) 874-2539

CONTACT: Lindsey Galloway, Editor   **DESCRIPTION:** Published by Royal Bank of Canada. Trade Magazine. Internal magazine for Royal Bank of Canada employees. Focus is on business stories and personnel issues that affect the bank and its' employees.

INTERFACE
425 rue De La Gauchetiére Est   **PHONE:** (514) 849-0045
Montreal, PQ H2L 2M7   **FAX:** (514) 849-5558

CONTACT: Sophie Malavoy, Editor   **DESCRIPTION:** Published by Association canadienne-francaise pour l'avancement des sciences. Circulation 9,000. French language publication. Issued 6 times a year. Established in 1984.
WRITERS: 30% freelance written. Buys 60 articles annually. Byline must be negotiated. Writers hired on assignment. Articles range from 1,200-1,500 words. Pays $80 per double-spaced page. Regular columns and features include: interviews; science clips; science monde; transferts; CD-ROM. Writers may query over the phone, by fax or mail. "We only cover research done in Canada, mainly concentrating on French Canadian scientists." No guidelines available.
PHOTOGRAPHERS: Stock photography is purchased. Photographers are hired on assignment. Uses all colour formats. Prefers matte 5x7 or 8x10 b&w prints. Model releases and captions are preferred. Payment in negotiated. Credit line is not given. Contact by sending a resumé, business card and samples.
NOTES: Buys one-time rights. Unsolicited materials will be returned with SASE. Previously published work will not be considered. A sample copy is free upon request.

INTERIOR DESIGN ONTARIO
717 Church Street   **PHONE:** (416) 921-2127
Toronto, ON M4W 2M5   **FAX:** (416) 921-3660

CONTACT: Lori Theoret, Production Manager   **DESCRIPTION:** Published by Association of Registered Interior Designers of Ontario. Circulation 6,400. Design industry publication featuring trends, association issues, and people in the business. Published 9 times a year. Established in 1985.
WRITERS: "We have a small budget for writing but we do have quite a string of contractors and freelancers on line now. We purchase maybe 18-20 per year and those are very small. It's a small publication now so there is not the need for a lot of people." Phone inquiries are welcome. "We are looking for a journalism graduate, somebody who has written freelance articles before with possibly a design focus background and/or some environmental and business issues." Maximum length is 750-1,000 words.
PHOTOGRAPHERS: "There is very little market in that we don't have a budget for writing or photogrpahy. We have a repertoire of photographers we have used in the past. We are looking for background experience in editorial photography. I like to see a portfolio if I am going to hire someone." Phone calls are welcome.
NOTES: "This publication has been sized down to newsletter size. We have a limited number of copies available free upon request."

INTERNATIONAL JOURNAL
15 King's College Circle   **PHONE:** (416) 979-1851
Toronto, ON M5S 2V9   **FAX:** (416) 979-8575

CONTACT: Gayle Fraser, Editor   **DESCRIPTION:** Published by Canadian Institute of International Affairs. Circulation 1,800. A quarterly international relations publication with articles from the scholarly community.

WRITERS: "Most of the work in the journal is commissioned and written by academics. We don't accept unsolicited material."
NOTES: Editor's note: This publication is very specific and is not open to queries.

INUIT ART QUARTERLY
2081 Merivale Road
Neapean, ON K2G 1G9

PHONE: (613) 224-8189
FAX: (613) 224-2907

CONTACT: Marybelle Mitchell, Editor   **DESCRIPTION:** Published by The Inuit Art Foundation. Circulation 4000. "The only magazine devoted exclusively to Inuit art. Each issue contains: one or more feature articles on the art, the people, or the issues; interviews; reviews of exhibitions and publications; and a news update." Published quarterly. Established in 1986.
WRITERS: 75% freelance written. Buys 10-15 articles per year. Byline is given. Writers are hired on assignment, expenses negotiated. Articles range from 500-3000 words. Pays: books & exhibition reviews $75-100; features $500-700. Contact the editor by phone or query by phone or fax. "Since Inuit Art Quarterly assumes reader familiarity with the art, contributors must also be well-informed on the subject."Writers' guidelines available.
PHOTOGRAPHERS: Photography purchased from stock and photographers hired on assignment. Uses all formats colour transparencies and b&w prints. Model releases are preferred. Captions are required. Pays up to $50 for colour inside and $200-500 for colour cover. Credit line is given. Contact the editor with query letter, brochure, flyer or samples. "Photographers should be familiar with the style and standard of photography published in Inuit Art Quarterly. Submissions for the *Views* page are welcome.
NOTES: Buys first North American serial rights. Unsolicited materials will be returned with SASE. Does not consider previously published work or simultaneous submissions. For sample copy send $7.25 (includes postage).

INUKTITUT MAGAZINE
170 Laurier Avenue West #510
Ottawa, ON K2P 5V5

PHONE: (613) 238-8181
FAX: (613) 234-1991

CONTACT: Jim Taylor, Project Coordinator   **DESCRIPTION:** Circulation 7,000. The cultural and educational magazine of Canadian Inuit. Publishes work of Inuit writers, photographers and artists and promotes the exchange of information of past and present Inuit life. "We do a lot of traditional and cultural articles and articles on Inuit leaders and models for other Inuit. The main purpose of this magazine is to share with other Inuit and other people the Inuit way of life or the past way of life." Published 3-4 times a year.
WRITERS: "We sometimes purchase freelance writing, maybe 10 per year. We are currently changing our rates. We want all kinds of cultural stories or experiences. We welcome poetry and fiction." Writer's guidelines are available.
PHOTOGRAPHERS: "We look for cultural photographs, and photographs of northern people. We use both black & white and colour." Payment is negotiable.
NOTES: Freelancers should contact the project coordinator, Jim Taylor by phone or mail.

INVESTMENT EXECUTIVE

208 Carlton Street   **PHONE:** (416) 962-4103
Toronto, ON M5A 2L1   **FAX:** (416) 962-4165

CONTACT: Tessa Wilmott, Editor   **DESCRIPTION:** Published by Investment Executive. A tabloid newspaper that goes out nationally to financial service professionals. Our focus is product news, industry trends, profiles of people and companies in the business. Published monthly. Established in 1989.
WRITERS: 80% freelance written. Byline is given. Writers are hired on assignment. Negotiated expenses are paid. Articles range from 800-1,000 words. Pays 50¢ a word. Profiles of industry professionals are usually a flat rate of $400. Query by phone or fax. Send resumé with samples and business card. "I am looking for writers who have specific knowledge of the financial markets and financial products. Although I accept story ideas, I generally assign specific stories." Guidelines are not available.
PHOTOGRAPHERS: 100% freelance. Pay is negotiated, approximately $100 for inside and cover work. Credit line is given. Contact by sending brochure, flyers or tear sheets. "I use photographs of the professional we are profiling, usually in an environment other than work. Photographs are assigned. I would like to know of available news-style photographers across Canada."
NOTES: Buys one-time rights. Unsolicited materials will be returned with SASE. Will not consider previously published work or simultaneous submissions. Sample copy is free upon request.

ISLAND NEWS FOR SENIORS

Main Street
North Rustico, PE C0A 1X0

NOTES: Could not locate. Phone number is not in service (902) 963-3102.

ISLAND PARENT MAGAZINE

941 Kings Road   **PHONE:** (604) 388-6905
Victoria, BC V8T 1W7   **FAX:** (604) 388-4391

CONTACT: James Holland, Editor   **DESCRIPTION:** Published by Krayenhoff-Holland Enterprises Ltd. A local resource magazine for Vancouver Island parents. Covers education, arts, entertainment, parenting issues. Published monthly. Established in 1988.
WRITERS: "We purchase on occasion but usually it's local. We get way more unsolicited material than we can use. We pay $25 for 500-800 words. We really look for local stuff; reflections on parenting or practical parenting. Priority is given to local writers."
PHOTOGRAPHERS: No photography is accepted.
NOTES: Does not consider previously published work. For a sample copy send 9x12" SASE with appropriate postage.

J'AIME LIRE

3995 Ste-Catherine Est   **PHONE:** (514) 522-3936
Montreal, PQ H1W 2G7   **FAX:** (514) 522-1761

CONTACT: Suzanne Spino   **DESCRIPTION:** Published by Bayard Presse Canada. Circulation 15,000. French language publication for children 7 to 12 years. Issued 10 times a year. Established in 1987.

WRITERS: Writers are hired on assignment. Publishes fiction and non-fiction for children. Stories are 12 double spaced pages in length. Pays $1000. Contact the editor with a query letter.
PHOTOGRAPHERS: Photography is not used.
NOTES: Buys all rights. Unsolicited materials will be returned with SASE. Will not consider previously published work. Considers simultaneous submissions. For sample send 6x9" SASE and $2 CDN postage.

JEWELLERY WORLD see Canadian Jeweller

JOBBER NEWS
1450 Don Mills Road   **PHONE:** (416) 445-6641
Don Mills, ON M3B 2X7   **FAX:** (416) 442-2213

CONTACT: Bob Blans, Editor   **DESCRIPTION:** Published by Southam. Circulation 11,200. A magazine devoted to the distribution segment of the automotive aftermarket. ie. the distribution of automotive parts, accessories and anything in the automotive line. Published monthly. Established in 1931.
WRITERS: "We very seldom purchase writing but we do occasionally assign once or twice a year. Most of the time it would be a profile on a company or an event that needs to be covered in another part of the country." Contact the editor with samples of work to be kept on file.
PHOTOGRAPHERS: "We sometimes look for colour cover shots, any format. We seldom buy inside shots."
NOTES: "We do have a lot of freelancers that we can call on." Sample copies of this publication are available free upon request.

THE JOURNAL
33 Russell Street #2053   **PHONE:** (416) 595-6053
Toronto, ON M5S 2S1   **FAX:** (416) 593-4694

CONTACT: Ian Kinross, Editor   **DESCRIPTION:** Circulation 10,700. "Reports on trends in the addictions field in Ontario and around the world. It is distributed to professionals and interested members of the public. Reports on a range of substances from alcohol and tobacco, to illegal drugs and the abuse of prescription drugs. Includes information on prevention programs and treatment of people who have serious problems. A tabloid published 6 times a year in English and French. Established in 1972.
WRITERS: "We have just recently started to assign some stories to freelancers. There are maybe 6 or 7 articles per issue. We pay around $200 for a news story, 600 words or so. It depends, I negotiate a final price with the writer after discussing what it will take to do the story and how many people will need to be interviewed. We never accept work on spec. We are looking for solid reporting experience. I want someone who is first-of-all a competent reporter and writer, and secondly who can use that skill to do an assignment relating to the addictions field. A knowledge of science is an asset." Fax a letter and resumé including relevant experience to (416) 595-6892 or mail it. "We are just gradually expanding our freelance component at the moment."
PHOTOGRAPHERS: "We use 2 or 3 freelance black & white photos or illustrations per issue. These are assigned based on our story list for the upcoming issue. Pay rates range from $100-$200. I am looking for someone who has done some news photography as opposed to artistic photography. Someone who has sold photos to a newspaper or worked

as a news photographer." Fax a letter and resumé including relevant experience to (416) 595-6892 or mail it.
NOTES: Someone with both written and photography skills is also considered. A sample copy is free upon request. Purchases exclusive rights. May consider work that was previously published.

LE JOURNAL DE L'ASSURANCE
353 St.-Nicolas St #4   **PHONE:** (514) 289-9595
Montreal, PQ H2Y 2P1   **FAX:** (514) 289-9527

CONTACT: Serge Therrien, Editor   **DESCRIPTION:** Published by Les Editions du Journal de l'Assurance Inc. Circulation 18,000. French language publication. Articles on Canadian insurance issues that may impact Quebec. Published monthly. Established in 1992.
WRITERS: "We don't have any need for freelance writers right now."
PHOTOGRAPHERS: "We have our own full-time photographer."

JOURNAL DENTAIRE DU QUEBEC
625 René-Lévesque Blvd. W, 15 Fl.   **PHONE:** (514) 875-8511
Montreal, PQ H3B 1R2   **FAX:** (514) 393-9248

CONTACT: Dr. Denis Forest, Editor   **DESCRIPTION:** Circulation 4,700. French language publication. Issued 10 times a year. Established in 1963.

JOURNAL OF CANADIAN PETROLEUM TECHNOLOGY
3400 de Maisonneuve Blvd W #1210   **PHONE:** (514) 939-2710
Montreal, PQ H3Z 3B8   **FAX:** (514) 939-2714

CONTACT: Perla Gantz, Editor   **DESCRIPTION:** Published by Canadian Institute of Mining, Metallurgy and Petroleum. Circulation 4,400. Published 10 times a year. Established in 1962.

JOURNAL OF CANADIAN POETRY
9 Ashburn Drive   **PHONE:** (613) 224-6837
Nepean, ON K2E 6N4   **FAX:** (613) 829-7783

CONTACT: David Staines, Editor   **DESCRIPTION:** Published by Borealis Press. Circulation 500. An bilingual annual review of the year's poetry, poetry criticism as well as new articles on Canadian poetry.
WRITERS: "This is a critical review of books of poetry so reviews are contracted. We will accept critical articles on Canadian poetry addressed to the editor by fax or mail. No payment is given."
PHOTOGRAPHERS: No photography is used.

THE JOURNAL OF SCHOLARLY PUBLISHING
10 St. Mary Street #700
Toronto, ON   M4Y 2W8

PHONE: (416) 978-2232
FAX: (416) 978-4738

CONTACT: Hamish Cameron, Editor   **DESCRIPTION:** Published by University of Toronto Press. Circulation 1,500. Semi-academic journal published for scholarly writers, publishers, librarians and university administrators. Published quarterly.
WRITERS: Contact with query letter. Unable to pay but inquiries welcome. Byline given. Guidelines available.

JOURNAL OF THE CANADIAN DENTAL ASSOCIATION
1815 Alta Vista Drive
Ottawa, ON   K1G 3Y6

PHONE: (613) 523-1770
FAX: (613) 523-7736

CONTACT: Dr. P. Ralph Crawford, Editor   **DESCRIPTION:** Published by Canadian Dental Association. Circulation 18,000+. A journal focusing on dentistry. Published monthly in French and English. Established in 1935.
WRITERS: "We do accept articles, mostly scientific and clinical articles concerning dentistry. There is also a practice management success column and book reviews. Contact the editor with a query letter."
PHOTOGRAPHERS: "We rarely purchase photography. We have a photographer that takes cover photos for us."

JUNIOR
785 Plymouth Avenue #310
Town of Mount-Royal, PQ   H4P 1B3

PHONE: (514) 735-5191
FAX: (514) 342-9406

CONTACT: Ronald Lapierre   **DESCRIPTION:** Published by Les Editions Presstissimo Inc. French language publication. Issued quarterly. Established in 1991.
WRITERS: "We do purchase articles."

KEY TO KINGSTON
Box 1352
Kingston, ON   K7L 5C6

PHONE: (613) 549-8442
FAX: (613) 549-1608

CONTACT: Mary Laflamme, Editor   **DESCRIPTION:** Published by Kingston Publications. Circulation 17,000. Includes restaurant reviews, shopping guides, and tours. Published eight times a year for visitors.
NOTES: This publication accepts freelance work on occasion.

KICK IT OVER
Box 5811 Station A
Toronto, ON   M5W 1P2

NOTES: Could not locate.

KIDS CREATIONS
8270 Mountain Sights #101   **PHONE:** (514) 731-7774
Montreal, PQ H4P 2B7   **FAX:** (514) 731-7459

CONTACT: Lisa Peters, Editor   **DESCRIPTION:** Published by Cama Inc. A magazine focusing on children's apparel. Published quarterly in English and French. Established in 1959.
NOTES: This publication does accept freelance material. Formerly called Kids Parade.

KIDS TORONTO
542 Mount Pleasant Corp. #401
Toronto, ON M4S 2M7

NOTES: Could not locate.

KIDS TRIBUTE
900A Don Mills Road #1000   **PHONE:** (416) 445-0544
Don Mills, ON M3C 1V6   **FAX:** (416) 445-2894

CONTACT: Sandra I. Stewart, Editor   **DESCRIPTION:** Published by Tribute Publishing Inc. Circulation 300,000. A general interest magazine for kids with an emphasis on film and a preview of the upcoming films for kids. Published quarterly. Established in 1989.
WRITERS: "We have a small base of freelancers which we draw from. We very rarely take submissions. People are welcome to query us."
PHOTOGRAPHERS: "We never purchase photography."

KINESIS
1720 Grant Street, #301   **PHONE:** (604) 255-5499
Vancouver, BC V5L 2Y6   **FAX:** (604) 255-5511

CONTACT: Fatima Jaffer, Editor   **DESCRIPTION:** Published by Vancouver Status of Women. Circulation 3,000. A national news magazine for feminists. Published 10 times a year. Provides a fresh look at what women are doing with their lives through investigative reports, timely interviews, cultural affairs and national and international news.
WRITERS: "We accept unpaid submissions but not a lot of unsolicited work, maybe 10 a year. Phone or write us. Before taking on an article contact us with an outline. We look for timely news items like legislation that affects women as well as commentaries on different issues."
PHOTOGRAPHERS: "We purchase photos with the articles. We prefer black & white."
NOTES: Sample copies of this publication are free upon request with a 9x12" SASE.

LABORATORY PRODUCT NEWS
1450 Don Mills Road   **PHONE:** (416) 445-6641
Don Mills, ON M3B 2X7   **FAX:** (416) 442-2213

CONTACT: Rita Tate, Editor   **DESCRIPTION:** Published by Southam Inc. Circulation 17,700. A publication dealing with new products for laboratories. Published 6 times a year. Established in 1971.
NOTES: No freelance material is purchased for this publication.

LABOUR TIMES
240 Edward Street
Aurora, ON L4G 3S9

PHONE: (905) 841-6481
FAX: (905) 841-5078

CONTACT: Beth Marlin, Managing Editor   **DESCRIPTION:** Published by Law Times Inc., Stewart Morrison. Circulation 14,700. Monthly national newspaper on industrial relations. News, profiles, features, opinion, columns and gossip. Published monthly. Established in 1989.
WRITERS: 50% freelance written. Byline is given. Hires on assignment; expenses paid. Average length 600-800 words. Pays $150-175; will negotiate more for more involved pieces. Contact editor by phone or with query letter or fax. "Don't call me directly unless you have a good story idea that can be quickly sold verbally. Writers should have some experience in this area. I am especially interested in writers who can write analytically and put stories into context." Writers' guidelines available.
PHOTOGRAPHERS: 90% of photos taken by photographers hired on assignment. Uses colour prints and b&w prints. Model releases and captions are not necessary. Pays $75 for inside photo. Credit line is given. Contact the editor with a sample portfolio. "I like photographers who can portray/reveal something about an individual without being boring!" Photo guidelines available.
NOTES: Buys first North American serial rights. Unsolicited materials will be returned with SASE. Does not consider previously published work or simultaneous submissions.

LABOUR/LE TRAVAIL: Journal of Canadian Labour Studies
Memorial University
Department of History
St. John's, NF A1C 5S7

PHONE: (709) 737-2144
FAX: (709) 737-4569

CONTACT: Gregory S. Kealey   **DESCRIPTION:** "A bilingual refereed scholarly journal primarily with labour history as its focus; the labour movement, work, and workers. Articles include: book notes, archival notes, and an annual bibliography of Canadian labour studies. Published twice a year.
WRITERS: "We don't publish freelance material. We are a scholarly journal and people are lusting to be published because they get career awards. We do publish material but we don't pay."

LANDMARK
1777 Victoria Avenue #1000
Regina, SK S4P 4K5

PHONE: (306) 584-1000

CONTACT: Tom Steve, Editor   **DESCRIPTION:** Published by Charlton Communications Inc. Publication for those in the land care industry such as landscape architects and contractors for golf courses, amusement parks and playground facilities. Published bi-monthly.
WRITERS: "We may purchase one or two articles per issue. Freelancers should contact the editor with a story idea. Payment varies."
PHOTOGRAPHERS: "We don't purchase photography."
NOTES: Sample copies of this publication are available free upon request. Also publishes Prairie Landscape, DC Magazine and Canadian Resources Review.

LANDSCAPE ARCHITECTURAL REVIEW
24 Kensington Avenue
Willowdale, ON M2M 1R6

PHONE: (416) 223-3956
FAX: (416) 225-8103

CONTACT: Nick Van Vliet, Editor **DESCRIPTION:** Circulation 1,400. Presents ideas and topics related to landscape architecture and the environmental sciences. Published five times a year in English and French. Established in 1980.

LANDSCAPE TRADES
7856 Fifth Line South RR4
Milton, ON L9T 2X8

PHONE: (905) 875-1805
FAX: (905) 875-3942

CONTACT: Linda Erskine, Editor **DESCRIPTION:** Published by Landscape Horticultural Trades Association. "We cover: profiles of landscaping companies and projects; report on new technology, environmental practices and integrated test management programs; and total plant health care." Published 9 times a year. Established in 1979.
WRITERS: "We do purchase from writers, probably 1-2 per articles per issue. We hire on assignment. We have a focus every month, for example the landscape contractor or the retail gardening centre. We first want to see an outline of an article and we decide from there. Our pay rate is 15¢ per word payable upon publication. Our articles are between 1,000-1,500 words. Because we are industry specific normally we have industry people writing for us. Once an article is submitted we like to see photos or graphics that will help round out the article. I prefer articles to be submitted on 3.5 disks (Word Perfect) or as hard copy. Writers should follow Canadian capitalizations and spelling." Guidelines are available.
PHOTOGRAPHERS: "We use colour and black & white photos with articles. We pay $5 for inside photos and $20 for the cover photo."
NOTES: Sample copies are available free upon request. "We purchase one-year, three-year and five-year rights." Considers previously published work with the appropriate permission.

LATITUDES
252 Ave. des pins E
Montreal, PQ H2W 1P3

PHONE: (514) 281-0905
FAX: (514) 281-0682

CONTACT: Louis Gauthier, Editor-in-Chief **DESCRIPTION:** Published by Plan B Strategies, Eve Howse. Circulation 275,000. A travel publication published 4 times a year in English and French. Distributed across Canada. Established in 1993.
NOTES: This publication purchases both writing and photography. Please look at a sample before making queries or submissions.

LAW TIMES
240 Edward Street
Aurora, ON L4G 3S9

PHONE: (905) 841-6481
FAX: (905) 841-5078

CONTACT: Beth Marlin, Managing Editor **DESCRIPTION:** Published by Law Times Inc., Stewart Morrison. Circulation 14,700. Weekly legal affairs newspaper for Ontario's legal profession. News, profiles, features, case analysis, opinion, columns and gossip. Published weekly. Established in 1989.
WRITERS: 50% freelance written. Buys 2,000 articles per year. Byline is given. Hires on assignment; expenses paid. Average length 600-800 words. Pays $150-175; will negotiate

more for more involved pieces. Contact editor by phone or with query letter or fax. "Don't call me directly unless you have a good story idea that can be quickly sold verbally. Writers should understand the legal system and have some experience in this area. I am especially interested in writers who can write analytically and put stories into context." Writers' guidelines available.

PHOTOGRAPHERS: 90% of photos taken by photographers hired on assignment. Uses colour prints and b&w prints. Model releases and captions are not necessary. Pays $75 for inside photo. Credit line is given. Contact the editor with a sample portfolio. "I like photographers who can portray/reveal something about an individual without being boring!" Photo guidelines available.

NOTES: Buys first North American serial rights. Unsolicited materials will be returned with SASE. Does not consider previously published work or simultaneous submissions.

THE LAWYERS WEEKLY

75 Clegg Road
Markham, ON L6G 1A1

PHONE: (905) 415-5804
FAX: (905) 479-3758

CONTACT: Beverley Spencer   **DESCRIPTION:** Published by Butterworths Canada Ltd. Circulation 8,000. "Our focus is on case law, all stories are law related." Readers are mostly judges, lawyers and other interested professionals. Published weekly. Established in 1983.

WRITERS: 50% freelance written. Byline given. Writers are hired on assignment and expenses paid. Average article length is 800-1,000 words paying 15¢ per word. A kill fee is paid if an article is cancelled. Writers can contact the publication by query letter with resumé, or by phone/fax or by sending completed articles on spec. "We are interested in anything that may be of interest to the legal community and it must be current." Writers' guidelines are not available.

PHOTOGRAPHERS: Purchases 3 photos per issue. 100% assigned to freelance photographers. Colour formats used: 35mm transparencies, 5x7 colour prints. B&W formats used: 5x7 prints, 8x10 prints, glossy, matte. Model releases are preferred. Pay ranges from $50-75 per b&w photo. Credit line is never given. Approach the company with a query letter. "We have photographers for most of the provinces." Photo guidelines are available. Contact Ann Macaulay, Copy Coordinator.

NOTES: For a sample copy send 9x12" SASE with appropriate postage. Purchases exclusive rights. Returns unsolicited materials with a SASE. Considers simultaneous submissions.

LBMAO REPORTER

4500 Sheppard Avenue East
Scarborough, ON M1S 3R6

PHONE: (416) 298-1731
FAX: (416) 298-4865

CONTACT: Stephen Johns, Editor   **DESCRIPTION:** Published by Lumber and Building Materials Association of Ontario. Circulation 1,350. An association owned and produced publication. Covers issues of interest to the industry and includes new product information. Published bi-monthly.

NOTES: "Much of the material is generated by the office and the association. The association represents the Ontario-based retail lumber, building supply and hardware industries. Typically we do not pay for editorial material."

LEADERSHIP IN HEALTH SERVICES
17 York Street #100   **PHONE:** (613) 241-8005
Ottawa, ON K1N 9J6   **FAX:** (613) 241-5055

CONTACT: Michelle Albagli, Editor   **DESCRIPTION:** Published by Canadian Hospital Association. Circulation 7,800. Business publication for health care boards and professionals. Published 6 times a year. Established in 1924.
WRITERS: "We don't have a budget for freelance writers now. Everything is done by medical professionals. We are more of a journal than a magazine."
PHOTOGRAPHERS: "We occasionally purchase colour or black & white photography. Query by mail with samples of work or stock list."
NOTES: Sample copies of this publication are available free upon request. Merged with Dimensions in Health Service and Hospital Trustee.

LEGION
359 Kent Street #407   **PHONE:** (613) 235-8741
Ottawa, ON K2P 0R6   **FAX:** (613) 233-7159

CONTACT: Mac Johnston, Editor   **DESCRIPTION:** Published by Canvet Publications. Circulation 485,900. "Our readers are of all ages (20-60), from boomers to seniors." Published monthly. Established in 1926.
NOTES: "We have many ways of finding freelance people and I am not prepared to answer these questions. They are of no benefit to me."

LEISURE WORLD
1253 Ouellette Avenue   **PHONE:** (519) 971-3207
Windsor, ON N8X 1J3   **FAX:** (519) 977-1197

CONTACT: Douglas O'Neil, Editor-in-Chief   **DESCRIPTION:** Published by Canadian Automobile Association. Circulation 340,000. Focus is on travel, leisure, and recreation. Published 6 times a year. Established in 1988.
WRITERS: "We usually buy unsolicited articles, we don't assign stories. We look for articles around 1,100 to 1,600 words. We are only interested in travel destination inside and outside the country covering recreational travel and soft adventure pieces. Leisure World is looking for travel and destination features that not only serve as accurate accounts of real-life experiences, but are also dramatic narratives, peopled by compelling characters. Non-fiction short stories brought home by writers who have gone beyond the ordinary verities of descriptive travel writing to provide an intimate glimpse of another culture. We don't cover business travel. You are better off with text/photo packages or just photos, we usually don't buy text only. The best way to contact us is by query letter and samples that show me you are capable of doing what you say you can do." Rates vary $200-500. Guidelines are available.
PHOTOGRAPHERS: "We purchase colour photography. We prefer transparencies on spec. Primarily use 35mm slides but larger formats are welcome. We look for photos to go with the stories we are doing. We are open-minded about photos coming in separately. Pays $75, $150 for colour cover. The best way to contact us is by query letter." Guidelines are available.
NOTES: "The best way to become familiar with the kind of material we publish is to read a recent issue or two from cover to cover. This will give you an accurate picture of the magazine's scope, approach and style." Sample copies of this publication are available

for $3. Purchases one-time rights. Considers previously published work if it didn't appear in the same geographic market.

LEISUREWAYS

2 Carlton Street #801   **PHONE:** (416) 595-5007
Toronto, ON   M5B 1J3   **FAX:** (416) 924-6308

CONTACT: Deborah Milton, Editor   **DESCRIPTION:** Published by Canada Wide Magazines. Circulation 643,000. Consumer publication for Ontario members of the Canadian Automobile Association. Includes leisure activity information as well as travel tips. Published 7 times a year. Established in 1982.
WRITERS: 75% freelance written. Buys 35 articles per year. Byline is given. Does not hire on assignment. Send articles on spec. Average article length 1,500. Pays 50¢ a word. "Editorial line-ups are prepared in Sept-Oct every year. Stories should be under 1,500 words."Writers' guidelines are available. Send SASE.
PHOTOGRAPHERS: Buys photography. 25% from stock. 70% included with stories. Uses 35mm, 2¼x2¼, 4x5 colour transparencies and 5x7, 8x10 glossy b&w prints. Pay is negotiable. Credit line in given. Send query letter with a detailed subject list. "Most photography comes with travel stories. Need to know who has what in travel destination photography - will call those on file if we need photos." Photo guidelines are available. Send SASE.
NOTES: Buys one-time rights or first North American serial rights. Unsolicited materials will be returned with SASE. Does not consider previously published work or simultaneous submissions. For sample copy send 9x12" SASE with $1.40 CDN postage. Sold in conjunction with Westworld.

LIFESTYLES MAGAZINE 5754

9005 Leslie Street #211   **PHONE:** (416) 881-3070
Richmond Hill, ON   L4B 1G7   **FAX:** (416) 731-6000

CONTACT: Jeanette Friedman, Editor   **DESCRIPTION:** Published by Lifestyles Magazine. Circulation 120,000 US and 90,000 Canadian by subscription only. A Jewish magazine published 6 times a year. "We interview Jewish personalities from around the world who have contributed something to society. We also cover events which have taken place in the Jewish community." Established in 1973.
WRITERS: "We do purchase stories on assignment. We pay $300 an article and $500 for a cover story. The length depends on the profile of the person, from one page to five or six pages. Freelancers should submit samples of work. Our themes are of Jewish subjects only."
PHOTOGRAPHERS: "We very rarely purchase photography. Most is done free of charge and we simply credit the photographer."
NOTES: "We give sample copies to people we assign articles to, and to the people we are interviewing."

LIFESTYLES PAST 50

Box 1291   **PHONE:** (506) 658-0754
Saint John, NB   E2L 4H8   **FAX:** (506) 633-0868

CONTACT: Ernie Maber, Editor   **DESCRIPTION:** Published by EMC Marketing Associates. Circulation 20,000. A general interest tabloid for New Brunswick seniors.

Published bi-monthly. Includes a cross-section of information including medical and human interest. Established in 1989.
WRITERS: We do not purchase work as a rule. At times we exchange articles for ad space. We have a number of regular contributors that write for us.
PHOTOGRAPHERS: All photography is done in-house.

THE LIGHT
228 Main Street   **PHONE:** (902) 895-7948
Bible Hill, NS B2N 4H2   **FAX:** (902) 893-1427

CONTACT: Karen Fulton, Editor   **DESCRIPTION:** A community paper focusing on the north shore area of Nova Scotia. Published once a month.
NOTES: May purchase freelance work on occasion. Also publishes Central Nova Business News and Truro Magazine.

LIGHTING MAGAZINE
395 Matheson Blvd. East   **PHONE:** (905) 890-1846
Mississauga, ON L4Z 2H2   **FAX:** (905) 890-5769

CONTACT: Bryan Rogers, Editor   **DESCRIPTION:** Published by Kerrwil Publications Ltd. Circulation 7,400. Published strictly for the lighting industry. Published 6 times a year. Established in 1987.
NOTES: Also publishes Formula, CAD Systems, Canadian Yachting, Electrical Business, Electrical Bluebook, Energy Manager, Manufacturing and Process Automation and La Monde.

LIMOUSIN LEADER
1935-32 Avenue NE   **PHONE:** (403) 291-6770
Calgary, AB T2E 7C8   **FAX:** (403) 291-6744

CONTACT: Randy Bollum, Editor   **DESCRIPTION:** Published by Bollum Marketing Inc. Circulation 3,000. Informative "how-to" and success stories about purebred and commercial Limousin cattle business. Includes business, breed info and people profiles. Published 11 times a year. Established in 1973.
WRITERS: 10% freelance written. Purchases 10 articles annually. Byline is given. Writers are hired on assignment, expenses are paid while on assignment. Average article is 1,200 words. Pays $100. Send completed articles on spec, fax or send query letter. "Knowledge of purebred and commercial cattle business would usually be mandatory to be able to complete a satisfactory article."
PHOTOGRAPHERS: Photos are included with text/photo packages. Uses 3x5 colour or b&w prints. Captions are required. Model releases not necessary. Pays $100 for text/photo package. Send query letter and subject list. "Photographer must usually have a basic understanding of the purebred and commercial cattle business to organize, set up and supply satisfactory photos."
NOTES: Buys one-time rights. Unsolicited material is not returned. Considers previously published work and simultaneous submissions. Sample copy available. Please send 9x12" SASE with $3 postage.

LIVING SAFETY
Canadian Safety Council
1020 Thomas Spratt Place
Ottawa, ON K1G 5L5

PHONE: (613) 739-1535
FAX: (613) 739-1566

CONTACT: Jack Smith, Editor   **DESCRIPTION:** Circulation 100,000. Covers a wide range of off-the-job safety information. Focuses on home safety, the environment, traffic, and recreational safety topics. There is an editorial slant to consumer information ie. what is new in safety. Published quarterly in a French edition as well.
WRITERS: "We purchase 30 articles a year. Short articles are 1,500 words and features are 2,500 words. We pay depending on the writer's skill and the abstract they provide, we pay between $240-$500. Writers can phone, fax or send me a query letter." Writer's guidelines are available.
PHOTOGRAPHERS: "We don't purchase photography. We have a photographer on contract."
NOTES: "We request all Canadian rights, since our membership often asks permission to reproduce the information in a newsletter." Considers previously published work if disclosed to the editor. Considers simultaneous submissions. Sample copies of this publication are available free upon request.

LOGGING AND SAWMILLING JOURNAL
Box 86670, 622 - West 22 Street
North Vancouver, BC Z7L 4L2

PHONE: (604) 990-9970
FAX: (604) 990-9971

CONTACT: Norm Poole, Editor   **DESCRIPTION:** Circulation 16,000. Nationwide forest management publication. Issued nine times per year. Articles deal with forest management, logging and sawmilling, manufacturing and technical updates.
WRITERS: 100% freelance written. Contact with query letter. Pay negotiable. Byline given. Send 9x12" SASE with appropriate postage for a sample copy.
PHOTOGRAPHERS: 98% text/photo packages. Contact with query letter. Colour prints preferred.
NOTES: "We do not do articles on pulp and paper."

LONDON BUSINESS MONTHLY MAGAZINE
Box 7400
London, ON N5Y 4X3

PHONE: (519) 472-7601
FAX: (519) 473-2256

CONTACT: Janine Foster, Managing Editor   **DESCRIPTION:** Published by Bowes Publishers Ltd. Circulation 14,100. Published monthly. Established in 1987.

LONDON GUIDEBOOK
231 Dundas Street, Main Floor
London, ON N6A 1H1

PHONE: (519) 679-4901
FAX: (519) 434-7842

DESCRIPTION: Features cycling, outdoor activities, events in London, theatre, parks and tourist attractions.
NOTES: Also publishes London Magazine, The Business Times and Cover Story.

LONDON MAGAZINE
231 Dundas Street #203　　　　　　　　PHONE: (519) 679-4901
London, ON N6A 1H1　　　　　　　　FAX: (519) 434-7842

CONTACT: Jackie Skender, Editor   DESCRIPTION: Published by London Magazine. Circulation 35,000. Features food, homes, leisure, city issues, health issues, business and fashion in London, Ontario. Readers include those from an upper to mid-class income, and are predominately young women "though we would like to increase our male readership." Published monthly. Established in 1985.
WRITERS: "The majority is freelance written, 90%. Article lengths range up to 2,000 words. Contact us through mail or fax. We don't usually publish unsolicited work, most is by assignment. Research the market and the magazine and get a knowledge of what we have done in the past." Guidelines are available.
PHOTOGRAPHERS: "Our photography is assigned, both colour and black & white. Contact Barbara Moore, the art director."
NOTES: Purchases first North American serial rights. Sample copies of this publication are available free upon request. Considers previously published work. Also publishes London Guidebook, The Business Times and Cover Story.

LUAC FORUM
41 Lesmill Road　　　　　　　　　　PHONE: (416) 444-5251
Don Mills, ON M3B 2T3　　　　　　　FAX: (416) 444-8031

CONTACT: Val Osbourne   DESCRIPTION: Published by Life Underwriter's Association of Canada. Circulation 18,000. Published 10 times a year. Established in 1914.
WRITERS: Does not purchase articles or hire on assignment.
PHOTOGRAPHERS: Buys approximately 10 photographs annually. Purchases from stock or hires on assignment. Uses all formats colour and b&w. Credit line is given. Contact the editor with a query letter.
NOTES: Unsolicited materials will be returned with SASE. Considers previously published work and simultaneous submissions. Sample copy is available, free upon request.

LUGGAGE, LEATHERGOODS AND ACCESSORIES
501 Oakdale Road　　　　　　　　　　PHONE: (416) 746-7360
Downsview, ON M3N 1W7　　　　　　　FAX: (416) 746-1421

CONTACT: Virginia Hutton, Editor   DESCRIPTION: Published by Laurentian Media Inc. Trade magazine focusing on leathergoods retailing. Issued quarterly.

LE LUNDI
7 Bates Road　　　　　　　　　　　　PHONE: (514) 270-1100
Outremont, PQ H2V 1A6　　　　　　　FAX: (514) 270-6900

CONTACT: Michelle Lemieux   DESCRIPTION: Published by Publicor. Circulation 90,000. French language publication. "We mostly write about local artists from Quebec. We carry a lot of interviews and chronicles." Published weekly. Established in 1976.
WRITERS: "All work is done by our freelance journalists on assignment. Contact the editor with a letter and CV or by phone."
PHOTOGRAPHERS: "All photography is done in-house."
NOTES: Sample copies of this publication are available free upon request.

MA REVUE DE MACHINERIE AGRICOLE
26 Meunier
St-Nice, PQ J2A 1H6

PHONE: (819) 478-2136
FAX: (819) 478-4819

CONTACT: Jean-Marc Beland **DESCRIPTION:** Published by Rubricor Inc. Circulation 35,000. French language publication. A trade magazine for agriculture.
NOTES: Freelance material is not purchased.

MACHINERY & EQUIPMENT MRO
(Maintenance and Repair Overhaul)
1450 Don Mills Road
Don Mills, ON M3B 2X7

PHONE: (416) 442-2089
FAX: (416) 442-2214

CONTACT: William Roebuck, Editor **DESCRIPTION:** Published by Southam Business Communications. Circulation 21,000+. Serves readers with information on maintenance and engineering. Our primary focus is the aftermarket of machinery items. We cover topics such as fittings and valves, bearing repair, gear motors, casters, aspects of hydraulics, extreme weather maintenance, lubrication, chains and drive systems, pumps, belts etc. Published bi-monthly. Established in 1985.
WRITERS: "We have a minimal freelance budget. Contact the editor directly. We find often information gets rehashed and that is not going to grab the reader's attention unless it is ground breaking material. People must keep in mind that it is an aftermarket magazine and that things geared toward maintenance, ease of maintenance and prolonging equipment life is usually what readers enjoy reading and we get the most response from."
PHOTOGRAPHERS: "We are using more photography to make the magazine more appealing. We use both black & white and colour. Usually clients supply photographs or we used computerized and animated drawings. We may be interested in photos for the cover." Contact the editor directly.
NOTES: Sample copies of this publication are available for $7.

MACLEAN'S
777 Bay Street, 7th Fl.
Toronto, ON M5W 1A7

PHONE: (416) 596-5311
FAX: (416) 596-7730

CONTACT: Robert Lewis, Editor **DESCRIPTION:** Published by Maclean Hunter Ltd. Circulation 570,000. Features Canadian news events, trends, and issues as well as international coverage. Canada's most read news magazine. Published weekly. Established in 1905.
WRITERS: Occasionally freelancers accepted in areas of business, sports, science, medicine, entertainment and technology. Submit query letters to Robert Lewis, Editor. If you request and send SASE they will return unused work. Pays on acceptance. Gives a byline. Purchases all rights; reprints with permission only.
PHOTOGRAPHERS: Send portfolio to Peter Bragg, Photo Editor. Buys first-time rights from freelancers.

MADAME AU FOYER
25 Sheppard Avenue West #100
North York, ON M2N 6S7

PHONE: (416) 733-7600
FAX: (416) 733-8683

CONTACT: Sally Armstrong, Editor-in-Chief **DESCRIPTION:** Published by Telemedia Communication Inc. Circulation 300,000. "We consider ourselves the thinking woman's magazine. It usually carries features of events taking place now. We also carry food, beauty, decor, fashion, and health features." The French version of Homemaker's Magazine. Published 8 times a year. Established in 1965.
WRITERS: "We purchase material. Unsolicited manuscripts welcome. If there is something we feel can be used in the magazine in some way or another we will contact the writer. We prefer to have a proposal letter before the full manuscript is sent. Length of article and payment is negotiable." Guidelines are available.
PHOTOGRAPHERS: "We very, very rarely purchase. We don't accept freelance inquiries."
NOTES: Sample copies available free upon request. Purchases first North American serial rights. Considers previously published work. Does not consider simultaneous submissions.

LE MAGAZINE CARGUIDE
447 Speers Road #4
Oakville, ON L6K 3S7

PHONE: (905) 842-6591
FAX: (905) 842-6843

CONTACT: Alan McPhee, Editor **DESCRIPTION:** Published by Formula Publications Ltd. French language publication. Issued 6 times a year. Sold in conjunction with Carguide. Distributed at Salon International de L'Auto de Quebec & Ottawa-Hull Auto Show.

LE MAGAZINE ENFANTS QUEBEC
300 Arran St
St-Lambert, PQ J4R 1K5

PHONE: (514) 672-7027
FAX: (514) 672-5442

CONTACT: Mireille Leduc, Editor **DESCRIPTION:** Published by Magazine Enfants Quebec Inc. Circulation 48,300. French language publication. Issued 10 times a year. Established in 1988.

MAGAZINE EXPEDITION PLEIN AIR
#210-225 Notre Dame W
Montreal, PQ H2Y 1T4

NOTES: Could not reach. Number is not in service. (514) 982-6063.

LE MAGAZINE JEUNESSE
7383 Rue de la Roche
Montreal, PQ H2R 2T4

NOTES: Could not locate. Phone number is not in service (514) 989-9795.

MAGAZINE LE CLAP
2360 Chemin Ste-Foy
Ste-Foy, PQ G1V 4H2

PHONE: (418) 653-2470
FAX: (418) 653-6018

CONTACT: Michel Aubé, Editor **DESCRIPTION:** Published by Cinéma Le Clap. Circulation 99,500. French language publication. Issued 8 times a year. Established in 1986.
WRITERS: All writing handled in-house.
PHOTOGRAPHERS: Only uses photos from movies.
NOTES: Do not submit query letters, resumés, or portfolios. They are not interested.

LE MAGAZINE PME see PME Magazine for Quebec

LE MAITRE D'OEUVRE
1250 rue Nobel
Boucherville, PQ J4B 5K1

PHONE: (514) 599-5106
FAX: (514) 599-5157

CONTACT: Marcel Soucy, Editor **DESCRIPTION:** Published by Groupe Ro-na Dismat. Published 4 times a year in French. Established in 1989.
WRITERS: They are happy to accept a faxed resumé or a query letter. They will give a byline. They purchase exclusive rights. No kill fee. They publish 2 regular issues with house plans, a country cottage house issue, deck plan issue, and an English issue at the beginning of May, as part of Le Maitre d'Oeuvre.
PHOTOGRAPHERS: Have an in-house photographer. Welcomes portfolios of photographers with expertise in house design, renovations and the like. Colour transparencies are preferred. Captions not necessary. Negotiable pay.
NOTES: "I really appreciate when I receive some ideas for an article and if the ideas sound good to me then maybe the writer can have an order for that article. If I receive some information from a writer I would like them to specialize in house designs or renovations." Send a SASE with $5.95 to receive a free copy of their publication.

LE MAITRE ELECTRICIEN
c/o 8735 Lucien Plante
Montreal, PQ H2M 2M7

PHONE: (514) 738-2184
FAX: (514) 383-7691

CONTACT: Chantale Baar, Editor **DESCRIPTION:** Published by Corporation of Master Electricians of Quebec. Circulation 9,500. French language publication. Issued 8 times a year. Established in 1954.

LE MAITRE IMPRIMEUR
255 Monteé Séraphin, Unit 13
Ste-Adéle, PQ J0R 1L0

PHONE: (514) 227-7300
FAX: (514) 229-4710

CONTACT: Charles-Henri Dubé, Editor Jules Coté, Publisher **DESCRIPTION:** Published by L'Association des Arts Graphicques du Quebec Inc. Circulation 4,500. French language publication. Publishes articles on a graphics arts theme about printing or pre-press operations. Published monthly. Established in 1937.
WRITERS: Will accept query letters or a faxed resumé to be kept on file.

PHOTOGRAPHERS: Will accept a portfolio of material from professional photographers. Looking for "a profile of major enterprises in colour (slides or prints). We need a caption for proper identification please." Payment negotiable.
NOTES: Unsolicited materials will not be returned with SASE. Sample copy available if you are a graphics arts writer.

MALAHAT REVIEW
University of Victoria
Box 1700
Victoria, BC   V8W 2Y2

PHONE: (604) 721-8524
FAX: (604) 721-8653

CONTACT: Derk Wynand, Editor
Marlene Cookshaw, Assoc. Editor   **DESCRIPTION:** Published by University of Victoria. Circulation 2,000.   Literary magazine established in 1967.
WRITERS: Publishes fiction, poetry and book reviews in a variety of styles. Send 5-10 poems and up to 20 pages of fiction or drama. Pays $25 per magazine page. Unsolicited material welcome, however, submit only one manuscript at a time. 100% freelance work, approximately 30 features per issue. No expenses paid. Preference given to Canadians. "We have no preconceived notions, we will publish anything as long as it is not offensive. The only thing we are concerned with is excellence." Will give a byline. Send your submission with SASE. No query letters please. "We return all material and will comment on it. Please use Canadian stamps on return envelopes if mailing from the US. If we accept your work we always publish it." Simultaneous submissions accepted.
PHOTOGRAPHERS: Stock photography is purchased. Send portfolio. Submissions will be returned quickly if you send SASE. Any format accepted. Pays $100 for a cover; $25 per inside page.
NOTES: For sample copy send SASE and a $7 cheque.

MANITOBA BUSINESS
8 Donald Street
Winnipeg, MB   R3L 2T8

PHONE: (204) 477-4620
FAX: (204) 284-3255

CONTACT: Ritchie Gage, Editor   **DESCRIPTION:** Published by Canada Wide Magazines Ltd.   Circulation 3,700.   General business magazine focusing on the Manitoba reader. Articles include profiles of companies, personality profiles, and how-to stories related to the business world. Published 10 times a year. Established in 1978.
NOTES: Contact by phone before submitting a portfolio. Do not submit unsolicited manuscripts. Pay is negotiable. Byline is given. Purchases first North American serial rights.

MANITOBA CO-OPERATOR
Box 9800, 220 Portage Avenue
Winnipeg, MB   R3C 3K7

PHONE: (204) 934-0401
FAX: (204) 934-0480

CONTACT: John W. Morriss, Editor   **DESCRIPTION:** Published by Manitoba Cooperator Publications/Division of Manitoba Pool Elevators.   Circulation 37,000.   Contains rural Manitoba-based articles. A weekly agricultural newspaper established in 1925.
WRITERS: Freelance writers are seldom used. Almost never buys on spec. Pay varies. Materials returned with SASE.

PHOTOGRAPHERS: Uses freelance photographers who have been with the publication for a long time. Will accept new submissions, in portfolio form, from those who understand what the publication needs. Colour photos used only for cover; buy 51 a year. Formats include: 8x10 or 5x7 b&w's which are professionally developed. $50 per photo.
NOTES: "I hate query letters. There is nothing worse than someone who queries you and has never seen your publication." Sample copy available, send SASE.

MANITOBA HIGHWAY NEWS see Western Canada Highway News

MANITOBA RESTAURANT NEWS see Western Restaurant News

THE MANITOBA TEACHER   **PHONE:** (204) 888-7961
191 Harcourt Street   **FAX:** (204) 831-0877
Winnipeg, MB R3J 3H2

CONTACT: Raman Job, Managing Editor   Joy Montgomery, Production Editor
DESCRIPTION: Published by Manitoba Teachers' Society. Circulation 18,600. Focuses on education in Manitoba. Readers include teachers and others involved in education. Articles are geared to public school teachers and others interested in public school education in Manitoba. Published 9 times a year. Established in 1919.
WRITERS: Freelance articles accepted but are not paid for. Nine articles accepted annually by query letter. Unsolicited materials returned with SASE. Sample copy available with SASE.
PHOTOGRAPHERS: Stock photographers may submit query letter or portfolio. Pay is minimal.

MANITOULIN EXPOSITOR
Box 369   **PHONE:** (705) 368-2744
Little Current, ON P0P 1K0   **FAX:** (705)368-3822

CONTACT: Jane Story, Editor   **DESCRIPTION:** Circulation 5,350. Publishes human interest stories. Issued weekly.
WRITERS: 10-20% freelance written. Contact with faxed resumé or query letter. Pay negotiable under $50. Byline is given.
PHOTOGRAPHERS: Use their own photographers; however you may submit a portfolio for consideration.
NOTES: Sample copy available with SASE.

MANITOULIN RECORDER
P.O. Box 235   **PHONE:** (705) 282-2003
Gore Bay, ON P0P 1H0   **FAX:** (705) 282-2432

CONTACT: Margaret Robinson, Editor   **DESCRIPTION:** Published by Manitoulin Media Inc. Circulation 4,500. A general interest newspaper with articles pertaining to seniors' issues, "how-to" in areas from photography to environmental issues. Weekly newspaper.

WRITERS: 2% new freelance writers hired each year. A faxed query letter or resumé is fine. Pay is negotiable. Publish a byline. Will return unused materials if requested and SASE.
PHOTOGRAPHERS: Photographers not hired. Do not send submissions.
NOTES: "I'm looking for special things, you know last year we did a series on photography that was done by a freelancer. We have a high senior population and this is a high tourism area - something like 'eco-tourism'. Submissions must be good quality and aimed at a general interest audience."

MANUFACTURING AND PROCESS AUTOMATION
395 Matheson Blvd. East   **PHONE:** (905) 890-1846
Mississauga, ON L4Z 2H2   **FAX:** (905) 890-5769

CONTACT: Klaus Pirker, Publisher   **DESCRIPTION:** Published by Kerrwil Publications. Circulation 14,878. Published 6 times a year. Established in 1986.

MARIAGE QUEBEC
740 Ouest Notre-Dame Suite 780   **PHONE:** (514) 392-9030
Montreal, PQ H3C 3X6   **FAX:** (514) 392-0328

CONTACT: Janine Saine, Editor   **DESCRIPTION:** Published by Key Publishing, Suzanne Hurst, Publisher. Circulation 22,300. French language publication focusing on the future bride and groom. Covers all the details of wedding preparation. Published twice a year. Established in 1989.
WRITERS: 50-100% freelance written. "We probably assign eight stories an issue to freelance writers, about four of them from new freelancers. Some are features, some are not. The editor writes for us and hands out everything else to freelance writers." Contact the publisher, or the editor about new work." A query letter, faxed resumé or sample article is acceptable. "If someone sends us an idea or summary of what they have in mind we will definitely respond to it." Pays $100-$500 for articles.
PHOTOGRAPHERS: Jean-Marc Martin, Art Director or Suzanne Hurst, Publisher will accept portfolios and query letters about photography work. "If you can come in, we will set up an appointment for portfolio viewing." 4x5 transparencies are ideal, although we also reproduce from prints." Captions preferred. Photographers are hired on team assignments. "We have gone to Greece and France." Approximately 20 photos purchased annually.
NOTES: "The one thing I do not like is when writers or photographers phone us and say, 'I am in town today, can you see me today', obviously we can't always do that. If they say, 'I'll be in Montreal a month or two weeks from now,' I can coordinate a meeting." Copies of the publication are available for $3.95 with SASE.

MARINE TRADES
5805 Whittle Road, Suite 208
Mississauga, ON L4Z 2J1

NOTES: Could not reach. Phone number is not in service (416) 568-4131.

MARKET AND WATERFRONT
320 Danforth Avenue #204
Toronto, ON M4K 1P3

NOTES: Could not reach. Phone number is not in service (416) 461-1090.

MARKETING
777 Bay Street
Toronto, ON M5W 1A7

PHONE: (416) 596-5858
FAX: (416) 593-3170

CONTACT: Wayne Gooding, Editor   **DESCRIPTION:** Published by Maclean Hunter Ltd. Circulation 11,800. Magazine covering marketing news and trends across Canada. Published weekly. Established in 1908.
WRITERS: For news stories, contact Stan Sutter; for feature stories, contact Margaret Bream.
PHOTOGRAPHERS: Contact Dean Mitchell for photography.
NOTES: A query letter to the above names is most appropriate.

MARKETNEWS
364 Supertest Road 2 Fl.
North York, ON M3J 2M2

PHONE: (416) 667-9945
FAX: (416) 667-0609

CONTACT: Robert Franner, Editor   **DESCRIPTION:** Published by Bomar Publishing Inc. Circulation 10,100. Consumer electronics and home computing publication. Is also distributed to retail stores. Published monthly. Established in 1975.
WRITERS: "40% freelance written. Articles are assigned. We presently have a number of regular contributors. Contact the editor directly by phone, fax or mail. We want someone with a knowledge of consumer electronics or the computing area." Writers' guidelines are not available. "Once we have qualified a writer then we will supply them with sample copies."
PHOTOGRAPHERS: "Most of our photography comes from equipment suppliers."

MARKHAM MONTH
3335-14 Avenue Suite #1
Markham, ON L3R 0H3

PHONE: (905) 475-1743
FAX: (905) 475-1029

CONTACT: Deborah Smith, Editor   **DESCRIPTION:** Published by Thornhill Publications, Peter Grosskurth, Publisher. Circulation 24,000. Published monthly. Established in 1979.
WRITERS: 2% new freelance writers used. Resumé and sample of work preferred. No kill fee. Does not purchase rights.
PHOTOGRAPHERS: Send portfolio or query letter for new submissions. Black and white prints preferred.
NOTES: Unsolicited materials will not be returned with SASE. Also publishes Thornhill Month, and Richmond Hill Month. Community-based newspapers with the same requirements for photographers and writers as those listed above. Some preference is given to local people who know the area.

MARQUEE ENTERTAINMENT MAGAZINE

77 Mowat Avenue #621   **PHONE:** (416) 538-1000
Toronto, ON M6K 3E3   **FAX:** (416) 538-0201

CONTACT: Jack Gartner, Managing Editor **DESCRIPTION:** Published by Marquee Publications Ltd. Circulation 698,000. Features stories, previews, and profiles of upcoming movies and personalities, music and fashion. Distributed in Sun newspapers across Canada. Published 9 times a year. Established in 1976.
WRITERS: "We don't purchase often, maybe 5 articles per year. We are looking for star profiles, interviews with personalities, and set location interviews. We use 500-700 words and our fee ranges." Writers' guidelines are not available. Contact the editor with submissions or a query.
PHOTOGRAPHERS: "We very rarely purchase photos. We do if colour photos come with the article."

LE MART

300 Laurentian Blvd   **PHONE:** (514) 747-5580
St Laurent, PQ H4M 2L4

CONTACT: Gilles Verronneau **DESCRIPTION:** Published by Communications Vero Inc. French language publication. Business tabloid with new product information for the construction and mining industries. Published monthly.
WRITERS: "Most of our editorial comes from freelancers, 6 articles with photos per issue. We have two or three regular contributors. Writers may solicit us with ideas on topics related to the magazine, if it's interesting we will negotiate a price. Most of our publications have editorial themes; stories are ordered ahead of time. Contact us by phone with supporting documentation by fax. All of our publications are trade magazines. Most assignments are action stories, job description and on-sight reporting. We prefer it on diskette, Mac or IBM, in WordPerfect or Microsoft Word. Stories don't go beyond three type-written pages, double spaced. We have a standard rate of $40 per typewritten page, depending on the writer. If there are expenses involved we will give a higher rate." Guidelines are not available.
PHOTOGRAPHERS: "Most of the time we buy photography with the article. If we have a three page text we will ask for at least one photo, or more depending on the subject."
NOTES: "Usually we buy exclusive rights for one issue. We may consider previously published work if it wasn't in a competitive magazine." Sample copies are available free upon request. Also publishes La Fournee, L'Hospitlite and La Revue Municipale.

MASTHEAD

1606 Sedlescomb Drive #8   **PHONE:** (905) 625-7070
Mississauga, ON L4X 1M6   **FAX:** (905) 625-4856

CONTACT: Doug Bennet, Editor **DESCRIPTION:** Published by North Island Publishing Ltd. Circulation 4,200. Trade magazine focusing on the Canadian magazine publishing industry. Articles include news happenings in the publishing world, major trends, concerns and people profiles. Readers are managers and publishers. Published 10 times a year. Established in 1987.
WRITERS: 20% freelance written. Contact editor with query letter. Returns unsolicited materials with SASE. Pays $75-$500, depending upon length. A 50% kill fee is offered. Byline is given. Guidelines available. Send 9x12" SASE for a sample copy.

PHOTOGRAPHERS: Occasionally hires photographers on assignment. Contact with query letter. Pay is negotiable.
NOTES: "We use: correspondents outside of Toronto who report on the magazine industry; 'first-person' opinion pieces about what it's like to work in the industry; and the occasional feature article commissioned to 'experts' in the magazine publishing field." Also publishes The Graphic Monthly and Mississauga Business Times.

MATERIAL HISTORY REVIEW

National Museum of
Science & Technology
Box 9724, Ottawa Terminal
Ottawa, ON K1G 5A3

PHONE: (613) 991-3079
FAX: (613) 990-3636

CONTACT: Geoff Rider, Managing Editor **DESCRIPTION:** Focuses on new methods of research through the documentation of cultural artifacts. Includes social history, history of technology and architecture, anthropology, geography, and art history. Published bi-annually.

MATERIALS MANAGEMENT & DISTRIBUTION

777 Bay Street 6 Fl.
Toronto, ON M5W 1A7

PHONE: (416) 596-5708
FAX: (416) 596-5554

CONTACT: Rob Robertson, Editor   **DESCRIPTION:** Published by Maclean Hunter Ltd. Circulation 19,000. Focuses on material distribution, handling and storage. Published monthly. Established in 1956.
WRITERS: 10-24% freelance written. Pays $100-$500 for articles. Guidelines available; phone inquiries welcome.
PHOTOGRAPHERS: Photography accepted. Send query with samples of work.

MATURITY

313 Archer Street
New Westminster, BC V3L 4Y7

PHONE: (604) 540-7911
FAX: (604) 540-7912

CONTACT: Audrey Gill, Editor   **DESCRIPTION:** Published by CYN Investments Ltd. Circulation 155,000. Complimentary publication available at the Bank of Montreal, targeting the 50+ age group. Articles include financial and travel features. Published 6 times a year. Established in 1984.
WRITERS: Contact with query letter and sample of work with SASE. Writers' guidelines are available.
PHOTOGRAPHERS: Uses colour cover photos. Cover submissions accepted with SASE.

MCGILL NEWS

3605 Mountain Street
Montreal, PQ H3G 2M1

PHONE: (514) 398-3549
FAX: (514) 398-7338

CONTACT: Janice Paskey, Editor **DESCRIPTION:** Published by The Graduate Society of McGill University. Circulation 120,000. Features articles on current affairs, entertainment, book and CD reviews, medical and scientific research as well as alumni profiles. Published quarterly.

WRITERS: Buys 2 freelance pieces per issue. Accepts query letters followed by a call. "I tend to approach writers who are alumni in the field. Generally if we have a good query we will consider it." Byline is given. Pay $500 per 1,500 word article. 10% kill fee. Submissions returned with SASE. Purchases one-time rights. "We generate most of the ideas. Not a lot of our really good stuff has come in through query letters. Interesting query letters take a certain talent, you must give us a different slant on a subject that has been done before. We use French and English." Writers' guidelines not available.
PHOTOGRAPHERS: 100% freelance. Phone inquiries welcome. Submissions returned with SASE. Pays $100-200 per photo. Colour or b&w accepted. Captions preferred. Rarely use stock photography.
NOTES: Send 9x12" SASE with appropriate postage for a sample copy.

LE MEDECIN DU QUEBEC
1440 St. Catherines Street West
Suite 1000
Montreal, PQ   H3G 1R8

PHONE: (514) 878-1911
FAX: (514) 878-4455

CONTACT: Dr. Georges Boileau, Editor-in-Chief   **DESCRIPTION:** Published by The Federation of General Practitioners of Quebec. Circulation 19,350. French language publication. Professional magazine for General Practitioners in the province of Quebec. Features a section on Continuing Medical Education and a news section which deals with social affairs and health issues. Published monthly. Established in 1965.
NOTES: All writing and photography is done in-house.

LE MEDECIN VETERINAIRE DU QUEBEC
795 Ave. du Palais #200
Saint-Hyacinthe, PQ   J2S 5C6

PHONE: (514) 774-1427
FAX: (514) 774-7635

CONTACT: Dr. Guy-Pierre Martineau   **DESCRIPTION:** Published by Corp. professionelle des médecins vétérinaires du Quebec. Circulation 2,200. French language publication. Focuses on veterinary medicine. Issued quarterly. Established in 1971.

MEDIA WAVE
1497 Marine Drive #300
West Vancouver, BC   V7T 1B8

NOTES: Could not reach. Phone number is not in service (604) 926-8765.

MEDIA WEST
3151 Westmount Place West
Vancouver, BC   V7V 3G4

NOTES: Could not reach. Phone number is not in service (604) 926-8765.

THE MEDICAL POST

777 Bay Street
Toronto, ON   M5W 1A7

PHONE: (416) 596-5767
FAX: (416) 593-3177

CONTACT: Derek Cassels, Editor   **DESCRIPTION:** Published by Maclean Hunter. Circulation 44,000. Tabloid publication containing news and features of interest to Canadian physicians. Articles focus on research, education, political and economic issues. Published 44 times a year. Established in 1965.
WRITERS: All writing is done in-house.
PHOTOGRAPHERS: "We need good cover shots. Phone or fax work to Pat Rich, Assignment Editor (416) 596-5771. We use colour prints."

MEDICINE NORTH AMERICA

Catherine Addleman, Managing Editor
400 McGill Street, 3rd Fl.
Montreal, PQ   H2Y 2G1

PHONE: (514) 397-9393
FAX: (514) 397-0228

CONTACT: Dr. Ian R. Hart, Editor   **DESCRIPTION:** Published by Parkers Publishing. Circulation 30,000. Published monthly. Established in 1980.
NOTES: This publication never accepts freelance material.

MEDISCAN

1867 Alta Vista Drive
Ottawa, ON   K1G 3Y6

PHONE: (613) 731-9331
FAX: (613) 523-0937

CONTACT: Debbie A. Rupert, Managing Editor   **DESCRIPTION:** Published by Canadian Medical Association. Circulation 5,400. Journal for medical students. Published 3 times a year. Established in 1980.
NOTES: We are not welcoming new submissions.

MEETINGS AND INCENTIVE TRAVEL

777 Bay Street, 5th Floor
Toronto, ON   M5W 1A7

PHONE: (416) 596-2697
FAX: (416) 596-5810

CONTACT: Lori Bak, Editor   **DESCRIPTION:** Published by Maclean Hunter Ltd. Circulation 9,200. Business publication for meeting, convention and incentive travel planners. Published seven times a year. Established in 1972.
WRITERS: "We purchase five stories an issue. Everything is assigned and all rates are negotiable. We never accept anything that is unsolicited. The best thing is to write me with a solid story idea and don't forget that we are a corporate business publication not a vacation travel magazine. I don't have a great need for material right now." No phone calls please.
PHOTOGRAPHERS: "We normally buy photography with the story, colour preferred. We also hire on assignment."
NOTES: Sample copy free upon request.

MEETINGS MONTHLY
Box 365
Montreal, PQ H2Y 3H1

PHONE: (514) 274-0004
FAX: (514) 274-5884

CONTACT: Guy J. Jonkman, Chief Editor   **DESCRIPTION:** Published by Publicom Inc. Circulation 12,200. Monthly meeting-planners trade publication. Articles include how to hold a meeting, choosing restaurants, accommodation and other issues relating to planning meetings. Issued 10 times a year. Established in 1988.
WRITERS: "Regular freelancers are already established, however, writers could submit a query letter and samples of their work. No phone inquiries please. Articles are 800 words in length. Fees negotiable. Guidelines are available. Sample copy free with SASE.
PHOTOGRAPHERS: Send portfolio or write a query letter. No phone calls please.
NOTES: Also publishes Congré Mensuel.

MEMO
3715 Lacombe Avenue #200
Montreal, PQ H3T 1M3

PHONE: (514) 341-7916
FAX: (514) 341-2644

CONTACT: Michel Guénard   **DESCRIPTION:** Published by Les Editions du Rineva. Circulation 22,000. In-flight magazine for Air Aviance, the original carrier for Air Canada. Contains articles on Quebec technology, industry and the economy. Published 6 times a year. Established in 1989.
WRITERS: 80% freelance written. Contact editor with query letter. Pay is negotiable. Returns unsolicited materials with SASE. Send 9x12" SASE for a sample copy.
PHOTOGRAPHERS: 95% assigned to in-house photographers. Contact editor with query letter. Returns unsolicited colour prints with SASE. Purchases 20 photos per year.
NOTES: "I occasionally need a photographer to cover a location shoot outside of the Quebec area."

MENZ
4880 Lacombe Ave.
Montreal, PQ H3W 1R5

PHONE: (514) 449-0722
FAX: (514) 449-1177

CONTACT: Tina Costakos, Editor-in-Chief **DESCRIPTION:** Published by L'integrale Services Graphiques. Circulation 60,000. The only men's lifestyle publication in Canada. Articles on health, lifestyle, gastronomy, and club scenes. Targets the 19 to 49 year old male. Published 6 times a year. Established in 1984.
WRITERS: Writers please fax with a sample of work. "Tell your writers to inundate me. I am under the impression we have no Canadian writers left. I am especially in the market for writers. We like to give new people a chance." Byline is given. Pay is negotiable.
PHOTOGRAPHERS: Freelance photographers may submit a portfolio or send a query letter. No phone calls please.
NOTES: "Read the publication before you contact me. We prefer articles on Mac diskettes."

METALWORKING PRODUCTION & PURCHASING
135 Spy Court
Markham, ON L3R 5H6

PHONE: (905) 477-3222
FAX: (905) 477-4320

CONTACT: Maurice Holtham, Editor   **DESCRIPTION:** Published by Action Communications. Circulation 18,100. Published bi-monthly. Established in 1974.

NOTES: "Everything we need is provided for in-house and we do not foresee a time when we will need to look outside for more help."

METROPOLITAN TORONTO BUSINESS JOURNAL
#1 First Canadian Place, Box 60   **PHONE:** (416) 366-6811
Toronto, ON M5X 1C1   **FAX:** (416) 366-5620

CONTACT: Steve Bernhut   **DESCRIPTION:** Published by Metropolitan Toronto Board of Trade. Circulation 12,000. Special interest magazine. This award-winning publication is aimed at a sophisticated audience that includes Canada's business leaders. Features include: business; personality profiles; and economic news pertaining to greater Toronto area.
WRITERS: "We don't currently purchase work."
PHOTOGRAPHERS: "We are looking for editorial photography to illustrate stories - mostly people shots. For a cover or major full-page shot we pay $350 for black & white or colour." Contact the art director, Rodney Frost by phone.

LE MEUNIER
2323 Versant Nord Boul.   **PHONE:** (418) 688-9221
Ste-Foy, PQ G1N 4P4   **FAX:** (418) 688-3575

CONTACT: André J. Pilon, Editor   **DESCRIPTION:** Published by L'Association Professionnelle des Meuniers du Quebec Local 115. Circulation 16,000. French language publication. Focuses on agriculture. Distributed mainly in Quebec. Established in 1964.
NOTES: "We don't purchase freelance material."

MICRO-GAZETTE
434A Isabey Street   **PHONE:** (514) 735-2992
Saint-Laurent, PQ H4T 1V3   **FAX:** (514) 735-1269

CONTACT: Gérald Gauthier, Editor   **DESCRIPTION:** Published by Micro-Gazette Inc. Circulation 12,000. French language publication. A computer magazine. Issued monthly. Articles for professional and amateur computer buffs. Established in 1986.
WRITERS: Submit writing samples by mail or fax only. Gives byline. Sample copies available with SASE. Pay is negotiable.
PHOTOGRAPHERS: Requirements handled in-house.

MILL PRODUCT NEWS
122625 Ingleton Avenue   **PHONE:** (604) 298-3004
Burnaby, BC V5C 4L8   **FAX:** (604) 291-1906

CONTACT: Toni Dabbs, Editor   **DESCRIPTION:** Published by Baum International Media. Circulation 18,197. Articles focus on pulp, paper and wood products. Published 6 times a year. Established in 1990. **NOTES:** All writing and photography is done in-house.

MINING IN ONTARIO
920 Yonge Street, 6th Floor
Toronto, ON M4W 3C7

NOTES: NO LONGER PUBLISHED

MINING REVIEW
3109B West 3 Ave.   **PHONE:** (604) 737-4759
Vancouver, BC V6K 1N2   **FAX:** 1(800)709-5551

CONTACT: Wendy Melanson, Editor   **DESCRIPTION:** Published by BC & Yukon
Chamber of Mines, Naylor Communications Ltd. Circulation 3,500. The articles are
chosen by the BC & Yukon Chamber of Mines and are related to the mining industry.
Published quarterly. Established in 1981.
WRITERS: If an article is of interest we present it to the association committee. If they
give the go-ahead we will run it. "If we hire somebody to write an article we own all rights.
We have a few writers who keep the rights, but generally we wouldn't do that." Byline
is given. Pay is negotiable - "As low as we can get it".
PHOTOGRAPHERS: All photography is done in-house.

MISSISSAUGA BUSINESS TIMES
1606 Sedlescomb Drive, #8   **PHONE:** (905) 625-7070
Mississauga, ON L4X 1M6   **FAX:** (905) 625-4856

CONTACT: Adam Gutteridge, Editor   **DESCRIPTION:** Published by North Island
Publishing Ltd. Circulation 20,000+. Provides business to business news for the area.
Published ten times a year. Established in 1983.
WRITERS: "We purchase 2 or 3 articles per month. We usually pay $250 per 1,000 words.
Contact us by phone or mail. I would like writers to send a published sample and one un-
edited sample. Our articles are all assigned." Writers' guidelines are available.
PHOTOGRAPHERS: "We do use a freelance photographer and have someone on staff
who takes photos as well. We generally request that writers include photos with their material.
We prefer colour prints."
NOTES: Sample copy free upon request depending on availability. Also available at select
restaurants, banks and hotels in the area. Also publishes The Graphic Monthly and Masthead.

MODEL AVIATION CANADA
5100 South Service Road Unit 9   **PHONE:** (905) 632-9808
Burlington, ON L7L 6A5   **FAX:** (905) 632-3304

CONTACT: Peter Perry, Editor   **DESCRIPTION:** Published by Model Aeronautics
Association of Canada. Circulation 13,000. A magazine for radio controlled model airplane
enthusiasts. Published 6 times a year. Established in 1955.
NOTES: This publication never purchases freelance material.

MODERN DAIRY

3269 Bloor Street West #205
Toronto, ON M8X 1E2

PHONE: (416) 239-8423
FAX: none

CONTACT: Ian Macnab, Editor **DESCRIPTION:** Published by Maccan Publishing Co. Ltd. Circulation 2,000. Published 5 times a year. Established in 1923.

MODERN DRAMA

University of Toronto Press,
Journals Dept., 5201 Dufferin Street
North York, ON M3H 5T8

PHONE: (416) 978-7984
FAX: (416) 667-7832

CONTACT: Dorothy Parker, Alan Thomas, David Blostein **DESCRIPTION:** Features bibliographies, essays, and interviews with famous theatrical creators, critics, and scholars from 1850 to present. Published quarterly. Established in 1958.
WRITERS: "Completed articles can be sent to the editors."
NOTES: Sample copy available free upon request.

MODERN PURCHASING

777 Bay Street 7 Fl.
Toronto, ON M5W 1A7

PHONE: (416) 596-5792
FAX: (416) 596-5866

CONTACT: Joe Terrett, Editor **DESCRIPTION:** Published by Maclean Hunter Ltd. Circulation 20,000. Business publication for private and public sector supply management professionals. Articles include professional/management, legal issues, industry, transportation, and office systems information for purchasing professionals. Published 10 times a year. Established in 1959.
WRITERS: Contact by sending resumé and samples of your work. Purchases 30 non-fiction articles a year. Hires writers on assignment and pays reasonable expenses. Gives byline. Average article 1,200 words.
PHOTOGRAPHERS: Stock photography is purchased. Photographers are hired on assignment. Purchases 5 or 6 photos per year. Colour transparencies, 4x5, preferred. Model releases and captions not necessary. Credit line is given. Contact with query letter, resumé and samples.

MODERN WOMAN

777 Bay Street 8 Fl.
Toronto, ON M5W 1A7

PHONE: (416) 596-5425
FAX: (416) 593-3197

CONTACT: Charlotte Empey, Editor **DESCRIPTION:** Published by Maclean Hunter Publishing. Circulation 500,000. "We are a national women's service magazine. We cover food, fashion, beauty, health, fitness, home decor, relationships, and parenting issues." Distributed with home-delivered Edmonton, Calgary, Ottawa and Toronto Sunday Sun newspapers. On newsstands everywhere.
WRITERS: "We purchase 5 or 6 articles per issue. Our pay scales are competitive. I prefer to negotiate a fee based on individual pieces because sometimes they may be short and require an enormous amount of research and that needs to be recognized; sometimes they may be longer but they are a first-person piece which requires very little research. Fax or mail a query letter. Samples of previous work is helpful. What makes our magazine different from other women's magazines is that when we do features, whether it's a health

or relationship piece, it's women's stories that are the focus of the piece, then we ask for expert overviews in a box or side bar. It's the anecdotes that really are the key to our pieces, this is very important. The other thing writers should be aware of and if they look at back issues it will become apparent is that we are a national magazine. I am looking for women's stories as well as expert resources across this country. I am not particularly interested in Toronto-centred stories. I am looking to find out what women in Vancouver, Calgary, Winnipeg and St. John think, not just women in Toronto. I tend not to assign on spec however I am quite happy to receive a finished manuscript especially if it is a writer who is just starting out and hasn't yet built a byline or portfolio. If they have an idea and go to the trouble of putting it together, I can see if they understand our magazine. Get copies of the magazine because we do things differently, more closely aligned with British mass market books than American magazines. It certainly makes me feel that someone has done their homework when I get story ideas that indicate the writer clearly understands what makes us us and not Chatelaine or Good Housekeeping." Writers' guidelines are available.

PHOTOGRAPHERS: "We hire on assignment and use primarily colour photos. For spot or portrait photography we pay $200; for features or service pieces such as fashion or beauty we pay $1,200 a day and $450 a half day. That includes film unless that is negotiated separately. Photographers should send us a mailer or sample. We are particularly looking to build photographers outside of the Toronto area. I am interested in fashion, beauty and people photographers.

NOTES: Considers previously published work. Considers simultaneous submissions. Purchases first North American French and English rights and electronic transmission rights.

MOGENSEN'S FARMERS ALMANAC
1172 Rose Marie Avenue
Sudbury, ON P3A 4E2

NOTES: NO LONGER PUBLISHED

MON BEBE
2260 des Patriotes Ste-Rose   **PHONE:** (514) 622-0091
Laval, PQ H7L 3K8   **FAX:** (514) 622-0099

CONTACT: Manon Leymone, Editor   **DESCRIPTION:** Published by Family Communications Inc. Circulation 53,000. French language publication. Focuses on post-natal care for expecting and new mothers. Published twice a year. Established in 1951.
WRITERS: "We usually have health specialists writing for us, however we do purchase occasionally. Send complete article (on spec) or submit a proposal. Articles must relate to baby and new mothers; health, new born care etc. We pay usually $75 per page."
PHOTOGRAPHERS: Purchases from stock. Uses colour and b&w. "We obtain our photos from a number of sources including stock agencies. We pay around $150 for an inside photo, covers are negotiated. Payment also depends on whether we use it for both the English and French magazines."
NOTES: This is the french version of Best Wishes.

MONARCHY IN CANADA

3050 Yonge Street, #206
Toronto, ON M4N 2K4

PHONE: (416) 482-4157
FAX: (416) 482-4157

CONTACT: Arthur Bousfield, Editor or Garry Toffoli, Associate Editor **DESCRIPTION:** Published by Fealty Enterprises in cooperation with the Monarchist League. Circulation 6,000. "A magazine about the monarchy, both historical and contemporary. We cover all royal tours, current constitutional and commonwealth issues, and international developments. We publish extensive book reviews and occasional articles on art exhibits etc." This quarterly magazine looks at the monarchy from a Canadian perspective.
WRITERS: "We occasionally buy articles. We have our own staff writers and have connections with people who often write for free. We are open to submissions of articles and we will pay, but we don't often buy. Contact the editor with a query idea. Article length averages 2,000 words. Payment is negotiable. Often we print articles from book writers and publish in exchange for advertising." Guidelines are available.
PHOTOGRAPHERS: "We have some staff photographers scattered around the country who provide photos of the royal tours. We do purchase stock and pay anywhere from $40-60 black & white inside. For colour we usually use our own pictures. We publish colour on the front and back covers and black & white inside. Often an author will provide their own illustrations or we use standard photos from our own collection. Generally photos have to be something we can't access ourselves. For royal tours or special events if there is a good picture we will pay for it. Photographers should contact the editor with a photocopy of the picture, a description and the price they have in mind. If they are local they can just phone." Guidelines are available.
NOTES: Purchases one-time rights. Unsolicited materials will be returned with SASE.

MONDAY MAGAZINE

1609 Blanshard Street
Victoria, BC V8W 2J5

PHONE: (604) 382-6188
FAX: (604) 381-2662

CONTACT: Sid Tafler, Editor **DESCRIPTION:** Published by Monday Publications Ltd. Circulation 49,000. Regional weekly news magazine with political, entertainment and business news. Established in 1975.
WRITERS: Up to 25% freelance written. "We have three writers on staff and have a number of regular freelancers. We suggest writers look at our paper to see our style and content and then just submit something." Pays $50-$500 for articles.
PHOTOGRAPHERS: They have an in-house photographer but would accept a query letter or portfolio of work from a photographer.
NOTES: Sample issue available for $1.49 plus large SASE.

LE MONDE DE L'AUTO

7575 Trans Canada Hwy #401
St Laurent, PQ H4T 1V6

PHONE: (514) 956-1361
FAX: (514) 956-1461

CONTACT: Luc Gagne, Editor **DESCRIPTION:** Published by World of Wheels Publishing. Circulation 30,000. French language publication. "A consumer magazine for car enthusiasts. Contains new model descriptions, road tests, feature stories about automotive topics, the vehicle industry, and phenomena that are in some way related to the automotive scene at large. We also publish motor sport and technology information." Published 6 times a year. Established in 1985.

WRITERS: "We occasionally purchase articles, up to 10 long and short pieces per issue. Most of it is on assignment and most writers have been regular contributors for the past 6 years. Our pay rate is 40¢ a word. Length depends on the topic. Call or write us with an idea. Though stories written in French are preferable we can translate. They are never as punchy as the original."

PHOTOGRAPHERS: "We do purchase photography. We prefer colour slides or prints and black & white prints. We look for vehicle, people and component shots. We pay $50 for photos. We don't buy much photography because our budget isn't large." Contact by mail or phone.

NOTES: Sample copy available free upon request. "We purchase exclusive rights, but it depends on the source."

LE MONDE JURIDIQUE

7423 de Fougeray   **PHONE:** (514) 353-3549
Anjou, PQ   H1K 3K2   **FAX:** (514) 353-4159

CONTACT: André Gagnon, Editor   **DESCRIPTION:** Published by Le Monde Juridique Inc. French language publication. A legal magazine for lawyers and judges in Quebec. Published monthly. Established in 1984.

WRITERS: "We have a number of regular writers. This is a very specialized field. Writers can call or fax a proposal."

PHOTOGRAPHERS: "We purchase photography. We both assign and purchase from stock. We buy 10 or more per month. We are covered in Montreal but elsewhere we are looking for ideas and photographs. Freelancers can call or send a fax describing their proposed project."

NOTES: This magazine can be found on newsstands in Quebec.

MONTREAL BUSINESS MAGAZINE

275 St. Jacques Street West #43   **PHONE:** (514) 286-8038
Montreal, PQ   H2Y 1M9   **FAX:** (514) 286-8038

CONTACT: Michael Carin, Editor   **DESCRIPTION:** Circulation 16,000. Directed to the managerial levels of Montreal businesses. Published bi-monthly in English. Established in 1988.

WRITERS: "We purchase an average of 3 articles per issue. We assign all our articles. We prefer a one-page proposal. We are interested in corporate profiles, wealth management issues, finance issues, business to business communication. Much of the publication is written by contributors in the business community. We look at anything that would be of interest to the Montreal business community - What's in it for me?" A style sheet is available.

PHOTOGRAPHERS: "Most of our subjects are happy to provide us with quality photographs."

NOTES: Sample copy available free upon request. This magazine is distributed through the Quebec edition of the Globe and Mail.

MONTREAL MIRROR
400 McGill Street, 1st Floor   **PHONE:** (514) 393-1010
Montreal, PQ H2Y 2G1   **FAX:** (514) 393-3173

CONTACT: Peter Scowen, Managing Editor   **DESCRIPTION:** Published by Communications Gratte-Ciel Ltée. Circulation 80,000. A weekly tabloid featuring articles on major issues written from a local perspective. Reviews restaurants, film, art, shows, books, and new music.
WRITERS: Contact editor with query letter or fax. Byline is given. Pay is negotiable.
PHOTOGRAPHERS: Contact editor with query letter or fax. Black and white prints, colour prints for cover. Freelancers sometimes hired on assignment. Pay is negotiable.

MONTREAL PLUS
5 Ville Marie Place #12500 Plaza Level   **PHONE:** (514) 871-4000
Montreal, PQ H3B 4Y2   **FAX:** (514) 871-1255

CONTACT: Joelle Ganguillet, Editor   **DESCRIPTION:** Published by Board of Trade of Metropolitan Montreal. Circulation 10,000. A bilingual trade publication featuring Board of Trade activities and profiles of the members. Published 8 times a year in English and French. Established in 1992.
WRITERS: Contact editor with query letter. Byline is given. Pays per word, will be negotiated when you are commissioned for an article.
PHOTOGRAPHERS: Not welcoming new submissions.
NOTES: Does not consider simultaneous submissions.

MONTREAL SCOPE
1253 McGill College #232   **PHONE:** (514) 933-3333
Montreal, PQ H3B 2Y5   **FAX:** (514) 931-9581

CONTACT: Nicolas Evreinow, Editor   **DESCRIPTION:** Published by Plaza Metro Ltd. Circulation 41,000. A city magazine featuring food, entertainment, people, places, and events. The monthly pocket-sized city guide is published in English and French. Established in 1976.
WRITERS: "We purchase work from four freelance writers. We don't need new writers at this time."
PHOTOGRAPHERS: All photography is done in-house.

MOSAIC: A JOURNAL FOR THE INTERDISCIPLINARY STUDY OF LITERATURE
Room 208, Tier Bldg.   **PHONE:** (204) 474-9763
University of Manitoba   **FAX:** (204) 261-9086
Winnipeg, MB R3T 2N2

DESCRIPTION: Circulation 1,000. A scholarly journal providing insights into a wide variety of disciplines.
Highlights the practical and cultural relevance of literary works. Published quarterly.
WRITERS: Does not pay. Byline is given. Returns unsolicited materials with SASE. No sample copies.
PHOTOGRAPHERS: All photography is done in-house.

MOTO JOURNAL
86 Parliament Street #3B   PHONE: (416) 362-7966
Toronto, ON M5A 2Y6   FAX: (416) 362-3950

CONTACT: Claude Leonard, Editor   DESCRIPTION: Published by Turbopress Inc.
Circulation 10,300. French language publication. Issued 10 times a year. Established in
1972.
NOTES: Also publishes Motorcycle Dealer & Trade.

MOTONEIGE QUEBEC
99 rue Brouillard   PHONE: (514) 252-3163
Vaudreuil, PQ J7V 6T5   FAX: (514) 254-2066

CONTACT: Pierre Vaillancourt, Editor-in-Chief   DESCRIPTION: Published by Les
Editions Motoneige Quebec Inc. Circulation 60,000. French language publication. Focuses
on snowmobiles and the sport. Six issues published in the fall/winter season. Established
in 1974.
WRITERS: Contact by phone with your ideas. Up to 25% freelance written. Pay is
negotiable. Byline is given. "One page of magazine is equal to three typed pages (25 lines
of 60 characters per line)." The rest of the guidelines will be discussed over the phone.
I would prefer to receive a well-written story with photographs taken by the writer. We
are open to new ideas. It should be written in French. However, if there was a story about
a snowmobile race between St. Paul, Minneapolis and Sault Ste. Marie, and a freelancer
could travel there and do the story in English then I will translate the story."
PHOTOGRAPHERS: Welcome new submissions for covers only.
NOTES: Purchases one-time rights.

MOTOR CARRIER MANAGER
920 Yonge Street, 6th Floor
Toronto, ON M4W 3C7

NOTES: NO LONGER PUBLISHED

MOTOR IN CANADA
1077 St. James Street, Box 6900
Winnipeg, MB R3C 3B1

NOTES: Could not locate. Phone number is not in service.

MOTOR TRUCK
1450 Don Mills Road   PHONE: (416) 445-6641
Don Mills, ON M3B 2X7   FAX: (416) 442-2213

CONTACT: Lou Smyrlis   DESCRIPTION: Published by Southam Business
Communications Inc. Circulation 31,000. A magazine for private and for hire trucking
fleets in Canada. Published monthly. Established in 1934.
WRITERS: "We do purchase material, 4-5 articles per issue. The people who write these
articles are on contract for an entire year. Sometimes someone will come in with a great
story idea and we will run with it. Produce a story line and call the editor. We may purchase

an article on spec, and pay when it runs. Our standard length is 1,000 words at around 30-40¢ a word. The best idea for a freelancer is to find a story angle that helps managers run trucking companies profitably." Contact with a query letter. Guidelines are available.
PHOTOGRAPHERS: "We do purchase some photography but not on a regular basis, maybe 1-2 a year where we hire a photographer to do our cover." Contact with a query letter.
NOTES: Buys first publishing rights. Sample copy available free upon request or check your local library.

MOTORCYCLE DEALER & TRADE

86 Parliament Street, Studio 3B	**PHONE:** (416) 362-7966
Toronto, ON M5A 2Y6	**FAX:** (416) 362-3950

CONTACT: Larry Tate, Editor   **DESCRIPTION:** Published by Turbopress Inc. Circulation under 10,000. Trade publication which is the "voice of what's happening" in Canada's motorcycle industry. Published six times a year. Established in 1978.
WRITERS: Contact editor with query letter. Less than 10% freelance written. Pays from $50-$500 for articles.
PHOTOGRAPHERS: Contact editor with query letter.
NOTES: Also publishes Moto Journal.

MOVING TO..

44 Upjohn Road	**PHONE:** (416) 441-1168
Don Mills, ON M3B 2W1	**FAX:** (416) 441-1641

CONTACT: Lorraine Hunter, Editor   **DESCRIPTION:** Published by Moving Publications Ltd. Circulation varies from city to city. Annual publication that helps people relocate in unfamiliar communities. Articles cover shopping, dining, education, real estate, and transportation. Separate editions serving Alberta, Hamilton area, Toronto area, Vancouver and BC, Winnipeg and Manitoba, Montreal and Ottawa. Established in 1973.
NOTES: Not looking for new contributors at this time.

MSOS JOURNAL

697 Carter Avenue, Suite B	**PHONE:** (204) 453-8502
Winnipeg, MB R3M 2C3	**FAX:** (204) 475-6853

CONTACT: Irvin Kroeker, Editor Ray Gislason, Advertising Director **DESCRIPTION:** Published by Manitoba Society of Seniors. Circulation 30,000. Aimed at Manitobians 55+. Publishes legal, financial, travel, recreation, and health news. "The mandate of the Manitoba Society of Seniors is to be an advocacy organization for seniors and the issues that concern seniors. Their main purpose is to improve the quality of life for seniors." Published 12 times a year. Established in 1979.
WRITERS: "We welcome a query letter or faxed resumé." Will return any material with SASE. Pays under $50 for articles. Guidelines are available. If you publish elsewhere, a courtesy line. Byline is given.
PHOTOGRAPHERS: "We are always looking for good stuff. It's a struggle to come up with new, good, creative ideas, so we are interested in seeing new photographs. We have done photo spreads in past issues. We purchase about a dozen photos per year. Either b&w or colour prints, 5x7 minimum size. Captions are preferred."

NOTES: "We shy away from anything that gives a negative image of seniors. We move toward a positive image of seniors and we don't deal with frailty, we deal with health. We shy away from photos or writing about people in the hospital."

MTL
8270 Mountain Sights Avenue, Suite 201
Montreal, PQ H4P 2B7

NOTES: Could not locate. Phone number is not in service.

MUNICIPAL BUSINESS CANADA
Jerry Skinner, Editor
Calgary, AB   **PHONE:** (403) 236-7298
T2C 2X5 (403) 279-5151

CONTACT: 200 Rivercrest Drive S.E., Suite 240 **DESCRIPTION:** Circulation Published quarterly.
NOTES: All writing and photography is done in-house.

MUNICIPAL MONITOR
80 West Beaver Creek #18   **PHONE:** (905) 771-7333
Richmond Hill, ON L4B 1H3   **FAX:** (905) 771-7336

CONTACT: Dennis Mellersh, Editor   **DESCRIPTION:** Published by Association of Municipal Clerks and Treasurers of Ontario, Kenilworth Publishing Inc. Circulation 2,500. A business magazine. Articles include municipal government issues. Published 6 times a year. Established in 1967.
WRITERS: Mostly done in-house. Contact editor with query letter. Byline is given. Pay is negotiable.
PHOTOGRAPHERS: Mostly done in-house. Contact editor with query letter.
NOTES: Also publishes Grainmaster, Signs, SPI Plastics, and Registered Nurse.

MUNICIPAL WORLD
Box 399   **PHONE:** (519) 633-0031
St. Thomas, ON N5P 3V3   **FAX:** (519) 633-1001

CONTACT: Michael J. Smither, Editor   **DESCRIPTION:** Published by Municipal World Inc. Circulation 7,000. Journal for elected and appointed staff of local and provincial government as well as taxpayers. Articles about municipal law. Published monthly. Established in 1891.
WRITERS: Contact this publication by mail. Will return articles with SASE if requested. Less than 10% freelance written. Byline is given. Pay is negotiable. Considers simultaneous submissions. Send $4.10 and 9x12" SASE for a sample copy.
PHOTOGRAPHERS: All photography is done in-house.
NOTES: "We are looking for freelance writers who can take photos to go with their article. It must be relevant and well-written, pertaining to our subject areas. We may hold an article for up to six months before we use it."

MUSCLE MAG INTERNATIONAL
52 Bramsteele Unit 2
Brampton, ON L6W 9M5

NOTES: Could not locate. Phone number is not in service (416) 457-3030.

MUSE
280 Metcalfe Street #400   PHONE: (613) 567-0099
Ottawa, ON K2P 1R7   FAX: (613) 233-5438

CONTACT: Aline Michaud, Managing Editor DESCRIPTION: Published by Canadian Museums Association. Circulation 2,000. Contains museum-based photography and visuals, feature articles and commentary, regular exhibition and book reviews, and sections providing practical information. Published quarterly in English and French. Established in 1983. WRITERS: Articles written by people who work in Canadian museums. No payment given. Returns unsolicited materials with SASE.
PHOTOGRAPHERS: Receives photographs from the museum community. Does not pay for them.

MUSIC EXPRESS MAGAZINE
219 Dufferin Street, Ste. 100
Toronto, ON M6K 3J1

NOTES: Could not locate. Phone number is not in service (416) 538-7500.

MUSIC MAGAZINE
219 Dufferin #100
Toronto, ON M6K 3J1

NOTES: Could not locate. Phone number is not in service (416) 323-9790.

MUSICWORKS: THE JOURNAL OF SOUND EXPLORATION
179 Richmond Street West
Toronto, ON M5V 1V3

NOTES: Could not locate. Phone number is not in service (416) 533-0192.

MUSKOKA BUSINESS MAGAZINE
Box 1600   PHONE: (705) 645-4463
Bracebridge, ON P1L 1V6   FAX: (705) 645-3928

CONTACT: John Challis, Editor DESCRIPTION: Published by Muskoka Publications Group Inc. Circulation 2,200. A business magazine for the Muskoka area. Published bi-monthly. Established in 1987.
NOTES: All writing and photography is done in-house.

MUSKOKA LIFE

Box 1600
Bracebridge, ON P1L 1V6

PHONE: (705) 645-4463
FAX: (705) 645-3928

CONTACT: John Challis, Editor   **DESCRIPTION:** Published by Muskoka Publications Group Inc. Circulation 20,000. Annual insert in the Muskoka Sun.
NOTES: All writing and photography is done in-house.

THE MUSKOKA SUN

Box 1600
Bracebridge, ON P1L 1V6

PHONE: (705) 645-4463
FAX: (705) 645-3928

CONTACT: John Challis, Editor   **DESCRIPTION:** Published by Muskoka Publications Group Inc. Circulation 20,000. Weekly tabloid published seasonally from Victoria Day to Thanksgiving. Articles geared to summer residents in Muskoka, featuring conversations with notable cottagers who live on the lake, heritage stories, cottage building, summer dining, health and environmental issues.
WRITERS: Contact editor with query letter. Publishes two 1,500-word articles per week; and shorter articles 500-1,000 words. Byline is given. Pay is minimal.
PHOTOGRAPHERS: Submit sample colour prints with SASE. Occasionally purchases stock. Minimal pay negotiated. "We are always on the look-out for a good cover photograph. Summer activities involving people - canoeing, fishing, swimming - would be great. All we seem to get from some of the local photographers are landscape or wildlife photos."
NOTES: Send $2 and 9x12" SASE for a sample copy. Also publishes The Active Generation.

THE MYSTERY REVIEW

Box 233
Colborne, ON K0K 1S0

PHONE: (613) 475-4440
FAX: (613) 475-3400

CONTACT: Barbara J. Davey, Editor   **DESCRIPTION:** Published by C. Von Hessert & Assoc. Circulation 2,000. Offers information and entertainment for mystery and suspense readers. Book reviews, author profiles and kids' features can be found inside this quarterly publication.
WRITERS: 80% freelance written. Contact editor with query letter. Byline is given. Pays honorarium. Purchases all rights. Sample copies not available. "Our magazine is available in bookstores, please do not request sample copies. We do not like to receive unsolicited articles. Find out what our needs are first."
PHOTOGRAPHERS: All photography is done in-house.

NANAIMO MAGAZINE

352 Commercial Street
Nanaimo, BC V9R 5G3

NOTES: Could not locate. Phone number is not in service (604) 754-9868.

NATIONAL
777 Bay Street 5 Fl.
Toronto, ON M5W 1A7

PHONE: (416) 596-5247
FAX: (416) 593-3162

CONTACT: J. Stuart Langford, Editor **DESCRIPTION:** Published by The Canadian Bar Association & Maclean Hunter. Circulation 35,400. Business publication with a unique look at legal news in Canada. Published 8 times a year in English and French.

NATIONAL INDUSTRIAL MAGAZINE
801 York Mills Road #201
Don Mills, ON M3B 1X7

PHONE: (416) 446-1404
FAX: (416) 446-0502

CONTACT: W.R. Bryson, Editor **DESCRIPTION:** Published by Brymell Publications Inc. Circulation 23,700. Industrial trade publication. Features articles on business, environmental and safety concerns related to the Canadian manufacturing industry. Published monthly. Established in 1976.
WRITERS: In-house writers. Articles are supplied. No payment attached. Returns unsolicited material with SASE.
PHOTOGRAPHERS: Photographs provided by agencies or writers.
NOTES: Formerly Ontario Industrial Magazine.

NATIONAL RADIO GUIDE
Box 48417 Bentall Centre
Vancouver, BC V7X 1A2

PHONE: (604) 688-0382
FAX: (604) 688-3105

CONTACT: Ms. C. Robertson, Editor **DESCRIPTION:** Circulation 40,000. CBC radio guide for listeners published monthly. Along with listings, readers will find articles about performers, information about upcoming programs and calendars for dramas, opera etc.
NOTES: All writing and photography is done in-house.

NATIONAL RUGBY POST
13228-76 Street
Edmonton, AB T5C 1B6

PHONE: (403) 476-0268
FAX: (403) 473-1066

CONTACT: David Graham, Editor **DESCRIPTION:** Published by National Rugby Post. Circulation 6,000. Dedicated to rugby football, mostly Canadian with some international coverage. Published 6 times a year. Established in 1985.
WRITERS: "We have several volunteer writers."
PHOTOGRAPHERS: "We pay a flat $50 fee for photographers whether we use one or more photographs."
NOTES: For a sample copy send 9x12" SASE with appropriate postage.

NATURAL LIFE
195 Markville Road
Unionville, ON L3R 4V8

NOTES: Could not locate. Phone number is not in service (416) 470-7930.

NATURE CANADA
1 Nicholas Street #520
Ottawa, ON K1N 7B7

PHONE: (613) 562-3447
FAX: (613) 562-3371

CONTACT: Barbara Stevenson, Editor **DESCRIPTION:** Published by Canadian Nature Federation. Circulation 15,000. Covers a broad range of natural history articles about animals and their habitats. Includes how-to stories and keeps readers up-to-date on the latest conservation and environmental issues. Published quarterly. Established in 1972.
WRITERS: Contact editor with query letter. Uses 20 features per year; 5-20 smaller articles freelance written. Pays 25¢ per word. Byline is given. Guidelines available. Kill fee offered if assigned article not run.
PHOTOGRAPHERS: Contact editor with query letter. Ask for photographer's guidelines. Purchase stock photography. Uses colour transparencies or 5x7 & 8x10 prints. Pays $40-100 colour inside.
NOTES: Purchases one-time rights. Send $5 and 9x12" SASE for a sample copy. "Keep in mind we use Canadian content only. Seasonal material must be received 6 months in advance. No fiction writing accepted."

NETWORK
920 Yonge Street, 6th Floor
Toronto, ON M4W 3C7

PHONE: (416) 961-1028
FAX: (416) 924-4408

CONTACT: Lori Knowles, Editor
DESCRIPTION: Published by Naylor Communications. Published annually.

NETWORK
237-8 Avenue SE
Calgary, AB T2G 5C3

PHONE: (403) 264-3270
FAX: (403) 264-3276

CONTACT: Richard Bronstein, Editor   **DESCRIPTION:** Published by OT Communications. Circulation under 10,000. Industry publication for cemeteries, monument builders, bronze makers and service supply companies. Published 6 times a year. Established in 1986.
WRITERS: Call with ideas or fax, either a query letter or resumé would be accepted. Pays $50-$100 for articles.
PHOTOGRAPHERS: All photography is done in-house.
NOTES: Sample copy available with SASE.

NETWORK
287 MacPherson Avenue
Toronto, ON M4V 1A4

PHONE: (416) 928-2909
FAX: (416) 928-1357

CONTACT: Stephen Hubbard, Editor **DESCRIPTION:** Published by Canadian Controlled Media Communications. Circulation 149,400. Entertainment magazine features pop/rock music interviews and reviews as well as some movie and video coverage. Published 6 times a year. Majority of magazines are distributed to Sam the Record Man retail stores.

NETWORK WORLD
501 Oakdale Road
North York, ON M3N 1W7

PHONE: (416) 746-7360
FAX: (416) 746-1421

CONTACT: John Pickett, Editor-in-Chief   **DESCRIPTION:** Published by Laurentian Technomedia Inc. Circulation 7,900. Published monthly. Established in 1991.
WRITERS: "This is a technical publication. We only buy freelance work occasionally. Primarily technical in nature, often reviews of consumer products, software and hardware. Writers must have a technical background because we serve a technical audience. Rates are substantially lower than CIO. 30¢ a word for 400-1,000 words."
PHOTOGRAPHERS: All photography is done in-house.
NOTES: Also publishes CIO Canada, Computerworld, Info Canada and Reseller World.

NEW BIOTECH
Box 7131, Station J
Ottawa, ON K2J 3L3

NOTES: Could not locate. Phone number is not in service (613) 567-1417.

THE NEW BRUNSWICK ANGLICAN
773 Glengarry Place
Fredericton, NB E3B 5Z8

PHONE: (506) 459-5358
FAX: (506) 459-5358

CONTACT: Ana Watts, Editor   **DESCRIPTION:** Published by Diocese of Fredericton. A church publication issued ten times a year. Established in 1977.
WRITERS: "No work is purchased. We have a lot of material submitted free of charge by people in the Diocese."
PHOTOGRAPHERS: "No photography is purchased."

NEW EQUIPMENT NEWS
204 Richmond Street West
Toronto, ON M5V 1V6

PHONE: (416) 599-3737
FAX: (416) 599-3730

CONTACT: Barrie Lehman, Editor   **DESCRIPTION:** Published by Canadian Engineering Publications Ltd. Circulation 23,000. Tabloid style magazine featuring new industrial products. Published 10 times a year. Established in 1940.
NOTES: "Our publication does not lend itself to the freelance market. I do use technical stories on product applications but they generally come from the company trying to promote the product."

NEW FREEMAN
1 Bayard Drive
Saint John, NB E2L 3L5

PHONE: (506) 653-6806
FAX: (506)

CONTACT: W.L. Donovan, Editor   **DESCRIPTION:** Published by New Freeman Ltd., Diocese of Saint John, Moncton, Bathurst & Edmundston. Circulation 6,850. Published weekly. Established in 1900.
NOTES: All writing and photography is done in-house. "I do not wish to accept any submissions at this time."

NEW INTERNATIONALIST

1011 Bloor Street West, Suite 300
Toronto, ON M6H 1M1

PHONE: (416) 588-6478
FAX: (416) 537-6435

CONTACT: Editors: Richard Swift, Wayne Ellwood, Editors   **DESCRIPTION:** Circulation 75,000. Monthly magazine provides information on major issues concerning international development. Includes the politics of aid, militarism, and national and multinational exploitation of the developing countries.
WRITERS: Contact editor with query letter. Pays $275 per 1,000 words. Byline is given. Purchases one-time rights.
PHOTOGRAPHERS: Most work assigned to in-house photographers. Contact editor with query letter. Returns unsolicited colour transparencies with SASE.
NOTES: Send 9x12" SASE for a sample copy.

NEW MARITIMES

Box 31269
Halifax, NS B3K 5Y5

PHONE: (902) 425-6622

CONTACT: Scott Milsom   **DESCRIPTION:** Published by The New Maritimes Editorial Council. Circulation 2,000. Contains in-depth features on issues of interest to Maritimers. Includes politics, labour, history, culture, media and books. Published 6 times a year.
WRITERS: "We purchase 6 articles per year. Payment and length varies and is negotiated. Contact by phone or by mail with samples of work. We aren't interested in lifestyle material. We are interested in regional politics and culture.
PHOTOGRAPHERS: "We very occasionally purchase black & white material. We prefer photos with submitted articles." Contact the editor with a query letter.
NOTES: Sample copy available free upon request. Purchases all rights. Considers previously published work. Considers simultaneous submissions.

NEW MOTHER

269 Richmond Street West
Toronto, ON M5V 1X1

PHONE: (416) 596-8680
FAX: (416) 596-1991

CONTACT: Holly Bennett   **DESCRIPTION:** Published by Today's Parent Group. Focuses on newborns and first year baby care, breastfeeding, feeding, health and safety, clothing, and furnishings and parent care. Published bi-annually. French counterpart is Mere Nouvelle.
NOTES: Unsolicited manuscripts will not be returned. The magazine will not accept responsibility for lost manuscripts, photos or drawings.

THE NEW PACIFIC

1155 Robson Street #401
Vancouver, BC V6E 1B5

NOTES: NO LONGER PUBLISHED

NEW QUARTERLY
The University of Waterloo
ELPP, PAS 2082
Waterloo, ON N2L 3G1

PHONE: (519) 885-1211 EXT.2329

CONTACT: Mary Merikle   **DESCRIPTION:** Literary magazine promotes new kinds of writing and new writers by publishing poetry, essays on writing, short fiction and interviews. Published quarterly.
WRITERS: Freelance written. Contact this publication by phone or query letter. $100 per story; $20 for "postcard fiction" or poems. "We are not a university journal. We publish people from all over, including Canada, the US, Australia, Wales and Isle of Mann."
PHOTOGRAPHERS: All photography is done in-house.
NOTES: Purchases one-time rights. Send $5 & 9x12" SASE for a sample copy. We don't encourage simultaneous submissions.

NeWEST REVIEW
Box 394, R.P.O. University
Saskatoon, SK S7N 4J8

PHONE: (306) 934-1444
FAX: (306) 242-5004

CONTACT: Gail Youngberg, Editor Doris Larson, Manager   **DESCRIPTION:** Published by 1,000. Cultural magazine of news and opinion on arts, literature, social and political issues important to the prairie provinces. Publishes short stories, book, theatre, music reviews, and short features on prairie issues. Published 6 times a year. Established in 1975.
WRITERS: About 50% freelance written. Contact editor with query letter or faxed resumé. Payment for reviews and articles ranges from $25-$100. Kill fee offered. Writers' guidelines also available with SASE.
PHOTOGRAPHERS: We have done photo spreads in past issues. Submit a portfolio or fax a query letter. We use 5-10 photos per issue. Prefer b&w prints of any size. Prefer captioned material.
NOTES: Will return unsolicited material with SASE. Send $3 and a SASE for the latest issue. "We do pay people but not very much, unfortunately. We pay flat rates."

NEWFOUNDLAND AND LABRADOR BUSINESS JOURNAL
74 O'Leary Avenue
St John's, NF A1C 5W2

NOTES: Could not locate. Phone number is not in service (709) 722-6433.

THE NEWFOUNDLAND HERALD
Box 2015, Logy Bay Road
St. John's, NF A1C 5R7

PHONE: (709) 726-7060
FAX: (709) 726-8227

CONTACT: Karen Dawe   **DESCRIPTION:** Published by The Sunday Herald. Circulation 43,600. Weekly news and entertainment magazine focusing on local issues.
WRITERS: Buys approximately 8-10 articles per week. "Our articles are 1-2 pages or 2,000 words. Columns are staff written. Contact by phone." Writers' guidelines are available.
PHOTOGRAPHERS: "Photography is purchased, presently we have a number of photographers we regularly call on."

NEWFOUNDLAND LIFESTYLE BUSINESS MAGAZINE see Atlantic Lifestyle Business Magazine

NEWFOUNDLAND STUDIES
English Department, Memorial University   **PHONE:** (709) 737-2600
St. John's, NF A1C 5S7   **FAX:** (709) 737-7000

CONTACT: Patrick O'Flaherty   **DESCRIPTION:** Circulation 500. "An interdisciplinary journal devoted to publishing clear and well-written essays about the culture of Newfoundland. It's a scholarly journal and the articles are refereed." Published twice yearly.
WRITERS: "Essays and reviews must be submitted in duplicate copies, double-spaced with bibliographical references. Submissions are welcome in English or French on disk in Wordperfect."
NOTES: Sample copy available free upon request.

NEWS AND VIEWS
180 Yorkland Blvd.   **PHONE:** (416) 491-4301
North York, ON M2J 1R5   **FAX:** (416) 494-4948

CONTACT: Elizabeth Alexander, Editor   **DESCRIPTION:** Published by Metropolitan Toronto Police Association. Circulation 9,500. Association magazine featuring articles on law enforcement, health, safety, and nutrition. Published monthly. Established in 1962.
WRITERS: Contact editor with query letter. Byline is given. Pay is negotiable.
PHOTOGRAPHERS: Majority done by in-house photographers. Contact editor with query letter. Returns unsolicited materials with SASE. For front cover vertical, colour prints are preferred. "We are always looking for good cover shots."
NOTES: Send 9x12" SASE for a sample copy.

NEWS CANADA
366 Adelaide Street #606   **PHONE:** (416) 599-9900
Toronto, ON M5V 1R9   **FAX:** (416) 599-9700

CONTACT: Linda Kroboth, Editor   **DESCRIPTION:** Published by News Canada Inc. Circulation 1,250 . "We are a media news-service publication distributed to newspaper editors." Published monthly. Established in 1981.
NOTES: "Everything is done in-house, all of the copy and photos are supplied by our clients."

NEWS FOR SENIORS
1324 - 11 Avenue S.W. Suite 309
Calgary, AB T3C 0M6

NOTES: Could not locate. Phone number is not in service (403) 228-9121.

NIAGARA ANGLICAN
67 Victoria Avenue South
Hamilton, ON L8N 2S8

PHONE: (905) 521-9598
FAX: (905) 521-9598

CONTACT: Larry Perks, Editor   **DESCRIPTION:** Published by Anglican Diocese of Niagara. Circulation 18,500. Tabloid newspaper focusing on current events in the Anglican Church. Published 10 times per year. Established in 1954
WRITERS: Text/photo submissions common for this publication. All writing is done by local volunteers.
PHOTOGRAPHERS: 100% assigned to in-house photographers.

NIAGARA BUSINESS REPORT
4309 Central Avenue, Box 400
Beamsville, ON L0R 1B0

PHONE: (905) 563-5393
FAX: (905) 984-3133

CONTACT: Rannie Specialty Products c/o Molly Harding, Editor   **DESCRIPTION:** Published by Rannie Magazines and Specialty Publications. Circulation 14,500. Quarterly publication focuses on Niagara businesses. Articles include marketing, real estate and business in the Niagara area. Established in 1993.
NOTES: "I am not soliciting outside help of any sort."

NIAGARA FARMERS' MONTHLY
Box 52, 131 College Street
Smithville, ON L0R 2A0

PHONE: (905) 957-3751
FAX: (905) 957-0088

CONTACT: Ivan Carruthers   **DESCRIPTION:** Published by Carruthers Printing. Circulation 18,000. A rural farm publication serving the area. Published 11 times a year.
WRITERS: "Writing is sometimes purchased. Call or send in a query letter. We do have 2 reporters on staff."
PHOTOGRAPHERS: "Most photography is supplied."

NINE TO FIVE
P.O. Box 364
Kingston, ON K7L 4W2

PHONE: (613) 634-1405
FAX: (613) 634-7256

CONTACT: Mrs. M. Paul   **DESCRIPTION:** Circulation 7,000. Publication features local business news and views, business and personality profiles, and new products reviews. Published monthly.
WRITERS: 50% freelance written. Contact editor with query letter. Pay is negotiable. Byline is given. Does not consider simultaneous submissions.
PHOTOGRAPHERS: Contact editor with query letter. Returns unsolicited prints or slides with SASE. Hires photographers on assignment. Pays negotiated expenses.
NOTES: Send 9x12" SASE for a sample copy.

NORTH ISLAND WOMAN
RR1, Site 168, C-11
Comox, BC V9N 5N1

NOTES: Could not locate. Phone number is not in service (604) 339-5313.

NORTH WEST FARMER-RANCHER
Box 430
North Battleford, SK S9A 2Y5

PHONE: (306) 445-4401
FAX: (306) 445-1977

CONTACT: Lorne Cooper, Editor   **DESCRIPTION:** Directed towards the rural farming population and urban areas of Battleford and North Battleford. Published quarterly.
WRITERS: Most of our work is done in-house and by syndicated columnists. A query letter or resumé is accepted. Byline is given. Purchases one-time rights. "Most of the articles we get on spec are too long. We need 500-600 words, max. We just don't have the space."
PHOTOGRAPHERS: "Occasionally the local professionals offer us photos to run as publicity. Our readers also send photos. We also get submissions from the local camera club. Black and white prints preferred. Captions not necessary."
NOTES: Send 9x12" envelope for a sample copy.

NORTHERN AQUACULTURE
4611 William Head Road
Victoria, BC V9B 5T7

PHONE: (604) 478-9209
FAX: (604) 478-1184

CONTACT: Peter Chettleburgh, Editor   **DESCRIPTION:** Published by Harrison House Publishers. North American cold water fish farming industry publication. Covers fish health, advice and company profiles. Distributed to cold water fish farmers. Includes trout, salmon and shellfish in the northern part of North America. Published monthly. Established in 1985.
WRITERS: "We purchase maybe 5 or 6 news items per issue and a couple of features or columns. We appreciate a degree of technical knowledge. We pay 15¢ a word." Short articles are 100-400 words, features 3,000. Columns and short features 800-1,500 words. Bylines are given. Guidelines are available. Query the editor by phone or with a written proposal.
PHOTOGRAPHERS: Purchases photography on occasion. "We prefer black & white glossies that complement the article being submitted."
NOTES: May possibly consider previously published work. Purchases first North American serial rights. Also publishes Cottage Magazine.

NORTHERN JOURNAL
Box 5215 Whitehorse, YK
Y1A 4Z1

NOTES: Could not locate. Phone number is not in service (403) 668-7336.

THE NORTHERN MINER
1450 Don Mills Road
Don Mills, ON M3B 2X7

PHONE: (416) 445-6641
FAX: (416) 442-2175

CONTACT: Vivian Danielson, Editor   **DESCRIPTION:** Published by Published weekly. Circulation 15,400. Mining industry publication reporting the news and issues. Published monthly. Established in 1915.
NOTES: All writing and photography is done in-house.

NORTHERN ONTARIO BUSINESS

158 Elgin Street
Sudbury, ON P3E 3N5

PHONE: (705) 673-5705
FAX: (705) 673-9542

CONTACT: Mark Sandford, Editor   **DESCRIPTION:** Published by Laurentian Publishing Co. Circulation 11-12,000. Business news in northern Ontario. Key topics are mining, forestry, general small business items and economics. Published monthly. Established in 1980.
WRITERS: Contact by phone or by sending a query letter or fax. Welcomes unsolicited articles with SASE. Byline is given. Pay is negotiable. We have an editorial calendar set a year in advance. New ideas are always welcome but they have to fit within the parameters we have set. Writers are always sought in Timmins, Thunder Bay, Fort Francis, Kenora, and Sault Ste. Marie."
PHOTOGRAPHERS: Contact by phone or by sending a query letter or fax. Purchases 10 photos per issue. Purchases stock images.
NOTES: Send 9x12" SASE for a sample copy.

NORTHERN WOMEN JOURNAL

Box 144
Thunder Bay, ON P7C 4V5

PHONE: (807) 346-8809

CONTACT: Jane Saunders   **DESCRIPTION:** Published by an independent non-profit collective. Circulation 200. "A feminist newspaper focusing on women's concerns: health, violence, employment, law reform, daycare, isolation at home and in the workforce. Regular features include interviews, book reviews and poetry." Published quarterly.
WRITERS: "We accept submissions from women writers but we are unable to pay. We publish short stories and fiction but we also would like reviews, analysis of issues etc." Writers' guidelines are available. Takes up to a month for a reply.
PHOTOGRAPHERS: Does not purchase.
NOTES: "No phone calls please."

NORTHPOINT

10 Four Seasons Place, #404
Etobicoke, ON M9B 6H7

PHONE: (416) 621-9621
FAX: (416) 621-8694

CONTACT: Robert Fowler, Editor   **DESCRIPTION:** Published by Ontario Association of Certified Technicians & Technologists. Circulation 1,200. A magazine for survey technicians and civil technologists. Published quarterly. Established in 1964.
WRITERS: "Our budget has been cut back so we don't purchase much. We do most of it in-house. We are open to inquiries. We look for someone who has written about current innovative technology. Articles are paid for upon acceptance, preferably 1,000 words." Writers' guidelines are not available.
PHOTOGRAPHERS: "We purchase a very limited amount."
NOTES: Sample copy available free upon request. Also publishes Ontario Technologist.

NORTHWARD JOURNAL

439 Wellington Street West, 3rd Floor
Toronto, ON M5V 1E7
NOTES: Could not locate. Phone number is not in service (416) 593-2730.

NORTHWEST BUSINESS
Box 22082   **PHONE:** (403) 538-0539
Grande Prairie, AB T8V 6X1   **FAX:** (403) 539-2393

CONTACT: Donald C. Sylvester, Editor   **DESCRIPTION:** Published by Sylvester
Publications Ltd. Circulation 10,000+. Focuses on people in business and industry. Articles
include oil and gas, logging, agriculture, anything related to business and industry. Published
6 times a year. Established in 1994.
WRITERS: Freelance writing is used. Send a faxed resumé and a sample of your work.
"We like as natural a style as possible. Read the magazine for examples. Very upbeat,
very positive. The magazine is very people-oriented; we tell people stories. All articles
are features."
PHOTOGRAPHERS: Freelance photographers are used. Send a portfolio with a query
letter. Either slides or colour 5x7 or 8x10 prints preferred. Captions preferred.
NOTES: Send 9x12" SASE with postage for a sample copy.

NOVA SCOTIA BUSINESS JOURNAL
6029 Cunard Street   **PHONE:** (902) 420-0437
Halifax, NS B3K 1E5   **FAX:** (902) 423-8212

CONTACT: Ken Partridge, Editor   **DESCRIPTION:** Published by Bilby Holdings
Ltd. Circulation up to 50,000. A monthly tabloid circulated in Nova Scotia. Focuses
on all areas of business, government policy, successful entrepreneurs, business innovation
and techniques, new company profiles. Published monthly.
WRITERS: "We do purchase some work, 20-30% freelance. I prefer to assign. I accept
query letters by mail or fax. Average length is 500 words. For a new writer the rate is
10¢ a word; once we have some experience with a writer we will slowly increase the rate.
I like to see an inquiry first."
PHOTOGRAPHERS: "We purchase very little."
NOTES: Considers previously published work. Sample copy available free upon request.
Purchases one-time rights.

NOW
150 Danforth Avenue   **PHONE:** (416) 461-0871
Toronto, ON M4K 1N1   **FAX:** (416) 461-2886

CONTACT: Michael Hollett, Editor-Publisher   **DESCRIPTION:** Published by Now
Communications Inc. Circulation 101,000. An alternative news and entertainment weekly.
Featuring articles on films, music reviews, theatre, art galleries, books, fashion, and news.
Established in 1981.
WRITERS: 25% freelance written (Unionization in the past year has caused some freelancers
to become full-time employees, thus decreasing the need for writers). Contact with query
letter and samples of work. Kill fee of 50% for assigned articles that are cancelled. Fees
negotiable. Gives byline. Buys one-time rights. Send 9 x 12" SASE to receive sample copy.
PHOTOGRAPHERS: We have our own freelance photographers. However, new submissions
are welcome. Phone or query Irene Granger, Photo Editor. B&w captioned prints are
preferred. Get a copy of the publication to learn the style we use.

NURSING B.C.

2855 Arbutus Street
Vancouver, BC   V6J 3Y8

PHONE: (604) 736-7331
FAX: (604) 738-2272

CONTACT: Bruce Wells, Editor   **DESCRIPTION:** Published by Registered Nurses Association of British Columbia. Circulation 35,400. Association magazine. "Nursing and health from the professional prospective." Articles cover nursing issues, education, research and news focusing on the province of B.C. Published 5 times a year. Established in 1968.
WRITERS: Freelance written. Contact with query letter or phone or fax with a story outline which includes how it fits our mandate. "My main interest is in writers who have written in the health care field and who already have a story idea in mind. Pay is negotiable. Guidelines are available. "We assume rights once we accept an article. Writers can re-do the article in another format and submit it elsewhere. I entertain writers who come up with a story idea much more than 'If you ever need a writer' inquiries. I'm not interested in anything outside the health care field in B.C." Gives a byline.
PHOTOGRAPHERS: Hires freelance photographers. "Particularly those who live outside mainland Vancouver. Prefer submissions of colour transparencies. Captions are preferred. Credit is given. Our arrangements with the photographer is negotiable."
NOTES: "We are looking for writers and photographers who live in British Columbia outside the lower mainland. Not from Vancouver, we've got those areas pretty well saturated." Send 9x12" SASE to receive sample copy of publication.

NURSING QUEBEC

4200 Dorchester Blvd W
Montreal, PQ   H3Z 1V4

PHONE: (514) 935-2501
FAX: (514) 935-2055

CONTACT: Guylaine Chabot   **DESCRIPTION:** Published by Order of Nurses of Quebec. Circulation 70,000. French language publication. Focuses on the health needs of Quebecers and issues affecting nurses. Published 6 times a year.
WRITERS: "We occasionally purchase work. We usually receive a completed article and we have an editorial committee that reviews it. Articles range from 1-2 type-written pages up to 6-10 pages. Our contributors are usually nurses."
PHOTOGRAPHERS: "We occasionally buy photos."
NOTES: Contact with query by phone or mail.

OCTANE

101-6 Avenue SW, Suite 2450
Calgary, AB   T2P 3P4

PHONE: (403) 266-8700
FAX: (403) 266-6634

CONTACT: David Coll, Editor   **DESCRIPTION:** Published by Maclean Hunter Ltd. Circulation 7,500. Analysis of issues affecting the downstream petroleum industry in Canada. Published quarterly. Established in 1987.
WRITERS: 50% freelance written. Query letters or phone inquiries are welcome. Purchases first North American Rights. Only industry-related material please. Kill fee is offered. Byline is given. Writers' guidelines not available.
PHOTOGRAPHERS: Stock images purchased. 10% freelance photography. Phone calls accepted. Colour slides and captioned preferred. Model releases not required.
NOTES: Sample copy available to anyone working for the publication.

OFF-ROAD CANADA MAGAZINE
895 Sandy Beach Road #12E
Pickering, ON L1W 3N6

NOTES: Could not locate. Phone number is not in service (416) 420-0508.

OFFICE SUPPLIES BUSINESS
70 Gibson Drive, Unit 5
Markham, ON L3R 4C2

NOTES: Could not locate. Phone number is not in service (416) 477-4349.

OFFICE SYSTEMS AND TECHNOLOGY
777 Bay Street
Toronto, ON M5W 1A7

NOTES: NO LONGER PUBLISHED

OHS (Occupational Health and Safety) CANADA
1450 Don Mills Road   **PHONE:** (416) 445-6641
Don Mills, ON M3B 2X7   **FAX:** (416) 442-2200

CONTACT: Margaret Nearing, Editor   **DESCRIPTION:** Published by Southam Information and Technology Group. Circulation 9,900. Health and safety industry publication for managers and professionals in business and government. Published 7 times a year. Established in 1985.
WRITERS: Pays $300-$900 for articles. Phone inquiries welcome.
PHOTOGRAPHERS: Photography is not accepted.

OHS BULLETIN
34 Parkview Avenue   **PHONE:** (416) 226-9011
Willowdale, ON M2N 3Y2   **FAX:** (416) 226-2740

CONTACT: Meribeth Clow, Editor   **DESCRIPTION:** Published by Ontario Historical Society. Circulation 3,000. Features news and information about the Ontario Heritage Community. This includes genealogical, archaeological, and historical information. Published 6 times a year. Established in 1968.
WRITERS: Occasionally uses freelance work. A query letter and sample of work is preferred. Pay must be negotiated.
PHOTOGRAPHERS: In-house photographers. New submissions not being accepted.
NOTES: Sample publications available with SASE. Also publishes Ontario History.

OIL PATCH
17560 - 107th Avenue, 2nd Floor
Edmonton, AB T5S 1E9

PHONE: (403) 486-1295
FAX: (403) 484-0884

CONTACT: L.H. Hyman, Editor **DESCRIPTION:** Published by Master Publications. Circulation 21,000. An international magazine for decision makers dealing with oil, gas, the environment and safety. Published 6 times a year. Established in 1978.
NOTES: No freelance material is purchased for this magazine.

OIL WEEK
101 - 6 Ave. S.W. Suite 2450
Calgary, AB T2P 3P4

PHONE: (403) 266-8700
FAX: (403) 266-6634

CONTACT: David Coll, Editor **DESCRIPTION:** Published by Maclean Hunter. Analysis of issues affecting the upstream petroleum industry in Canada. Quarterly publication.
WRITERS: Contact editor with query letter. Articles must be industry-related. Byline is given.
PHOTOGRAPHERS: Phone calls accepted. Stock images purchased. Mail captioned, colour slides.
NOTES: Purchases first North American serial rights. Send 9x12" SASE for a sample copy.

OKANAGAN BUSINESS MAGAZINE
Box 1479 Station A
Kelowna, BC V1Y 7V8

PHONE: (604) 861-5399
FAX: (604) 868-3040

CONTACT: J. Paul Byrne, Editor-Publisher **DESCRIPTION:** Published by Byrne Publishing Group. Circulation 18,000. Business publication. Articles features entrepreneurs, new businesses, business events and humour columns. Published 8 times a year. Established in 1989.
WRITERS: Contact this publication with query letter or by fax. Submissions not returned. Pay is negotiable. Byline is given. Guidelines are available.
PHOTOGRAPHERS: Submissions of local Okanagan-area photography accepted. Pay is negotiable.
NOTES: Buys one-time rights. Send 9x12" SASE for a sample copy.

OKANAGAN LIFE
Box 1479, Station A
Kelowna, BC V1Y 7V8

PHONE: (604) 861-5399
FAX: (604) 868-3040

CONTACT: Holly McNeil, Editor   **DESCRIPTION:** Published by Byrne Publishing Group. Circulation 20,000. City magazine focusing on readers in the Okanagan. Personality profiles, local events, sports and local issues are covered. Published seasonally with a Bride Magazine, City Guide and Homes Issue as inserts. Established in 1988.
WRITERS: 100% freelance written. Pay is negotiable. Guidelines are available.
PHOTOGRAPHERS: Local photography submissions accepted. Pay is negotiable.
NOTES: Buys one-time rights. Send 9 x 12" SASE for a sample copy.

OLD AUTOS
348 Main Street, Box 419
Bothwell, ON N0P 1C0

PHONE: (519) 695-2303
FAX: (519) 695-3716

CONTACT: Murray McEwan, Editor   **DESCRIPTION:** Published by Old Autos. Circulation 14,000. Tabloid featuring articles about antique cars and their owners. Features include everything from nostalgia items to the cars themselves. Published twice a month. Established in 1987.
WRITERS: 75% freelance written. Contact this publication by phone first, then mail in a sample of work. "We get a number of free stories from hobbyists." Pay is negotiable. Writers' guidelines available.
PHOTOGRAPHERS: Have in-house photographers. New submissions welcomed, however many stories submitted have photos taken by the author. Query letter or phone call preferred. Colour prints with captions preferred. **NOTES:** Send 9x12" SASE for sample publication.

OLDTIMER'S HOCKEY NEWS
Box 951
Peterborough, ON K9J 7A5

PHONE: (705) 743-2679
FAX: (705) 748-3470

CONTACT: Dave Tatham, Publisher   **DESCRIPTION:** Published by Tatham Publications Inc. The focus is on recreation hockey for adult and oldtimer hockey teams 30 years and older. Reports on tournaments and related news. Published 8 times a year Canada-wide. Established in 1975.
WRITERS: "We occasionally purchase writing. We take unsolicited material, however if we see something we like we may pay $25-$50 for it. I prefer to speak with the freelancer myself. The biggest problem is that freelancers fail to ask for a fee when they first contact me. I would prefer that they tell me their fee for what they are proposing upfront."
PHOTOGRAPHERS: "We haven't purchased much in the past few years. We have a hall of fame in which we run photos. We are also open to someone who may have a tremendous action photo of oldtimers hockey. They can send me a photocopy or a fax so I can see it; if I like it I will buy it. I prefer to speak with freelancers personally."
NOTES: Sample copy available free upon request.

L'OMNIPRATICIEN
1425 René-Lévesque West
Montreal, PQ H3G 1T7

PHONE: (514) 878-2595
FAX: (514) 878-8270

CONTACT: Lyse Savard, Editor   **DESCRIPTION:** Published by Thomason Healthcare Communications. Circulation 10,500. French language publication aimed at General Practitioners. Articles are news-related or clinical in nature. Published 24 times a year. Established in 1993.
WRITERS: Contact editor with query letter. Byline is given. Pays $70 per 250 words. "We need writers who can write about family medicine in French. Writers must be sure that their statements are backed up by doctors, unless they are doctors themselves."
PHOTOGRAPHERS: Call for appointment to show portfolio or send colour prints or transparencies. Unsolicited submissions are returned with SASE.
NOTES: Send 9x12" envelope with appropriate postage for a sample copy.

ON COURT
1200 Sheppard Avenue East, Suite 400
Willowdale, ON M2K 2S5

NOTES: Could not locate. Phone number is not in service (416) 497-1370.

ONSET
154 Parliament Street
Toronto, ON M5A 2Z1

PHONE: (416) 601-9865
FAX: (416) 601-9967

CONTACT: Vincent Hempsall, Editor   **DESCRIPTION:** Published by Onset Publishing Ventures Ltd. Circulation 70,000. Magazine for adults with a career and lifestyle focus. Published 6 times a year. Established in 1993.
WRITERS: Up to 5% freelance written. A query letter, phone call or fax is acceptable. Pay is negotiable.
PHOTOGRAPHERS: Will accept new submissions. Query letter or phone call is best.

ONTARIO BEEF
130 Malcolm Road
Guelph, ON N1K 1B1

PHONE: (519) 824-0334
FAX: (519) 824-9101

CONTACT: Sandra Eby, Editor   **DESCRIPTION:** Published by Ontario Cattleman's Association. Circulation 22,000. A primary source of communication for the Association. Contains information on issues, the industry and trends in business. Published 6 times a year. Established in 1963.
WRITERS: Mostly written in-house or by association contributors; 5% volunteer freelance written. Average article length 800 words. Contact with a query letter or send article on spec. "We like newsy current issues that are short and readable."
PHOTOGRAPHERS: 90% assigned to in-house photographers. 10% included in text\photo submissions. Uses 35mm transparencies or 5x7 b&w prints.

ONTARIO BEEF FARMER MAGAZINE
Box 7400
London, ON N5Y 4X3

PHONE: (519) 471-8520
FAX: (519) 473-2256

CONTACT: Paul Mahon, Editor **DESCRIPTION:** Published by Bowes Publishers Inc. Circulation 13,000. Magazine featuring articles about the beef farming industry in Ontario. Published quarterly. Established in 1993.
NOTES: All writing and photography is done in-house. Also publishes Ontario Farmer, Ontario Dairy Farmer and Ontario Hog Farmer. "We are farmers first and writers second."

ONTARIO BUSINESS JOURNAL
100 Main Street East, 40th Fl.
Hamilton, ON L8N 3W6

PHONE: 1-800-494-6397
(905) 526-8600
FAX: (905) 526-0086

CONTACT: Mark Higgins, Assistant Editor David Harris, Editor **DESCRIPTION:** Published by Ontario Press Ltd. Circulation 104,000. Features business news and products, new business and entrepreneur profiles. A tabloid with five different editions published 11 times a year. Established in 1993.
WRITERS: Contact assistnat editor with query letter. He will keep all information on file and call you when he needs you. Byline is given. Purchases one-time rights. Pay is negotiable. Send 9x12 SASE for a sample copy.
PHOTOGRAPHERS: 95 % assigned to in-house photographers. Contact editor with query letter. Occasionally hires photographers on assignment.
NOTES: "Preference is given to local photographers and writers who we can call and assign to a particular feature."

ONTARIO CRAFT
35 McCaul Street, Chalmers Bldg
Toronto, ON M5T 1V7

PHONE: (416) 977-3551
FAX: (416) 977-3552

CONTACT: Ann McPherson, Editor **DESCRIPTION:** Published by Ontario Crafts Council. Features a broad range of craft subjects including ceramics, textiles, metal working; plus reviews of artists, art teachers, textile artists and craftspeople. Published quarterly.
WRITERS: Freelance written. Contact editor with query letter. Byline is given. Does not return unsolicited material. Pay is negotiable. Writers' guidelines are available. "Our writers must be people with knowledge and expertise in the art world. Articles must be based in Ontario."
PHOTOGRAPHERS: Majority assigned to in-house photographers. Hires photographers on assignment.
NOTES: Send $4 & 9x12" SASE for a sample copy.

ONTARIO DAIRY FARMER
Box 7400
London, ON N5Y 4X3

PHONE: (519) 473-0010
FAX: none

CONTACT: Paul Mahon, Editor **DESCRIPTION:** Published by Bowes Publishers Ltd. Circulation 14,000. Ontario magazine geared to the dairy farmer of Ontario. Published 6 times a year. Established in 1987.
NOTES: All writing and photography is done in-house. Also publishes Ontario Farmer, Ontario Hog Farmer, and Ontario Beef Farmer. "We are farmers first and writers second."

ONTARIO DENTIST
4 New Street
Toronto, ON M5R 1P6

PHONE: (416) 922-3900
FAX: (416) 922-9005

CONTACT: Jim Shosenberg, Editor   **DESCRIPTION:** Published by Ontario Dental Association. Circulation 5,500. A technical journal with practice management, personal finance, health, and some feature stories. Published 10 times a year. Established in 1925.
NOTES: "Most work is done internally and by dentists."

ONTARIO FARMER
Box 7400
London, ON N5Y 4X3

PHONE: (519) 473-0010
FAX: (519) 473-2256

CONTACT: Paul Mahon, Editor   **DESCRIPTION:** Published by Bowes Publishers Ltd. Circulation 34,500. Weekly newspaper featuring articles on the farming industry in Ontario. Established in 1968.
NOTES: All writing and photography is done in-house. Also publishes Ontario Beef Farmer, Ontario Dairy Farmer and Ontario Hog Farmer. "We are farmers first and writers second."

ONTARIO FISHERMAN
85 Scarsdale Road, #100
Toronto, ON
M3B 2R2 (416) 445-5702

PHONE: (416) 445-0753
FAX: Transcontinental Publications Ltd.

CONTACT: Matthew Nicholls, Editor   **DESCRIPTION:** A magazine published 7 times a year. Covers stories and photographs of fishing in Ontario.
WRITERS: "We assign stories but most of them are done by regular correspondents. Call first with a query to see if there is any interest."
PHOTOGRAPHERS: Call with a query.
NOTES: Doesn't consider previously published work. For a sample copy please send the $2.95 cover price of the magazine plus SASE. Also publishes Hockey News.

ONTARIO GOLF NEWS
2 Billingham Road #400
Etobicoke, ON M9B 6E1

PHONE: (416) 232-2380
FAX: none

CONTACT: Ken McKenzie   **DESCRIPTION:** Published by Ontario Golf News. Circulation 30,000. Association magazine distributed free at golf courses. All articles are golf-related. Published 5 times a year.
NOTES: All writing and photography is done in-house or is provided free by golf courses and members.

ONTARIO HOG FARMER
Box 7400
London, ON N5Y 4X3

PHONE: (519) 473-0010
FAX: none

CONTACT: Paul Mahon, Editor   **DESCRIPTION:** Published by Bowes Publishers Ltd. Circulation 10,000. Published 6 times a year. Established in 1988.

NOTES: All writing and photography is done in-house. Also publishes Ontario Farmer, Ontario Beef Farmer, and Ontario Dairy Farmer. "We are farmers first and writers second."

ONTARIO HOME BUILDER see Homes

ONTARIO INDUSTRIAL MAGAZINE see National Industrial Magazine

ONTARIO LAND SURVEYOR
1043 McNicoll Avenue
Scarborough, ON M1W 3W6

PHONE: (416) 491-9020
FAX: (416) 491-2576

CONTACT: Brian Munday, Editor **DESCRIPTION:** Published by Association of Ontario Land Surveyors. Circulation 1,600. A membership publication primarily focusing on issues related to land surveying and management in Ontario. Published quarterly. Established in 1957.
NOTES: "We rarely purchase material. If something comes up that is land surveying oriented we may consider it, but beyond that we generally don't buy material."

ONTARIO LAWYERS WEEKLY
75 Clegg Road
Markham, ON L6G 1A1

PHONE: (905) 479-2665
FAX: (905) 479-3758

CONTACT: Don Brillinger, Editor **DESCRIPTION:** Published by Butterworth's Canada. Published weekly.

ONTARIO MEDICAL REVIEW
525 University Avenue #300
Toronto, ON M5G 2K7

PHONE: (416) 599-2580
FAX: (416) 599-9309

CONTACT: Jeff Henry, Editor **DESCRIPTION:** Published by Ontario Medical Association. Circulation 11,400. Publication aimed at physicians, to keep them informed about pertinent medical developments. Published monthly. Established in 1922.

ONTARIO MEDICINE
777 Bay Street
Toronto, ON M5W 1A7

NOTES: NO LONGER PUBLISHED

ONTARIO MILK PRODUCER
6780 Campobello Road
Mississauga, ON L5N 2L8

PHONE: (905) 821-8970
FAX: (905) 821-3160

CONTACT: Bill Dimmick, Editor **DESCRIPTION:** Published by Ontario Milk Marketing Board. Circulation 11,500. Glossy magazine focusing on Ontario's dairy industry with

the main emphasis on dairy farmers. Includes articles on production, politics and economics as related to the Ontario dairy industry. Published monthly. Established in 1925.
WRITERS: Majority is assigned to in-house writers. Contact editor with query letter. Byline is given. Pay is negotiable.
PHOTOGRAPHERS: Not accepting new submissions. All photography is handled in-house.

ONTARIO MOTOR COACH REVIEW
920 Yonge Street, Suite 600   **PHONE:** 1(416) 961-1028
Toronto, ON M4W 3C7

CONTACT: Lori Knowles, Editor   **DESCRIPTION:** Published by Ontario Motor Coach Association. Circulation 3,000. Targets the bus and bus tour operator industry. "We are not about Winnebagos."
WRITERS: Contact editor with query letter. Writers' guidelines are available. Byline is given. Buys all rights. Editor wants to be able to use the story again if she needs to. Considers simultaneous submissions.
PHOTOGRAPHERS: Contact editor with query letter.
NOTES: Send 9x12" SASE for a sample copy. Also publishes Aquatic Link, Construction Comment, and Network.

ONTARIO OUT OF DOORS
227 Front Street East #100   **PHONE:** (416) 368-0185
Toronto, ON M5A 1E8   **FAX:** (416) 941-9113

CONTACT: Burt Myers, Editor   **DESCRIPTION:** Published by Special Interest Publications, Maclean Hunter Ltd. Circulation 89,800. Magazine published 10 times a year for Ontario's hunters and anglers. Articles include boating, firearms, backroad touring, how-to, and where-to. Established in 1969.

THE ONTARIO PSYCHOLOGIST
730 Yonge Street #221   **PHONE:** (416) 961-5552
Toronto, ON M4Y 2B7   **FAX:** (416) 961-5516

CONTACT: Dr. Donald Rudzinski, Editor   **DESCRIPTION:** Published by Ontario Psychological Association. Circulation 1,500. Psychology-based magazine intended to inform members and others about news and events in the Ontario Psychological Association. Published 6 times a year. Established in 1969.
NOTES: All writing and photography is done in-house.

ONTARIO RESTAURANT NEWS
2065 Dundas Street East #101   **PHONE:** (905) 206-0150
Mississauga, ON L4X 2W1   **FAX:** (905) 206-9972

CONTACT: Stephen Law, Editor   **DESCRIPTION:** Published by Ishcom Publications. Circulation 17,000. A trade publication serving Ontario's foodservice and hospitality industry. Published monthly. Established in 1986.
WRITERS: "We purchase minimal work. We like feature length and news stories that pertain to our readers. Write us with an idea in bullet format saying what you are going to address. Have an idea in mind first."

PHOTOGRAPHERS: "We purchase occasionally."
NOTES: Considers previously published work. Sample copy available free upon request.

ONTARIO SNOWMOBILER MAGAZINE
RR3 Centre Road   **PHONE:** (905) 473-7009
Mount Albert, ON L0G 1M0   **FAX:** (905) 473 5217

CONTACT: Mark Lester, Managing Editor   **DESCRIPTION:** Published by Ontario Snowmobiler Publishing Ltd. Circulation 80,000. Official organ of the Ontario Federation of Snowmobile clubs. Consumer magazine emphasizing snowmobiling in Ontario. Published 5 times a year. Established in 1986.
WRITERS: "We rarely use freelance writers."
PHOTOGRAPHERS: "We do buy some photos. We are looking for anything to do with snowmobiling in Ontario, either colour or black & white." Call the editor with a query.
NOTES: Sample copy available for $2.50.

ONTARIO TECHNOLOGIST
10 Four Seasons Place #404   **PHONE:** (416) 621-9621
Etobicoke, ON M9B 6H7   **FAX:** (416) 621-8694

CONTACT: Ruth Klein, Editor   **DESCRIPTION:** Published by Ontario Association of Certified Engineering Technicians & Technologists. Circulation 20,000. "A house organ of the Association. The editorial base is engineering and technology, professional issues, new products, and legal issues." Published 6 times a year. Established in 1958.
WRITERS: "Our budget has been cut back so we don't purchase much. We do most of it in-house. We are open to inquiries. We look for someone who has written about current innovative technology. Articles are paid for upon acceptance, preferably 1,000 words." Writers' guidelines are not available.
PHOTOGRAPHERS: "We purchase a very limited amount."
NOTES: Sample copy available free upon request. Also publishes Northpoint.

ONTARIO TENNIS
1185 Eglinton Avenue East   **PHONE:** (416) 426-7135
North York, ON M3C 3C6   **FAX:** (416) 426-7370

CONTACT: Peter Budreo, Editor   **DESCRIPTION:** Published by Ontario Tennis Association. Circulation 16,000. Tabloid sized magazine features news and opinions from members of the association. Published four or five times a year. Established in 1969.
WRITERS: Majority is assigned to in-house writers. Contact editor with query letter. Byline is given. Does not pay for articles.
PHOTOGRAPHERS: 100% assigned to in-house photographers.

OPERA CANADA
366 Adelaide Street East #434   **PHONE:** (416) 363-0395
Toronto, ON M5A 3X9   **FAX:** (416) 363-0396

CONTACT: Rick Amis, Executive Director   **DESCRIPTION:** Published by Opera Canada Publications. Circulation 5,500. Follows the growth and development of Canadian opera companies and professionals. Covers national and international opera. Articles include:

special features; international calendar of events; reviews of books, recordings of all types and formats; personal profiles; and world-wide coverage of operas. Covers issues pertinent to Opera both from a consumer and trade point of view. Columns include Debut which deals with up-and-coming Canadian talent; Grand Tradition deals with the historical aspect of Opera from a Canadian perspective; plus others. Published quarterly. Established in 1960.
WRITERS: "We purchase both columns and features; usually 5 pieces per issue." Pays maximum $400 for a feature, $175 for a column and $50 for cd/book reviews, Opera reviews are $25 plus 2 tickets. "We will look at unsolicited material, but prefer an outline. We want to see material with a Canadian focus. There had better be a relationship to Canadian Opera. Writers must know something about Opera. We occasionally accept fiction and poetry if it is Opera related."
PHOTOGRAPHERS: "Most of our material is supplied by the Opera companies."
NOTES: Purchases one-time rights and in some cases joint copyright. Sample copy is available for $5.95. Also available on newsstands across Canada.

OPERATIONS FORESTIERES/SCIERIE

1 Pacifique
Ste. Anne de Bellevue, PQ H9X 1C5

PHONE: (514) 457-2211
FAX: (514) 457-2558

CONTACT: Guy Fortin **DESCRIPTION:** Circulation 5,000. French language publication. Focuses on logging and sawmilling in Quebec, eastern Ontario, and western New Brunswick. Published 6 times a year.
WRITERS: 80% freelance written. Contact editor with query letter. Would prefer not to receive unsolicited manuscripts. Pay is negotiable. Byline is given. Buys first-time Canadian rights.
PHOTOGRAPHERS: All photography is done in-house.
NOTES: Send $2 & 9x12" SASE for a sample copy.

OPPORTUNITIES CANADA

2550 Goldenridge Road #42
Mississauga, ON L4X 2S3

PHONE: (905) 277-5600
FAX: (905) 277-3397

CONTACT: Robert Sinclair **DESCRIPTION:** Published by The Type People Inc. Circulation 25,000. Business franchise and dealership guide. Articles are written by lawyers and bankers with an emphasis on franchising and starting a business. Published 3 times a year. Established in 1990.
WRITERS: Majority assigned to in-house writers. Contact editor with query letter, resumé and sample article(s).
PHOTOGRAPHERS: All photography is done in-house.

OPTICAL PRISM

31 Hastings Drive
Unionville, ON L3R 4Y5

PHONE: (905) 475-9343
FAX: (905) 477-2821

CONTACT: Allan Vezina, Editor **DESCRIPTION:** Published by Vezcom Inc. Circulation 7,400. A national publication for optometrists, ophthalmologists opticians and suppliers. Contains information about business, management and marketing. Published 9 times a year. Established in 1983.

WRITERS: Articles desired are in the areas of management, marketing, and merchandising; personal, wholesale and retail success stories; eye, contact lens, eyeglass and optical lens articles of interest to the consumer; articles on fitting eyeglasses, contact lenses and clinical optometric/ophthalmological articles. "I need retail stories and I need technical stories from the standpoint of fitting eyeglasses, and the dispensing end of things. We have a lot of industry profiles but not a lot of retail profiles and success stories." Complete articles may be submitted on spec or submit a story outline. Articles are 1,500-15,000+ words. "Read a number of articles from the magazine before submitting." Pays 10¢ a word to a maximum of $500.
PHOTOGRAPHERS: "We only use photography if it comes with an article."
NOTES: Purchases one-time rights.

OPTION SERRE MAGAZINE
151 Lecavalier
Varennes, PQ J3X 1B4

PHONE: (514) 652-3055
FAX: (514) 652-5980

CONTACT: George O'Shaughnessy, Editor-in-Chief   **DESCRIPTION:** Published by Editions versicolores Inc. Circulation 1,316. French language publication. Published 6 times a year. Established in 1988.

ORAH MAGAZINE
1310 Greene Avenue #900
Westmount, PQ H3Z 2B8

PHONE: (514) 937-9431
FAX: (514) 933-6483

CONTACT: Lily Frank   **DESCRIPTION:** Published by Hadassa-WIZO Organization of Canada. Published quarterly. Established in 1960.
NOTES: All writing and photography is done in-house.

ORAL HEALTH
1450 Don Mills Road
Don Mills, ON M3B 2X7

PHONE: (416) 445-6641
FAX: (416) 442-2214

CONTACT: Jana Binelli, Editor Erla Kay, Publisher   **DESCRIPTION:** Published by Southam Business Communications Ltd. Circulation 16,900. Clinical journal for dentists and oral surgeons. Published monthly. Established in 1911.
WRITERS: Majority assigned to in-house freelancers. Contact editor with query letter. "Only those with technical expertise in the dental field should submit a query letter."
PHOTOGRAPHERS: All photography is done in-house.

L'ORATOIRE
3800 Queen Mary Road
Montreal, PQ H3V 1H6

PHONE: (514) 733-8211
FAX: (514) 733-9735

CONTACT: Madame Thérése Baron, Editor   **DESCRIPTION:** Published by Fathers of Holy Cross of St. Joseph's Oratory of Mount Royal. Circulation 8,500 English Edition, 58,000 French Edition. Two-part publication. The first part deals with pastoral point-of-view on general problems facing congregation members. The second part profiles saints, shrines, and important religious sites of interest to those of the Catholic faith. Emphasis

on Christian values would appeal to those of all faiths. Published 6 times a year in French and English. Established in 1912.
WRITERS: Majority assigned to in-house writers. Contact editor with query letter to Madame Thérése Baron. Pays $55 per article. We prefer articles to be no more than two pages.
PHOTOGRAPHERS: Majority assigned to in-house photographers. Contact editor with query letter. Hires on assignment once or twice a year.
NOTES: "We have around two million visitors and pilgrims every year to St. Joseph's Oratory. The magazine is a way to continue the pilgrimage." Considers simultaneous submissions. Send 9x12" SASE for a sample copy.

OSMT ADVOCATE
234 Eglinton Avenue East #600
Toronto, ON M4P 1K5

PHONE: (416) 485-6768

CONTACT: Kathryn Robins **DESCRIPTION:** Published by Ontario Society of Medical Technologists. Circulation 4,000. Special interest publication for medical technologists. Published 4 times a year.
NOTES: "Most of our material is contributed by members, free of charge."

OTTAWA BUSINESS MAGAZINE
192 Bank Street
Ottawa, ON K2P 1W8

PHONE: (613) 234-7751
FAX: (613) 234-9226

CONTACT: Mark Sutcliff, Editor **DESCRIPTION:** Published by Pegasus Publishing Ltd. Circulation 20,000. Magazine with emphasis on local business issues. Published 6 times a year. Established in 1982.
WRITERS: 25% freelance written. Contact editor with query letter. Pay is negotiable. Byline is given.
PHOTOGRAPHERS: Majority assigned to in-house photographers. Contact editor with query letter and subject lists.

OTTAWA BUSINESS NEWS
77 Auriga Drive #3
Nepean, ON K2E 7Z7

PHONE: (613) 727-1400
FAX: (613) 727-1010

CONTACT: Darrin Denne, Editor **DESCRIPTION:** Published by Laurentian Publishing Ltd. Circulation 12,000. Newspaper featuring regional business news, business and personality profiles, and regular special reports. Published twice monthly.
WRITERS: 10% freelance written. Contact editor with query letter with resumé and sample articles. Pays $50-$100 for articles. Guidelines available.
PHOTOGRAPHERS: All photography is done in-house.
NOTES: Purchases one-time rights. Send 9x12" SASE for a sample copy.

OTTAWA LIVING
400 Cumberland Street
Ottawa, ON K1N 8X3

NOTES: NO LONGER PUBLISHED

OTTAWA MAGAZINE
192 Bank Street, 2nd Floor
Ottawa, ON K2P 1W8

PHONE: (613) 234-7751
FAX: (613) 234-9226

CONTACT: Mark Sutcliff, Editor   **DESCRIPTION:** Published by Pegasus Publishing Inc. Circulation 38,000. Featuring articles on local issues, lifestyle, film, restaurants, fashion, and gourmet cooking. Published monthly. Established in 1979.
WRITERS: Partially freelance written. Contact editor with query letter. Byline is given. Pay is negotiable.
PHOTOGRAPHERS: Majority assigned to in-house photographers. Contact editor with query letter and subject lists.
NOTES: Also publishes Ottawa Business Magazine.

THE OTTAWA TRANSCRIPT
1511 Merivale Road #205
Nepean, ON K2G 3J3

PHONE: (613) 224-3460
FAX: (613) 224-1076

CONTACT: Mark Buckshon, Editor   **DESCRIPTION:** Published by Business Park News Publishing Co. Circulation 8,500. Focus is on construction and real estate news. Published monthly. Established in 1993.
NOTES: All writing and photography is done in-house. "We are getting too many solicitations from writers and photographers. We do not want submissions, thankyou."

OUR FAMILY
Box 249
Battleford, SK S0M 0E0

PHONE: (306) 937-7772
FAX: (306) 937-7644

CONTACT: Father Nestor Gregoire   **DESCRIPTION:** Circulation 10,000. Special interest magazine. Articles are family centred and include: living within the Catholic faith; difficulties and hopes of family life; marriage; relationships; child raising; care of the elderly; prayer; humour; and human interest.
WRITERS: 60% freelance written; around 10% new writers. "When it comes to writing about family life people have a lot of stories to tell. We use a format similar to Reader's Digest." Send query letter, or complete article with SASE; it will be returned if not needed. "If I purchase an article, I use it." Pays 7-11¢ per word. Writers' guidelines on request.
PHOTOGRAPHERS: Mostly use in-house people. Send a portfolio of new materials. Any format. Captions not necessary.
NOTES: Buys one-time North American serial rights. Sample copies for $2.50 with SASE.

OUR TIMES
390 Dufferin Street
Toronto, ON M6K 2A3

PHONE: (416) 531-5762
FAX: (416) 533-2397

CONTACT: Lorraine Endicott, Editor   **DESCRIPTION:** Published by Our Times Publishing Ltd. Circulation 2,600. Canada's only independent labour magazine devoted to unions and the labour movement in Canada. Articles include: labour relations; health and safety; union organizing; plant closures; pay equity and technological change. Published 6 times a year. Established in 1981.
WRITERS: "We purchase some work. Contact with a query letter with your angle. We are looking for stories of interest to workers on work issues and union organizing." Features

are 1,500-2,500 words. Opinion columns no more than 900 words. Notes and reviews 600-800 words. Writers' guidelines are available. "We pay honouriums, \$75-300."
PHOTOGRAPHERS: "We purchase colour covers and black & white inside. Photos usually accompany the article." Photo guidelines are not available.
NOTES: Sample copy available free upon request. Considers previously published work.

OUTDOOR CANADA
703 Evans Avenue, #202   **PHONE:** (416) 695-0311
Toronto, ON M9C 5E9   **FAX:** (416) 695-0382

CONTACT: Ms. Teddi Brown, Editor or James Little   **DESCRIPTION:** Published by The Publishing Division Outdoor Canada. Circulation 100,000. "We are a magazine for the Canadian sportsman and his family. We stress fishing but also cover hunting, camping, photography, canoeing and outdoor destinations. Every issue lets readers learn by sharing the experiences of experts." Published 8 times a year. Established in 1972.
WRITERS: 100% freelance written. "We assign stories to some of our regular freelance writers. If we are not familiar with you we ask for material on spec. If it works out that's good, and if not you can always try again. We are interested in anything to do with Canada's outdoors, ie. wildlife, fishing, canoeing, camping, hunting and any outdoor activity. If you are interested in working with us, send us something in the mail." Writers' guidelines are available.
PHOTOGRAPHERS: "We prefer text/photo packages. We have our own photo files, and occasionally assign a photographer to do certain pieces. We prefer 35mm or larger transparencies. We are demanding when it comes to wildlife shots. We deal with Canada's best wildlife photographers. We are often looking for people-in-action shots, not just scenics." Photo guidelines are available.
NOTES: Unsolicited materials will be returned with SASE.

OUTDOOR EDGE
5829-97 Street   **PHONE:** (403) 448-0381
Edmonton, AB T6E 3J2   **FAX:** (403) 438-3244

CONTACT: Kevin Rolfe, Editor   **DESCRIPTION:** Published by Keywest Marketing Ltd. Circulation 60,000. "A general interest outdoors publication taking in hunting, fishing, camping etc. for western Canada." Published 6 times a year. Established in 1991.
WRITERS: "100% freelance written. We have about 55 contributors. At times we assign articles but usually we accept queries. We prefer a query letter by mail with an outline of writing done in the past. We ask writers to supply us with 4-6 photos along with the article. Pay rates average \$200 for articles; that depends on the value of the article and how much work has gone into it. Features are 1,500-1,750 words. What we try to incorporate in most of our articles is not just a 'me and Joe' story but more of a how-to and where-to component."
PHOTOGRAPHERS: "We purchase photography all the time, both black & white and colour. We like to see samples of slides and prints. We like articles that have accompanying photos. For individual photos we pay from \$80-\$200."
NOTES: Sample copy available free upon request. Purchases first North American serial rights.

OUTSIDE GUIDE
117 Indian Road
Toronto, ON M6R 2V5

PHONE: (416) 538-2293
FAX: (416) 538-2475

CONTACT: Iain MacMillan, Editor **DESCRIPTION:** Published by Solstice Publishing Inc. Circulation 100,000. "A spring and summer magazine focusing on sport interests such as mountain biking, in-line skating, trekking etc. across Canada." Published twice a year.
WRITERS: "We accept unsolicited submissions, if we know the writer we will assign. Contact the editor with samples of work and story ideas. "Rates depend on the expertise of the writer, anywhere from $100 for a small article up to $1,000 for feature articles." Guidelines are available.
PHOTOGRAPHERS: Buys photography. "Pay rates depend on the expertise of the photographer. A cover photo would typically bring about $400 down to $75 for a small shot used in our news section." Guidelines are available.
NOTES: "We mostly use freelance contributors and freelance photographers. If someone has an interest in healthy outdoor sports we would like to hear from them." Contact the editor for a free sample copy. Does not return unsolicited writing. Considers previously published work but has never published something that has previously run elsewhere. Also publishes Ski Canada and Le Ski.

OWL
179 John Street #500
Toronto, ON M5T 3G5

PHONE: (416) 971-5275
FAX: (416) 971-5294

CONTACT: Keltie Thomas, Managing Editor Nyla Ahmad, Editor **DESCRIPTION:** Published by Diane Davy. Circulation 100,000. Children's magazine. Readers are children from 8-13 years. Owl is an award-winning science and nature magazine aimed at helping young people discover the world around them, with a focus on appreciating nature and the environment. The articles are exciting and informative and are surrounded with activities, games, photographs and illustrations. Owl magazine has earned a world-wide recognition for the quality of its presentation and its entertaining and informative content. Published 10 times a year.
WRITERS: Contact editor with query letter with specific outline of what you propose. Byline is given. A kill fee of 50% is offered if an assigned article is not run. "Before submitting any articles a person should read the magazine and really learn the particular style that we use."
PHOTOGRAPHERS: New photographers should send sample portfolio of captioned transparencies, with SASE. Takes 6-8 weeks to respond. Stock images purchased. Send subject list of your photographs.
NOTES: Returns unsolicited materials with SASE. Purchases one-time rights. Send $4.25 and 9x12" SASE for a sample copy. Also publishes Chickadee Magazine.

PACIFIC AFFAIRS
University of British Columbia
2029 West Mall
Vancouver, BC V6T 1Z2

PHONE: (604) 822-4534
FAX: (604) 822-5207

CONTACT: Bernice Chisholm **DESCRIPTION:** Scholarly journal which publishes research papers containing social, cultural, political, and economic issues of the Pacific

region. Nearly half of the text is devoted to book reviews. Published quarterly. Established in 1927.
NOTES: "We do not welcome submissions of any sort, either written or photographic. "

PACIFIC GOLF MAGAZINE
401-4180 Lougheed Hwy
Burnaby, BC V5C 6A7

PHONE: (604) 299-7311
FAX: (604) 299-9188

CONTACT: Bonnie Irving, Editor   **DESCRIPTION:** Published by Canada Wide Magazines Ltd. Circulation 16,000. Published 6 times a year. Established in 1994.

PACIFIC TRIBUNE
1726 East Hastings Street, Suite 100
Vancouver, BC V5L 1S9

NOTES: Could not locate. Phone number is not in service (604) 251-1186.

PACIFIC YACHTING
1132 Hamilton Street, #202
Vancouver, BC V6B 2S2

PHONE: (604) 687-1581
FAX: (604) 687-1925

CONTACT: Stewart Snow, Editor   **DESCRIPTION:** Published by O.P. Publishing Ltd. Circulation 18,500. "Boating magazine focused on cruising the west coast of Canada, Washington and Alaska. Emphasis is on how-to items for a knowledgeable boating public; for example how-to repair your boat or cruising knowledge and information. " Published monthly. Established in 1968.
WRITERS: Freelance written. Pay is negotiable. Byline published. Contact by phone or fax. "Writers should submit photos with an article." Guidelines available. "I would encourage anyone who wants to query us to read the magazine first. "
PHOTOGRAPHERS: "Generally, we like to buy photography with articles. We are definitely looking for cover material. Subject matter should be the BC coast and boating, preferably with some human interest, not just a boat. " Formats include 35mm and medium format transparencies. Captions preferred.
NOTES: Purchases one-time rights. Sample copy for $3.00 with SASE.

PACKAGING FOR DISTRIBUTION
777 Bay Street
Toronto, ON M5W 1A7

NOTES: NO LONGER PUBLISHED

LES PAPETIERES DU QUEBEC
3300 Côte Vertu #4105
St. Laurent, PQ H4R 2B7

PHONE: (514) 339-1399
FAX: (514) 339-1396

CONTACT: Jaclin Ouellet, Editor   **DESCRIPTION:** Published by Southam Business and Communications Group Inc. Circulation 3,900. French language publication. Issued quarterly. Established in 1990.

PARACHUTE

4060 boul. Saint-Laurent #501   **PHONE:** (514) 842-9805
Montreal, PQ H2W 1Y9   **FAX:** (514) 287-7146

CONTACT: see below   **DESCRIPTION:** Circulation 5,000. Bilingual contemporary art quarterly. Articles include the theory and practice of art today, with interviews, music, cinema, photography, theatre, dance, and video features.
WRITERS: "We will look at unsolicited work. Pays: exhibition reviews 1,000 words at $100; in-depth essays 4000-5,000 at $500. Call us to see if we are interested in your proposed material."
PHOTOGRAPHERS: "We very rarely purchase work. We usually deal with art galleries and they supply us with photos."
NOTES: English Editor: Jim Drobnick, French Editor: Chantel Pontbrian.

PARAGRAPH-THE CANADIAN FICTION REVIEW

137 Birmingham Street   **PHONE:** (519) 273-7083
Stratford, ON N5A 2T1

CONTACT: Beverly Daurio, Acting Editor   **DESCRIPTION:** Circulation 1,200. Canadian contemporary fiction. Published 3 times a year. Reflects the diversity of Canadian writing by including interviews, essays, criticism, and a review section.
WRITERS: Send completed material to the editor with SASE. "If someone would like to do book reviews for the magazine they should query first."
PHOTOGRAPHERS: "No photography is purchased."
NOTES: Sample copy is available for $3.95 plus GST.

PARALLELOGRAMME

183 Bathurst Street, 1st Floor
Toronto, ON M5T 2R7

NOTES: Could not locate. Phone number is not in service (416) 896-1275.

PARENT-TO-PARENT

Box 85324   **PHONE:** (905) 335-3549
Burlington, ON L7R 4K5   **FAX:** (905) 336-0761

CONTACT: Angela Greenway, Editor   **DESCRIPTION:** Published by Positive Parenting Inc. Circulation 40,000. "Our mandate is very specific. It focuses on the emotional well-being between parents and children." Published 6 times a year. Established in 1987.
WRITERS: "All our writers are therapists with the specific skills we need."
NOTES: Not accepting queries or submissions at this time.

THE PARKHURST EXCHANGE

400 McGill 3 Fl.   **PHONE:** (514) 397-8833
Montreal, PQ H2Y 2G1   **FAX:** (514) 397-8833

CONTACT: David Elkins   **DESCRIPTION:** Published by Parkhurst Publishing. Circulation 38,000. A trade journal for physicians across Canada. Published 10 times a year. Established in 1993.

WRITERS: "We use specialized material written by physicians."
NOTES: No freelance work is purchased. "We are unique because we run a lot of cartoons. We are also a forum for Canadian artists. We run 2-3 paintings by Canadian artists in every issue. Contact Beth Katz."

PARLONS AFFAIRES BAS ST. LAURENT/GASPESIE/I'ISLET

16 du Domaine Road
Riviere du Loup, PQ G5R 2P5

PHONE: (418) 862-1774
FAX: (418) 862-4387

CONTACT: Nadine Nolet, Editor Georges Fraser, Managing Editor **DESCRIPTION:** Published by Quebecor. French language publication. Issued 6 times a year. Established in 1988.
WRITERS: Majority assigned to in-house writers. Contact editor with query letter.
PHOTOGRAPHERS: Majority assigned to in-house photographers. Contact editor with query letter.
NOTES: Also publishes Le Portage and St. Laurent Echo.

PARLONS AFFAIRES LAURENTIDES

612 St.-Jacques St
Montreal, PQ H3J 4M8

PHONE: (514) 436-3303
FAX: (514) 436-5904

CONTACT: Diane Bougie, Editor **DESCRIPTION:** Published by Les Editions Hebcor Inc. Circulation 5,000. French language publication. Issued monthly. Established in 1984.
WRITERS: Majority assigned to in-house writers. Contact editor with query letter. Byline is given. Pay is negotiable.
PHOTOGRAPHERS: Majority assigned to in-house photographers. Contact editor with query letter.

PATHWAYS

238 Lakeshore Road East
Oakville, ON L6J 1H8

NOTES: NO LONGER PUBLISHED

PATIENT CARE

1120 Birchmount Road #200
Scarborough, ON M1K 5G4

PHONE: (416) 750-8900
FAX: (416) 751-8126

CONTACT: Vil Meere, Editor   **DESCRIPTION:** Published by Thomson Healthcare Communications. Circulation 27,000. A how-to publication for physicians. Published monthly. Established in 1990.
WRITERS: "Most of our material is written by doctors or science and medical writers. If a writer is specialized and has medical knowledge, that gives them an inside edge. Contact us by phone or mail."
PHOTOGRAPHERS: "We use medical illustrations."
NOTES: For a sample copy send 9x12" SASE with appropriate postage.

PEACE MAGAZINE
736 Bathurst Street
Toronto, ON M5S 2R4

PHONE: (416) 533-7581
FAX: (416) 531-6214

CONTACT: Metta Spencer **DESCRIPTION:** Circulation 1,000. Volunteer, non-profit organization magazine. Features interviews, commentary, and articles pertaining to nuclear disarmament and the arms trade. Also features peace-keeping or conflict resolution articles related to various geographic areas. Published six times a year.
NOTES: All writing and photography is done in-house.

PEDAL MAGAZINE
2 Pardee Avenue #204
Toronto, ON M6K 3H5

PHONE: (416) 530-1350
FAX: (416) 530-4155

CONTACT: Benjamin Sadavoy, Editor **DESCRIPTION:** Covers all aspects of cycling, competitive road and track, mountain bike and product reviews. Also features triathlon events and recreational, commuting and touring information. Provides advice on repair and maintenance. Published 9 times a year. Established in 1986.
NOTES: Also publishes Skitrax and Bike Trade Canada.

PEDIGREE MAGAZINE
19607-88 Avenue
Langley, BC V3A 6Y3

NOTES: NO LONGER PUBLISHED

THE PEGG
10060 Jasper Avenue, Scotia Place
15th Floor, Tower One
Edmonton, AB T5J 4A2

PHONE: (403) 426-3990
FAX: (403) 426-1877

CONTACT: Nordhal Flakstad, Editor **DESCRIPTION:** Published by The Association of Professional Engineers, Geologists & Geophysicists of Alberta. Circulation 31,200. Information for members, industry news and trends. A tabloid published ten times a year.
WRITERS: "We do purchase some material. Writers can send us a letter outlining the kinds of articles they normally write. We assign our articles."
PHOTOGRAPHERS: "We do purchase photography. Contact us by fax or mail or they can call to set up an appointment."
NOTES: Sample copy available free upon request.

PENINSULA PRIME
101-1440 George Street
White Rock, BC V4B 4A3

PHONE: (604) 531-1711
FAX: (604) 531-7977

CONTACT: Diane Strandberg, Editor **DESCRIPTION:** Published by The Peace Arch News. Circulation 28,500. Monthly magazine distributed as an insert in the Peace Arch Newspaper. Features publication with people profiles, food, fashion and books.
WRITERS: 10% freelance written. Contact editor with query letter. Byline is given. Payment negotiable.

PHOTOGRAPHERS: Submit a portfolio. Quality b&w prints. Does not purchase stock photography. "The only time we use freelancers is when our main photographer is sick or on holidays."
NOTES: Send 9x12" SASE for a sample copy.

PERCEPTION

441 MacLaren, 4th Floor   **PHONE:** (613) 236-8977
Ottawa, ON   K2P 2H3   **FAX:** (613) 728-9387

CONTACT: Nancy Perkins, Editor   **DESCRIPTION:** Published by Canadian Council on Social Development. A bilingual quarterly for those who want to be informed about Canada's changing social environment. Focuses on Canada's economic and social policies and programs. Provides thought-provoking research and insights. Established in 1977.
WRITERS: Majority handled in-house. Contact editor with query letter. Does not pay.
PHOTOGRAPHERS: Majority handled in-house. Contact editor with query letter.

PERFORMANCE

30 St. Clair Avenue West, #805   **PHONE:** (416) 926-7595
Toronto, ON   M4V 3A1   **FAX:** (416) 926-0407

CONTACT: Laurie Payne, Editor   **DESCRIPTION:** Published by St. Clair Investments Group Inc. Program distributed free at performances. House program for Toronto's O'Keefe Centre, Home of The National Ballet of Canada and The Canadian Opera Company. Published quarterly.
WRITERS: 100% freelance written. Contact editor with query letter and sample article with SASE. Do not send large manuscripts. Byline is given. Purchases all rights. "Writers need to be very familiar with live entertainment and the arts. If they live in Toronto or close that would be terrific."
PHOTOGRAPHERS: All photography is done in-house.

PERFORMANCE RACING NEWS

593 Yonge Street   **PHONE:** (416) 922-7223
Toronto, ON   M4Y 1Z4   **FAX:** (416) 922-8001

CONTACT: John Hopkins, Editor   **DESCRIPTION:** Published by Buy & Sell Newspaper Publishing. Circulation 15,700. Covers the entire spectrum of motorsports; car, motorcycle, powerboat and snowmobile racing. An authority on motor racing in Canada, it features coverage and photographs from around the world. Published 16 times a year. Established in 1989.
WRITERS: Contact editor with query letter. Follow-up with a phone call 10 days later. Byline is given. Pay is negotiable.
PHOTOGRAPHERS: Contact editor with query letter. Follow-up with phone call 10 days later. Sample colour prints returned with SASE.
NOTES: "We try to get coverage of some of the smaller, localized motorsport race tracks across Canada. If we have people writing offering reports or photos from a particular race track, then that is ideal. General sports articles are also welcome." Send 9x12" SASE for a sample copy.

PERFORMING ARTS & ENTERTAINMENT IN CANADA
104 Glenrose Avenue   **PHONE:** (416) 484-4534
Toronto, ON M4T 1K8   **FAX:** (416) 484-6214

CONTACT: Karen Bell, Editor   **DESCRIPTION:** Published by Canadian Stage & Arts. Circulation 44,000. Articles include theatre, dance, opera, ballet, and film. Also profile individual performers, companies, and troupes. Published quarterly. Established in 1961.
WRITERS: 75% freelance written. Contact editor with query letter. Byline is given. Pays $75-$175 for articles. Does not pay for unsolicited articles. Considers simultaneous submissions.
PHOTOGRAPHERS: All photography is done in-house or photos included with text/photo submissions.

PETS MAGAZINE
10 Gateway Blvd. #490   **PHONE:** (416) 696-5488
North York, ON M3C 3T4   **FAX:** (416) 696-7395

CONTACT: Margaret Williamson, Editor   **DESCRIPTION:** Published by Moorshead Magazines. Circulation 55,000. A magazine for Canadian pet owners with advice, help and guidance. Published 6 times a year. Established in 1983.
WRITERS: "We purchase 50 articles per year. Articles average 900 words paying 17¢ a word." Prefer work on disk, Wordperfect 5.1 or 6.1 or MS Word. Include hard copy of the story and any photography. "Before going to the trouble of sending an unsolicited article, send a query letter first."
PHOTOGRAPHERS: "We purchase approximately 25 photos per year. We pay $10 per photo."
NOTES: Doesn't return unsolicited material "due to volume of mail" and doesn't accept previously published work or simultaneous submissions. Also publishes Computing Now and Government Purchasing Guide.

PETS QUARTERLY MAGAZINE
151-8333 Jones Road   **PHONE:** (604) 244-7450
Richmond, BC V6Y 1L5   **FAX:** (604) 244-7450

CONTACT: Val Wilson, Editor   **DESCRIPTION:** Published by PQM Pets Quarterly Magazine. Circulation 70,000. Focuses on pet owners (primarily cats and dogs). Features are regular veterinary columns, and other articles regarding the health, exercise and training of animals. Published quarterly. Established in 1992.
WRITERS: Most writing is done in-house. Veterinary columns are written by vets. Query letter or sample of work preferred. Will return work with SASE. Writers' guidelines available. Pay is negotiable.
PHOTOGRAPHERS: Publishes photos, but generally does not pay unless it is a very unusual photograph which they cannot find elsewhere. "Original photo ideas are considered. Colour transparencies or prints are acceptable. "We have a feature called 'The Family Album' where people send their pet photos in. Some of them are just excellent and so it is a huge resource."
NOTES: Buys one-time rights. Send 9x12" SASE for a sample copy.

PHARMACIST NEWS

777 Bay Street 5 Fl.   **PHONE:** (416) 596-2662
Toronto, ON M5W 1A7   **FAX:** (416) 596-2589

CONTACT: Polly Thompson, Editor   **DESCRIPTION:** Published by Maclean Hunter Ltd. Circulation 17,700. A monthly publication covering news, professional and clinical issues for Canada's retail and hospital pharmacists. Established in 1993.
WRITERS: "I have a number of freelancers I work with regularly. Any freelancers who are interested in contacting me should just call me at 596-5950 or send a query letter. Retail pharmacy news in Canada is the subject area and that is the only subject interested freelancers should contact me about."
PHOTOGRAPHERS: "I hire on assignment. Contact with a phone call or a query letter."

PHARMACY POST

1120 Birchmont Road #200   **PHONE:** (416) 750-8900
Scarborough, ON M1K 5G4   **FAX:** (416) 751-8126

CONTACT: Karen Welds, Managing Editor   **DESCRIPTION:** Published by Thomson Healthcare Communications. Circulation 16,600. Monthly publication geared to pharmacists and drug store managers. Articles focus on pharmacy news and merchandising trends. Established in 1993.
WRITERS: 80% freelance written. Contact this publication by faxing a query letter. Byline is given. Pay is negotiable.
Buys exclusive rights. Send 9x12" SASE for a sample copy.
PHOTOGRAPHERS: 85% assigned to in-house photographers. Contact this publication by faxing a query letter with subject lists.
NOTES: "Please do not send photos or articles. We keep subject lists, resumés and query letters on file until we need them." Also publishes Hospital Pharmacy Practice (written by pharmacists).

PHARMACY PRACTICE

1120 Birchmount Road #200   **PHONE:** (416) 750-8900
Scarborough, ON M1K 5G4   **FAX:** (416) 751-8126

CONTACT: Anne Bokma, Editor   **DESCRIPTION:** Published by Thomson Healthcare Communications. Circulation 17,000. Professional journal written for the pharmacist with the purpose of improving professional expertise in the field of pharmacy. Established in 1985.
WRITERS: 25% freelance written. Contact this publication by faxing a query letter. Byline is given. Pay is negotiable.
PHOTOGRAPHERS: 85% assigned to in-house photographers. Contact this publication by faxing a query letter with subject lists.
NOTES: Buys exclusive rights. Send 9x12" SASE for a sample copy.

PHILATELIE QUEBEC
Box 1000 Station M
Montreal, PQ H1V 3R2

PHONE: (514) 252-3035
FAX: none

CONTACT: Jean-Pierre Durand, Editor   **DESCRIPTION:** Published by Les Editions Phibec Inc. Circulation 3,000. French language publication for rare stamp collectors in the province of Quebec. Published 10 times a year. Established in 1974.
WRITERS: Majority assigned to in-house photographers. Contact editor with query letter. Byline is given.
PHOTOGRAPHERS: All photography is done in-house.

PHOTO DEALER NEWS
130 Spy Court
Markham, ON L3R 5H6

PHONE: (905) 475-8440
FAX: (905) 475-9246

CONTACT: Jim Dominey, Editor   **DESCRIPTION:** Published by Carmar Publications Ltd. Circulation 4,200. Published bi-monthly. Established in 1990.
NOTES: Trade magazine aimed at photo dealers across Canada.

PHOTO DIGEST; The Photographer's Magazine
Toronto Dominion Center, Suite 2550
Toronto, ON M5K 1E7

PHONE: (416) 287-6357
FAX: (416) 287-6359

CONTACT: Jacques Thibault   **DESCRIPTION:** Published by Apex Publications. Circulation 40,000. "The photographers magazine" is aimed at photo enthusiasts. "We try to cover all aspects of photography; powerful new techniques, equipment reviews and tips, photo composition and design, news, a reader's gallery and portfolios. Open to all suggestions. Regular features on travel, nature, equipment." The magazine is written by photographic journalists for people who love photographs. "We do two things with Photo Digest, we have how-to articles and we get a lot of reader participation. The content is very much determined by reader interest." Established in 1990.
WRITERS: We have a number of regular contributing editors; payment is negotiated as a special agreement. Unsolicited manuscripts are sometimes used; payment averages $300. Articles usually include 4-5 photos and approximately 1000 words. Occasionally very good articles from Photo Selection are translated for use in Photo Digest and vise versa. "Every month we look at approximately 100 submissions. We prefer a query letter with photos and article. No submissions are ever accepted without us evaluating the photos first." Send SASE. Buys first rights, with 6 month North American exclusivity. If article is translated, the writer is paid an additional 50% fee.
PHOTOGRAPHERS: "Our purpose is to promote Canadian talent, to give Canadian photographers a chance to be published." Send in photo packages for consideration in readers sections. Consult back issues to see the types of submissions used.
NOTES: Also publishes *NATIONAL PHOTO BUYERS GUIDE*. This is a product related magazine, published annually. Focuses on all types of equipment and acessories including: 35mm SLRs, medium formats, film, accessories. Submissions will also be considered for this publication. Articles must be equipment related. Circulation 60,000.

PHOTO LIFE

130 Spy Court
Markham, ON L3R 5H6

PHONE: (905) 475-8440
FAX: (905) 475-9246

CONTACT: Jerry Kobalenko, Editor   **DESCRIPTION:** Published by Phil Whaylen, Publisher: Camar Publications Ltd. Circulation 40,000. Special interest consumer magazine. Focuses on the needs of advanced amateur and professional photographers. Articles include: how-to's, portfolios, corporate reviews and general articles (see back issues). Published 8 times a year. Established in 1976.

WRITERS: "Most of our articles are written either by professional photographers or by writers with excellent research skills and a knowledge of photography. Articles should be easy to read but dense with information. No travelogues please." Writers are generally responsible for tracking down the photographs to illustrate articles. "The magazine has very high standards. We have a core of really strong contributors. It is not easy to break in. Research stories are something we are definitely interested in." Query with good solid ideas.

PHOTOGRAPHERS: Hires on assignment and buys from stock. Pays $50-100 for colour, $300 for colour cover, $500 for text/photo packages. Uses all formats of colour transparencies, custom colour prints and 8x10 b&w prints. Reports in 6-8 weeks. "We run one portfolio per issue and are always interested in the work of new photographers. Please get familiar with the magazine before you query."

NOTES: Guidelines are available. Please send SASE. Do not contact unless you have researched back issues of the magazine.

PHOTO RETAILER

Toronto Dominion Center, Suite 2550
Toronto, ON M5K 1E7

PHONE: (416) 287-6357
FAX: (416) 287-6359

CONTACT: Don Long   **DESCRIPTION:** Published by Apex Publications. Circulation 5200. Trade magazine distributed to photo dealers and chains. Published 4 times a year. Articles cover new equipment and photo products.

NOTES: All writing and photography is done in-house.

PHOTO SELECTION

850 Pierre Bertrand Blvd.
Ville De Vanier, PQ G1M 3K8

PHONE: (418) 687-3550

CONTACT: Jacques Thibault   **DESCRIPTION:** Circulation 17,000. French language publication. Consumer photography magazine. Published 8 times a year. "We try to cover all aspects of photography; powerful new techniques, equipment reviews and tips, photo composition and design, news, a reader's gallery and portfolios. Open to all suggestions. Regular features on travel, nature, equipment. The magazine is written by photographic journalists for people who love photographs. The content is very much determined by reader interest."

WRITERS: We have a number of regular contributing editors; payment is negotiated as a special agreement. Unsolicited manuscripts are sometimes used; payment averages $300. Articles usually include 4-5 photos and approximately 1,000 words. Occasionally very good articles from Photo Digest are translated for use in Photo Selection and vise versa. Content of Photo Selection is 90% unique. "Every month we look at approximately 100 submissions. We prefer a query letter with photos and article. No submissions are ever accepted without us evaluating the photos first." Send SASE. Buys first rights, with 6 month

North American exclusivity. If article is translated, the writer is paid an additional 50% fee.

PHOTOGRAPHERS: "Our purpose is to promote Canadian talent, to give Canadian photographers a chance to be published." Send in photo packages for consideration in readers sections. Consult back issues to see the types of submissions used.

PHYSICAL EDUCATION DIGEST
111 Kingsmount Blvd.   **PHONE:** (705) 675-7055
Sudbury, ON P3E 1K8   **FAX:** (705) 675-5539

CONTACT: Dick Moss, Editor   **DESCRIPTION:** Published quarterly.
NOTES: All writing and photography is done in-house.

PHYSICIAN'S MANAGEMENT MANUALS
777 Bay Street   **PHONE:** (416) 596-5724
Toronto, ON M5W 1A7   **FAX:** (416) 596-3162

CONTACT: Will Koteff, Editor   **DESCRIPTION:** Published by Maclean Hunter Ltd. Circulation 41,100. Highly specialized, technical publication in the field of medicine. Published monthly. Established in 1976.
WRITERS: 99% assigned to in-house writers. Contact editor with query letter. Byline is given.
PHOTOGRAPHERS: All photography is done in-house.

PHYSICS IN CANADA
151 Slater Street, #903   **PHONE:** (613) 237-3392
Ottawa, ON K1P 5H3   **FAX:** (613) 238-1677

CONTACT: J.S.C. McKee, Editor   **DESCRIPTION:** Published by Canadian Association of Physicists. Circulation 8,000. Publication focusing on scientific advancements in physics. Published 6 times a year in English and French. Established in 1946.
NOTES: All writing and photography is done in-house.

PHYSIOTHERAPY CANADA
890 Yonge Street 9 Fl.   **PHONE:** (416) 924-5312
Toronto, ON M4W 3P4   **FAX:** (416) 924-7335

CONTACT: Diane Charter, Editor   **DESCRIPTION:** Published by Canadian Physiotherapy Association. Circulation 3,500. Academic journal of physiotherapy. Published quarterly in English and French. Established in 1923.
NOTES: All writing and photography is done in-house.

PIONEER CHRISTIAN MONTHLY
RR4
Cambridge, ON N1R 5S5

PHONE: (519) 622-1777
FAX: (519) 622-1993

CONTACT: Rev. Jeff Kingswood **DESCRIPTION:** Free publication containing special events, issues and news of the Reformed Church of Canada. Published monthly. Established in 1951.
NOTES: All writing and photography is done in-house.

PISCINES & SPA
270 Esmond Park East
Markham, ON L3R 1H3

PHONE: (905) 513-0090
FAX: (905) 513-1377

CONTACT: André LaPierre, Editor **DESCRIPTION:** Published by Hubbard Marketing & Publishing. Circulation 1,000. French language publication issued 4 times per year. Articles feature "everything you always wanted to know about pools & spas."
WRITERS: Contact editor with query letter.
PHOTOGRAPHERS: Contact editor with query letter.

LES PLAISANCIERS
970 Montée de Liesse #310
Ville St. Laurent, PQ H4T 1W7

PHONE: (514) 856-0788
FAX: (514) 856-0790

CONTACT: Claude Leonard, Editor **DESCRIPTION:** Published by Power Boating Canada. Circulation 15,000. French language publication. Focuses on boating techniques, boat tests and reviews. Published five times a year. Established in 1986.
WRITERS: 99% assigned to in-house writers. Contact editor with query letter, to be kept on file.
PHOTOGRAPHERS: 99% assigned to in-house photographers. Contact editor with query letter, to be kept on file.
NOTES: "We do everything in-house unless we are really in a bind." Also publishes Power Boating Canada and Vie En Plein Air.

PLAN-LE MENSUEL DE GENIE QUEBECOIS
2020 University St. 18 Fl.
Montreal, PQ H3A 2A5

PHONE: (514) 845-6141
FAX: (514) 845-1833

CONTACT: Jean-Marc Papineau, Editor **DESCRIPTION:** Published by Ordre des ingénieurs de Quebec. Circulation 40,000. Free engineering publication for the Order of Engineers in Quebec. Published 10 times a year in French. Established in 1963.
WRITERS: Majority assigned to in-house writers. Contact editor with query letter. Byline is given. Pay is negotiable.
PHOTOGRAPHERS: Majority assigned to in-house photographers. Contact editor with query letter.

THE PLANET THIS WEEK
665 Davis Street
Newmarket, ON L3Y 2R2

NOTES: Could not locate. Phone number is not in service (416) 727-8901.

PLANS DE MAISONS DU QUEBEC
7 Bates Road
Outremont, PQ H2V 1A6

PHONE: (514) 270-1100
FAX: (514) 270-6900

CONTACT: Claude Leclerc, Editorial Director   **DESCRIPTION:** Published by Publicor. Circulation 27,600. French language publication. Contains house plans and articles about renovations and building construction. Published quarterly. Established in 1976.
WRITERS: Majority assigned to in-house writers. Contact editor with query letter. Byline is given. Pay is negotiable.
PHOTOGRAPHERS: Majority assigned to in-house photographers. Contact editor with query letter.
NOTES: Send 9x12 SASE for a sample copy.

PLANT
777 Bay Street
Toronto, ON M5W 1A7

PHONE: (416) 596-5777
FAX: (416) 596-5552

CONTACT: Wayne Karl, Editor   **DESCRIPTION:** Published by Maclean Hunter Ltd. Circulation 36,300. Trade magazine aimed at manufacturing and industrial plants. Articles aimed at increasing cost effectiveness, production, and product quality. Readers include plant managers, engineers, and trainers. Published 18 times a year. Established in 1941.
WRITERS: Majority assigned to in-house writers. Contact editor with query letter. Pay is negotiable. Writers' guidelines available.
PHOTOGRAPHERS: Majority assigned to in-house photographers. Contact editor with query letter.
NOTES: Also publishes Plant Maintenance, Plant Automation, and Plant Controls and Instrumentation.

PLANT AND GARDEN
1 Pacifique
Ste-Anne-de-Bellevue, PQ H9X 1C5

PHONE: (514) 457-2744
FAX: (514) 457-6255

CONTACT: Barbara Paul, Publisher   **DESCRIPTION:** Published by Gardenvale Publishing Co. Circulation 36,700. Articles on planning and enhancing your garden give advice to all green thumbs. Published quarterly. Established in 1988.
WRITERS: 50% freelance written. Contact editor with query letter and resumé. Byline is given. Pay is negotiable.
PHOTOGRAPHERS: 50% freelance. Contact editor with query letter and subject lists. Do not send photos in the mail.
NOTES: Formerly TLC.. for plants

PLANT ENGINEERING & MAINTENANCE

277 Lakeshore Road East
#209 Royal Life Bldg.
Oakville, ON L6J 6J3

PHONE: (905) 842-2884
FAX: (905) 842-8226

CONTACT: Rae Robb, Editor **DESCRIPTION:** Published by Clifford Elliot & Associates Ltd. Circulation 20,000. An industrial editorial publication for plant managers, engineers, and production operations across Canada. Published 7 times a year.
WRITERS: "Freelance work is purchased. Contact the editor by phone, mail or fax."
PHOTOGRAPHERS: "We do purchase photography." Contact the editor by phone, mail or fax.
NOTES: Must have a knowledge of the publication before making contact.

PLASTICS BUSINESS

1450 Don Mills Road
Don Mills, ON M3B 2X7

PHONE: (416) 445-6641
FAX: (416) 442-2213

CONTACT: Michael Shelley, Editor **DESCRIPTION:** Published by Southam Business Communications Inc. Circulation 9,800. Trade publication dealing with the plastics industry. Published quarterly. Established in 1980.
WRITERS: Majority done by in-house writers. Contact editor with query letter, bearing in mind the comments below.
PHOTOGRAPHERS: All photography is done in-house.
NOTES: "We are a trade publication for the plastics industry and people with expertise in this area are few and far-between. We don't want to be inundated with offers that are not appropriate to our needs." Read the publication before making any queries.

PLASTICS IN CANADA

406 North Service Road East #1
Oakville, ON L6H 5R2

PHONE: (905) 844-9773
FAX: (905) 944-5672

CONTACT: Larry Bonikowsky, Editor **DESCRIPTION:** Published by Kay Publishing. Circulation 8,000. A trade publication for the plastics processing industry in Canada. Published 6 times a year.
WRITERS: "We don't frequently use freelance writers."
PHOTOGRAPHERS: "We do purchase photographs but not for editorial."
NOTES: Also publishes Coatings.

PLAYBACK

366 Adelaide Street West #500
Toronto, ON M5V 1R9

PHONE: (416) 408-2300
FAX: (416) 408-0870

CONTACT: Mary Maddever, Editor **DESCRIPTION:** Published by Brunico Communications Inc. Published 25 times a year. Established in 1986.
WRITERS: "We usually assign our articles. We are so specialized that it is not appropriate for freelancers to send us unsolicited material."
PHOTOGRAPHERS: Does not purchase photography.
NOTES: Also publishes Video Innovations, Playback International and Canada on Location.

PLAYBACK INTERNATIONAL
366 Adelaide Street West #500
Toronto, ON M5V 1R9

PHONE: (416) 408-2300
FAX: (416) 408-0870

CONTACT: Mary Maddever, Editor **DESCRIPTION:** Published by Brunico Communications Inc. Circulation 2,100. Published twice a year. Established in 1990.
WRITERS: "We usually assign our articles. We are so specialized that it is not appropriate for freelancers to send us unsolicited material."
PHOTOGRAPHERS: Does not purchase photography.
NOTES: Also publishes Video Innovations, Playback and Canada on Location, and Strategy.

PLAYBOARD
7560 Lawrence Drive
Burnaby, BC V5A 1T6

PHONE: (604) 420-6115
FAX: (604) 420-6115

CONTACT: Chuck Davis, Editor **DESCRIPTION:** Published by Arch-Way Publishers Ltd. Circulation 44,500. Monthly arts magazine. Features behind-the-scenes articles and interviews with key performers for concert and theatre goers. Established in 1966.
NOTES: All writing and photography is done in-house.

PME MAGAZINE FOR QUEBEC
1100 René-Lévesque Blvd W 24 Fl.
Montreal, PQ H3B 4X9

PHONE: (514) 392-9000
FAX: (514) 393-9430

CONTACT: Denis Dubé, Editor **DESCRIPTION:** Published by Transcontinental Publications Inc. Circulation 30,000. French language publication. A business magazine for owners of small and medium-sized businesses. Issued 10 times a year. Established in 1984.
WRITERS: 100% freelance written. "We hire on assignment and accept queries from journalists. Contact us by phone or mail. I would like to receive a plan of a proposed article with a resumé and samples of articles published." Writers' guidelines are not available.
PHOTOGRAPHERS: "We purchase colour photography by assignment only. Contact our Artistic Director, Louise Rouleau by mail or phone."
NOTES: Sample copy available free upon request.

POCKET PRO GOLF MAGAZINE
85 West Wilmot Street #14
Richmond Hill, ON L4B 1K7

PHONE: (905) 764-5409
FAX: (905) 764-5462

CONTACT: Bruce Longhurst, Editor **DESCRIPTION:** Published by Longhurst Golf Corp. Circulation 142,500. A pocket sized guide for golfers to use as they play a golf course. Distributed at golf courses. Published annually.
NOTES: No freelance material is used in this publication. However, this publisher is developing a new magazine which will be open to query letters from writers and photographers. The magazine will focus on golf courses only.

POETRY CANADA

Box 1061
Kingston, ON K7L 4Y5

PHONE: (613) 548-8429
FAX: (613) 548-1556

CONTACT: Barry Dempster, Editor   **DESCRIPTION:** Circulation 1,500. Quarterly publication which features Canada's best poets and new writers. Also publishes reviews and news and in-depth interviews.
WRITERS: Contact editor with query letter and subject lists. Pays $10 per page; $15 per poem. Byline is given. Purchases one-time rights. Returns unsolicited articles with SASE in 8-12 weeks. Poetry editor: Barry Dempster. Prose editor: Bob Hilderley.
PHOTOGRAPHERS: "We don't want any original photography to be sent because we don't want to be responsible for anything that goes missing. Perhaps a quality reproduction that does not have to be returned would be better."
NOTES: Send $5 and 9x12" SASE for a sample copy. They also publish Quarry Magazine and Canadian Fiction Magazine.

POINT OF VIEW MAGAZINE

Holt Renfrew, 50 Bloor Street West
Toronto, ON M4W 1A1

PHONE: (416) 960-2917
FAX: (416) 922-3240

CONTACT: Nancy Moore, Publisher   **DESCRIPTION:** Published by Holt Renfrew. Circulation 130,000 for Women's Point of View and 120,000 for Men's Point of View. A fashion magazine directly related to the Holt Renfrew Chain. A women's version and a men's version are published. Issued a total of 4 times a year in English and French. Established in 1987.
WRITERS: "We do purchase freelance work. Because we have writers on staff we only purchase two or three times a year."
PHOTOGRAPHERS: "We do hire photographers on assignment. All of the photography is freelanced; at least 400 pages a year." Contact the art director, Gerry Mamone at (416) 368-1137.
NOTES: Sample copy available free upon request.

POLICY OPTIONS

1470 Rue Peel #200
Montreal, PQ H3A 1T1

PHONE: (514) 985-2461
FAX: (514) 985-2559

CONTACT: Alfred LeBlanc, Editor   **DESCRIPTION:** Published by The Institute for Research on Public Policy. Circulation 2,500. A leading forum for the debate of public policy.
NOTES: All writing and photography is obtained in-house.

POMME D'API QUEBEC

3995 Ste-Catherine Est
Montreal, PQ H1W 2G7

PHONE: (514) 522-3936
FAX: (514) 522-1761

CONTACT: Suzanne Spino   **DESCRIPTION:** Published by Bayard Presse Canada Inc. Circulation 8,000. French language publication. Aimed at children 3 to 7 years. Includes a supplement for parents in each issue. Published 10 times a year. Established in 1991.

WRITERS: 80% freelance written. Contact editor with query letter or phone to pitch a story idea. Byline is given.
PHOTOGRAPHERS: All photography is done in-house.
NOTES: Pay is negotiable. Send 9x12" SASE for a sample copy.

POOL & SPA LIFESTYLE

270 Esmond Park Drive, #12   **PHONE:** (905) 513-0090
Markham, ON L3R 1H3   **FAX:** (905) 513-1377

CONTACT: David Barnsley, Editor **DESCRIPTION:** Published by Hubbard Marketing & Publishing. Circulation 2,000. Pool and spa lifestyle publication. Published up to 4 times per year.
WRITERS: Contact editor with query letter. Byline is given. Pay is negotiable. Returns unsolicited articles with SASE if requested. Purchases all rights.
PHOTOGRAPHERS: Contact editor with query letter. Returns unsolicited photos with SASE, if requested. "Photo subjects would be anything involving the pool or spa." Purchases first-time rights.
NOTES: Send 9x12" SASE for a sample copy. Also publishes Pool & Spa Marketing and Piscines & Spa.

POOL & SPA MARKETING

270 Esmond Park Drive #12   **PHONE:** (905) 513-0090
Markham, ON L3R 1H3   **FAX:** (905) 513-1377

CONTACT: David Barnsley, Editor **DESCRIPTION:** Published by Hubbard Marketing & Publishing. Circulation 9,000. Geared to pool and spa industry owners and operators in Canada and the eastern United States. Features include everything from how to run pool and spa businesses to the more technical side of the chemicals and equipment involved. Published 7 times a year.
WRITERS: 20% freelance written. Purchases 5 articles per year. Purchases all rights; reprints with permission only.
PHOTOGRAPHERS: Purchases 6 photos per year. Contact editor with query letter. Returns unsolicited colour prints with SASE. Pay is negotiable. Purchases first-time rights.
NOTES: Send 9x12" SASE for a sample copy.

PORT HOLE

26 Golden Gate Court   **PHONE:** (416) 293-2438
Scarborough, ON M1P 3A5   **FAX:** none

CONTACT: Diana Zonnenberg, Managing Editor **DESCRIPTION:** Published by Canadian Power and Sail Squadrons. Circulation 24,900. Published quarterly by Canadian Power and Sail Squadrons to promote safe boating. Articles include new products and equipment. Published in English and French. Established in 1952.
NOTES: "Canadian Power and Sail Squadrons is a charitable organization that uses entirely volunteer staff."

LE PORTEFEUILLE D'ASSURANCES

30 rue Logan #3   **PHONE:** (514) 465-8869
St. Lambert, PQ J4P 3P4   **FAX:** (514) 465-9656

CONTACT: Pierre M. Chaput, Editor   **DESCRIPTION:** Published by L. Chaput, Fils et Cie Ltd. Circulation 6,200. Trade publication focusing on financial services and banking. Published quarterly in English(20%) and French(80%).
WRITERS: 20% assigned to freelance writers. Contact this publication by sending or faxing a query letter with a resumé. Byline is given. Pay is negotiable.
PHOTOGRAPHERS: Majority assigned to in-house photographers. Contact editor with query letter or fax with subject lists.
NOTES: Send 9x12 SASE for a sample copy. "Do not send unsolicited sample photos or articles please."

PORTS ANNUAL

1434 St. Catherine Street West #512   **PHONE:** (514) 861-6715
Montreal, PQ H3G 1R4   **FAX:** (514) 861-0966

CONTACT: Megan Perkins, Editor   **DESCRIPTION:** Published by Canadian Marine Publications Ltd. Published annually.
NOTES: All writing and photography is done in-house. Also publishes Great Lakes Navigation.

POTTERSFIELD PORTFOLIO

151 Ryan Court
Fredericton, NB E3A 2Y9

NOTES: Could not locate. Phone number is not in service (506) 472-9251.

POWER BOATING CANADA

2585 Skymark Avenue #306   **PHONE:** (905) 624-8218
Mississauga, ON L4W 4L5   **FAX:** (905) 624-6764

CONTACT: Pam Cottrell, Editor   **DESCRIPTION:** Published by Camping Canada Inc. Circulation 40,000. Bi-monthly magazine featuring stories on waterskiing, powerboat performance and evaluation of new equipment and boating techniques. Aimed at the powerboat enthusiast. Established in 1986.
WRITERS: "A large portion is freelance by assignment. I prefer writers to query with samples before making any submissions. Article length ranges from 1,200-1,500 words. Pay rates negotiated depending on the writer and the subject matter. We are looking for articles with a Canadian slant applicable to the enjoyment of power boating." Guidelines are not available.
PHOTOGRAPHERS: "We don't purchase photos individually. They come as part of an arrangement we make with the writer. A lot of our writers are photographers as well. Colour is preferred."
NOTES: May consider previously published work. Prefers single submissions. Sample copies are given to those who are on assignment. Also publishes Camping Canada and Hot Water Magazine.

PRACTICAL ALLERGY & IMMUNOLOGY
3333 Cote Vertu Blvd. #300   PHONE: (514) 331-4561
Montreal, PQ H4R 2N1   FAX: (514) 336-1129

CONTACT: Inara Palieps, Managing Editor   DESCRIPTION: Published by Medicopea
International Inc. Circulation 3,500. Clinical publication with allergy updates, AIDS updates
and other medical news. Published 6 times a year. Established in 1986.
WRITERS: 10% freelance written. Contact editor with query letter, resumé and samples.
Pay is negotiable. Guidelines available.
PHOTOGRAPHERS: All photography is done in-house.
NOTES: "Do not send articles in the mail. We will contact you when we need you for
a particular story." Also publishes Ophthalmic Practice & Practical Optometry.

PRACTICAL OPTOMETRY
3333 Cote Vertu Blvd. #300   PHONE: (514) 331-4561
St. Laurent, PQ H4R 2N1   FAX: (514) 336-1129

CONTACT: Inara Palieps, Managing Editor   DESCRIPTION: Published by Medicopea
International Inc. Circulation 3,500. Published 6 times a year. Established in 1986.
WRITERS: 10% freelance written. Contact editor with query letter, resumé and samples.
Pay is negotiable.
PHOTOGRAPHERS: All photography is done in-house.
NOTES: "Do not send articles in the mail. We will contact you when we need you for
a particular story." Also publishes Ophthalmic Practice and Practical Allergy & Immunology.

PRAIRIE BOOKS NOW
100 Arthur Street, #404   PHONE: (204) 947-3335
Winnipeg, MB R3B 1H3   FAX: (204) 942-1555

CONTACT: Maureen Devanik   DESCRIPTION: Circulation 40-50,000. "Tabloid
featuring articles and reviews about books written or published in, or about the Prairies."
Published 3 times per year. Administered through the offices of the Association of Manitoba
Book Publishers.
WRITERS: "We will look at freelance information. In the past we have generally contracted
out all of the works. All freelance writers have to be aware that we also publish electronically
in the internet and they have to be willing to give us the electronic rights. Lengths and
pay rates vary. Contact with an outline of the article."
PHOTOGRAPHERS: "We usually have someone shoot on assignment. We would accept
queries from photographers. They can be from anywhere. Contact by letter."
NOTES: Copies are available at most book stores, libraries and some alternative outlets
like theatres and cafes.

PRAIRIE FIRE
100 Arthur Street, #423   PHONE: (204) 943-9066
Winnipeg, MB R3B 1H3   FAX: (204) 942-1555

CONTACT: Andris Taskans, Editor   DESCRIPTION: Circulation 1,400. Literary
magazine featuring poetry, fiction, essays, interviews, reviews, and criticism by established,
as well as new Canadian authors. Published quarterly. Established in 1978.

WRITERS: 90% freelance written. Returns unsolicited materials with SASE. Pay is negotiable. Byline is given. Writers' guidelines are available with SASE. Purchases first North American serial rights.
PHOTOGRAPHERS: All photography is done in-house.

PRAIRIE FORUM

Canadian Plains Research Center
University of Regina
Regina, SK S4S 0A2

PHONE: (306) 585-4795
FAX: (306) 585-4699

CONTACT: Dr. Patrick Douaud, Editor   **DESCRIPTION:** Circulation 350. Prairie Forum is a multi-disciplinary, scholarly journal serving as an outlet for research relating to the Canadian Prairie region. Published twice a year. Established in 1976.
WRITERS: 100% freelance written. Contact editor with query letter. Returns unsolicited materials with SASE. Does not pay. Byline is given.
PHOTOGRAPHERS: All photography is done in-house.
NOTES: "We do not publish fiction. Articles must be well-researched, documented and related to the prairies. We don't take reminiscences. Articles are sent out to two external examiners before publication and must pass very stringent guidelines."

PRAIRIE LANDSCAPE MAGAZINE

1777 Victoria Avenue #1000
Regina, SK S4P 4K5

PHONE: (306) 584-1000

DESCRIPTION: Published by Charleton Communications Ltd. Publication for tree nurseries and florist shops. Published bi-monthly. Established in 1977.
NOTES: No freelance material is purchased for this publication.

PRAIRIE MESSENGER

Box 190
Muenster, SK S0K 2Y0

PHONE: (306) 682-1770
FAX: (306) 682-5285

CONTACT: Andrew Britz, Editor   **DESCRIPTION:** Published by Order of St. Benedict Muenster-Sask. Circulation 9,000. A Catholic weekly newspaper for Saskatchewan and Manitoba. Published 46 times a year. Established in 1923.
WRITERS: Phone pitches or query letters for new submissions are welcome.
PHOTOGRAPHERS: Normally use 35 photos per issue. Only 10% from outside sources. Buys stock photography. Phone call preferred. Uses b&w prints. Captions not necessary.

PREMIERE

1314 Britannia Road East
Mississauga, ON L4W 1C8

PHONE: (905) 564-1033
FAX: (905) 564-3398

CONTACT: Catherine Puddy, Editor   **DESCRIPTION:** Published by Premiere Video Magazine Inc. Circulation 8,000. "We are a trade publication for the home entertainment industry in Canada. Our magazine goes to video retailers, rental stores, specialty stores, mass merchants, buyers and industry associated people." Published monthly. Established in 1984.

WRITERS: "We plan to start purchasing more. We have trouble finding writers that are film literate or who have a working knowledge of entertainment technologies. We are interested in emerging home entertainment technologies like CD ROM, satellite and retail operations. We might do an article on customer service. Remember the focus is general home entertainment. Freelancers can fax or write us. If you have a proposal for an article I would prefer it by fax with samples of your work."
PHOTOGRAPHERS: "All our photography is supplied by entertainment companies."
NOTES: Sample copy available. Send 9x12" SASE with $2 postage.

PRESBYTERIAN RECORD
50 Wynford Drive
North York, ON M3C 1J7

PHONE: (416) 441-1111

CONTACT: John Congram, Editor   **DESCRIPTION:** Published by The Presbyterian Church in Canada. Circulation 59,000. A national magazine for the Presbyterian church of Canada. Published monthly. Established in 1876.
WRITERS: "We give an honorarium for articles. It ranges from $25-$55. People can send articles on spec to the editor." Writers' guidelines are available.
PHOTOGRAPHERS: "We don't purchase photography."
NOTES: For a sample copy send 9x12" SASE with $1.40 postage.

PRESS REVIEW
Box 368, Station A
Toronto, ON M5W 1C2

PHONE: (416) 368-0512
FAX: (416) 366-0104

CONTACT: Sheila Johnston, Editor   **DESCRIPTION:** Published by Press Review Ltd. Published quarterly. Established in 1976.
NOTES: This publication is not accepting freelance material at this time.

PREVIEW/REVIEW see Review

PRIMETIME
5308 Calgary Trail South, Riviera Plaza
Edmonton, AB T6H 4J8

PHONE: (403) 434-7424
FAX: (403) 437-0123

CONTACT: Ruth Kelly, Editor   **DESCRIPTION:** Published by PrimeTime Publishing Ltd. Circulation 191,400. Stories on entertainment and the pay-TV industry compliment monthly pay-TV listings. Published monthly. Established in 1983.
WRITERS: "We purchase freelance work a couple of times a year. Freelancers can call or fax us. We look for bios on entertainers, actors and actresses."
PHOTOGRAPHERS: "Occasionally we purchase cover photography. We look for photos of the feature movie of the month."
NOTES: Sample copy available free upon request.

PRIMEURS

2100 Sainte-Catherine Street West 9 Fl.   **PHONE:** (514) 939-5036
Montreal, PQ H3H 2T3   **FAX:** (514) 939-1515

CONTACT: Marvin Boisvert, Editor   **DESCRIPTION:** Published by Les Publications Feature Ltée. Circulation 220,800. French language publication. Pay television magazine. Published 9 times a year. Established in 1983.
WRITERS: All writing is done in-house.
PHOTOGRAPHERS: "We purchase movie photos from stock agencies."

PRINTACTION

2240 Midland Avenue #201   **PHONE:** (416) 299-6007
Scarborough, ON M1B 4R8   **FAX:** (416) 299-6674

CONTACT: Julian Mills, Editor **DESCRIPTION:** Published by Youngblood Publishing Co. Circulation 16,000. Focuses on the graphic art industry features technological and business news. Published monthly. Established in 1971.
WRITERS: This publication very occasionally purchases material. Articles average 1,500 words and pay approximately $300. Query with a letter.
NOTES: Purchases first North American serial rights. Also publishes Electronic Composition & Imaging (EC&I).

PRISM INTERNATIONAL

University of British Columbia   **PHONE:** (604) 822-2514
Dept. of Creative Writing   **FAX:** (604) 822-3616
1866 Main Mall, E462
Vancouver, BC V6J 1W5

CONTACT: Leah Postman, Editor   **DESCRIPTION:** Circulation 1,100. Quarterly literary journal publishing innovative fiction, poetry, drama, creative non-fiction, and translation from Canadian and international authors. Established in 1959.
WRITERS: "We accept anything that is geared toward a literary audience. We don't accept genre fiction or science fiction. Pays $20 per printed page. Writers' guidelines are available.
PHOTOGRAPHERS: "We do cover art so we would accept photography for the cover only. Both colour and black & white. Send us slides of your work. The type of image is quite flexible."
NOTES: Sample copies of this publication are available for $5.

PRO-FARM

4401 Albert Street #201   **PHONE:** (306) 586-5866
Regina, SK S4S 6B6   **FAX:** (306) 586-2707

CONTACT: Chris Dodd, Editor   **DESCRIPTION:** Published by Western Canadian Wheat Growers Association. Circulation 9,000. Farm magazine featuring articles aimed at helping farmers understand agricultural policy and production. Published 6 times a year. Established in 1985.
WRITERS: Those with extensive knowledge about agricultural policies may submit query letter or sample of work with SASE. Pay is negotiable.
PHOTOGRAPHERS: All photography is done in-house.

PROBE

96 Centre Point Drive   **PHONE:** (613) 224-5515
Nepean, ON K2G 6B1   **FAX:** (613) 224-7283

CONTACT: Janice Edgar, Managing Editor   **DESCRIPTION:** Published by Canadian Dental Hygienists' Association. Circulation 6,500. A scientific journal for the Canadian Dental Hygienists' Association. Published 6 times a year. Established in 1966.
WRITERS: "Articles are written by Canadian dental hygienists and are peer reviewed. Articles are sent on spec. We also publish case studies and news mostly from hygienists. We do not have a freelance budget. If someone wishes to submit we are open to ideas."

PROBE POST

12 Madison Avenue
Toronto, ON M5R 2S1

NOTES: Could not locate. Phone number is not in service (416) 926-1647.

LE PRODUCTEUR DE LAIT QUEBECOIS

555 Boul. Roland-Therrien   **PHONE:** (514) 679-0530
Longueuil, PQ J4H 3Y9   **FAX:** (514) 670-4788

CONTACT: Jean Vigneault, Editor   **DESCRIPTION:** Published by La Fédération des producteurs de lait du Quebec. Circulation 14,000. French language publication. Issued 11 times a year. Established in 1980.
WRITERS: "We do purchase writing, 3 or 4 articles per issue. Most articles are from agronomists or specialists in dairy production. It's a very specialized field of writing. Contact editor by phone or fax. If a good writer has a good subject idea I will listen. We pay around $60 per 25 line page. It depends on the subject and the type of research needed." Guidelines are not available.
PHOTOGRAPHERS: "We have a photography library. When a subject is out of our area I may need to assign a photographer. I try to fix a price for the whole shoot, not per photograph. We do buy individual photos. Usually a photographer will send us photos and we will select what we want." Contact editor before submitting material. Guidelines are not available.
NOTES: Sample copies are free for potential writers or photographers, speak to the editor.

LE PRODUCTEUR PLUS

Box 147, 455-A rue St-Hilaire   **PHONE:** (514) 293-8282
Farnham, PQ J2N 2R4   **FAX:** (514) 293-8554

CONTACT: Leonard Pigeon, Editor   **DESCRIPTION:** Published by Les Editions Imago Inc. Circulation 22,000. French language publication. Agricultural publication covering all aspects of Quebec farming. Published 10 times a year. Established in 1991.
WRITERS: Majority assigned to in-house writers. Contact editor with query letter. Pay is negotiable.
PHOTOGRAPHERS: Majority assigned to in-house photographers. Contact editor with query letter or by phone.
NOTES: Send 9x12" SASE for a sample copy.

PRODUCTION IMPRIMEE
4316 St.-Laurent Blvd. #400
Montreal, PQ H2W 1Z3

PHONE: (514) 842-5873
FAX: (514) 842-2422

CONTACT: Patrick Pierra, Editor Bruno Gautier, Publisher   **DESCRIPTION:** Published by Editions Info Presse Inc. Circulation 6,500. Published twice a year.

PROFESSIONAL RENOVATION
178 Main Street
Unionville, ON L3R 2G9

PHONE: (905) 479-4663
FAX: (905) 479-4482

CONTACT: Rise Levy   **DESCRIPTION:** Published by Homes for Sale Ltd. Features home renovation articles; profiles completed renovation projects. Provides advice on hiring professionals. Published twice a year. Serves the greater Toronto area.
WRITERS: All writing is done in-house.
PHOTOGRAPHERS: "Some photography may be purchased. Contact the editor."

PROFESSIONAL SOUND
67 Mowat Avenue #350
Toronto, ON M6K 3E3

PHONE: (416) 533-8303
FAX: (416) 533-1630

CONTACT: Shauna Kennedy, Editor   **DESCRIPTION:** Published by Norris-Whitney Communications Inc. Circulation 12,400. A magazine for the high-end audio, live and recorded sound market. Published quarterly. Established in 1990.
WRITERS: "I do purchase work, however I do have stringent guidelines that writers must follow. They must be musically and technically literate with a recording or engineering degree. I prefer writers to send me copies of their published work." Writers' guidelines are not available, read the publication.
PHOTOGRAPHERS: Hires on assignment. Contact the editor by mail.
NOTES: Contact this address for sample copy: 23 Hannover Drive Unit 7, St. Catharines, ON L2W 1A3. Also publishes Canadian Musician and Canadian Music Trade.

PROFIT
777 Bay Street
Toronto, ON M5W 1A7

PHONE: (416) 596-5999
FAX: (416) 596-5152

CONTACT: Rick Spence, Editor   **DESCRIPTION:** Published by CB Media Ltd. Circulation 90,600. Articles covering management topics and issues of interest to owners and managers of small to medium-sized businesses. Published quarterly. Established in 1981.

PROFIT HOME BUSINESS
777 Bay Street
Toronto, ON M5W 1A7

NOTES: NO LONGER PUBLISHED

PROFIT: THE MAGAZINE FOR CANADIAN ENTREPRENEURS
17 - 35 Riviera Drive
Markham, ON L3R 8N4

DESCRIPTION: Focuses on all aspects of management for owners and managers of independent businesses. Articles include finance, tax, marketing, and political issues. Published quarterly.

PROPANE/CANADA
700-4 Avenue SW #1600
Calgary, AB T2P 3J4

PHONE: (403) 263-6881
FAX: (403) 263-6886

CONTACT: Scott Jeffrey   **DESCRIPTION:** Published by Northern Star Communications. Published 6 times a year. Established in 1968.

PROPERTY MANAGEMENT NEWS
789 West Pender Street #720
Vancouver, BC V6C 1H2

PHONE: (604) 669-7671
FAX: (604) 681-9535

CONTACT: Kelly Reynolds, Editor   **DESCRIPTION:** Published by K-Rey Publishing Inc. Circulation 5,000. Focuses on BC building owners and property managers; anyone involved in residential or commercial property management. Published 6 times a year. Established in 1992.
WRITERS: "All of our writers are volunteers."
PHOTOGRAPHERS: All photography is done in-house.

PROPOS DE CUISINE
Box 1010
Victoriaville, PQ G6P 8Y1

PHONE: (819) 752-4243
FAX: (819) 758-8812

CONTACT: Claude Roy **DESCRIPTION:** Published by Editions C.R. Inc. Circulation 1,700. French language publication. Issued quarterly. Established in 1983.

PROSPECTIVE
1 Westmount Square #500
Montreal, PQ H3Z 2P9

PHONE: (514) 932-4277
FAX: (514) 932-6400

CONTACT: Louis Garneau, Editor   **DESCRIPTION:** Published by l'Association des intermédiaires en assurance de personnes du Québec. Circulation 13,000. A publication for the Quebec life underwriters. Covers the industry, finance, production and distribution of financial products. Published 9 times a year in mostly French with some English.
WRITERS: All writing handled in-house.
PHOTOGRAPHERS: "We do not purchase stock photography. We work with freelance photographers on covers for every issue. We also need photos of the people we interview and some inside illustrative photos. Payment is negotiable. We would be interested in receiving queries from freelancers in the area." Contact Josee Marquis.
NOTES: Sample copies of this publication are available free upon request with a 9x12" SASE.

THE PROSPECTOR EXPLORATION & INVESTMENT
1268 West Pender Street   **PHONE:** (604) 688-2271
Vancouver, BC   V6E 2S8   **FAX:** (604) 688-2038

CONTACT: Adrian Leonard, Editor   **DESCRIPTION:** Published by K.W. Publishing Ltd. Circulation 25,000. A technical trade publication for mining and investment. Published 6 times a year. Established in 1980.
WRITERS: "We very rarely purchase work. A freelancer can contact me by fax or mail. I do accept unsolicited material however it is rare that anyone sends me something appropriate. Articles should be 600-800 words."
PHOTOGRAPHERS: "We occasionally purchase black & white photography. I accept query letters."
NOTES: Also publishes the Independent Senior.

PUBLIC SECTOR MANAGEMENT
Toronto, ON   **PHONE:** (416) 932-3667
M4P 1E8   (416) 932-3666   **FAX:** Institute of Public Administration of Canada

CONTACT: J.M. Galimberti
150 Eglinton Avenue East #305   **DESCRIPTION:** Circulation 3,000. A magazine for members of the Institute of Public Administration of Canada. Published quarterly.
WRITERS: "No freelance work is purchased. Magazine is written on a contribution/request basis."
PHOTOGRAPHERS: "We occasionally purchase, sometimes one per issue and other times none."

PUBLIQUIP
582-90 Avenue #202   **PHONE:** (514) 367-0882
LaSalle, ON   H8R 2Z7   **FAX:** (514) 367-3655

CONTACT: Gilles Chevigny   **DESCRIPTION:** Published by Publiquip Inc. Circulation 26,600. French language publication. Focuses on trucks and heavy equipment. Issued monthly. Established in 1983.

THE PUBLISHER
90 Eglinton Avenue East #206   **PHONE:** (416) 482-1090
Toronto, ON   M4P 2Y3   **FAX:** (416) 482-1908

CONTACT: Dave Dejong   **DESCRIPTION:** Published by Canadian Community Newspapers Association. Circulation 2,100. A publication for association members. Issued ten times a year.
NOTES: All writing and photography is done in-house.

PULP & PAPER CANADA
3300 Cote Vertu, #410   **PHONE:** (514) 339-1399
St. Laurent, PQ   H4R 2B7   **FAX:** (514) 339-1396

CONTACT: Graeme Rodden, Editor   **DESCRIPTION:** Published by Southam Business Information and Communication Group Ltd. Circulation 10,000. Focuses on the pulp

and paper industry; includes profiles, innovations and research, technology, management and financing. Published monthly. Established in 1903.
WRITERS: "We assign articles approximately 5 times a year." Contact the editor by phone or mail.
PHOTOGRAPHERS: "We don't purchase photography."
NOTES: Sample copies available free upon request.

PULP & PAPER JOURNAL see Canadian Papermaker

PUNCH DIGEST FOR CANADIAN DOCTORS see Stitches

PURCHASING MANAGEMENT see Plant Engineering & Maintenance

QALAM
42 Rosepac Avenue   **PHONE:** (905) 840-6778
Brampton, ON L6Z 2S4   **FAX:** (905) 840-6778

CONTACT: Khizar Hayat, Editor   **DESCRIPTION:** Published by Qalam International Inc. Circulation 8,000. Quarterly publication on the art, architecture and history of the Islamic world. Established in 1992.
WRITERS: "We accept freelance writing. Writers can fax or phone me. We look for articles on art, travel, architecture, and personalities. Length and pay rates depend on the article." Writers' guidelines are not available.
PHOTOGRAPHERS: "Most photography is supplied by the writers."
NOTES: For a sample copy send 9x12" SASE.

QUARRY
Box 1061   **PHONE:** (613) 548-8429
Kingston, ON K7L 4Y5   **FAX:** (613) 548-1556

CONTACT: Mary Cameron, Editor   **DESCRIPTION:** Circulation 1,200. Quarterly magazine publishes new and innovative poetry, essays, and fiction by young Canadian writers. Also features interviews, photo-essays and translations.
WRITERS: "We don't have guidelines. We prefer that people look at back issues. Quarry is open to all kinds of writing. We are open to interviews, essays, stories, poetry, reviews and photo essays. We want everything on spec. For interviews a query letter is acceptable. For poetry send 8-12 poems per submission. Generally it takes 2-3 months for us to respond with SASE's. Take a look at the magazine before submitting anything."
PHOTOGRAPHERS: "We are open to all types of photography essays and journalism. We excerpt some material from exhibitions." Contact Bob Hilderley.
NOTES: Available at large magazine stores and libraries. Also publishes Canadian Fiction Magazine and Poetry Canada.

QUARTER HOURSE JOURNAL see Horses All

QUEBEC ENTERPRISE
715 Square Victoria #507
Montreal, PQ H2Y 2H7

PHONE: (514) 842-5492
FAX: (514) 842-5375

CONTACT: Daniel Boisvert, Editor   **DESCRIPTION:** Circulation 25,000. French language publication. Issued six times a year. Established in 1992.

QUEBEC FARMER'S ADVOCATE
Box 80
Ste.-Anne-de-Bellevue, PQ H9X 3L4

PHONE: (514) 457-2010
FAX: (514) 398-7972

CONTACT: Susanne Brown, Managing Editor   **DESCRIPTION:** Published by Quebec Farmers Association. Circulation 2,500. "We are the only English language agricultural publication serving the Quebec agricultural market." Published ten times a year. Established in 1980.
NOTES: All writing and photography is done in-house. "We don't purchase material."

QUEBEC PHARMACIE
4378 Pierre de Coubertin
Montreal, PQ H1V 1A6

PHONE: (514) 254-0346

CONTACT: Daine Blais, Editor   **DESCRIPTION:** Published by Les Publications Codex. Circulation 6,300. French language publication. Issued 10 times a year. Established in 1953.

QUEBEC SCIENCE
425 de la Gauchetiére Est
Montreal, PQ H2L 2M7

PHONE: (514) 843-6888
FAX: (514) 843-4897

CONTACT: Raymond Lemieux   **DESCRIPTION:** Published by La Revue Quebec Science. Circulation 13,600. French publication covering current science and how it affects the lives of people. Published 10 times a year. Established in 1969.
WRITERS: "We assign articles. We accept calls or query letters. The magazine is done mostly by freelancers."
PHOTOGRAPHERS: "We purchase photography. Some is assigned and some comes from a photo bank."
NOTES: Available on newsstands.

QUEBEC VERT MAGAZINE
6538 de Lanaudiére
Montreal, PQ H2G 3A9

PHONE: (514) 495-1985
FAX: (514) 495-3819

CONTACT: Bertrand Dumont, Editor-in-Chief **DESCRIPTION:** Published by Editions versicolores inc. Circulation 2,865. French language publication. A trade magazine published 7 times a year. Established in 1977.

QUEBEC YACHTING VOILE & MOTEUR

1100 boul. René-Lévesque West 24 Fl.   **PHONE:** (514) 392-9000
Montreal, PQ H3B 4X9   **FAX:** (514) 392-4726

CONTACT: Henri René De Cotret, Editor   **DESCRIPTION:** Published by Transcontinental Publications Inc. Circulation 8,000. French language publication. A magazine for boaters, powerboaters and sailers. Focuses on: navigation and pleasure boating in general, new products, cruising guides etc. Articles include yacht maintenance, and news on the sport. Issued six times a year. Established in 1978.
WRITERS: "We do purchase work. We have freelancers who submit regularly. Freelancers can either send a completed article or a query with outline. Let us know whether or not photos are available to illustrate the article. Writers should provide a selection of titles, headings and sub-headings. The longest article is 5-6 double spaced pages. We pay $40 per published page." Writers' guidelines are available.
PHOTOGRAPHERS: "Most of our writers provide us with photos, but there is a possibility we may purchase additional photos. They can be about Quebec or Canada. We touch on subjects outside of Quebec's geographical boundaries. We like to have horizontal and vertical shots which gives us flexibility. Prefer 35mm transparencies. We favour photographs of people boating or sailing, not just a sail boat far on the horizon. We put a preference on human interest photographs. Photographs are paid on publication: $40 for each inside photograph less than a full page. A full page inside $100. A cover shot is $250."
NOTES: Sample copies available free upon request. Available on newsstands in Quebec.

QUEEN'S QUARTERLY

184 Union Street, Queen's University   **PHONE:** (613) 545-2667
Kingston, ON K7L 3N6   **FAX:** (613) 545-6822

CONTACT: Boris Castel, Editor   **DESCRIPTION:** Published by Queen's Quarterly Committee. Circulation 2,800. Canada's oldest scholarly journal features articles of wide general interest. Topics include politics, history, science, the humanities, music, original poetry, fiction, and book reviews. Published quarterly. Established in 1893.
WRITERS: "We pay upon publication. For fiction $100-$200 and for poetry $60-$100. Article rates are negotiated with the editor. We don't pay for book reviews. Unsolicited work can be mailed to us with a SASE. If it is accepted for publication we require it on disk. Guidelines available.
PHOTOGRAPHERS: Photography is not used.
NOTES: Sample copy available for $6.50 including postage.

QUILL & QUIRE

70 The Esplanade, 2nd Floor   **PHONE:** (416) 360-0044
Toronto, ON M5E 1R2   **FAX:** (416) 360-8745

CONTACT: Ted Mumford, Editor   **DESCRIPTION:** Published by Key Publishers Co. Ltd. Circulation 7,000. Monthly journal for the Canadian book trade. Features news, reviews, lists of published and upcoming books. Also profiles authors, distributors, and publishing houses. Established in 1935.
WRITERS: "60% freelance written. All work is assigned. Inquiries for news coverage can be directed to the news editor, Scott Anderson. People who are interested in reviewing can contact the book review editor Stephen Smith with a query letter.

PHOTOGRAPHERS: "We do purchase black & white photos with our articles. Occasionally we assign some work. Query to Ted Mumford with a flyer or mailer."
NOTES: Available at most libraries and some newsstands.

QUINCAILLERIE-MATERIAUX
777 Bay Street
Toronto, ON M5W 1A7

PHONE: (416) 596-5094
FAX: (416) 596-2642

CONTACT: Jo-ann Marchand, Editor   **DESCRIPTION:** Published by Maclean Hunter Ltd. Circulation 5,100. French language publication. Keeps readers informed of latest developments in the world of hardware manufacturing, includes marketing tips and new products showcase. Published 6 times a year. Established in 1987.
NOTES: French version of Hardware Merchandising.

RADDLE MOON
2239 Stephens Street Upper
Vancouver, BC   V6K 3W5

PHONE: (604) 736-9769

CONTACT: Susan Clark, Editor   **DESCRIPTION:** International magazine that prints untranslated writing, short stories, poetry and criticism from Spain, Sweden, Chile, India, Japan, Mexico, and many other countries. Published twice a year.
WRITERS: "We get a lot of inappropriate material. We publish poetry and short stories. Unless people know the avant-garde poetry world quite well they won't know what we want. Our suggestion is to read the magazine."
PHOTOGRAPHERS: Does not purchase photography.
NOTES: Sample copy available for $6 including postage.

RATHERBY
Box 2849
Huntsville, ON P0A 1K0

NOTES: NO LONGER PUBLISHED

RE NEW see Century Home

READER'S DIGEST
215 Redfern Avenue
Westmount, PQ H3Z 2V9

PHONE: (514) 934-0751
FAX: (514) 934-3637

CONTACT: Alexander Farrell   **DESCRIPTION:** Published by Reader's Digest Magazines Ltd. Circulation 1,354,000. General interest magazine. Articles include nature, science, politics, advice, self-improvement, and prominent people. Published monthly.
WRITERS: Most articles are reprints of articles found in other publications. Query with copies of published work. Read the magazine to see what types of articles are used. Buys one-time rights for republished work, all rights for original manuscripts. Average article length is 3,000-5,000 words. Let the editor know if you have photos to go with an article. Does not publish fiction. "We do not read unsolicited manuscripts." Guidelines are available.

PHOTOGRAPHERS: 98% assigned to in-house photographers. Contact with query letter to Rachel Irwin, Art Director. Do not send unsolicited photos.

THE READERS SHOWCASE
17317-107 Street   **PHONE:** (403) 486-5802
Edmonton, AB T5S 1E5   **FAX:** (403) 481-9276

CONTACT: Dave Suggitt, Editor   **DESCRIPTION:** Published by Suggitt Publishing Ltd. Circulation 40,000. Focuses on the book industry. Distributed nationally through SmithBooks. Published 12 times a year.
WRITERS: "We purchase 5 articles per issue. Our standard rate is 10¢ a word for 800-1,000 words a page. That varies depending on the writer." Contact the editor by letter or phone. Writers' guidelines are available.
PHOTOGRAPHERS: "Most of our photography is supplied."
NOTES: Sample copy free upon request. Does not consider previously published work.

REAL ESTATE NEWS
1400 Don Mills Road   **PHONE:** (416) 443-8113
Don Mills, ON M3B 3N1   **FAX:** (416) 443-9185

CONTACT: Laura Morrison **DESCRIPTION:** Published by Toronto Real Estate Board. Circulation 74,438. Real estate, industry/market and municipal news of metro and suburban Toronto. Includes articles on renovation, decorating, architecture, and interior design.
NOTES: All writing and photography is done in-house.

REAL ESTATE VICTORIA
1609 Blanshard Street   **PHONE:** (604) 382-9171
Victoria, BC V8W 2J5   **FAX:** (604) 382-9172

CONTACT: Glenda Turner   **DESCRIPTION:** Published by Monday Publications Ltd. Circulation 20,000. Pulished weekly. Established in 1977.
NOTES: All writing and photography is done in-house. "Please do not contact."

REAL MARKET REVIEW
744 West Hastings Street #218
Vancouver, BC V6C 1A5

NOTES: Could not locate. Phone number is not in service (604) 684-0412.

RECREATION CANADA
1600 James Naismith Drive
Gloucester, ON K1B 5N4

NOTES: Could not locate. Phone number is not in service (613) 746-0060.

RECYCLING PRODUCT NEWS

1625 Ingleton Avenue
Burnaby, BC   V5C 4L8

PHONE: (604) 291-9900
FAX: (604) 291-1906

CONTACT: Dan Kennedy, Editor   **DESCRIPTION:** Published by Baum Publications Ltd. Circulation 14,000. A tabloid published six times a year. Established in 1992.
NOTES: "It would be a wasted call for any photographers or writers. We have never used anyone outside our staff. The only chance is if it applies to our specific needs and if writers want to get it published for free. The companies selling the products we feature provide us with write-ups and features."

REGARDS\LA REVUE DE L'ASSURANCE

300 Leo Pariseau #801
Montreal, PQ   H2W 2N1

NOTES: NO LONGER PUBLISHED

REGISTERED NURSE

80 W. Beaver Creek #18
Richmond Hill, ON   L4B 1H3

PHONE: (905) 771-7333
FAX: (905) 771-7336

CONTACT: Dennis Mellersh, Editor   **DESCRIPTION:** Published by Kenilworth Publishing. Circulation 24,600. Published 6 times a year. Established in 1967.
WRITERS: Majority of writing done in-house. Contact with query letter. Byline is given. Pay is negotiated.
PHOTOGRAPHERS: Majority assigned to in-house photographers. Contact with query letter.
NOTES: Also publishes Municipal Monitor, Grainmaster, Signs, and SPI Plastics.

REHAB & COMMUNITY CARE MANAGEMENT

101 Thorncliffe Park Drive
Toronto, ON   M4H 1M2

PHONE: (416) 421-7944
FAX: (416) 421-0966

CONTACT: Caroline Tapp-McDougall, Editor   **DESCRIPTION:** Published by BCS Communications Ltd. Circulation 19,100. Published quarterly. Established in 1992.

REHABILITATION DIGEST

45 Sheppard Avenue #801
Toronto, ON   M2N 5W9

PHONE: (416) 250-7490
FAX: (416) 229-1371

CONTACT: Heather Stonehouse, Editor   **DESCRIPTION:** Published by Canadian Rehabilitation Council for the Disabled. Circulation 1,800. Profiles programs, technology and people in rehabilitation. Covers disability issues for health care professionals and consumers with disabilities. Published quarterly.
WRITERS: "We purchase 2-3 articles per issue. We pay $250 for a feature and $50 for book reviews. Features average 1,500 words. We assign all articles. If you have a solid idea a phone call is the best." Writers' guidelines are not available.
PHOTOGRAPHERS: "We don't purchase photography."
NOTES: Sample copy available free upon request.

REM MAGAZINE
115 Thorncliffe Park Drive
Toronto, ON M4H 1M1

PHONE: (416) 425-3504
FAX: (416) 425-0040

CONTACT: Jim Adair, Editor   **DESCRIPTION:** Published by House Magazine Inc. A national trade publication aimed at real estate agents and brokers. Published 12 times a year. Established in 1989.
WRITERS: "We purchase 10 articles per issue. We assign stories; the length and payment is negotiated. A kill fee is offered if we cancel an article. Writers should send query and resumé to editor. Queries should be specific to agents and brokers. We don't want to know what is happening in the real estate market, we want to know about the industry itself."
PHOTOGRAPHERS: "We rarely purchase photography. Cover is colour, inside is b&w. We buy covers several times a year. Photographers could send some information about themselves, this will be kept on file."
NOTES: Sample copy available free upon request. Considers previously published work. Considers simultaneous submissions. Formerly called Real Estate Marketing Magazine.

RENDEZ-VOUS
310 Dupont Street
Toronto, ON M5R 1V9

PHONE: (416) 968-7252
FAX: (416) 968-2377

CONTACT: Edith Baxter, Editor-in-Chief   **DESCRIPTION:** Published by Baxter Publishing. Published annually. Established in 1981.
NOTES: All writing and photography is done in-house.

RENOVATION BRICOLAGE
7 Bates Road
Outremont, PQ H2V 1A6

PHONE: (514) 270-1100
FAX: (514) 270-6900

CONTACT: Claude LeClerc   **DESCRIPTION:** Published by Publicor. Circulation 37,500. French language publication. Issued 10 times a year. Established in 1976.
NOTES: Also publishes Femme Plus, Filles d'aujourd'hui, Clin d'oeil, Les Idees De Ma Maison, Decorations Chez-soi, Plans de Maisions Quebec and En Route.

RENOVATION MAGAZINE
178 Main Street
Unionville, ON L3R 2G9

PHONE: (905) 479-4663
FAX: (905) 479-4482

CONTACT: Rise Levy, Editor   **DESCRIPTION:** Published by Homes Publishing Group. Circulation 50,000. Toronto-based magazine featuring articles on home and business renovation.
WRITERS: 99% assigned to in-house writers. Contact with query letter.
PHOTOGRAPHERS: 99% assigned to in-house photographers. Contact with query letter.
NOTES: Do not send unsolicited manuscripts or photography to this publication.

REPORT BUSINESS QUARTERLY

875 Main Street West
Hamilton, ON L8S 4R1

PHONE: (905) 522-6117
FAX: (905) 529-2242

CONTACT: Elizabeth Kelly, Editor   **DESCRIPTION:** Published by Town Publishing Inc. Contains local business stories, computer articles and anything that relates to business in the Hamilton area. Published quarterly.
WRITERS: "We purchase 2-3 articles per issue; the length and pay rate depends on the type of article. Either send samples or a letter to the editor. We like to see general lifestyle and entertainment stories and opinion columns. We're not too big on sports or political articles although we have done a bit in the past."
PHOTOGRAPHERS: "We purchase two or three photos per issue from freelance photographers and 1 or 2 from stock agencies. Transparencies are great - we can use almost any format. Our freelancers usually take people photos and our stock photos are chosen to go with a story line. Payment is negotiable - depends on what it is being used for. Contact the editor either by phone or mail."
NOTES: Also publishes Hamilton This Month. This publication is presently looking for freelance artists, contact the editor to show portfolio.

REPORT ON BUSINESS MAGAZINE

444 Front Street West
Toronto, ON M5V 2S9

PHONE: (416) 585-5406
FAX: (416) 585-5641

CONTACT: David Olive, Editor   **DESCRIPTION:** Published by The Globe and Mail. Circulation 300,000. Monthly magazine covering the national business scene and international developments affecting Canada. Articles include profiles of business and political personalities, book reviews, personal finance and national opinion. Established in 1984.
WRITERS: "70% freelance written. We pay roughly $1 a word for articles 2,500-5,000 words. Write to us with a query letter and a story in mind." Writers' guidelines are not available.
PHOTOGRAPHERS: "Almost all of our photography is freelanced on assignment. Contact the art director to show your portfolio." Contact Kaspar De Line, Art Director.
NOTES: Purchases first Canadian serial rights. This magazine is inserted in the Globe and Mail on the last Friday of the month. Look at several copies before sending queries.

THE REPORTER

65 St. Clair Avenue East
Toronto, ON M4T 2Y8

PHONE: (416) 925-2493
FAX: (416) 925-7764

CONTACT: Aleda O'Connor, Editor   **DESCRIPTION:** Published by Ontario English Catholic Teachers' Association. Circulation 34,000. A trade magazine for members published five times a year. Established in 1975.
WRITERS: "We are not in the market. We don't have a budget for freelance writers however we accept submissions without payment. Material on education and education matters and separate school issues."

REPORTER
4500 Sheppard Avenue East
Scarborough, ON M1S 3R6

PHONE: (416) 298-1731
FAX: (416) 298-4865

CONTACT: Steven Johns, Executive Director & Editor **DESCRIPTION:** Circulation 1,300. An association publication for the Lumber and Building Materials Association of Ontario. Covers member news, association events and programs, industry news, new products, supplier profiles, and retailer profiles. Published 6 times a year.
NOTES: All writing and photography is done in-house.

RESELLER WORLD
501 Oakdale Road
North York, ON M3N 1W7

PHONE: (416) 746-7360
FAX: (416) 746-1421

CONTACT: John Pickett, Editor-in-Chief **DESCRIPTION:** Published by Laurentian Technomedia Inc. Circulation 15,000. Aimed at organizations that sell computer and communications products, both hardware and software, to end user organizations.
WRITERS: "This is a technical publication and most of our contributors are in the business. We do take a limited amount of freelance work. It is technical in nature, often reviews of consumer products, software and hardware. There is a fairly specific technical background requirement. Rates average 30¢ a word for 400-1,000 words on those rare occasions when we do purchase freelance."
PHOTOGRAPHERS: All photography is done in-house.
NOTES: Also publishes CIO Canada, Computerworld, Info Canada, and Network World.

RESIDENCES
554 Grosvenor Avenue
Westmount, PQ H3Y 2S4

PHONE: (514) 935-1171
FAX: (514) 935-4504

CONTACT: Daniele Adam, Publisher **DESCRIPTION:** Published by Marketing U.S.P Inc. Circulation 69,700. Quebec lifestyle publication. Feature articles include travel, gourmet food, attractions, shopping, and book reviews. Published 5 times a year in English and French. Established in 1990.
WRITERS: 10% freelance written. Contact with query letter, resumé and sample articles. Returns unsolicited materials with SASE. Byline is given. Purchases all rights.
PHOTOGRAPHERS: Does not purchase stock images. Hires photographers on assignment. Contact with query letter and sample colour prints.
NOTES: Send 9x12" SASE for a sample copy.

RESOURCES FOR FEMINIST RESEARCH/ DOCUMENTATION SUR LA RECHERCHE FEMINISTE
Ontario Institute for Studies &
Education, 252 Bloor Street West
Toronto, ON M5S 1V6

PHONE: (416) 923-6641 ext. 2277
FAX: (416) 926-4725

CONTACT: Philinda Masters **DESCRIPTION:** Circulation 2,000. A bilingual journal of feminist research papers, abstracts, reviews, reports of works in progress, and bibliographies. Published quarterly. Two issues are devoted to interdisciplinary collections of new feminist research, one to a special theme in women's studies and one is an annual book review issue.

WRITERS: "We don't have a budget to pay but writers get complimentary copies of the issue. Write or telephone us. Sometimes the process to review is lengthy. We will send the manuscript out to 2-3 different readers and get feedback." Writers' guidelines are available and the information is all in the first page of the journal.

PHOTOGRAPHERS: "We do publish some photography. We prefer black & white glossy prints to accompany articles."

NOTES: The journal is in some book stores and libraries. Sample copy available for $10 each. Anything addressed to this journal should be clearly marked RESOURCES FOR FEMINIST RESEARCH.

RETAIL DIRECTIONS
777 Bay Street
Toronto, ON M5W 1A7

NOTES: NO LONGER PUBLISHED

REVUE COMMERCE: QUEBEC'S FIRST BUSINESS MAGAZINE
1100 René Lévesque Blvd W 24 Fl.   **PHONE:** (514) 392-9000
Montreal, PQ H3B 4X9   **FAX:** (514) 392-4726

CONTACT: Danielle Thibault, Editor   **DESCRIPTION:** Published by Transcontinental Publications Inc. Circulation 41,300. French language publication. High profile business publication for Quebec. Articles feature management, marketing, and business trends and forecasts. Issued monthly. Established in 1898.
WRITERS: Contact by sending a query letter. Pay is negotiable. Byline is given. "We are looking for writers in the Quebec area."
PHOTOGRAPHERS: Contact with query letter and subject list.
NOTES: For sample copy send $5 & 9x12" SASE.

LA REVUE D'ARCHITECTURE ARQ
1463 Prefontaine   **PHONE:** (514) 523-6832
Montreal, PQ H1W 2N6   **FAX:** (514) 523-2312

CONTACT: Pierre Boyer-Mercier, Editor   **DESCRIPTION:** Published by ARQ Magazin Ltée. Circulation 4,500. Architect's Association of Quebec publication. Issued 6 times a year in French and English. Established in 1981.
WRITERS: "Occasionally we purchase work. Contact us with a letter and samples, including interests and what kinds of articles you write."
PHOTOGRAPHERS: "We do purchase some photography. We look for photos of buildings, both interiors and exteriors and architecturally designed landscapes. We usually commission photography. Send a letter of interest with a few samples of work in the domain of building architecture. We use black & white but photographers can send colour slides or prints."
NOTES: Sample copy available free upon request for freelancers.

LA REVUE ECONOMIQUE
1555 Chomedy Blvd. #200
Laval, PQ H7V 3Z1

NOTES: No longer published. May resume publishing in fall of 1995.

LA REVUE MUNICIPALE
1600 Henri-Bourassa Blvd. #420   **PHONE:** (514) 332-8376
Montreal, PQ H3M 3E2   **FAX:** (514) 332-2666

CONTACT: Gilles Verronneau   **DESCRIPTION:** Published by Communications Vero Inc. Circulation 11,500. French language publication. A municipal and public works magazine aimed at municipal administrators and managers as well as elected officials. Established in 1922.
WRITERS: "Most of our editorial comes from freelancers, 6 articles or pictures per issue. We have two or three regular contributors who we call upon for assignments. If we get a query or finished article that interests us we will negotiate a price. Most of our publications have editorial themes and stories are ordered ahead of time. The most expedient way to contact us is by phone with supporting documentation by fax. All of our publications are trade magazines. Most of our assignments are for action stories, job descriptions and on-sight reporting. We prefer diskettes, Mac or IBM, in WordPerfect or Microsoft Word. Average story length is three double spaced typed pages. We have a standard rate of $40 per page. If expenses are involved we will cover incidental costs." Guidelines are not available.
PHOTOGRAPHERS: "We try to buy photography together with the article. If we have a three page text we will ask for at least one picture or more depending on the subject."
NOTES: Buys first North American serial rights. "We consider previously published work if it wasn't in a competitive magazine." Sample copies are available free upon request. Also publishes La Fournee, L'Hospitlite and La Mart.

LA REVUE OCCASIONS D'AFFAIRES
425 St.-Amable St #145   **PHONE:** (418) 640-1686
Quebec, PQ G1R 5E4   **FAX:** (418) 640-1687

CONTACT: Pierre Bhérer, Editor   **DESCRIPTION:** Published by La Revue Occasions D'affaires Ltée. Circulation 50,000. French language publication aimed at those wishing to start and run a successful franchise business. Articles are written by lawyers, accountants, and consultants. Two regular feature columns are written by The Canadian Franchise Association and The Quebec Franchise Association. Published 6 times. Established in 1993.
WRITERS: All writing is done in-house.
PHOTOGRAPHERS: 95% assigned to in-house photographers. Hires photographers on assignment. Contact with a query letter, resumé, and small portfolio of colour prints.
NOTES: "We have a photographer to handle the Quebec City area. We need photographers from Montreal and Toronto. The photographer must be French-speaking."

RICHMOND HILL MONTH
3335- 14 Avenue, Suite #1   **PHONE:** (416) 475-1743
Markham, ON L3R OH3   **FAX:** (416) 475-1029

CONTACT: Deborah Smith, Editor   **DESCRIPTION:** Published by Thornhill Publications Inc. Circulation 12,000. Local news and views of the Richmond Hill area of Ontario. Published quarterly. Established in 1992.
WRITERS: 2% freelance written. Contact with query letter and resumé. Does not return unsolicited manuscripts. Byline is given. Pay is negotiable.
PHOTOGRAPHERS: 98% assigned to in-house photographers. Send query letter and sample portfolio of b&w prints.
NOTES: Also publishes Markham Month and Thornhill Month.

RICKY MCMOUNTAIN BUYER'S GUIDE
42 Steinway Blvd. Unit 12   **PHONE:** (416) 798-1772
Etobicoke, ON M9W 6Y6   **FAX:** (416) 798-1773

CONTACT: Ylva Van Buuren, Editor   **DESCRIPTION:** Published by Ricky McMountain Enterprises Ltd. Circulation 700,000. Contains straight-forward information on various businesses. Also contains lifestyle articles. "Our main function is to recommend to the people of Toronto contractors that are good to do business with. The editorial is pretty broad based and we have something for everybody." Published 5 times a year. Established in 1988.
WRITERS: "We do purchase freelance work. We have almost a dozen regular contributors. We assign most of our articles, a few are sent in on spec. Contact the editor with a query and samples."
PHOTOGRAPHERS: "We don't purchase photography."
NOTES: For a sample copy send 9x12" SASE.

ROTUNDA: THE MAGAZINE OF THE ROYAL ONTARIO MUSEUM
100 Queen's Park   **PHONE:** (416) 586-5590
Toronto, ON M5S 2C6   **FAX:** (416) 586-5863

CONTACT: Sandra Shaul, Executive Editor   **DESCRIPTION:** Published by Royal Ontario Museum. Circulation 25,000. Quarterly magazine. Articles focus on art, archaeology, the earth and life sciences, and astronomy. Reports the latest information on world-wide research and presents full-colour photography of artifacts, specimens and places. Established in 1968.
NOTES: All writing and photography is done in-house. Submissions are not welcome at this time.

THE ROUGHNECK
700-4th Avenue SW 16th Floor   **PHONE:** (403) 263-6881
Calgary, AB T2P 3J4   **FAX:** (403) 263-6886

CONTACT: Scott Jeffery   **DESCRIPTION:** Published by Roughneck Publications Ltd. Circulation 6,000. An oil and gas related publication. Published monthly. Established in 1952.

WRITERS: Mainly written in-house. Contact with query letter. Pay is negotiable. Writers' guidelines are available. Sample publication not available.
PHOTOGRAPHERS: Contact by phone before sending sample photos.

ROUNDUP
CFB Calgary
Calgary, AB   T3E 1T8

NOTES: Could not locate. Phone number is not in service (403) 240-7715.

ROUTES ET TRANSPORTS
1595 Saint Hubert St. #100   **PHONE:** (514) 523-6444
Montreal, PQ   H2L 3Z2

CONTACT: Catherine Hirou   **DESCRIPTION:** Published by L'Association Quebecoise de Transport et des Routes Inc. French language publication. Issued quarterly. Established in 1965.

RPM WEEKLY
6 Brentcliffe Road   **PHONE:** (416) 425-0257
Toronto, ON   M4G 3Y2   **FAX:** (416) 425-8629

CONTACT: Walter Grealis, Editor   **DESCRIPTION:** Published by RPM Music Publications Ltd. A music trade journal for the entertainment business. Published weekly. Established in 1964.
NOTES: All writing and photography is done in-house.

RURAL ROOTS
Box 550   **PHONE:** (306) 764-4276
Prince Albert, SK   S6V 5R9   **FAX:** (306) 763-3331

CONTACT: Barb Gustafson, Editor   **DESCRIPTION:** Published by Prince Albert Daily Herald. Circulation 31,600. A weekly tabloid targeting the 60+ population. Features Prince Albert area articles about rural living, community profiles, food columns, and pioneer heritage. Established in 1991.
WRITERS: Contact with query letter. Buys occasionally. Payment MUST be negotiated.
PHOTOGRAPHERS: Contact with query letter or phone before submitting photographs. Have in-house photographers.

THE RURAL VOICE
Box 429, 136 Queen Street   **PHONE:** (519) 523-4311
Blyth, ON   N0M 1H0   **FAX:** (519) 523-9140

CONTACT: Keith Roulston   **DESCRIPTION:** Published by North Huron Publishing Co. Inc. Circulation 15,000. Regional monthly publication featuring agricultural news, politics, law, finances, marketing, profiles and home life. Established in 1975.
WRITERS: Contact with query letter. Byline is given. Pays 12¢ per word. "Articles must be about agriculture in Ontario." Guidelines available.

PHOTOGRAPHERS: In-house photographers. Photos often taken by their writers.
NOTES: Returns unsolicited materials with SASE. Send 9x12" SASE for a sample copy.
Purchases one-time rights.

SAFARIR
549 Grande Allée Est   **PHONE:** (418) 522-1062
Quebec, PQ G1R 2J5   **FAX:** (418) 522-3597

CONTACT: Claude Desrochers, Editor-in-Chief **DESCRIPTION:** Published by Les
Artistocrates Inc. Circulation 60,000. French publication for young adults in Quebec
and New Brunswick. Articles have a humorous focus. Published monthly. Established in
1987.
WRITERS: Contact with query letter. Byline is given. Pays $75 per page for articles.
Purchases one-time rights.
PHOTOGRAPHERS: Photos not accepted.
NOTES: "Read the magazine to find out our style."

SAILING CANADA
12 Mill Street South
Port Hope, ON L1A 3J6

NOTES: Can't locate. Phone number is not in service (416) 885-7948.

SALES FORCE MANAGER
1200 Markham Road #301   **PHONE:** (416) 439-4083
Scarborough, ON M1H 3C3   **FAX:** (416) 439-4086

CONTACT: Stephen Beatty **DESCRIPTION:** Published by CDMN Publishing. Circulation 15,000. Focuses on how to manage a sales team to produce higher results and lower
costs. Published 8 times a year. Established in 1994.

SALON MAGAZINE
146 Parliament Street   **PHONE:** (416) 869-3131
Toronto, ON M5A 2Z1   **FAX:** (416) 869-3008

CONTACT: Alison Wood, Editor **DESCRIPTION:** Published by Salon Communications
Inc. Circulation 27,300. Trade magazine for the professional beauty salon industry. Articles
focus on hair, skin, nails and tanning. Feature articles are geared to the salon owner and
include a gallery of 'best picks' for different looks and trends. Published 6 times a year.
Established in 1992.
WRITERS: 95% assigned to in-house writers. Contact with a query letter and resumé.
Pay is negotiable. Byline is given.
PHOTOGRAPHERS: 85% assigned to in-house photographers. Contact with query letter.
**Unsolicited photos will not be returned. Pay is negotiable.

SANITATION CANADA
1735 Bayly Street #7A
Pickering, ON L1W 3G7

PHONE: (905) 831-4711
FAX: (905) 831-4725

CONTACT: Tanja Nowotny, Editor   **DESCRIPTION:** Published by Perks Publishing Co. Ltd. Circulation 4,000. Published 6 times a year.
NOTES: Not welcoming new submissions from photographers or writers.

SANTE
5148 Saint-Laurent Blvd.
Montreal, PQ H2T 1R8

PHONE: (514) 273-9773
FAX: (514) 273-3408

CONTACT: Héléne Matteau, Editor   **DESCRIPTION:** Published by Les Editions du Feu Vert. Circulation 34,100. French language publication. Focuses on health and lifestyle. Published 10 times a year. Established in 1984.

SANTE QUEBEC
531 Sherbrooke Street East
Montreal, PQ H2L 1K2

PHONE: (514) 282-9511

CONTACT: Madelaine Pelletier, Editor   **DESCRIPTION:** Published by Order des Infirmiéres et Infirmiers Auxiliaires du Quebec. Circulation 20,000. Published 3 times a year in French and English. Established in 1974.
NOTES: Does not purchase freelance material.

SASKATCHEWAN BUSINESS
2207 Hanselman Court
Saskatoon, SK S7L 6A8

PHONE: (306) 244-5668
FAX: (306) 653-4515

CONTACT: Heather Sterling, Editor   **DESCRIPTION:** Published by Sunrise Publishing. Circulation 8,800. "We like to cover all facets of business and the economy. For each issue we pick an editorial theme and focus on that sector of the economy. We are entertaining as well as fact-informative. We report on new businesses, inventive business ideas and those who are prospering in spite of uncertain times." Published quarterly. Established in 1994.
WRITERS: "Feature stories are 1,500-2,500 words; our *In Business* section runs 300-400 words." Pays 20¢ a word. Writers hired on assignment. Occasionally accepts articles on spec. Bylines are given. Contact by phone or fax. "We are interested in articles about the ingenuity of a business or the people behind the business. As you read the article you should be able to create a mental check list of things that will help other businesses." Guidelines are not available.
PHOTOGRAPHERS: "If a freelance writer hired on assignment is not confident in their photographic abilities we will hire someone to take photos. Formats include colour and black & white prints. Payment is negotiated." Contact by phone or fax. Guidelines are not available.
NOTES: "We are open to freelance writers and photographers calling us with story ideas or photographs that may work." Purchases first North American serial rights. Sample copy available free upon request to those in the industry. Considers previously published work, depending on where it appeared.

SASKATCHEWAN FARM LIFE
4-75 Lenore Drive
Saskatoon, SK S7K 7Y1

PHONE: (306) 242-5723
FAX: (306) 244-6656

CONTACT: Larry Hyatt   **DESCRIPTION:** Published by Saskatchewan Farm Life. A tabloid published every second week. Established in 1981.
NOTES: "We handle all photography and writing in-house."

SATURDAY NIGHT
184 Front Street East #400
Toronto, ON M5A 4N3

PHONE: (416) 368-7237
FAX: (416) 368-5112

CONTACT: Kenneth White, Editor   **DESCRIPTION:** Published by Hollinger Inc. Circulation 408,000. Magazine featuring politics, business, entertainment and the arts. Published 10 times a year. Established in 1887.
WRITERS: 50-100% freelance written. Contact with query letter. Pay is negotiable. Byline is given. Guidelines available. Purchases one-time rights. Returns unsolicited materials with SASE.
PHOTOGRAPHERS: All photography is assigned or done in-house. If you are outside Toronto submit a query letter to Carmen Dunjko, Art Director. Torontonians may phone for an appointment.
NOTES: "If you have an article and good accompanying photographs let us know in a query letter. Do not send photographs. We do not like to take responsibility for loss of unsolicited material. We do not have time to respond to faxes." Sample copies are not available.

SCARLET AND GOLD
1215 Alder Bay Walk
Vancouver, BC V6H 3T6

PHONE: (604) 738-4423

CONTACT: Mrs. J. Murphy, Editor   **DESCRIPTION:** Published by RCMP Veteran Association. Circulation 1,800. Contains association news, events, and reminiscences. Published annually.
NOTES: All writing and photography is done in-house.

SCENE
Box 2302
London, ON N6A 4E3

PHONE: (519) 642-4780
FAX: (519) 433-1284

CONTACT: N. Breton Downe, Editor   **DESCRIPTION:** Published by Scene Communications. A local weekly news, arts and entertainment magazine. Established in 1989.
NOTES: Some freelance work is purchased. Contact by mail. "Freelancers should be very specific with ideas and upfront about what they want to accomplish, what they are interested in and what they expect."

SCHOOL MAGAZINE
4040 Creditview Road #11, Box 1800   **PHONE:** (905) 569-1800
Mississauga, ON L5C 3Y8   **FAX:** (905) 569-1818

CONTACT: Hugh Parkinson, Publisher or Eleanor Parkinson, Editor **DESCRIPTION:** Published by Sawmill Creek Communications. Circulation 11,500. School publication featuring overview articles, new products, and installation or case history stories. Published 6 times a year. Established in 1993.
WRITERS: Contact with query letter and a business card. Follow-up phone call welcome. Articles range from 600-1,200 words. Pay is negotiable. Byline is given. Considers simultaneous submissions.
NOTES: Also publishes Government Business Magazine and Church Business Magazine.

SCOPE CAMPING NEWS
Box 39   **PHONE:** (519) 471-9109
Hyde Park, ON N0M 1S0

CONTACT: Harold Merton   **DESCRIPTION:** National camping magazine for beginners and experienced campers. Features stories on clubs, sites, and equipment. Published six times a year.
NOTES: All writing and photography is done in-house. Editors note: do not send queries, articles, photos. Unsolicited submissions are not welcome.

SCORE, CANADA'S GOLF MAGAZINE
287 MacPherson Avenue   **PHONE:** (416) 928-2909
Toronto, ON M4V 1A4   **FAX:** (416) 928-1357

CONTACT: Bob Weeks, Managing Editor   **DESCRIPTION:** Published by Canadian Controlled Media Communications. Circulation 125,000. Focuses on articles of interest to Canadian golfers, including instruction, travel, profiles, current and up-coming events. Published 7 times a year. Established in 1980.
WRITERS: 50-100% freelance written. Pays $200 per page (approximately 700 words). Kill fee is offered if assigned article is not used. Byline is given. Guidelines available when requested by mail. Purchases first North American serial rights. Send 9x12" SASE for a sample copy.
PHOTOGRAPHERS: All photography is done in-house or is assigned. Some stock images are purchased. Contact with query letter first.
NOTES: "Do not send SASE with U.S. postage. I will throw it out."

THE SCOREBOARD
Box 310, 34 Main Street West
Beeton, ON L0G 1A0

NOTES: NO LONGER PUBLISHED

SEAPORTS see Canadian Sailings

SEASONS

355 Lesmill Road
Don Mills, ON M3B 2W8

PHONE: (416) 444-8419
FAX: (416) 444-9866

CONTACT: Gail Muir, Editor   **DESCRIPTION:** Published by Federation of Ontario Naturalists. Circulation 15-16,000. A nature and environment magazine covering natural history, wildlife parks, wilderness and conversation in Ontario. "We focus on Ontario's environment, wildlife, parks and wilderness." Published quarterly.
WRITERS: "We purchase 3-4 features per issue plus a birding column. I like to see written queries with samples of past published work. Articles range from 1,500-3,000 words, and pay from $350-$700. I would like the writer to be familiar with the magazine. We focus only on Ontario and on nature. The query should be very focused, not general. Writers should understand our readers level of awareness. Readers are well-educated and have a basic understanding of natural history. The writer must be able to tell them something they don't already know." Guidelines are available.
PHOTOGRAPHERS: "We purchase wildlife, parks and wilderness photos taken in Ontario. I usually ask for a general submission of about 20-40 colour slides so that I can assess quality and relevance (ie. Ontario content). Credit lines are given. I want to see imaginative photography, not sunsets or chipmunks. Many of our photos are very specialized. We rarely hire on assignment, we just don't have the budget. For black & white we pay $40; for a half-page or less, colour $50; half to full page, colour $80; a spread $100 and for a cover $120." Guidelines are available.
NOTES: Samples are available for $7.20 (including GST & shipping) payable to the Federation of Ontario Naturalists. Very rarely considers previously published material, occasionally book excerpts. Purchases first North American serial rights.

SECOND IMPRESSIONS

12644-126 Street
Edmonton, AB T5L 0X7

PHONE: (403) 455-1718
FAX: (403) 451-4786

CONTACT: Michael Staley   **DESCRIPTION:** Circulation 10,000. A magazine designed for the graphic arts industry of western Canada. Covers photography, videography etc. Published bi-monthly. Established in 1985.
WRITERS: "We have one regular freelancer. We are open to queries from writers, but there is no remuneration. Writers can call, fax or send for next year's editorial outline."
PHOTOGRAPHERS: Photography is done in-house.
NOTES: Sample copy available free upon request.

SEL & POIVRE

7 Chemain Bates
Outremont, PQ H2V 1A6

PHONE: (514) 270-1100
FAX: (514) 270-6900

CONTACT: Danielle Lachance, Editor   **DESCRIPTION:** Published by Publicor. Circulation 25,000. French language publication. Focuses on food and good eating. Issued six times a year.
WRITERS: All writing is done in-house. Contact with query letter. Byline is given. Purchases one-time rights.
PHOTOGRAPHERS: All photography is done in-house. Contact with query letter. Credit line is given.

SELECT HOME DESIGNS

301, 611 Alexander St.
Vancouver, BC   V6A 1E1

PHONE: (604) 879-4144
FAX: (604) 251-3212

CONTACT: Brian Thorn   **DESCRIPTION:** Published by Select Home Designs. Circulation 100-200,000. Consumer publication focusing on single-family residential dwelling design. Features include residential construction, interior decorating, and residential renovations. Published annually. Established in 1983.
WRITERS: 10-24% freelance written. Contact with query letter. Pay is negotiable. Byline is given.
PHOTOGRAPHERS: Contact with query letter. Do not send photos.

SELECT HOMES AND FOOD see Canadian Select Homes

SELECTION READER'S DIGEST

215 Redfern Avenue
Westmount, PQ   H3Z 2V9

PHONE: (514) 934-0751
FAX: (514) 932-3637

CONTACT: Lise Verschelden, Editor   **DESCRIPTION:** Published by Reader's Digest Magazines. Circulation 1,460,000. French language publication. Issued monthly.

SENIORS REVIEW

Box 2511
St. Catherines, ON   L2M 7M8

PHONE: (905) 687-9861
FAX: (905) 687-6911

CONTACT: Elaine Irwin, Editor   **DESCRIPTION:** Circulation 40,000 for both editions. Geared toward the active 50 and over crowd in the Niagara region and Hamilton-Burlington. One edition is produced for each region. A bi-monthly tabloid established in 1987.
WRITERS: "I already have a number of contributing writers. Payment is negotiated. Poetry is accepted but we do not pay. Freelancers can phone or they can send material in, no more than 600 words. If I'm interested you'll hear from me. We don't do politics or debate, we try to stay middle-of-the-road. We focus on health and travel etc. and subjects pertinent to the area. I have a golf writer, a food writer and some seasonal material."
PHOTOGRAPHERS: "We don't pay for photographs."
NOTES: Readily available in area stores, senior centres and pharmacies.

SENIORS TODAY

232 Henderson Hwy
Winnipeg, MB   R2L 1L9

PHONE: (204) 982-4000
FAX: (204) 982-4001

CONTACT: Heather McCaine-Davies, Editor   **DESCRIPTION:** Published by McCaine Davies Communications Ltd. Circulation 40,000. A tabloid issued twice a month for the over-50 population of Manitoba. Established in 1982.
WRITERS: This publication accepts queries by mail from local seniors only.
PHOTOGRAPHERS: Photography is not purchased.

THE SENIORS' CHOICE
Box 1094, Station 'A'
Kelowna, BC V1Y 7P8

PHONE: (604) 765-6065
FAX: (604) 765-7346

CONTACT: Mrs. Rickard **DESCRIPTION:** Published by Egress Enterprises Inc.
Circulation 30,000. A tabloid sized magazine written by seniors, for BC's senior population.
Published monthly. Established in 1989.
WRITERS: Does not welcome new submissions. Less than 1% freelance written. Most
articles are written by seniors or syndicated columnists.
PHOTOGRAPHERS: All photography is done in-house.

SENIORSPLUS NEWSPAPER
Box 1112
Barrie, ON L4M 5E8

PHONE: (705) 725-9269
FAX: (705) 725-9684

CONTACT: Mike Garratty, Editor **DESCRIPTION:** Published by Wally Moran,
Publisher. Circulation 59,000. Seniors publication featuring articles on travel; luxury
and adventure, health, sports, recreation and current events. A monthly tabloid established
in 1992.
WRITERS: 25% freelance written. Contact with query letter. Byline is given. Pay is
negotiable.
PHOTOGRAPHERS: No submissions please.
NOTES: Returns unsolicited materials with SASE. Send 9x12" SASE for a sample copy.
Purchases first North American serial rights.

SENTIER CHASSE-PECHE
11450 Albert-Hudon
Montreal North, PQ H1G 3J9

PHONE: (514) 327-4464
FAX: (514) 327-0514

CONTACT: Jeannot Ruel, Editor **DESCRIPTION:** Published by Groupe Polygone
Editeurs Inc. Circulation 69,800. French language publication. Focuses on hunting, fishing
and the outdoors. Published monthly. Established in 1971.

THE SENTINEL
94 Sheppard Ave West
Willowdale, ON M2N 1M5

PHONE: (416) 223-1690
FAX: (416) 223-1324

CONTACT: Norman Ritchie, Editor **DESCRIPTION:** Published by British America
Publishing Co. Ltd. Circulation 6,100. A fraternal magazine. Official publication of the
Loyal Orange Association. Published 6 times a year. Established in 1875.
NOTES: All writing and photography is done in-house.

SEPT JOURS
2020 University #2000
Montreal, PQ H3A 2A5

PHONE: (514) 848-7164
FAX: (514) 848-9854

CONTACT: Claude J. Charron **DESCRIPTION:** Published by Trustar Ltd. Circulation
174,800. French language publication. Focuses on the arts, culture, health etc. Published
weekly. Established in 1989.

WRITERS: We use freelancers occasionally. Contact by telephone. "It is not very often that we use something."
PHOTOGRAPHERS: "We do purchase photos. We have our own photographer but we may have to get additional photos from the US or Canada."

SEQUELS
151 Yonge Street, Suite 802
Toronto, ON M5C 2W7

NOTES: Could not locate. Phone number is not in service (416) 860-0400.

SERVICE STATION & GARAGE MANAGEMENT
1450 Don Mills Road   **PHONE:** (416) 445-6641
Don Mills, ON M3B 2X7   **FAX:** (416) 442-2077

CONTACT: Gary Kenez, Editor   **DESCRIPTION:** Published by Southam Business Communications. Circulation 25,000. Focuses on service station management. Published monthly.
WRITERS: "I do purchase work. I am looking for articles on service, issues affecting the industry, environmental articles, and technical articles. The pay rate varies from nothing to $200-$300 for an article of 800-1,500 words."
PHOTOGRAPHERS: Photography purchased in conjunction with the articles. Uses mostly colour.

SHEEP CANADA
237-8 Ave SW #600   **PHONE:** (403) 264-3270
Calgary, AB T2G 5C3   **FAX:** (403) 264-3276

CONTACT: Patrick Ottmann, Publisher
DESCRIPTION: Published by OT Communications. Issued quarterly.
NOTES: All writing and photography is done in-house.

SHIFT MAGAZINE
174 Spadina Ave. #407   **PHONE:** (416) 504-1887
Toronto, ON M5T 2C2   **FAX:** (416) 504-1889

CONTACT: Evan Solomon, Editor   **DESCRIPTION:** Published by Shift Magazine Inc. Circulation 25,000. Media-lifestyles magazine covering television, new technology, film and literature throughout Canada. Established in 1992.
WRITERS: Contact with query letter and resumé. Byline is given. Pay is negotiable. "All articles will be published on the internet. We do not want to receive fiction articles."
PHOTOGRAPHERS: 100% assigned to freelance photographers. Contact with query letter. Submit b&w or colour prints. Pay is negotiable. "We do work across Canada so it's good to know photographers nationwide."
NOTES: Purchases first North American serial rights and electronic rights. Does not accept previously published work. Send 9x12" SASE for a sample copy.

THE SHIPPING WORLD see Canadian Sailings

SHORTHORN NEWS
Box 63
Qu'Appelle, SK S0G 4A0

NOTES: Could not locate. Phone number is not in service (306) 669-7110.

SHOWS AND EXHIBITIONS
777 Bay Street   **PHONE:** (416) 596-2686
Toronto, ON M5W 1S3   **FAX:** (416) 596-5158

CONTACT: Nancy Remnant, Editor   **DESCRIPTION:** Published by Maclean Hunter
Ltd. Circulation 6,000. "Comprehensive directory of Canadian and International trade
shows." Published annually. Established in 1964.
NOTES: All writing and photography is done in-house.

SI BUSINESS
2005 Sheppard Ave East 4 Fl.   **PHONE:** (416) 497-9562 ext. 350
Willowdale, ON M2J 5B1   **FAX:** (416) 497-9427

CONTACT: Patricia MacInnis, Editor   **DESCRIPTION:** Published by Plesman
Publications Ltd. Circulation 8,480. A trade magazine for value-added computer resellers.
Addresses the specific concerns of systems integrators, software developers, consultants
and in-house systems integrators. Focuses on the trends through case studies of successful
systems integrators, profiles of prominent companies and executives as well as vertical
market analysis. Published 10 times a year. Established in 1990.
WRITERS: "95% freelance. We have specific columns: product outlook, solutions, spotlight
on suppliers and a vertical market report. We have established features every issue. For
September it is Network Integration, for October Client Service computing etc. We are
always looking for ideas on other features or ideas on any of the columns. I prefer a query
letter with a story idea." Writers' guidelines and a schedule are available from Ursula James.
"The most important thing is to be organized when you are inquiring about something.
Familiarize yourself with the magazine before you start making suggestions. Make sure
you know the market well. Our writers must be reasonably technical with a good knowledge
of the computer industry."
PHOTOGRAPHERS: "We don't purchase photography."
NOTES: For a sample copy send 9x12" SASE.

SIGNAL
2536 Lapierre   **PHONE:** (514) 595-9110
Ville Lasalle, PQ H8N 2W9   **FAX:** (514) 595-3398

DESCRIPTION: Published by Ligue de Sécurité. Published quarterly in English and
French. Established in 1989.
NOTES: Plans are to resume publishing in the fall of 1995 when a new editor comes on
board.

SIGNS CANADA
80 W. Beaver Creek #18
Richmond Hill, ON L4B 1H3

PHONE: (905) 771-7333
FAX: (905) 771-7336

CONTACT: Kim Laudrum, Editor **DESCRIPTION:** Published by Sign Association of Canada, Kenilworth Publishing Inc. Published bimonthly for the Sign Association of Canada.
NOTES: This publication does not purchase freelance material often. All decisions are made by the Association's editorial board. Also publishes Greenmaster, Municipal Monitor and Registered Nurse.

SIMMENTAL COUNTRY
#13, 4101-19 Street NE
Calgary, AB T2E 7C4

PHONE: (403) 250-5255
FAX: (403) 250-5279

CONTACT: Ted Pritchett, Editor **DESCRIPTION:** Published by Pritchett Publications Ltd. Circulation under 10,000. Business magazine covering the Simmental cattle industry. Published monthly.
WRITERS: 98% freelance written. Contact with query letter. Pay is negotiable. Byline is given. Send 9x12" SASE for a sample copy.
PHOTOGRAPHERS: Contact with query letter. Colour prints preferred.

SITE SOUND
Box 23015 City Centre Mall
London, ON N6A 5N9

NOTES: Could not locate. Phone number is not in service (519) 657-7077.

LE SKI
117 Indian Road
Toronto, ON M6R 2V5

PHONE: (416) 538-2293
FAX: (416) 538-2475

CONTACT: Iain MacMillan, Editor **DESCRIPTION:** Published by Solstice Publishing Inc. Circulation 20,000. French language publication. Covers the national ski market with emphasis on Quebec. Published quarterly. Established in 1987.
WRITERS: "We accept unsolicited submissions, if we know the writer we will assign. Contact the editor with samples of work and story ideas. Rates depend on the expertise of the writer, anywhere from $100 for a small article up to $1,000 for feature articles." Guidelines are available.
PHOTOGRAPHERS: Uses freelance stock photography. "Pay rates depend on the expertise of the photographer. A small shot used in our news section is $75 up to $400 for a colour cover." Guidelines are available.
NOTES: "We mostly use freelance contributors and freelance photographers. If someone has an interest in ski sports or snow boarding we would like to hear from them." Contact the editor for a free sample copy. Does not return unsolicited writing. Considers previously published work but has never published something that has previously run elsewhere. Also publishes Ski Canada and Outside Guide. Editor's note: Writers should check out translation and language rights.

SKI CANADA
117 Indian Road
Toronto, ON M6R 2V5

PHONE: (416) 538-2293
FAX: (416) 538-2475

CONTACT: Iain MacMillan, Editor   **DESCRIPTION:** Published by Solstice Publishing Inc. Circulation 50,000. "We address the alpine ski market in Canada with content relating to ski travel, instruction, equipment reviews and tests, and competition. Also covers snow boarding, fashion, news plus Photo Gallery. Published 6 times a year in season beginning in September. Established in 1972.
WRITERS: "We accept unsolicited submissions, if we know the writer we will assign. Contact the editor with samples of work and story ideas. Rates depend on the expertise of the writer, anywhere from $100 for a small article up to $1,000 for feature articles." Guidelines are available.
PHOTOGRAPHERS: Uses freelance stock photography. "Pay rates depend on the expertise of the photographer. A small shot used in our news section is $75 up to $400 for a colour cover." Guidelines are available.
NOTES: "We mostly use freelance contributors and freelance photographers. If someone has an interest in ski sports or snow boarding we would like to hear from them." Contact the editor for a free sample copy. Does not return unsolicited writing. Considers previously published work but has never published something that has previously run elsewhere. Also publishes Le Ski and Outside Guide. Editor's note: Writers should check out translation and language rights.

SKI THE WEST
1510-2nd Street North
Cranbrook, BC V1C 3L2

PHONE: (604) 426-7253

CONTACT: Daryl Shellborn   **DESCRIPTION:** Published by Koocanusa Publications Inc. Circulation 39,300. A ski publication geared to a B.C. and Alberta audience. Published annually. Established in 1987.
WRITERS: 98% assigned to in-house writers. Contact with query letter. Byline is given.
PHOTOGRAPHERS: 98% assigned to in-house photographers. Purchases a few stock images.
NOTES: Send 9x12" SASE for a sample copy. Purchases one-time rights. Also publishes Sno Riders West and Fishing the West.

SKITRAX
2 Pardee Avenue #204
Toronto, ON M6K 3H5

PHONE: (416) 530-1350
FAX: (416) 530-4155

CONTACT: Benjamin Sadavoy, Editor   **DESCRIPTION:** Focuses on cross-country skiing in Canada and around the world. Includes product information, training advice and destination details. Published 4 times a year. Established in 1990.
NOTES: Also publishes Pedal Magazine and Bike Trade.

SKYLARK
2130 Charleroi #8
Beauport, PQ G1E 3S1

NOTES: NO LONGER PUBLISHED

SLATE
155 King Street East
Kingston, ON K7L 2Z9

PHONE: (613) 542-3717
FAX: (613) 542-1447

CONTACT: Sonia Dodich, Editor   DESCRIPTION: Published by Slate. An art gallery guide to Toronto and south western Ontario. Published 8 times a year. Established in 1979.
NOTES: No freelance material is purchased by this publication.

SNO RIDERS WEST
1510-2nd St. North
Cranbrook, BC V1C 3L2

PHONE: (604) 426-7253
FAX: (604) 489-3743

CONTACT: Bob Boxall, Editor   DESCRIPTION: Published by Koocanusa Publications Inc. This magazine focuses on the snowmobile sport in the provinces of B.C. and Alberta. Articles on touring and snowmobile activities in the mountains. Published annually. Established in 1990.
WRITERS: Contact with query letter. Byline is given. Send 9x12 SASE for a sample copy. Pay is negotiable. Purchases one-time rights.
PHOTOGRAPHERS: Contact with query letter. Colour prints preferred. Pay is negotiable. "Good, action snowmobile photos are welcomed."

SNOW GOER
130 Spy Court
Markham, ON L3R 0W5

PHONE: (905) 475-8440
FAX: (905) 475-9560

CONTACT: Chris Knowles, Editor   DESCRIPTION: Published by Camar Publications Ltd. Circulation 100,000. Canadian snowmobiling magazine featuring new products, travel events and activities. Published in English and French. Issued twice a year. Established in 1980.
WRITERS: Buys freelance material. Contact with query letter. Follow-up with phone call. Pay is negotiable. Byline is given.
PHOTOGRAPHERS: 98% assigned to in-house photographers. Contact with query letter. Slide format preferred. Pay is negotiable.
NOTES: Purchases first North American serial rights. "Articles in French may be submitted as well. Query letter in English, though, please." Also publishes Water Goer.

SNOWMOBILE SPORTS
447 Speers Road, Suite 4
Oakville, ON L6K 3S7

NOTES: Could not locate. Phone number is not in service (416) 842-6591.

THE SOCIAL WORKER\LE TRAVAILLEUR SOCIAL
383 Parkdale Avenue #402
Ottawa, ON K1Y 4R4

PHONE: (613) 729-6668
FAX: (613) 729-9608

CONTACT: Peni Sipkes, Managing Editor   DESCRIPTION: Published by Myropen Publications Ltd. Circulation 14,000. Professional journal for social workers. Published quarterly in English and French. Established in 1932.

WRITERS: 99% of the articles are written by social workers. Does not pay.
PHOTOGRAPHERS: Photos supplied by various agencies. Does not pay.
NOTES: Returns unsolicited materials with SASE.

SOHO
Box 67
Westmount, PQ H3Z 2T1

PHONE: (514) 933-3985
FAX: (514) 933-4369

CONTACT: Johanne de Luca, Editor-in-Chief   **DESCRIPTION:** Published by Les Publications JDL Inc. Circulation 75,000. French language publication. Focuses on information for small and home offices. Issued 10 times a year. Established in 1984.
NOTES: All writing and photography is done in-house.

SON HI-FI VIDEO MAGAZINE
5148 Saint-Laurent Blvd
Montreal, PQ H2T 1R8

PHONE: (514) 273-9773
FAX: (514) 273-9034

CONTACT: Claude Corbeil, Editor-in-Chief   **DESCRIPTION:** Published by Les Editions du Feu Vert. Circulation 15,000. French language publication. "A trade and consumer magazine aimed at all future video equipment buyers." Published 6 times a year. Distributed mainly in Quebec. Established in 1978.
WRITERS: "Most of our articles are freelanced." Hires on assignment. "We don't have standard pay rates or lengths. We use light but technical articles and equipment and CD reviews. Writers should query by fax or mail. Normally we assign articles. A 50% kill fee is offered if an article is cancelled." Writers' guidelines are not available.
PHOTOGRAPHERS: "100% freelance. Rates are negotiated."
NOTES: Sample copy available free upon request. Also publishes Sante, Good Times, and Le Bel Age.

SOU'WESTER
Box 128
Yarmouth, NS B5A 4B1

PHONE: (902) 742-7111
FAX: (902) 742-2311

CONTACT: Alain Meuse, Editor   **DESCRIPTION:** Published by Cameron Publications Ltd. Circulation 10,500. Fishing publication covering commercial in-shore fishing in Atlantic Canada and Quebec. A bi-weekly tabloid established in 1968.
WRITERS: 98% assigned to in-house freelance writers. Contact with query letter or fax. Pay is negotiable. Byline is given. Purchases first North American serial rights.
PHOTOGRAPHERS: 98% assigned to in-house photographers. Purchases stock images. Send b&w or colour prints of any size. Pays $10 per b&w photo.
NOTES: "We need a few new feature articles each year which can be kept on file until we need them. Articles must relate to the fishing industry in Atlantic Canada or Quebec."

SOUND AND VISION
99 Atlantic Avenue #302
Toronto, ON M6K 3J8

PHONE: (416) 535-7611
FAX: (416) 535-6325

CONTACT: Alan Lofft, Editor   **DESCRIPTION:** Circulation 30,000. A national special-interest consumer hi-fi and video magazine, technically oriented with product test

reports and stories on sound reproduction, video, CD reviews and acoustics. Published 6 times a year. Established in 1985. Distributed in a few U.S. cities as well as Canada. **WRITERS:** 60% Canadian freelancers; 40% U.S. freelancers. Contact with a fax, query letter or phone inquiry. Byline is given. Features pay $500-$1,000; columns $200-$500. "A lot of Canadian writers are lazy. We publish a technical magazine and I like stylish, lively writing, so I am particularly looking for someone with the ability to write about complex technical subjects in home entertainment and make them easily understandable to the layman. I have more U.S. writers than Canadians that fit that category. Fax me a query letter, but not an article. I prefer articles by modem or on a 5¼" or 3½" IBM, or Mac disk, ASCII text file.
PHOTOGRAPHERS: All photography is done in-house.
NOTES: Purchases first North American serial rights. Returns unsolicited materials with SASE. Send 9x12" SASE for a sample copy. Formerly Sound Canada.

SOUND CANADA see Sound and Vision

SOUNDING BOARD
999 Canada Place #400
Vancouver, BC V6C 3C1

PHONE: (604) 681-2111
FAX: (604) 681-0437

CONTACT: Ron Stanaitis, Editor Darcy Rezac, Editor-in-Chief **DESCRIPTION:** Published by Vancouver Board of Trade. Circulation 12,000. Tabloid covering Board of Trade events, and issues affecting trade and small business policy. Published 10 times a year. Established in 1935.
WRITERS: 98% assigned to in-house photographers. Hires writers on assignment. Contact with query letter, resumé and sample article. Pays 25¢ per word. Byline is given.
PHOTOGRAPHERS: 98% assigned to in-house photographers. Hires photographers on assignment. Contact with query letter. Follow up by phone. Returns unsolicited colour or b&w prints with SASE.
NOTES: Purchases first North American serial rights. Does not accept simultaneous submissions. Send 9x12" SASE for a sample copy.

SOURCES
4 Phipps St #109
Toronto, ON M4Y 1J

PHONE: (416) 964-7799
FAX: (416) 964-8763

CONTACT: Barrie Zwicker **DESCRIPTION:** Listings of information contacts for journalists, writers and editors. Published twice a year. Established in 1977.
NOTES: All writing and photography is done in-house. "We are not soliciting any photographers or writers and we do not want to be contacted."

SOUTHERN ALBERTA BUSINESS
Box 1203
Lethbridge, AB T1J 4A4

PHONE: (403) 327-3200
FAX: (403) 320-6049

CONTACT: Robert Byrne, Editor **DESCRIPTION:** Published by Byrne Publishing Group Inc. Circulation 8,500. Business magazine geared to the southern Alberta business

community. Includes profiles on entrepreneurs and articles about starting and running a small business. Published quarterly.
WRITERS: Contact with query letter. Byline is given. "Articles should focus on southern Alberta business."
PHOTOGRAPHERS: 95% text/photo submissions. Purchases 5% stock images.
NOTES: Returns unsolicited materials with SASE. Purchases one-time rights. Send 9x12" SASE for a sample copy. Also publishes Lethbridge Magazine.

SPORT MAGAZINE
22 Maberley Crescent
West Hill, ON M1C 3K8

NOTES: Could not locate.

SPORTING SCENE
22 Maberley Cres.   **PHONE:** (416) 284-0304
West Hill, ON M1C 3K8   **FAX:** (416) 284-1299

CONTACT: Peter Martens, Editor   **DESCRIPTION:** Published by Sporting Scene. Circulation 24,000. A monthly tabloid. Established in 1980.
NOTES: All writing and photos are contributed by our readers.

SPORTS BUSINESS
501 Oakdale Road   **PHONE:** (416) 746-7360
Downsview, ON M3N 1W7   **FAX:** (416) 746-1421

CONTACT: Bruce Etheridge, Editor   **DESCRIPTION:** Published by Laurentian Media Inc. Circulation 10,000. Publication directed at retailers. Features the newest sporting goods products. Also traces industry trends, and does company and sports personality profiles. Published five times a year. Established in 1973.
WRITERS: Purchases freelance material. Contact with query letter. Byline is given. Pay is negotiable. Guidelines available.
PHOTOGRAPHERS: Purchases stock photography. Occasionally hires photographers on assignment. Contact with query letter.
NOTES: Purchases all rights. Also publishes Outdoor Bound, Imprint Canada Sport Fishing Retailer, Sports Licensing Retailer and Foot Culture.

SPORTS JOURNAL
3419-26 Ave. SW   **PHONE:** (403) 240-3258
Calgary, AB T3E 0N3

CONTACT: Barry Whetstone   **DESCRIPTION:** Circulation 15,000. Tabloid-sized sports magazine covering football, hockey, and baseball in both the American and National leagues. Issued 5 times a year. Established in 1976.
WRITERS: Contact with query letter. Pay $25 per article.
PHOTOGRAPHERS: All photography is done in-house.

THE SPORTS PAGE
427-10 Ave. SE
Calgary, AB T2G 0W3

PHONE: (403) 233-8850
FAX: (403) 233-8859

CONTACT: Dave White, Editor **DESCRIPTION:** Published by D.W. Associates.
Circulation 40,000. A monthly tabloid. Established in 1990.
NOTES: Format is being changed. Unsure of photography or writing requirements.

SPOSA: THE WEDDING PLANNER
77 Mowat Avenue #410
Toronto, ON M6K 3E3

PHONE: (416) 534-1851
FAX: (416) 534-0262

CONTACT: Ross Skoggard, Editor **DESCRIPTION:** Published by Word Picture Inc.
Circulation 15,000. "Semi-annual wedding planner magazine. Distributed nationally in
Canada and to some US cities." Established in 1989.
WRITERS: "We seldom purchase writing. Nothing in the last year."
PHOTOGRAPHERS: "Photographers are hired on assignment for each issue." Contact
editor by phone and make arrangements for a portfolio showing. "We do fashion shots
and a few product shots, all in colour. We are looking for something with a European
look; we like to be a little bit ahead of the market."
NOTES: Copies are available on newsstands. Presently developing a new magazine called
CASA, a magazine for newlyweds.

SQUASH LIFE
1185 Eglinton Avenue East
North York, ON M3C 3C6

PHONE: (416) 495-4140
FAX: (416) 426-7393

CONTACT: Sherry Funston, Managing Editor **DESCRIPTION:** Published by Squash
Ontario. Circulation 5,000. Features news, views, and opinions on squash events,
tournaments, clinics, and leagues. Published five times a year. Established in 1981.
WRITERS: 100% in-house freelance written. Does not pay.
PHOTOGRAPHERS: 99% assigned to in-house photographers. Contact with query letter.
Purchases a few stock images. Pay is negotiable.

STARWEEK MAGAZINE
1 Yonge Street
Toronto, ON M5E 1E6

PHONE: 4936(Editorial)
(416) 869-4244
FAX: (416) 865-3635

CONTACT: Jim Atkins, Editor **DESCRIPTION:** Published by Toronto Star Newspapers.
Circulation 743,000. Toronto-based weekly television publication which focuses on top
entertainers plus articles on sports, music, videos, cooking, and kids' programming.
WRITERS: 5% freelance written. Contact with query letter. Byline is given. Purchases
first North American serial rights. Sample copies may be available from the Circulation
Department.
PHOTOGRAPHERS: All photography is done in-house.
NOTES: "Do not phone me. I keep queries on file a few months. I will call if I can use
your article."

STITCHES

16787 Warden Ave. RR3
Newmarket, ON L3Y 4W1

PHONE: (905) 853-1884
FAX: (905) 853-6565

CONTACT: Simon Hally, Editor   **DESCRIPTION:** Published by Stitches Publishing Inc. Circulation 40,900. Humour and lifestyle magazine for physicians. Published 10 times a year.
WRITERS: "We buy freelance, maybe 8-10 articles per issue. A fair bit is written by doctors on a freelance basis. We only look at manuscripts on spec. Because it's humour writing, we don't assign based on a query; we only look at manuscripts on spec. It's advantageous if stories have something to do with medicine or health care but not essential. The standard fee is 35¢ a word." Writers' guidelines are not available.
PHOTOGRAPHERS: "We don't purchase photography."
NOTES: Sample copy available free upon request. Purchases first North American serial rights. Formerly Punch Digest for Canadian Doctors.

STRATEGY

366 Adelaide Street West #500
Toronto, ON M5V 1R9

PHONE: (416) 408-2300
FAX: (416) 408-0870

CONTACT: Patrick Allossery, Editor   **DESCRIPTION:** Published by Brunico Communications Inc. Circulation 17,500. Published 25 times a year. Established in 1989.
NOTES: Also publishes Canada on Location, Playback, Playback International, Strategy and Video Innovations.

STUDIES IN POLITICAL ECONOMY

Social Sciences Research Building
#303 Carleton University
1125 Colonel By Drive
Ottawa, ON K1S 5B6

PHONE: (613) 788-2600 ext. 6625

CONTACT: Emer Killean, Editor   **DESCRIPTION:** Circulation 800. Academic journal. Focuses on contemporary and historical issues. Features debates in public policy, workers' history, feminism, the labour movement, international affairs, economics, and peace movement. Published 3 times a year.
NOTES: "We do not pay. We welcome submissions from university academics."

STUDIO MAGAZINE

124 Galaxy Boulevard
Toronto, ON M9W 4Y6

PHONE: (416) 675-1999
FAX: (416) 675-6093

CONTACT: Barbara Murray, Executive Editor   **DESCRIPTION:** Published by Roger Murray & Associates Inc. Circulation 10-12,000. Features articles on professional designers, illustrators, and photographers. Covers pre-press technology, computer graphics, and printing subjects. "Our magazine is designed for the professional illustrator, photographer, graphic designer, and art director. We carry profiles on leading professionals and information on new technology, paper and computers." Published 7 times a year. Established in 1982.

WRITERS: "We do purchase some work. We have in-house writers so it depends on someone's capability to do a good job. All work is assigned. If writers are interested send us a sample of your work with a cover letter." Writers' guidelines are not available.
PHOTOGRAPHERS: "All photography is done in-house."
NOTES: Studio is available on newsstands across Canada.

STYLE

1448 Lawrence Avenue East, Suite 302
Toronto, ON M4A 2V6

PHONE: (416) 755-5199
FAX: (416) 755-9123

785 Plymouth Ave. #301
Montreal, PQ H4P 1B3

PHONE: (514) 739-7766
FAX: (514) 342-0060

CONTACT: Deborah Fulsang, Fashion Director in Toronto or Marsha Ross, Editor in Montreal **DESCRIPTION:** Published by Style Communications. Circulation 12,000. Womenswear industry publication with fashion news and business features for retailers and manufacturers. Published fourteen times a year.
WRITERS: 10% freelance written. Contact with query letter; with follow-up phone call. Pay is negotiable. Byline is given. Send 9x12" SASE for a sample copy.
PHOTOGRAPHERS: 100% assigned to freelance photographers. Colour or b&w prints. Contact Marsha Ross, Editor by phone, or fax if in the Montreal area or in the Toronto area submit to Deborah Fulsang, Fashion Director.
NOTES: Their publications Footwear Forum, Canadian Jeweler and Floorcovering Plus use freelance writers extensively. Also publishes Buyer's Guide (once per year) and Jeanstyle (twice per year).

SUB-TERRAIN MAGAZINE

175 East Broadway #204A
Vancouver, BC V5T 1W2

PHONE: (604) 876-8710
FAX: (604) 879-2667

CONTACT: Brian Kaufman, Editor **DESCRIPTION:** Published by Sub-terrain Literary Collective Society. Circulation 3,000. Features work of writers, artists and photographers in North America. Published quarterly.
WRITERS: Most writing is done by members of the collective. Contact with query letter. Pay is negotiable. Payment of unsolicited manuscripts may be with free copies of the publication. Send $4.00 & 9x12 SASE for a sample copy.
PHOTOGRAPHERS: Most photography is done by members of the collective. Contact with query letter and 5x7's or contact sheets.
NOTES: "We suggest that you read our publication before you submit any writing or photography and make sure that the material you are sending us is suitable."

SUNDAY SUN TELEVISION MAGAZINE: CALGARY

2615-12 Street NE
Calgary, AB T2E 7W9

PHONE: (403) 250-4200
FAX: (403) 291-4116

CONTACT: Chris Nelson, Managing Editor Sean McCann, City Editor **DESCRIPTION:** Published by Calgary Daily Sun. Circulation 104,000. Features travel, trends, lifestyles, and Calgary-based articles. Published weekly. Established in 1980.
WRITERS: Call with news stories that are just "breaking" on the scene. Contact either Chris Nelson or Sean McCann. Pay is negotiable. Byline is given.

PHOTOGRAPHERS: Text/photo submissions common. Black and white or colour prints.
NOTES: "If something happens in Mexico City involving a Calgarian, and it's a good feature, we are more likely to be interested than in a general interest feature."

SUNDAY SUN TELEVISION MAGAZINE: EDMONTON
4990-92 Avenue   **PHONE:** (403) 468-0100
Edmonton, AB   T6B 3A1   **FAX:** (403) 468-0128

CONTACT: Tom Elsworthy   **DESCRIPTION:** Published by Edmonton Sun. Circulation 121,800. Published weekly. Established in 1978.

SUNDAY SUN TELEVISION MAGAZINE: OTTAWA
380 Hunt Club Road   **PHONE:** (613) 739-7000
Ottawa, ON   K1G 5H7

CONTACT: Rick Overall, Editor   **DESCRIPTION:** Published by Ottawa Sun. Circulation 56,500. Published weekly.
WRITERS: 99% assigned to in-house writers. Byline is given. Pay is negotiable.
PHOTOGRAPHERS: All photography is done in-house.
NOTES: "If there is a 'fast-breaking story', please call me right away."

SUNDAY SUN TELEVISION MAGAZINE: TORONTO
333 King Street East   **PHONE:** (416) 947-2333
Toronto, ON   M5A 3X5   **FAX:** (416) 947-3139

CONTACT: Gord Stimmell, Editor   **DESCRIPTION:** Published by Toronto Sun. Circulation 455,100. Published weekly.
NOTES: "All work is done in-house. The only outside influence is syndicated material we pick up. That includes photography as well."

SUNSPORTS see the Outside Guide

SUPERTRAX INTERNATIONAL
Box 20219
Hamilton, ON   L9C 7M8

NOTES: Could not locate. Phone number is not in service (905) 575-1621.

SUPPLY POST
108-19329 Enterprise Way   **PHONE:** (604) 533-5577
Surrey, BC   V3S 6J8   **FAX:** (604) 533-9533

CONTACT: Ken Kenward, Managing Editor   **DESCRIPTION:** Published by Ken Kenward Enterprises. Circulation 15,000. Trade newspaper geared toward the B.C. heavy equipment industry. Published 11 times a year. Established in 1971.
NOTES: All writing and photography is done in-house. They are not welcoming any submissions at this time.

SURFACE

1475 Maisonneuve
Val David, PQ J0T 2N0

PHONE: (819) 322-7940
FAX: (819) 322-1789

CONTACT: Richard Bolduc, Editor   **DESCRIPTION:** Published by Les Enterprises Surface. Circulation 6,300. French language publication. Trade magazine distributed to floor covering retailers, installers, architects and designers in the province of Quebec. Articles deal with floor covering and floor covering maintenance. Issued 8 times a year. Established in 1985.
WRITERS: Writers contact editor with query letter, fax or phone call. Pay is negotiated. Byline is given.
PHOTOGRAPHERS: In-house photographers.
NOTES: Send 9x12" SASE for a sample copy. Purchases first North American serial rights.

TAPESTRY

7181 Woodbine Avenue #230
Markham, ON L3R 1A3

NOTES: Could not locate. Phone number is not in service (416) 513-1200.

TEACHER'S MONEY MATTERS

70 Scriven Road
Bailieboro, ON K0L 1B0

NOTES: NO LONGER PUBLISHED

TEACHING TODAY

12644-126 Street
Edmonton, AB T5L 0X7

PHONE: (403) 455-1718
FAX: (403) 451-4786

CONTACT: Michael Staley   **DESCRIPTION:** Circulation 10,000. A resource magazine for teachers, published six times a year. Established in 1983.
WRITERS: "We purchase freelance material all the time. We look for material to help teachers." Payment must be negotiated.
PHOTOGRAPHERS: All photography is done in-house.

TEEN GENERATION see TG Voices of Today's Generation

TELECASTER

565 Windmill Road
Dartmouth, NS B3B 1B4
NOTES: Could not locate. Phone number is not in service (902) 461-0222.

TELEROMANS

2001 University Drive #900
Montreal, PQ H3A 2A6

PHONE: (514) 499-0561
FAX: (514)499-1844

CONTACT: Jean Louis Podlesak, Editor-in-Chief   **DESCRIPTION:** Published by Telemedia. Circulation 232,000 . French language publication. Focuses on the television industry, soapstars, personality profiles, movie and video reviews, children's programs, specials, sports, and pay T.V. Published weekly in four editions. Distributed in Quebec. **WRITERS:** 50% assigned to freelancers. Contact with query letter. Byline is given. Pay is negotiable. Guidelines available.
PHOTOGRAPHERS: Have access to free network of photos. Contact with query letter to Maryse Charette, Art Director. Do not send photos in the mail.
NOTES: Send 9x12" SASE to Agnes Blosch for a sample copy.

TG VOICES OF TODAY'S GENERATION

70 University Avenue, Suite 1050
Toronto, ON M5J 2M4

PHONE: (416) 487-3204

CONTACT: Stoney McCart   **DESCRIPTION:** Published by Teen Generation Inc. Circulation 150,400. National publication written and illustrated by youth, for youth. Published quarterly in English and French. Established in 1940.
WRITERS: All writing done by youth. Byline is given.
PHOTOGRAPHERS: All photographs are submitted by youth.
NOTES: "There is no payment for any of the submissions but we supply tear sheets to help young writers develop the skills they need if they want to go on to become professionals in any of these fields."

THIS MAGAZINE

16 Skey Lane
Toronto, ON M6J 3S4

PHONE: (416) 588-6580
FAX: (416) 588-6638

CONTACT: Naomi Klein, Managing Editor   **DESCRIPTION:** Published by The Red Maple Foundation. Circulation 8,000. News magazine includes investigative features and commentaries on culture, politics, labour, and international affairs. Published 8 times a year. Established in 1966.
NOTES: "We do purchase freelance material. The best thing for freelancers to do is to request our guidelines. We have them for both writers and photographers." Sample copy available for $3.95.

THIS WEEK IN BUSINESS

250 St-Antoine St. West
Montreal, PQ H2Y 3R7

PHONE: (514) 987-2512
FAX: (514) 987-2638

CONTACT: David Yates   **DESCRIPTION:** Published by The Gazette. A weekly tabloid insert in The Gazette. Articles focus on financial matters, mortgage rates and other business items. Established in 1987.
WRITERS: Contact with query letter.
PHOTOGRAPHERS: Contact with query letter to Barry Gray, Photo Editor.

THORNHILL MONTH
3335-14 Avenue #1   **PHONE:** (905) 475-1743
Markham, ON L3R 0H3

CONTACT: Deborah Smith, Editor   **DESCRIPTION:** Published by Thornhill Publications Ltd. Published monthly. Established in 1979.
WRITERS: Majority is assigned to in-house writers. Contact with query letter.
PHOTOGRAPHERS: Majority is assigned to in-house photographers. Contact with query letter.
NOTES: Also publishes Markham Month and Richmond Hill Month.

THUNDER BAY BUSINESS
1145 Barton Street   **PHONE:** (807) 623-2348
Thunder Bay, ON P7B 5N3   **FAX:** (807) 623-7515

CONTACT: Scott Sumner, Editor   **DESCRIPTION:** Published by North Superior Publishing Inc. Circulation 7,500. Monthly tabloid featuring current Thunder Bay and northwestern Ontario business. Features articles on the budget and how it affects business, reviews of successful companies, special monthly topics such as transportation or construction. Established in 1984.
WRITERS: Contact with query letter. Pay is negotiable. Byline is given. Purchases one-time rights. Send 9x12" SASE for a sample copy. Accepts simultaneous submissions if they were published outside of Thunder Bay and Ontario.
PHOTOGRAPHERS: Majority done by in-house photographers. Contact with query letter, and resumé. Black and white photos accepted. Small amount of stock purchased.
NOTES: "Don't submit unsolicited articles. Query us first." Also publishes Thunder Bay Car and Truck News, Thunder Bay Life, Thunder Bay Real Estate News.

THUNDER BAY CAR AND TRUCK NEWS
1145 Barton Street   **PHONE:** (807) 623-2348
Thunder Bay, ON P7B 5N3   **FAX:** (807) 623-7515

CONTACT: Scott Sumner   **DESCRIPTION:** Published by North Superior Publishing Inc. Circulation 20,000. Published twice monthly.
WRITERS: Contact with query letter. Byline is given. Pay is negotiable.
PHOTOGRAPHERS: 95% in-house photographers. Contact with query letter.
NOTES: Send 9x12" SASE for a sample copy. Also publishes Thunder Bay Business, Thunder Bay Life, and Thunder Bay Real Estate News.

THUNDER BAY GUEST
1126 Roland Street   **PHONE:** (807) 623-4424
Thunder Bay, ON P7B 5M4   **FAX:** (807) 622-3140

CONTACT: Debbie Junnila **DESCRIPTION:** Published by Guide Printing and Publishing, a Division of Algoma Publishing Ltd. Published monthly. Established in 1963.
NOTES: All writing and photography is done in-house. They also publish The Thunder Bay Post.

THUNDER BAY GUIDE

1126 Roland Street
Thunder Bay, ON P7B 5M4

PHONE: (807) 623-5788
FAX: (807) 622-3140

CONTACT: Debbie Junnila, Editor   **DESCRIPTION:** Published weekly. Established in 1965.
NOTES: All writing and photography is done in-house.

THUNDER BAY LIFE

1145 Barton Street
Thunder Bay, ON P7B 5N3

PHONE: (807) 623-2348
FAX: (807) 623-7515

CONTACT: Scott Sumner, Editor   **DESCRIPTION:** Published by North Superior Publishing Inc. Circulation 7,500. Published bi-monthly. Established in 1989.
WRITERS: Contact with query letter.
PHOTOGRAPHERS: Majority done by in-house photographers. Contact with query letter.
NOTES: Also publishes Thunder Bay Business, Thunder Bay Car and Truck News and Thunder Bay Real Estate News.

THUNDER BAY MAGAZINE

1186 Roland Street
Thunder Bay, ON P7B 5M4

PHONE: 807 623-8545
FAX: 807 623-7110

CONTACT: Mike Thompson, Editor   **DESCRIPTION:** Circulation 31,000. A full colour, glossy, consumer magazine. Focuses on city lifestyle including art, fashion, history, business, travel, finance, sports and people.
NOTES: All writing and photography is done in-house. Additional publications include: Circle Tour, Bear Country, Chamber of Commerce Progress Report, Curtain Call and Flyer's Hockey Program.

THUNDER BAY REAL ESTATE NEWS

1145 Barton Street
Thunder Bay, ON P7B 5N3

PHONE: (807) 623-2348
FAX: (807) 623-7515

CONTACT: Scott Sumner, Editor   **DESCRIPTION:** Published by North Superior Publishing Inc. A weekly real estate tabloid established in 1983.
WRITERS: Contact with query letter.
PHOTOGRAPHERS: 95 % in-house photographers. Contact with query letter.
NOTES: Also publishes Thunder Bay Business, Thunder Bay Car and Truck News, and Thunder Bay Life.

TIME MAGAZINE

175 Bloor Street East #602 North Tower
Toronto, ON M4W 3R8

PHONE: (416) 929-1115
FAX: (416) 929-0019

CONTACT: Sandra Berry, Managing Director   **DESCRIPTION:** Published by Time Canada Inc. Circulation 342,400. Published weekly.
NOTES: All writing and photography is done in-house. Editor's note: if you have a one-of-a-kind national or international news photo, call them.

TODAY'S BRIDE
37 Hanna Avenue, Suite 1   **PHONE:** (416) 537-2604
Toronto, ON M6K 1X1   **FAX:** (416) 538-1794

CONTACT: Shirley Ohannessian   **DESCRIPTION:** Published by Family Communications Inc. Circulation 107,500. Complete information resource planner for those about to be married. Published twice a year. Established in 1980.
WRITERS: "We do occasionally purchase material. Most is written in-house but we may freelance for lifestyle articles. For example *Wedding Stress Syndrome*. Articles like choosing music or flowers are done in-house. Contact me with a point-form query letter. We assign work of 1,000-1,200 words and we pay $250."
PHOTOGRAPHERS: "We purchase stock."
NOTES: Also publishes You, Expecting and Baby and Child Care Encyclopedia. Purchases unlimited rights. Copies are widely available on newsstands.

TODAY'S HEALTH
5915 Airport Road #700
Mississauga, ON L4V 1T1

NOTES: Could not locate. Phone number is not in service (416) 673-2500.

TODAY'S MATURITY see Today's Seniors

TODAY'S PARENT
269 Richmond St. West   **PHONE:** (416) 596-8680
Toronto, ON M5V 1X1   **FAX:** (416) 596-1991

CONTACT: Fran Fearnley, Editor-in-Chief   **DESCRIPTION:** Published by Today's Parent Group. Circulation 150,000. Consumer magazine for parents with children up to the age of 12. Provides positive and supportive information to parents. Published 9 times a year.
WRITERS: "Writers are advised to send query letters rather than completed manuscripts and to enclose samples of previously published work. Send SASE. Please do not phone or fax queries!" Responds within 6 weeks. Editorial line-up includes health, education, resources, marketplace, motherhood, fatherhood, family fun, cooking with kids. Columns run 900-1,200 words, pays $650-700; features 1,200 to 3,000 words, pays $700-1400. The fee will be negotiated when you are commissioned to write an article.
NOTES: Contact with query letter. Do not phone or fax.

TODAY'S SENIORS
467 Speers Road   **PHONE:** (905) 815-0555
Oakville, ON L6K 3S4   **FAX:** (905) 815-0026

CONTACT: Don Wall, Editor-in-Chief   **DESCRIPTION:** Published by Metroland Printing, Publishing & Distributing. Circulation 611,000. Publication for those over 50, with features pertinent to their lifestyle. A large emphasis on travel. A monthly tabloid.
WRITERS: Completely freelance written. Article length varies; pay varies with length, from $50-100. Query with letter and samples of work. "We are always willing to listen; we promote Canadian writers as much as possible." Submit clean copy - "no-time to edit

spelling and grammar." Interested in seniors' issues, special services with broad appeal, individual experience (issues involved and precautions for others to consider). No travel pieces: "nothing that puts seniors down." "We try to be upbeat and look for fun things." Accepts previously published work, "provided it belongs to the writer, not the publication; and only if it's a very special piece."
PHOTOGRAPHERS: "Most of our work is done by two in-house photographers. We are interested in stories with photography. If you have a story and a photo to go with it we will gladly look at it." Black & white prints are standard.

TODAY'S TIMES
Box 1198 Station A
Vancouver BC   V6E 2V27

NOTES: Could not locate. Phone number is not in service (604) 754-2387.

TODAY'S TRUCKING
452 Attwell Drive #100   **PHONE:** (416) 798-2977
Etobicoke, ON   M9W 5C3   **FAX:** (416) 798-3017

CONTACT: Rolf Lockwood, Editor   **DESCRIPTION:** Published by New Communications Group Inc. Circulation 29,000. Trucking magazine for fleets and owner-operators focusing on the business of heavy trucking. Published 10 times a year. Established in 1987.
NOTES: All writing and photography is done in-house.

TODAY'S WOMAN IN BUSINESS
Grandview Industrial Park,   **PHONE:** (506) 658-0754
113 Old Black River Road, Box 1291   **FAX:** (506) 633-0868
Saint John, NB   E2L 4H8

CONTACT: Carol Maber, Editor   **DESCRIPTION:** Published by EMC Marketing Associates. Circulation 10,000. A quarterly tabloid established in 1993. Articles are business-related featuring finances, stress management, and business seminars.
WRITERS: Contact with query letter. Does not pay.
PHOTOGRAPHERS: Contact with query letter. Does not pay. Colour or b&w prints will be returned with SASE if requested.

TOP FORTY FOCUS
17317-107 Avenue   **PHONE:** (403) 486-5802
Edmonton, AB   T5S 1E5   **FAX:** (403) 481-9276

CONTACT: Dave Suggitt, Editor   **DESCRIPTION:** Published by Suggitt Publishing Ltd. Circulation 40,000. A consumer-based publication focusing on the music industry with reviews and interviews with artists. Published 6 times a year and distributed in music stores in Alberta and BC. Established in 1992.
WRITERS: "We purchase 5 articles per issue. Our standard rate is 10¢ a word for 800-1,000 words a page. Payment is negotiated with the writer." Contact the editor by letter or phone. Writers' guidelines are available.
PHOTOGRAPHERS: "Most of our photography is supplied."
NOTES: Sample copy free upon request. Does not consider previously published work.

TOPS MAGAZINE
131 Park Street West
Windsor, ON N9A 5T6

NOTES: Could not locate. Phone number is not in service (519) 977-6035.

TORONTO COMPUTES!
99 Atlantic Avenue **PHONE:** (416) 588-6818
Toronto, ON M6K 3J8 **FAX:** (416) 588-4110

CONTACT: Mark Langton, Editor **DESCRIPTION:** Published by ConText Publishing Inc. Circulation 100,000. A newsmagazine which features articles on "low-end" personal computers, technologies, software reviews and local events.
WRITERS: Contact with query letter. Pays 15¢ per word. Byline is given. Unsolicited articles returned with SASE.
PHOTOGRAPHERS: Contact with query letter. Looking for good cover shots. Purchases at least one photo per month. Do not send sample photos in the mail.
NOTES: Purchases first North American serial rights. Send $2 and 9x12" SASE for a sample copy.

TORONTO CONSTRUCTION NEWS
280 Yorkland Blvd **PHONE:** (416) 494-4990
North York, ON M2J 4Z6 **FAX:** (416) 756-2767

CONTACT: Randy Threndyle, Editor **DESCRIPTION:** Published by Daily Commercial News, a division of Southam Information & Technology Group. Circulation 3,900. A publication listing construction starts in the Toronto area.
NOTES: Contact with query letter. Also publishes Daily Commercial News.

TORONTO GARDENS
1560 Bayview Avenue #302A **PHONE:** (416) 481-1955
Toronto, ON M4G 3B8 **FAX:** (416) 481-2819

CONTACT: Eric McMillan, Editor **DESCRIPTION:** Published by Bayview Media Inc. Circulation 50,000. "For people who grow things in the metro Toronto area." A tabloid published 8 times a year. Established in 1992.
WRITERS: "We purchase several articles every issue. We are looking for practical tips and information for people who do their own yard gardening." Send a query by mail or fax: should include clippings, an outline and proposal. "Features are around 1,500 words; we have shorter features; columns and reviews which run from 300-900 words. We commission an article at a certain length and work it out at 15¢ a word. That is the amount we pay whether it's edited down or the writer writes too much." Guidelines are not available.
PHOTOGRAPHERS: "We usually buy one shot per issue, colour or black & white. We are looking for human interest shots; not just a nice shot of a tulip, but someone planting a tulip." Payment is negotiable.
NOTES: Sample copy available free upon request. Purchases first North American serial rights. Also publishes We Compute.

TORONTO LIFE
59 Front Street East, 3rd Floor   **PHONE:** (416) 364-3333
Toronto, ON M5E 1B3   **FAX:** (416) 861-1169

CONTACT: John Macfarlane, Editor   **DESCRIPTION:** Published by Key Publishers Ltd. Circulation 90,000. Monthly city magazine featuring Toronto lifestyles. Articles include city politics, society, business, commerce, sports and shopping. Established in 1966.
WRITERS: "We purchase articles, approximately 5 per issue. Lengths vary from 400-2,000 words. Freelancers should send their resumé to the editor. We sometimes take articles on spec. All articles must be specific to Toronto."
PHOTOGRAPHERS: "We occasionally purchase photography, both colour and black & white." Contact Sandra Latini, Art Director.
NOTES: Sample copy available for $3. Rights purchased are negotiable.

TORONTO LIFE FASHION
59 Front Street East   **PHONE:** (416) 364-3333
Toronto, ON M5E 1B3   **FAX:** (416) 594-3374

CONTACT: Joan Harting Barham, Editor   **DESCRIPTION:** Published by Key Publishers Ltd. Circulation 130,000. National fashion and beauty magazine dealing with health, fitness, and other issues affecting women. Established in 1977. Published 6 times a year.
WRITERS: Contact with query letter to Jennifer David, Managing Editor. Do not send unsolicited material in the mail. Pay is negotiable.
PHOTOGRAPHERS: Contact Art Director, Brad MacIver by phone. Appointments to show work are Tuesdays and Thursdays. Photographers drop off portfolios in the morning, then pick up later that day. Out-of-town residents must contact Mr. MacIver before sending submissions in the mail.

TORONTO MAGAZINE
444 Front Street West   **PHONE:** (416) 585-5519
Toronto, ON M5V 2S9

CONTACT: Trevor Cole or John Doyle, Editor   **DESCRIPTION:** Circulation 100-200,000. Focuses on the people and events of Toronto. Published monthly.
WRITERS: Contact with query letter. Pay is negotiable. Guidelines available.
PHOTOGRAPHERS: All photography is done in-house.

TORONTO REVIEW OF CONTEMPORARY WRITING ABROAD
Box 6996 Station A   **PHONE:** (416) 483-7191
Toronto, ON M5W 1X7   **FAX:** (416) 483-7191

CONTACT: Mr. Vassanji, Editor   **DESCRIPTION:** Circulation 600. Publishes fiction, poetry, criticism, reviews and interviews pertaining to new Canadian and International writing. Publishes 3 issues per year.
WRITERS: Contact with query letter. Returns unsolicited materials with SASE. Pay $10 for unsolicited poems and $50 for articles, plus a free subscription. Pays slightly higher for commissioned articles. Byline is given. Do not send complete manuscripts. Considers simultaneous submissions.

PHOTOGRAPHERS: All photography is done in-house.
NOTES: Send $6.50 & 9x12" SASE for a sample copy. Formerly the Toronto South Asian Review.

TORONTO STOCK EXCHANGE REVIEW
2 First Canadian Place   **PHONE:** (416) 947-4660
The Exchange Tower 8 Fl.   **FAX:** (416) 941-0811
Toronto, ON M5X 1J2

CONTACT: Peter Traynor, Editor   **DESCRIPTION:** Published by The Toronto Stock Exchange. Published monthly. Established in 1934.
NOTES: All writing and photography is done in-house.

TORONTO TONIGHT
430 King Street West
Toronto, ON M5V 1L5

NOTES: NO LONGER PUBLISHED

TOURING
3281 Jean Béraud Avenue, Chomedey   **PHONE:** (514) 334-5912
Laval, PQ H7T 2L2   **FAX:** (514) 688-6269

CONTACT: André Ducharme, Editor-in-Chief Jeannette St. Pierre, Managing Editor
DESCRIPTION: Published by Consultants C.G.E.I Inc. Circulation 474,000. French (80%) and English (20%) automobile magazine, distributed to members of the CAA and others. Articles include tips and information on automobile travel and the automobile industry in general. Eleven pages are devoted to CAA members. Published quarterly.
WRITERS: Purchases freelance work. Contact with query letter. Returns unsolicited materials with SASE. Byline is given. Pay is negotiable. Text is accepted in English, however most articles are translated from French into English."
PHOTOGRAPHERS: Contact with query letter. Buys up to 20 photos per issue. Good cover shots needed. Purchases stock images. Pay is negotiable. "We need very good cover shots and good photos of cars (not like the ones in car ads). We do not want to receive unsolicited photos. Let us know what you have, and we'll call when we need something"
NOTES: Purchases first North American serial rights. Send 9x12" SASE for a sample copy.

TOURISME PLUS
1100 René Lévesque Blvd. West 24 Fl.   **PHONE:** (514) 392-9000
Montreal, PQ H3B 4X9   **FAX:** (514) 392-4726

CONTACT: Michel Villeneuve, Editor **DESCRIPTION:** Published by Transcontinental Publications Inc. Circulation 7,200. Touring magazine published weekly in French. Established in 1980.
NOTES: All writing and photography is done in-house.

TOURS ON MOTORCOACH
CP 365
Montreal, PQ H2Y 3H1

PHONE: (514) 274-0004
FAX: (514) 274-5884

CONTACT: Guy J. Jonkman, Editor   **DESCRIPTION:** Published by Publicom Inc. Circulation 6,400 French; 13,000 English. Reference book for tour group organizers. Published monthly. Established in 1988.
WRITERS: Contact with query letter. Fees negotiable. Guidelines available.
PHOTOGRAPHERS: Contact with query letter.
NOTES: Also publishes Meetings Monthly, Congré Mensuel, and a French edition called Excursions en Autocar.

TOYS & GAMES
501 Oakdale Road
North York, ON M3N 1W7

PHONE: (416) 746-7360
FAX: (416) 746-1421

CONTACT: Lynn Winston, Editor   **DESCRIPTION:** Published by Laurentian Media Inc. Circulation 6,500. A trade publication directed to independent toy retailers. Published bi-monthly. Established in 1973.
WRITERS: "We are not able to purchase from writers. Our budget is very limited."
PHOTOGRAPHERS: "We don't purchase photography."
NOTES: Also publishes Luggage, Leather Goods and Accessories, Marketnews, Sports Business.

TRADE AND COMMERCE
1700 Church Avenue
Winnipeg, MB R2X 3A2

PHONE: (204) 632-2606
FAX: (204) 694-3040

CONTACT: Laura Jean Stewart, Editor   **DESCRIPTION:** Published by Sanford Evans Communications Ltd. Circulation 10,000. Reports on economic development in Canada and on prosperous companies. Published 5 times a year.
WRITERS: Contact with query letter and resumé. Does not consider simultaneous submissions. Pay is negotiable. Byline is given. Send 9x12" SASE for a sample copy. Purchases one-time North American rights. Guidelines available.
PHOTOGRAPHERS: 98% assigned to in-house photographers. Contact with query letter. Purchases stock images - about 2 per issue.

TRADER'S POST
1 First Canadian Place, Box 60
Toronto, ON M5X 1C1

PHONE: (416) 368-1681
FAX: (416) 366-4906

CONTACT: Editor   **DESCRIPTION:** A newsletter distributed to the membership of the Toronto Junior Board of Trade.
NOTES: No freelance material is purchased.

TRAVEL A LA CARTE
136 Walton Street   **PHONE:** (905) 885-7948
Port Hope, ON L1A 1N5   **FAX:** (905) 885-7202

CONTACT: Donna Carter, Editor   **DESCRIPTION:** Published by Interpress Inc.
Circulation 90,000. National travel publication. Articles include how-to get there, see
the best attractions, eat the best food, stay in the best hotels and generally enjoy yourself
thoroughly. Published 6 times a year. Established in 1959.
WRITERS: Less than 50% freelance written. Contact with query letter. Do not send
unsolicited manuscripts. Purchases approximately six to twelve manuscripts per year. Photos
are provided by the author; no additional payment. Pays $125-300.
PHOTOGRAPHERS: All photography is provided in text/photo packages.
NOTES: "I get annoyed when people do not send proper postage with unsolicited materials."

TRAVEL COURIER
310 Dupont Street   **PHONE:** (416) 968-7252
Toronto, ON M5R 1V9   **FAX:** (416) 968-2377

CONTACT: Edith Baxter, Editor   **DESCRIPTION:** Published by Baxter Publishing.
Circulation 7,300. Published weekly. Established in 1982.
NOTES: All writing and photography is done in-house.

TRAVEL TRENDS MAGAZINE: NO LONGER PUBLISHED

TRAVELWEEK BULLETIN
282 Richmond Street East #100   **PHONE:** (416) 365-1500
Toronto, ON M5A 1P4   **FAX:** (416) 365-1504

CONTACT: Patrick Dineen, Editor   **DESCRIPTION:** Published by Concepts Travel
Media Ltd. Circulation 7,100. A magazine for the retail travel industry. Readers include
agents and industry suppliers. Published twice a week from August through April and then
once a week for the balance of the year. Established in 1973.
WRITERS: "We very occasionally purchase work. Rarely if it's unsolicited. We use
freelancers occasionally if we are too busy. We don't buy consumer travel articles. We
are a specialized trade magazine. Contact the editor by query letter with samples of work."
PHOTOGRAPHERS: "We don't use photography."
NOTES: Sample copy available free upon request.

TREE HOUSE FAMILY
179 John Street #500   **PHONE:** (416) 971-5275
Toronto, ON M5T 3G5   **FAX:** (416) 971-5294

CONTACT: Jane Weeks, Managing Editor Annabel Slaight, Editor **DESCRIPTION:**
Published by Owl Communications. Circulation 174,000. Family magazine, published
4 times a year. Focused on the parents of 3-to-11-year-olds. Activity-related articles, family
crafts, food columns, neighbours section. Established in 1992.
WRITERS: Pay is negotiable. Byline is given. "I want things that are different. Creative,
unique stories that are fun. For example, Fun Family Adventure Vacations is one article

we are doing; another article profiles a family of four living an idyllic country life." Writers' guidelines available.
NOTES: Send $2 and 9x12" SASE for a sample copy. Buys exclusive rights.

TRIBUTE MAGAZINE
900A Don Mills Road #1000   **PHONE:** (416) 445-0544
Don Mills, ON M3C 1V6   **FAX:** (416) 445-2894

CONTACT: Kim Greene, Editor   **DESCRIPTION:** Published by Tribute Publishing Inc. Circulation 600,000. Published 8 times a year and sent to every cinema across Canada. A movie magazine with primarily movie previews. Established in 1984.
WRITERS: "We have a number of regular writers that do most of our work." Please contact editor with a query letter.
PHOTOGRAPHERS: Never hires photographers.

TROT
2150 Meadowvale Blvd.   **PHONE:** (905) 858-3060
Mississauga, ON L5N 6R6   **FAX:** (905) 858-3089

CONTACT: Harold Howe, Editor   **DESCRIPTION:** Published by Canadian Trotting Association. Circulation 17,000. Monthly North American standardbred racing publication. Articles feature personality profiles, horse racing, and horses in many different aspects. Published monthly in French and English. Established in 1976.
WRITERS: Contact with query letter. Returns unsolicited material with SASE. Byline is given. Pay is negotiable. "Articles submitted in French may be accepted for our French edition."
PHOTOGRAPHERS: Contact with query letter and detailed subject list. Purchases stock images. Buy up to 30 photos per issue. Occasionally hires on assignment. Pay is negotiable.
NOTES: Purchases first North American serial rights. Send 9x12" SASE for a sample copy.

TRUCK LOGGER MAGAZINE
815 West Hastings Street #725   **PHONE:** (604) 682-4080
Vancouver, BC V6C 1B4   **FAX:** (604) 682-3775

CONTACT: David Webster, Editor   **DESCRIPTION:** Published by Truck Loggers Association of British Columbia. Circulation 6,500. Published bi-monthly. Established in 1948.

TRUCK NEWS
1450 Don Mills Road   **PHONE:** (416) 442-2062
Don Mills, ON M3B 2X7   **FAX:** (416) 442-2092

CONTACT: Ted Light **DESCRIPTION:** Published by Southam Business Communications. Circulation 40,000. Contains national information for truck owners and fleet operators. Published monthly. Established in 1981.
WRITERS: "We are looking for technical articles to do with trucking. We pay the going rate." Contact the editor with a query letter.
PHOTOGRAPHERS: Not interested in receiving queries for photography.

TRUCK WEST

1450 Don Mills Road
Don Mills, ON M3B 2X7

PHONE: (416) 442-2062
FAX: (416) 442-2092

CONTACT: Patricia Cancilla   **DESCRIPTION:** Published by Southam Business Communications. Circulation 22,000. A heavy-trucking publication distributed to semi-truck fleet owners. Covers Thunder Bay to BC. Technical articles are of interest to truckers and fleet owners; covers mostly mechanical, tire maintenance, computer issues. Tabloid sized magazine, published monthly. Established in 1981
WRITERS: "We purchase occasionally." Contact the editor with a query letter.
PHOTOGRAPHERS: "We are occasionally very much in need of western truck shots. We prefer colour." Contact the editor with a query letter.

TRURO MAGAZINE

228 Main Street
Bible Hill, NS B2N 4H2

PHONE: (902) 895-7948
FAX: (902) 893-1427

CONTACT: Karen Fulton, Editor   **DESCRIPTION:** Published by Advocate Printing & Publishing Co. Ltd. Circulation 10,000. "A monthly publication for the Truro area. Contains local human interest stories."
WRITERS: We purchase articles pertinent to Truro. Pay rates depend on the story and the amount of work that has gone into it. A phone call is the preferred method of contact. I wouldn't want writers wasting their time on a story I wouldn't use." Contact by phone or query letter. Byline is given.
PHOTOGRAPHERS: "Photographs should really have to do with the Truro area. Photographers should call me first. Usually the writers take photos to go with their story so we do not use photographers often." Contact this publication by phone first. Pay is negotiable.
NOTES: Considers simultaneous submissions. Purchases first North American serial rights. Send 9x12" SASE for a sample copy. Also publishes Central Nova Business News and The Light.

TURF & RECREATION

123 B King Street
Delhi, ON N4B 1X9

PHONE: (519) 582-8873
FAX: (519) 582-8877

CONTACT: Mike Jiggens, Editor   **DESCRIPTION:** Published by Turf & Recreation Publishing Inc. Circulation 14,500. Focuses on golf courses and grounds maintenance. Articles could feature golf courses, municipal parks, cemeteries, or athletic fields. Published 7 times a year. Established in 1988.
WRITERS: 98% assigned to in-house writers. Contact with query letter. Text/photo submissions sometimes looked at if queried first. Byline is given. Pay is negotiable. "My ideal writer would be someone who knows the subject area and who knows how to write!"
PHOTOGRAPHERS: 98% assigned to in-house photographers. Contact with query letter, possibly with a subject list of related photographs.
NOTES: Send 9x12" SASE for a sample copy. Simultaneous submission accepted unless they have gone to competing magazines.

TV GUIDE

25 Sheppard Ave. W. Suite 100
North York, ON M2N 6S7

PHONE: (416) 733-7600
FAX: (416) 733-3568

CONTACT: Bill Anderson, Features Editor   **DESCRIPTION:** Circulation 840,000. Canada's largest weekly television magazine. Sold on newsstands. Articles focus on the entertainment industry, sports, food, children's programming, and showbiz personalities.
WRITERS: Contact with query letter. We pay competitive rates according to a writer's experience. Byline is given. "If you don't think you are up to national magazine standards, don't apply. However, we welcome new submissions from people who know the entertainment business. There is a grave shortage of good writers in this area. We have problems getting the standard of writing we want."
PHOTOGRAPHERS: Contact with query letter. Follow-up with call for appointment if in Toronto area. Do not send photos in the mail. Toba Krasman-Lakier, Art-Director.
NOTES: Purchases first North American serial rights. Also purchases database rights.

TV WEEK MAGAZINE

4180 Lougheed Hwy #401
Burnaby, BC V5C 6A7

PHONE: (604) 299-7311
FAX: (604) 299-9188

CONTACT: Hardip Randhawa, Editor   **DESCRIPTION:** Published by Canada Wide Magazines. Circulation 90,000. Features television listings with local entertainment highlights. Published weekly.
WRITERS: "We do buy occasionally. I assign freelance stories every week. We do personality profiles, interviews, and stories on television series. Writers can fax their story ideas or outline."
PHOTOGRAPHERS: "Our photography is assigned by the art director, Kim Vizi. We use primarily colour."
NOTES: Sold on newsstands and by subscription.

TWO BY FOUR

Box 1010
Victoriaville, PQ G6P 8Y1

PHONE: (819) 752-4243
FAX: (819) 758-8812

CONTACT: Claude Roy   **DESCRIPTION:** Published by Editions C.R. Inc. Circulation 8,000. A bilingual publication issued 5 times a year.

UN PEU PLUS

130 Boul. De Mortagne #201
Bourcherville, PQ J4B 5M7

NOTES: NO LONGER PUBLISHED

UNION FARMER
250C - 2nd Avenue South
Saskatoon, SK S7K 2M1

PHONE: (306) 652-9465
FAX: (306) 664-6226

CONTACT: Kathy Bayliss, Editor   DESCRIPTION: Published by National Farmer's Union. Circulation under 10,000. Publication for farmers. Reports on agriculture and agricultural policy issues. Distributed to National Farmer's Union members. Quarterly magazine. Established in 1950.
WRITERS: 98% assigned to in-house writers. Contact with query letter. Writers occasionally hired on assignment. Byline is given. Pay is negotiable.
PHOTOGRAPHERS: 98% assigned to in-house photographers. Contact with query letter. Do not send photos in the mail.

THE UNITED CHURCH OBSERVER
84 Pleasant Blvd.
Toronto, ON M4T 2Z8

PHONE: (416) 960-8500
FAX: (416) 960-8477

CONTACT: Muriel Duncan, Editor   DESCRIPTION: Published by Observer Publications. Circulation 140,000. "The observer is the national magazine of The United Church of Canada. Its goals each month are to inform, challenge and entertain. It aims to be a forum for dialogue among members, to help people explore their faith and their spirituality, and apply it to the world around them." Published monthly. Established in 1925.
WRITERS: 20% freelance written. Buys 12-20 articles per year. Byline given. Occasionally hires on assignment. Contact with a query letter.
PHOTOGRAPHERS: 60% assigned to freelance photographers. Buys 50 photos per issue. Colour formats used: 35mm transparencies, 5x7 colour prints. Black and white formats used: 5x7 prints, glossy, matte. Model releases required. Captions required. Pays $60 per photo. Send brochure or tear sheets.
NOTES: Considers previously published work. Does not consider simultaneous submissions. Purchases one-time rights and first North American serial rights.

UNIVERSITY AFFAIRS
350 Albert Street #600
Ottawa, ON K1R 1B1

PHONE: (613) 563-1236
FAX: (613) 563-9745
E-mail ctausig@aucc.ca

CONTACT: Christine Tausig Ford, Editor   DESCRIPTION: Published by Association of Universities & Colleges of Canada. Circulation 31,000. Canada's higher education news magazine. Aimed at University faculty administrators and students. A tabloid published 10 times a year.
WRITERS: "We are about 25% freelance written. I prefer a query letter. I want to see someone who has read my publication before they contact me. I want to see issues oriented articles of interest to the higher education community. The pay rate varies depending on the length of the article and the complexity, between $200-$750. Features are 1,500-2,000 words but we also purchase shorter articles. Read the publication and become familiar with our needs." Do not send unsolicited articles.
PHOTOGRAPHERS: "We purchase very little photography, mostly black & white prints relating to the articles." A query letter is best or E-mail.
NOTES: Sample copy available free upon request. Purchases all rights.

UNIVERSITY MANAGER
250 The Esplanade #201   **PHONE:** (416) 867-1042
Toronto, ON M5A 1J2   **FAX:** (416) 867-1115

CONTACT: Andrea Kuch, Editor **DESCRIPTION:** Published by August Communications. A quarterly publication for University and College business officers. The official publication of the Canadian Association of University Business Officers.
WRITERS: "Some freelance work is purchased. There is no standard length and the rate is negotiable. Contact the editor with a query letter. We do take pitched articles from time to time."
PHOTOGRAPHERS: "We occasionally purchase photography." Contact the editor with a letter of inquiry.
NOTES: Sample copies available for serious potential writers.

UP-HERE, LIFE IN CANADA'S NORTH
Box 1350   **PHONE:** (403) 920-4652
Yellowknife, NT   X1A 2N9   **FAX:** (403) 873-2844

CONTACT: Rosemary Allerston, Editor   **DESCRIPTION:** Published by Marion Levine. Circulation 35,000. Up Here is an award-winning magazine focusing on adventure, wildlife, history and northern Canada's lifestyles. Profiles of northern personalities and native people and how they live. Articles explore northern communities and examine indigenous wildlife. Published 6 times a year.
WRITERS: 25-50% freelance written. Pays 20¢ to 25¢ per published word, for articles 750-3,000 words. Guidelines are available. We prefer query letters or a call. "We prefer a northern point of view, so writers should have travelled (if not lived) in the north. Only unusual travel stories are considered (no more "I drove the Dempster Highway" stories)."
PHOTOGRAPHERS: Twenty-five photos purchased per issue. Colour or b&w prints and transparencies. Prefers captions. Pay scale from $60 for a quarter-page colour and up. Commissioned cover could be $300-350. "If photographers have pertinent, relevant stock, we are very happy to look at it. Quite routinely people let us know if they are going on a trip, if we're interested we'll ask them to send us duplicates on spec. Sometimes I keep maybe 6-10 photos to select from. Usually wildlife, indigenous cultures, or scenics. Outdoor activities like skiing, hunting, fishing, all those things lend themselves to this kind of publication. Material must be authentically northern and of very high technical quality. It must be relevant to our publication. Look at the magazine first."
NOTES: Purchases North American serial rights. Sample copy available to those who send $3 with SASE.

UPTOWN MAGAZINE
101-457 Main Street   **PHONE:** (204) 949-8680
Winnipeg, MB R3B 1B5   **FAX:** (204) 957-0795

CONTACT: Nancy Westaway, Editor **DESCRIPTION:** Published by Canadian Publishers. Circulation 25,000. Reports on Winnipeg news and entertainment. Articles include a "What's Up" section, current news events, movie, music and computer reviews, and personality profiles. Published weekly.
WRITERS: 98% assigned to in-house photographers. Contact this publication by phone. Byline is given. Pay is negotiable.
PHOTOGRAPHERS: 98% assigned to in-house photographers. Contact this publication by phone. Do not send photos in the mail until you have contacted the editor.

URBA

680 Sherbrooke Street West #680
Montreal, PQ H3A 2M7

PHONE: (514) 282-7700
FAX: (514) 282-7711

CONTACT: Mr. Marin LaSalle, Editor   DESCRIPTION: Published by l'Union des municipalités de Quebec. Circulation 6,500. Trade publication dealing with issues involving urban municipalities in the Quebec area. Articles often feature legal and environmental issues. Published 9 times a year in French.
WRITERS: Contact with query letter or fax to the editor. Follow-up with phone call in 10 days. Byline is given. Send 9x12" SASE for a sample copy.
PHOTOGRAPHERS: Contact with query letter to the editor. Will return unsolicited colour prints with SASE.

URBAN SCENE

3C, 2020 Portage Ave.
Winnipeg, MB R3S 0K4

PHONE: (204) 885-7798
FAX: (204) 889-3576

CONTACT: Jim Watson, Managing Editor   DESCRIPTION: Published by Craig Kelman & Associates. Circulation 1,500. Quarterly publication focusing on issues related to Manitoba urban municipalities.
WRITERS: 98% assigned to in-house photographers. Contact with query letter. Byline is given.
PHOTOGRAPHERS: 98% assigned to in-house photographers. Contact with query letter.

L'USINE: LES NOUVELLES INDUSTRIELLES DU QUEBEC

1001 de Maisonneuve West, 10th Flr.
Montreal, PQ H3A 3E1

PHONE: (514) 729-8275
FAX: (514) 845-4393

CONTACT: Pierre Deschamps, Editor   DESCRIPTION: Published by Maclean Hunter. French trade publication featuring articles on general industry, industrial news and manufacturing. Published 6 times per year.
WRITERS: Majority assigned to in-house photographers. Contact with query letter. Submit sample portfolio of industrial-related photos.
PHOTOGRAPHERS: Established in 1993.
NOTES: Majority assigned to in-house writers. Contact editor with query letter, include a "story pitch". Pay is negotiable.

V CANADA

58 Silverbirch Avenue
Toronto, ON M4E 3K9

PHONE: (416) 699-1026
FAX: (416) 699-2649

CONTACT: Ted Graham, Editor   DESCRIPTION: Published by Graham Publications. Circulation 5,000. A national volleyball publication with physical training tips, news on national team and university programs and other news from the volleyball community. A tabloid published 6 times a year. Established in 1992.
WRITERS: "Most of our writers are volunteer; occasionally we pay for stories." Contact the editor by phone.
PHOTOGRAPHERS: "We do purchase some photography - we can use both colour and black & white. We are looking for action photos, it depends on the story; at times we need simple head shots. More people are participating in beach volleyball since volleyball has

been included in the Olympics. We are interested in seeing some shots of that." Payment is negotiable. Contact the editor by phone.
NOTES: Sample copy available free upon request.

VACANCES POUR TOUS
95 Chanoine-Coté
Vanier, PQ G1M 1T8

PHONE: (418) 686-1940
FAX: (418) 686-1942

CONTACT: Eric Sohier, Editor   **DESCRIPTION:** Published by Les Editions EJS . Circulation 42,000. French language publication. Travel articles deal with Canadian as well as international destinations. Issued 7 times a year. Established in 1971.
WRITERS: All writing is done in-house.
PHOTOGRAPHERS: Majority assigned to in-house photographers. Contact with query letter. They would like to purchase good cover photos. Pays $80-200. They currently purchase stock images from a stock agency and receives free photographs from Tourist Associations.

VALUE PLUS MAGAZINE
105 Kenneth Street
Duncan, BC V9L 1N5

PHONE: (604) 746-6463
FAX: (604) 746-7445

CONTACT: Frank Hird-Rutter, Editor   **DESCRIPTION:** Published by Value Plus Magazine Ltd. George Spong. Circulation 12,000. "A city magazine for Duncan and area. Feature local writers, plus national syndicated columnists, comics and other features." Published monthly. Established in 1993.
WRITERS: "I have staff writers, most freelancers submit without pay. The bulk of my writers are from this area and are locally known."
PHOTOGRAPHERS: "I have a photographer for assignments."

THE VANCOUVER CHILD
757 Union Street
Vancouver, BC V6A 2C3

NOTES: Could not locate. Phone number is not in service (604) 251-1760.

VANCOUVER MAGAZINE
West 12th Avenue #300 SE Tower
Vancouver, BC V5Z 4L4

PHONE: (604) 877-7732
FAX: (604) 877-4848

CONTACT: Jim Sutherland, Editor   **DESCRIPTION:** Published by Telemedia Publishing Inc. Circulation 68,000. Glossy magazine features current affairs, entertainment, politics, business, media, music and dining. Issued monthly.
NOTES: "We are completely inundated with writing and photographic material. Everyone in Vancouver knows us and anyone outside this area would not have enough knowledge about our publication's needs."

VELO MAG
1251 Rachel East
Montreal, PQ H2J 2J9

PHONE: (514) 521-8356
FAX: (514) 847-0242

CONTACT: Pierre Hamel, Editor   **DESCRIPTION:** Published by Les Editions Tricycle. French language publication. Focuses on cycling; includes information on competitions, training, and travel. Published 6 times a year.

VEN'D'EST
Box 430
Petit Rocher, NB   E0B 2E0

PHONE: (506) 783-4097
FAX: (506) 783-8386

CONTACT: Loic Vennin, Editor   **DESCRIPTION:** Published by Les Editions coopératives du Ven'd'est ltée. Circulation 4,500. Published quarterly. Established in 1985.
NOTES: "All our needs are taken care of by our staff. We are not welcoming submissions of any kind."

VENTURE
10155-102 Street
Edmonton, AB T5J 4L6

PHONE: (403) 427-0670
FAX: (403) 427-1529

CONTACT: Marylu Walters   **DESCRIPTION:** Published by Economic Development and Tourism. Circulation 35,000+. A bi-annual tabloid sized magazine featuring the Alberta business scene and showcasing the accomplishments of Alberta businesses. Offers information on opportunities in trade and investment. All aspects of economic development are discussed.
WRITERS: "The majority of writing is done by freelancers. We don't have a standard article length. We don't often do long features. Most of the work in on assignment. Contact the editor directly by phone at 452-5143 or fax 455-1097. We look for business writers and creative business writing."
PHOTOGRAPHERS: "We occasionally purchase photography, generally black & white although our cover is colour. We have almost a zero budget for photography so we often borrow photos - we give credit. For the cover we will often tender." Contact Susan Smitten by phone or fax or set up an appointment for a portfolio viewing."
NOTES: Sample copy available free upon request.

VETERINARIAN MAGAZINE
248 Mary Street
Rockwood, ON N0B 2K0

NOTES: NO LONGER PUBLISHED

VICE VERSA
CP991 Succa
Montreal, PQ H3C 2W9

NOTES: Could not locate. Phone number is not in service (514) 393-1853.

VICTORIA TODAY
200-770 Enterprise Cres
Victoria, BC V8Z 6R4

NOTES: Could not locate. Phone number is not in service (604) 727-3469.

VICTORIA'S BUSINESS REPORT
1609 Blanshard Street   **PHONE:** (604) 382-7777
Victoria, BC V8W 2J5   **FAX:** (604) 381-2662

CONTACT: Gerry Lemon, Editor   **DESCRIPTION:** Published by Monday Publications Ltd. Circulation 14,500. Business publication with emphasis on local business. Published monthly. Established in 1979.
NOTES: "Our needs are specialized, therefore we prefer to handle everything in-house. We do not welcome new submissions at this time."

VIDEO INNOVATIONS
366 Adelaide Street West #500   **PHONE:** (416) 408-2300
Toronto, ON M5V 1R9   **FAX:** (416) 408-0870

CONTACT: Mary Maddever, Editor   **DESCRIPTION:** Published by Brunico Communications Inc. Circulation 2,100. Published twice a year. Established in 1990.
WRITERS: "We usually assign writers. We are so specialized that it is not appropriate for freelancers to send us unsolicited material. We are a trade not a consumer magazine." Contact with query, resumé and samples.
NOTES: Also publishes Playback International, Playback and Canada on Location.

VIDEO NEWS AND REVIEWS
17317-107 Avenue   **PHONE:** (403) 486-5802
Edmonton, AB T5S 1E5   **FAX:** (403) 481-9276

CONTACT: Dave Suggitt, Editor   **DESCRIPTION:** Published by Suggitt Publishing Inc. Circulation 40,000. A consumer-based magazine focusing on the video rental industry with reviews and interviews with stars. Covers Alberta and BC. Published monthly.
WRITERS: "We have one writer who is in touch with Hollywood. We purchase 5 articles per issue. Our standard rate is 10¢ a word for 800-1,000 words." Contact the editor with query letter or by phone. Writers' guidelines are available.
PHOTOGRAPHERS: "Most of our photography is supplied by video wholesalers."
NOTES: Sample copy available free upon request. Does not consider previously published work.

VIDEO-PRESSE
3965 boul. Henri Bourassa est
Montreal, PQ H1H 1L1

NOTES: CEASED PUBLICATION JUNE 1995

LA VIE DES ARTS
200 St Jacques #600   **PHONE:** (514) 282-0205
Montreal, PQ H2Y 1M1   **FAX:** (514) 282-0235

CONTACT: Bernard Levy, Editor   **DESCRIPTION:** Published by La Vie des Arts. French language publication. Arts magazine featuring design, visual art and gallery information. Published quarterly.

VIE EN PLEIN AIR
970 Montee de Liesse   **PHONE:** (514) 856-0787
Ville St. Laurent, PQ H4T 1W7   **FAX:** (514) 856-0790

CONTACT: Claude Leonard **DESCRIPTION:** Published by Vie En Plein Air. Circulation 25,000. French language publication. Consumer magazine for RV owners and enthusiasts. Contains buyer information for RV vehicles; motorhomes, trailers, tent trailers, 5th wheels and anything that pertains to camping. Published 4 times a year.
WRITERS: "We purchase very little. Most material is translated from Camping Canada. Material can be submitted for review."
PHOTOGRAPHERS: "Photography is done in-house."
NOTES: A sister publication to Camping Canada. Also publishes Les Plaisanciers.

VISION
250 The Esplanade #201   **PHONE:** (416) 867-1042
Toronto, ON M5A 1J2   **FAX:** (416) 867-1115

CONTACT: Doug E. Bell, Editor   **DESCRIPTION:** Published by August Communications. A bi-monthly national publication. Official publication of the Opticians Association of Canada.
WRITERS: "Freelance writing is accepted. Contact the editor with a query letter."

VISION MODE
877 St-Pierre   **PHONE:** (514) 964-7590
Terrebonne, PQ J6W 1E6   **FAX:** (514) 964-2327

CONTACT: Robert Frosi, Editor   **DESCRIPTION:** Published by Groupe Magazines. French language publication. Focuses on fashion and travel. Issued 3 times a year.

VISITOR
75 King Street South #209   **PHONE:** (519) 886-2831
Kitchener, ON N2J 1P2

CONTACT: Janne Dean, Editor   **DESCRIPTION:** Published by Fairway Group. Visitors' information about Waterloo, Kitchener, Cambridge, Guelph, Stratford and the surrounding areas. Articles include shopping, festivals, hotels, shows and restaurants. Published five times a year.
WRITERS: "We purchase work. Articles must focus on this tourism area. Rates and lengths vary and are negotiated. Our publication is 20% editorial."
PHOTOGRAPHERS: "We purchase colour photography for the cover. Pays $175. Contact us by phone."

NOTES: Sample copy available free upon request and through Ontario Travel and local hotels/motels and Chambers of Commerce.

VISITOR'S CHOICE
999-8 Street SW #222   **PHONE:** (403) 244-7343
Calgary, AB T2R 1J5

DESCRIPTION: Published by I.G. Publications Ltd. Publishes Banff & Lake Louise; Calgary; Edmonton; Vancouver and Victoria editions.
WRITERS: "We use articles on local attractions, however we usually use the same information from year to year because not much changes." Contact Sharon Komori.
PHOTOGRAPHERS: "We buy colour photography if it is taken in Canada. We look for landscapes, cities, flora & fauna, and attractions. Photographers should send a letter requesting guidelines." Contact Elizabeth Hraptspead.
NOTES: Sample copy free upon request.

VOICE OF THE HURON FARMER
Box 490   **PHONE:** (519) 683-4485
Dresdan, ON N0P 1M0   **FAX:** (519) 683-4355

CONTACT: Peter Epp, Managing Editor   **DESCRIPTION:** Published by Leader Publications. Circulation approximately 14,000 per month. Agricultural publication featuring county-specific articles on agricultural specialties and crops, area farm meetings and farmer profiles.
WRITERS: Writers contact with query letter. Follow-up with a phone call. Byline is given. Pay is negotiable.
PHOTOGRAPHERS: Majority is assigned to in-house photographers. Contact with query letter plus subject list with prices. Purchases 3 photos per issue. Returns unsolicited b&w captioned prints with SASE. Hires photographers on assignment.
NOTES: Also publishes Voice of the Kent Farmer, Voice of the Lambton Farmer, Voice of the Middlesex Farmer, Voice of the Essex Farmer, Voice of the Huron Farmer, Voice of the Perth Farmer and Voice of the Oxford Farmer.

VOILA QUEBEC
185 St-Paul St.   **PHONE:** (418) 694-1272(
Quebec, PQ G1K 3W2   **FAX:** (418) 694-0083

CONTACT: Jo Ouellet, Editor   **DESCRIPTION:** Published by Publications Vacances Inc. Circulation 48,000. A hotel tourist guide. Published quarterly in English and French. Established in 1975.
NOTES: All writing and photography is done in-house.

VOIR MONTREAL
4130 St. Denis Street   **PHONE:** (514) 848-0805
Montreal, PQ H2W 2M5   **FAX:** (514) 848-9004

CONTACT: Richard Martineau, Editor   **DESCRIPTION:** Published by Communications Voir Inc. Circulation 90,000. French language publication. An alternative news weekly.

WRITERS: "Contact the editor or Jean-Francois Deschenes by phone or send completed articles. We work mostly with our own team but we occasionally may purchase something. It must be about cultural life in Montreal; social issues, trends, lifestyles etc. Articles range between 3-6 pages. We pay from $40-$60 per page."
PHOTOGRAPHERS: All photography is done in-house.

LA VOIX DU VRAC
710 Bouvier Street #215   **PHONE:** (418) 623-7923
Quebec City, PQ G2J 1C2   **FAX:** (418) 623-0448

CONTACT: André Lavoie   **DESCRIPTION:** Published by L'Association Nationale des Camionneurs Artisans Inc., André Lavoie. Circulation 9,870. French language publication. "A magazine for the bulk trucker of Quebec. We represent 4,000 truckers." Published 6 times a year. Established in 1972.
WRITERS: No articles are purchased.
PHOTOGRAPHERS: No photography is purchased.

VOTRE SUCCES
5174 Cote Des Neiges
Montreal, PQ H3T 1X8

NOTES: Could not locate. Phone number is not in service (514) 731-6099.

WASTE BUSINESS MAGAZINE
85 Somerset Avenue #200   **PHONE:** (416) 658-7519
Toronto, ON M6H 2R3   **FAX:** (416) 658-9708

CONTACT: Matthew Keegan, Editor   **DESCRIPTION:** Published by Eco-Lands Publishing. Circulation 40,000. Trade publication with environmental articles relating to hazardous waste remediation and transportation. Published 6 times a year. Established in 1990.
WRITERS: 50% freelance written. Contact with query letter. Does not pay for unsolicited articles. Articles should be two pages in length.
PHOTOGRAPHERS: All photography is done in-house.
NOTES: Media kit available. Send 9x12" SASE for a sample copy. Purchases first North American serial rights. Does not consider simultaneous submissions.

WATER GOER
130 Spy Court   **PHONE:** (905) 475-8440
Markham, ON L3R 5H6   **FAX:** (905) 475-9560

CONTACT: Chris Knowles   **DESCRIPTION:** Published by Camar Publications Ltd. Circulation 50,000. Publication for watercraft users. Published annually.
WRITERS: 10% freelance written. Contact with query letter. Pay is negotiable. Byline is given. "Articles may be submitted in French, but query in English please."
PHOTOGRAPHERS: 10% assigned to freelance photographers. Contact with query letter. Follow-up with a phone call. Slide format preferred.

NOTES: Purchases first North American serial rights. Returns unsolicited materials with SASE. Also publishes Snow Goer.

WATER WELL DRILLERS AND PUMP INSTALLERS

145 Thames Road West, Box 1060   **PHONE:** (519) 235-2400
Exeter, ON N0M 1S3   **FAX:** (519) 235-0798

CONTACT: Peter Darbishire, Managing Editor   **DESCRIPTION:** Published by AIS Communications. Circulation 1,300. Stories on ground water, well development, water treatment, and technical articles. A quarterly publication established in 1978.
WRITERS: Freelance work purchased very infrequently. "We are not really clamouring for stories. We tend to use some regular freelancers and if there's a need for something in a certain area, we put it into our travel plans for the next 12 months. We often work 12 months ahead on photos, with stories following later. Generally the stories are not time-sensitive." Query by mail or fax.
NOTES: Also publishes Canadian Rental Service, Glass Canada and Agri Book Magazine.

WE COMPUTE

1560 Bayview Avenue #302A   **PHONE:** (416) 481-1955
Toronto, ON M4G 3B8   **FAX:** (416) 481-2819

CONTACT: Eric McMillan, Editor   **DESCRIPTION:** Published by Bayview Media Inc. Circulation 80,000. "A very non-technical publication for home or small business computer users." A tabloid published 10 times a year.
WRITERS: "We purchase 6-7 articles per issue. Send me something by mail or fax, including clippings, an outline and proposal. We are looking for plain english articles with practical information." Features run up to 1,500 words; columns and reviews run from 300-900 words. We commission an article at a certain length and work it out at 15¢ a word. That is the amount we pay whether the article is edited down or the writer writes too much." Writers' guidelines are available.
PHOTOGRAPHERS: "We buy very little photography."
NOTES: Sample copy available free upon request. Purchases first North American serial rights. Also publishes Toronto Gardens.

WEDDINGBELLS

120 Front Street East, #200   **PHONE:** (416) 862-8479
Toronto, ON M5A 4L9   **FAX:** (416) 862-2184

CONTACT: Crys Stewart, Editor   **DESCRIPTION:** Published by Diane Hall. Circulation 110,000. National special interest magazine aimed at the bridal market and young couples starting out. Emphasis on planning for weddings and lifestyle issues. Published twice a year.
WRITERS: Contact with query letter, resumé and sample articles. Byline is given. Guidelines are not available.
PHOTOGRAPHERS: Contact with query letter. Hires photographers on assignment. "I am not interested in wedding photographers; only established professional fashion and table top photographers."
NOTES: Returns unsolicited materials with SASE. No sample copy - available on newsstands. Purchases one-time rights.

WEDDINGS & HONEYMOONS
65 Helena Avenue
Toronto, ON M6G 2H3

NOTES: Could not locate. Phone number is not in service (416) 922-7129.

WELDING AND FABRICATING CANADA
3500 Dufferin Street #103
Downsview, ON M3K 1N2

NOTES: Could not locate. Phone number is not in service (416) 633-2188.

WELLNESS MD
344 Edgeley Blvd. Unit16-17   PHONE: The Wellness Publishing Co.
Concord, ON L4K 4B7   FAX: 37,600

CONTACT: Gordon Bagley, Editor   DESCRIPTION: Published by Published 6 times
a year. Established in 1991.
NOTES: NO LONGER PUBLISHING. This magazine may resume publication in 1996.
Do not send inquiries or any material. It will not be returned.

WEST COAST LINE
2027 East Annex   PHONE: (604) 291-4287
Simon Fraser University   FAX: (604) 291-5737
Burnaby, BC V5A 1S6

CONTACT: Jacqueline Larson, Managing Editor   DESCRIPTION: Circulation 600.
A contemporary literary publication featuring poetry, short fiction, literary criticism, personal
essays and black & white photography. Published three times a year. Established in 1990.
WRITERS: "We pay $8 a page upon publication. We recommend that potential contributors
send a letter of inquiry before submitting a manuscript. Poems are up to 400 lines and
fiction to 7,000 words" Writers' guidelines are available with SASE.
PHOTOGRAPHERS: "We pay $100 for colour covers. Photos must be really interesting.
We don't buy many photos. Photographers should look at back issues."
NOTES: Sample copy available for $10. Can also be found in public libraries and book
stores. Any correspondence to this publication should include an SASE.

WESTBRIDGE ART MARKET REPORT
2339 Granville Street   PHONE: (604) 736-1014
Vancouver, BC V6H 3G4   FAX: (604) 734-4944

CONTACT: Anthony Westbridge   DESCRIPTION: Published by Westbridge Publications
Ltd. Art market newsletter. Published 6 times a year.
NOTES: "We are a very specialized newsletter with all our writing and photographic needs
handled in-house."

WESTBRIDGE ART REPORT

1683 Chestnut Street
Vancouver, BC V6J 4M6

PHONE: (604) 734-4944
FAX: (604) 731-4576

CONTACT: Anthony Westbridge **DESCRIPTION:** Art market news covering the national and international fine art market. Includes auction previews and results, and market trends. Published 10 times a year.
NOTES: All writing and photography is done in-house.

WESTCOAST FISHERMAN

1496 West 72 Avenue
Vancouver, BC V6P 3C8

PHONE: (604) 266-7433
FAX: (604) 263-8620

CONTACT: Michael Skog, Editor **DESCRIPTION:** Published by Westcoast Publishing. Circulation 5,000. Commercial fishing publication for BC and the rest of Canada. Highlights people in the industry. "Our readers are commercial fishermen, coverage is aimed directly at this group." Articles include: commercial fishing; features; environmental concerns; processing techniques; etc. Published monthly.
WRITERS: Mostly handled by regular freelancers. Contact with query letter.
PHOTOGRAPHERS: Mostly handled in-house. Contact with query letter.
NOTES: Also publishes Westcoast Mariner, Westcoast Logger, Partners With Poland, Good Morning News, Travel and Adventure Guide, Commercial Marine Directory.

WESTCOAST LOGGER

1496 West 72 Avenue
Vancouver, BC V6P 3C8

PHONE: (604) 266-8611
FAX: (604) 263-8620

CONTACT: Robert Allington **DESCRIPTION:** Published by Westcoast Publishing Ltd. Circulation 10,000. Aimed at BC's loggging community. Published monthly.
WRITERS: Majority done by in-house writers. Contact with query letter.
PHOTOGRAPHERS: Majority done by in-house photographers. Contact with query letter.

WESTCOAST REFLECTIONS

2604 Quadra Street
Victoria, BC V8T 4E4

PHONE: (604) 383-1149
FAX: (604) 388-4479

CONTACT: Jane Kezar, Associate Editor Jim Bisakowski,Publisher-Editor
DESCRIPTION: Published by Rand Communications. Circulation 15,000. Lifetime magazine for those "39-and-holding" who live on Vancouver Island. Articles feature news items, humour, decorating, health, finance, and personality profiles. Published monthly. Established in 1990.
WRITERS: Majority assigned to regular freelancers. Contact with query letter. Pays 10¢ per word. Articles should be 750-1,200 words. Accepts unsolicited manuscripts. "Most of our writers are already published and are very well-known. We accept most articles that apply to our active lifestyle; for example, if someone is an expert gardener and writes us a great article on how to grow roses, we'll look at it. We do not do articles on the downside of getting older - arthritis or other ailments. We would not print finance articles, for example on RRSP's. Many of our readers have an interest in computers."
PHOTOGRAPHERS: All photography is done in-house.

NOTES: Returns unsolicited materials with SASE. Purchases first North American rights. Send 9x12" SASE for a sample copy.

WESTERN AUTOBODY
1077 St. James Street, Box 6900
Winnipeg, MB R3C 3B1

NOTES: NO LONGER PUBLISHED

WESTERN AUTOMOTIVE REPAIR
59 Deering Close   **PHONE:** (204) 654-3573
Winnipeg, MB R2K 4K6   **FAX:** (204) 667-8922

CONTACT: Dan Proudly, Editor   **DESCRIPTION:** Published by New Horizons West Ltd. Circulation 11,000. Technical trade publication featuring articles on automotive repair and environmental issues. Published 6 times a year. Established in 1992.
NOTES: All writing and photography is done in-house.

WESTERN CANADA HIGHWAY NEWS
2020 Portage Avenue, Suite 3C   **PHONE:** (204) 885-7798
Winnipeg, MB R3J 0K4   **FAX:** (204) 889-3576

CONTACT: Terry Ross, Editor   **DESCRIPTION:** Published by Craig Kelman & Assoc. Ltd. Publishes articles specific to the trucking industry such as government initiatives, safety, equipment articles (trucks, tires, parts). Includes profiles, viewpoints on different issues with a western focus. Published quarterly. Established in 1971.
WRITERS: Occasionally uses freelance writers, especially from Western Provinces - 25 articles a year. Paid by word, varies with the job. Byline is given. Send a fax or resumé and follow-up with a call. Will always use work they agree to use - no kill fee necessary.
PHOTOGRAPHERS: Use stock photos approximately 2 times a year. Submit colour portfolio in any format. Will send back with SASE if not used.
NOTES: Unsolicited materials will be returned with SASE. Simultaneous submissions accepted. Sample copies available with SASE. Also publishes Professional Photographers of Canada, Urban Scene, Yardstick and Forest Products Carrier.

WESTERN CANADA OUTDOORS
1132-98 Street Box 430
North Battleford, SK S9A 2Y5

NOTES: NO LONGER PUBLISHED

WESTERN CATHOLIC REPORTER
8421-101 Avenue
Edmonton, AB T6A 0L1

PHONE: (403) 465-8030
FAX: (403) 465-8031

CONTACT: Glen Argan, Managing Editor   **DESCRIPTION:** Published by Great Western Press Ltd. Circulation 38,000. A Catholic newspaper with articles of interest and help to Catholic readers. Published weekly. Established in 1965.
WRITERS: "We have regular columnists. We buy fewer than 10 feature articles a year. It would have to be something that can't be done by our own staff. It is helpful if it relates to Alberta. We are not always able to respond but we try to with SASE material."
PHOTOGRAPHERS: "We purchase almost no photography."
NOTES: For a sample copy send 9x12" SASE.

WESTERN COLLISION REPAIR
59 Deering Close
Winnipeg, MB R2K 4K6

PHONE: (204) 654-3573
FAX: (204) 667-8922

CONTACT: Dan Proudley, Editor   **DESCRIPTION:** Published by New Horizons Ltd. Magazine focuses on collision repair. Circulated at body shops. Published 5 times a year. Established in 1992.
WRITERS: Majority of work done in-house. Contact with query letter. Byline is given. Pay is negotiable.
PHOTOGRAPHERS: All photography is done in-house.
NOTES: "Do not query us unless you have specific experience in the automotive trade or collision repair."

WESTERN COMMERCE AND INDUSTRY
945 King Edward Street
Winnipeg, MB R3H 0P8

PHONE: (204) 775-0387
FAX: (204) 775-7830

CONTACT: Kelly Gray, Editor   **DESCRIPTION:** Published by Mercury Publications Ltd. Circulation 10,600. "General business magazine with industrial/construction emphasis for the western Canadian market." Published 6 times a year. Established in 1949.
WRITERS: 50% freelance written. Byline given. No query letters. Submit resumé with phone call ten days later. One third kill fee if a commissioned article is not used. Buys exclusive rights. Send $5 and 9x12" SASE for a sample copy.
PHOTOGRAPHERS: Submit a portfolio with a follow-up phone call ten days later. Work must be captioned; prefers 120 colour transparencies. Pay is negotiable.
NOTES: "Do not send demanding queries." Also publishes Manitoba Restaurant News and Western Grocer.

WESTERN DAIRY FARMER QUARTERLY
4504-61 Ave.
Leduc, AB T9E 3Z1

PHONE: (403) 986-2271
FAX: (403) 986-6397

CONTACT: Susan Blackman, Editor   **DESCRIPTION:** Published by Bowes Publishers Ltd. Circulation 3,000. Magazine featuring articles on the dairy industry, with a specialty in Alberta. Published quarterly. Established in 1991.
WRITERS: 98% is freelance written. Contact with query letter and resumé. Byline is given. Do not phone please. Purchases all rights. Reprints with permission only.

PHOTOGRAPHERS: All photography is done in-house.
NOTES: Send 9x12" SASE for a sample copy.

WESTERN GROCER
945 King Edward Street   **PHONE:** (204) 775-0387
Winnipeg, MB R3H 0P8   **FAX:** (204) 775-7830

CONTACT: Kelly Gray, Editor   **DESCRIPTION:** Published by Mercury Publications
Ltd. Circulation 10,800. Management magazine focusing on the food industry in western
Canada. Provincial coverage of food processors, brokers, importers, distributors, events,
and new products. "The oldest magazine in Western Canada." Published 6 times a year.
WRITERS: Uses freelancers. Pay is negotiable.
PHOTOGRAPHERS: Uses freelancers. Pay is negotiable.

WESTERN HOG JOURNAL
10319 Princess Elizabeth Avenue   **PHONE:** (403) 474-8288
Edmonton, AB T5G 0Y5   **FAX:** (403) 471-8065

CONTACT: Wayne Arthurson, Editor   **DESCRIPTION:** Published by Alberta Pork
Producers Development Corporation. Circulation 9,000. A trade magazine for the hog
producers for Western Canada. Published quarterly. Established in 1972.
WRITERS: "Our columnists are experts in the industry."
NOTES: "We don't have a budget for freelance material."

WESTERN HOG PRODUCER
Box 2500
Saskatoon, SK S7K 2C4

NOTES: NO LONGER PUBLISHED

WESTERN INVESTOR
Box 10349   **PHONE:** (604) 669-8500
Vancouver, BC V7Y 1G5   **FAX:** (604) 669-2154

CONTACT: Tracy Chysik, Editor-Publisher **DESCRIPTION:** Published by Westward
Publications Ltd. Circulation 23,000. Financial, industrial, commercial and real estate
issues across Canada. Published monthly. Established in 1985.
WRITERS: Contact with query letter. Byline is given. Pay is negotiable. Purchases first
North American serial rights.
PHOTOGRAPHERS: Contact with query letter. Occasionally hires on assignment.

WESTERN LIVING
555 West 12th Avenue #300, SE Tower   **PHONE:** (604) 877-7732
Vancouver, BC V5Z 4L4   **FAX:** (604) 877-4849

CONTACT: Paula Brook, Editor **DESCRIPTION:** Published by Telemedia Publishing.
Circulation 270,000. General-interest and lifestyle magazine with an emphasis on homes

and lifestyle. Features food, cooking, travel, fashion, recreation, arts, home design and architecture. Published monthly. Established in 1971.

WRITERS: "Purchases about 6-8 articles per issue. We look for a broad range of short (50 words) to full-length features (3,000 words)." Pay rates are negotiated. "Stories must be written in an engaging, stimulation, sophisticated manner, to capture the attention of informed readers, both male and female. Wherever possible, we want a regional, western Canadian angle." Editorial areas open to freelancers are: Homes and Gardens; Living West; Western Travel (length 500-1500, pays $250 and up); World Travel (length 1,200-2,000, pays $600 and up) Recreation; The Arts; Features; Stylemakers. Rates begin at 50¢ a word. Do not send unsolicited completed articles. MUST query and if you are new to the editor provide a small sampling of work. Guidelines are available.

PHOTOGRAPHERS: "We take a great number of freelance contributions." Pays $50-400 depending on size and number used. Must be captioned including subjects' names, locations and other relevant details. Uses colour transparencies of any size. Photo guidelines are available.

NOTES: Buys first Canadian serial rights. "We want only the best writing, photography and illustration available.

WESTERN MUNICIPAL PRODUCT NEWS see Municipal Business Canada

WESTERN PEOPLE
Box 2500, 2310 Millar Avenue **PHONE:** (306) 665-3539
Saskatoon, SK S7K 2C4   **FAX:** (306) 653-8750

CONTACT: Michael Gillgannon, Editor **DESCRIPTION:** Published by Western Producer Publications. Circulation 100,000. Contains people features, historical articles and profiles and a little fiction. A weekly supplement to the Western producer.

WRITERS: "We freelance about 4 articles per week. Query by mail or telephone, whatever is quicker. We cover all of western Canada and we often carry stories of foreign agriculture as well. It is a fairly broad scope. We would be interested in hearing from someone in Canada or the western US."

PHOTOGRAPHERS: "We use a lot of freelance photos, averaging 5-6 per issue. We would like everything in colour but depending on the page it may run black & white. We like to have it in colour for flexibility." Contact with a query letter or phone call.

WESTERN PRODUCER
Box 2500, 2310 Millar Avenue **PHONE:** (306) 665-3535
Saskatoon, SK S7K 2C4   **FAX:** (306) 653-8750

CONTACT: Elaine Shein, Editor **DESCRIPTION:** Published by Western Producer Publications. Circulation 100,000. Weekly agricultural newspaper for western Canadian families. Focuses on modern rural life, agricultural news and issues. Articles include lifestyle, livestock, equipment, personality profiles, and fiction. Also history of western Canada and the people who explored, settled and developed the land.

WRITERS: "We freelance from 6-20 articles for the paper." Contact this publication by sending a query letter. Follow-up with a phone call. Returns unsolicited articles with SASE. Pay negotiable. Purchases one-time rights. Byline given.

PHOTOGRAPHERS: "We buy 7-8 photos per issue. Majority assigned to in-house photographers. Contact this publication by sending a query letter of with a phone call."

NOTES: Send $4 and 9x12" SASE for a sample copy.

WESTERN REPORT
17327 - 106A Avenue
Edmonton, AB   T5S 1M7

PHONE: (403) 486-2277
FAX: (403) 489-3280

CONTACT: Paul Bunner, Executive Editor   **DESCRIPTION:** Published by United Western Communications. Circulation 41,000. Weekly news magazine focuses on business, resources, law, education, religion, arts, politics, agriculture, sports, medicine and people. A sister publication of Alberta Report with Saskatchewan and Alberta news. Goes to readers outside of Alberta and BC.
WRITERS: "We don't often assign articles to unknown writers. Most is on assignment. We like writers to do a few articles first. Contact the executive editor with writing samples."
PHOTOGRAPHERS: "We have a network of freelance photographers in different cities. New photographers can contact us so we can look at their work."
NOTES: Sample copy available free upon request. Also publishes BC Report and Alberta Report.

WESTERN RESTAURANT NEWS
945 King Edward Street
Winnipeg, MB   R3H 0P8

PHONE: (204) 775-0387
FAX: (204) 775-7830

CONTACT: Kelly Gray, Editor   **DESCRIPTION:** Published by Mercury Publications. Circulation 12,000. A western Canadian management publication with a food service focus. Published quarterly.
WRITERS: Uses 50% freelance writers. Pays out-of-town per diem, gas and telephone costs. Publishes 20 freelance articles a year. Pays 20¢ per word. Byline is used. No query letters. Send a resumé with a cover letter. Follow-up with phone call 10 days later. Be persistent. Sometimes sends material back with SASE. We offer 1/3 kill fee. Purchases exclusive rights. Guidelines for writers not provided.
PHOTOGRAPHERS: Photo submissions are welcome, submit in portfolio form with a follow-up call. Prefers colour photographs; 120 transparencies are best. Captions are preferred. Pay rates negotiable.
NOTES: Sample copy available to those who want to send $5 and SASE. Also available in libraries. "Do not send demanding query letters."

WESTERN SKIER
1132 - 98 Street, Box 430
North Battleford, SK   S9A 2Y5

PHONE: (306) 445-4401
FAX: (306) 445-1977

CONTACT: Becky McIntosh McDonald   **DESCRIPTION:** Published by Rod McDonald. Circulation 25,000. Consumer publication focuses on skiing in western Canada. Articles feature where and how-to ski information, ski resorts, equipment, and fashions. Also features racing and event information. Published 4 to 5 times a year.
WRITERS: 50% freelance written. Contact with query letter with sample articles. We don't take simultaneous submissions. Kill fee offered for commissioned work. "We don't want, 'My First Day Out' articles. We won't use beginner how-to stories."
PHOTOGRAPHERS: 95% assigned to in-house photographers. Returns unsolicited slides or transparencies with SASE. Contact with query letter.
NOTES: Send 9x12" SASE for a sample copy.

WESTERN SPORTSMAN
Box 737
Regina, SK S4P 3A8

PHONE: (306) 352-2773
FAX: (306) 565-2440

CONTACT: Brian Bowman, Editor   **DESCRIPTION:** Published by Western Sportsman Ltd. Circulation 21,700. Hunting and fishing magazine focusing on the outdoor experience in Alberta, Saskatchewan and Manitoba. Published 6 times a year. Established in 1968.
WRITERS: Majority assigned to in-house writers. Contact with query letter. Returns unsolicited materials with SASE. Purchases one-time rights. Tear sheets given. Pay is negotiable.
PHOTOGRAPHERS: Majority assigned to in-house photographers. Contact with query letter and subject list. Returns unsolicited slides and 8 x 10"colour repros if SASE is provided. Pay is negotiable.

WESTWORLD MAGAZINE
4180 Lougheed Highway #401
Burnaby, BC V5C 6A7

PHONE: (604) 299-7311
FAX: (604) 299-9188

CONTACT: Robin Roberts, Editor   **DESCRIPTION:** Published by Canada Wide Magazines Ltd., Canadian automobile Association. Circulation 500,000. Articles are automobile-related with some travel features and destination information. Published quarterly.
WRITERS: "We purchase 4 articles per issue. Query first before submitting articles and include background information. We are looking for international travel features and automotive related articles such as auto theft. Length of 1,200 words is average. We pay 50¢ a word however we may go to a sliding scale for first-time writers. Writers should study back issues so they are not querying something that we have just run." Writers' guidelines are available.
PHOTOGRAPHERS: "Most often writers submit photos with their stories. If they don't we may purchase from photographers. We use colour slides. Photographers should contact us with a written query and stock list. We pay $75 for the first image used and $35 for each additional photo." Photo guidelines are available. Contact Cathy Mullaly, Art Director.
NOTES: Purchases first North American serial rights. Considers previously published work at a reduced rate. Considers simultaneous submissions. For a sample copy send 9x12" SASE.

WFCD COMMUNICATOR
Suite 107, 1090 Waverly St.
Winnipeg, MB R3T 0P4

PHONE: (204) 989-9300
FAX: (204) 989-9306

CONTACT: Robynne Eva, Editor   **DESCRIPTION:** Published by Canadian Association of Agri-Retailers. Circulation 3,400. Agriculture, fertilizer and chemical trade publication. Published quarterly.
WRITERS: 100% freelance written. Contact with query letter. Pay is negotiable. Returns unsolicited articles with SASE if requested. Send 9x12" SASE for a sample copy.
PHOTOGRAPHERS: Contact with query letter and sample of colour prints. Cover or ad photos are needed. Hires photographers on assignment. Pay is negotiable.

WHAT! A MAGAZINE

108-93 Lombard Avenue
Winnipeg, MB R3B 3B1

PHONE: (204) 942-2214
FAX: (204) 943-8991

CONTACT: Stu Slayen, Editor   **DESCRIPTION:** Published by What! Publications Inc. Circulation 200,000. Magazine distributed in high schools. Articles focus on sports, entertainment, career options, and profiles of unique individuals in unique situations. Published 6 times a year. Established in 1987.
WRITERS: Contact with query letter. Do not "pitch" us. Query guidelines available. Pay is negotiable. Byline is given. "I hate receiving unsolicited stuff. This magazine uses a blend of reader submissions and professional journalism. If people write in for Writers' guidelines I don't send them something about how to write, I send them information on, how to get an idea considered for What! A Magazine; we'll deal with the writing later."
PHOTOGRAPHERS: 95% assigned to in-house photographers. Contact this publication by phone call to Art Director, Brian Kauste. Further appointments may be arranged as necessary.
NOTES: Does not consider simultaneous submissions. Purchases first North American serial rights. Also publishes Kids World.

WHAT'S HAPPENING MAGAZINE

Box 171, 135-137 Main Street
Foxboro, ON K0K 2B0

PHONE: (613) 969-8896
FAX: (613) 969-1836

CONTACT: Jo Anne Lewis, Editor   **DESCRIPTION:** Published by Susan K. Bailey Enterprises Ltd. Circulation 15,000. Publication of events, food, business and people of the Belleville and Quinte areas. Published 4 times a year. Established in 1977.
WRITERS: 20% freelance written. Contact with query letter. Byline is given. Pay is negotiable.
PHOTOGRAPHERS: Majority assigned to in-house photographers. Contact with query letter.
NOTES: "We have a full complement of writers and photographers that we presently draw from." Also publishes Today's Seniors, The Weekender and Coffee News.

WHAT'S NEW IN WELDING

777 Bay Street
Toronto, ON M5W 1A7

PHONE: (416) 596-5713
FAX: (416) 596-5881

DESCRIPTION: Published by Maclean Hunter. Published 6 times a year.

WHAT'S UP NIAGARA

91 Geneva Street
St Catharines, ON L2R 4M9

NOTES: Could not locate. Phone number is not in service (416) 682-2685.

WHERE CALGARY

1 Palliser Square,
125 - 9th Avenue S.E. #250
Calgary, AB   T2G 0P6

PHONE: (403) 299-1888
FAX: (403) 290-0573

CONTACT: Jennifer McLeod, Editor   **DESCRIPTION:** Published by Thomas Tait. Circulation 25,000. Vistors magazine of events, attractions, restaurants, entertainment reviews, and shopping. Personality profiles of prominent Calgarians are also included. **WRITERS:** 10% freelance written. Byline is given. Pay is negotiable. "I prefer not to receive unsolicited manuscripts or articles without first talking to the writer." **PHOTOGRAPHERS:** Majority assigned to in-house photographers. Contact with query letter. "We are looking for good cover shots; new, creative shots of Calgary art or events."

WHERE HALIFAX/DARTMOUTH

5475 Spring Garden Road
Box 14 Suite 302
Halifax, NS   B3J 3T2

PHONE: (902) 420-9943
FAX: (902) 429-9058

CONTACT: Karen Janik, Editor   **DESCRIPTION:** Published by Sheila Pottie. Circulation 25,000. City magazine for visitors and tourists to Halifax and Dartmouth. Articles feature the sights to see, where to eat, and where to stay. Published 10 times a year. **WRITERS:** Contact with query letter with resumé and sample article(s). Returns unsolicited materials with SASE. Byline is given. Pay is negotiable. A 25% kill fee is offered. **PHOTOGRAPHERS:** Purchases stock images. Call for an appointment to show photos if you are local and have relevant photos. If not local, send a query letter with a small sample of your work and SASE. **NOTES:** "Ideally, people would have read our magazine and have a good idea of the kind of writing and photography we are looking for." Send 9x12" SASE for a sample copy.

WHERE OTTAWA-HULL

400 Cumberland Street
Ottawa, ON   K1N 8X3

PHONE: (613) 241-7888
FAX: (613) 241-3112

CONTACT: Marc Choma, Editor   **DESCRIPTION:** Published by Where International. Circulation 32,000. Monthly visitor's guide, with articles on sightseeing, shopping, dining, entertainment and the arts. Note: formerly What's On/Voici Ottawa-Hull. **WRITERS:** 10% freelance written. Contact with query letter. Byline is given. Purchases one-time rights. Pay is negotiable. **PHOTOGRAPHERS:** 90% assigned to in-house photographers. Contact with query letter. Do not send unsolicited colour prints in the mail. **NOTES:** Send 9x12" SASE for a sample copy. Also publishes Prélude Magazine

WHERE TORONTO

6 Church Street, 2nd Floor
Toronto, ON   M5E 1M1

PHONE: (416) 364-333
FAX: (416) 594-3375

CONTACT: Jacquelyn Waller-Vintar, Editor   **DESCRIPTION:** "Toronto's premiere travel and tourist magazine, distributed in over 110 city hotels. Articles include entertainment, shopping and dining." Readers are predominantly visitors to Toronto. Published monthly.

WRITERS: "We occasionally use freelance work. Writers should submit an article and if we are interested we will call. Payment is negotiable."
PHOTOGRAPHERS: "We use both assigned and freelance photos of Toronto, both colour and black & white." Contact the editor by mail with a query letter.

WHERE VANCOUVER

2208 Spruce Street   **PHONE:** (604) 736-5586
Vancouver, BC   V6H 2P3   **FAX:** (604) 736-3465

CONTACT: Louise Whitney, Editor   **DESCRIPTION:** Published by Where International. Circulation 40,000. Monthly visitor's guide to entertainment, attractions, shopping, dining, and art gallery listings.
WRITERS: Majority assigned to in-house writers. Phone before submitting anything, even a query letter.
PHOTOGRAPHERS: Majority assigned to in-house photographers. Phone before submitting anything, even a query letter.
NOTES: "I'm really not interested in people from outside the Vancouver area. If they are from Vancouver, they should call me first."

WHERE VICTORIA

1001 Wharf Street, 3rd Floor   **PHONE:** (604) 388-4324
Victoria, BC   V8W 1T6   **FAX:** (604) 388-6166

CONTACT: Janice Strong   **DESCRIPTION:** Published by Key Pacific Publishers. Circulation 25,000. Monthly visitor's magazine covering current events, shopping, dining and information on the cities sights.
WRITERS: Less than 5% freelance written. Contact with query letter. Pays 15¢ per word for articles 500-1,000 words. Purchases one-time rights.
PHOTOGRAPHERS: Purchases stock images. Pay is negotiable. Returns unsolicited prints or transparencies with SASE. Prefers captioned work. Purchases one-time rights.
NOTES: "We work on the *bug me* system here. The more often you contact me, the more chance we will remember you when we are in dire need." Send 9x12" SASE for a sample copy.

WHERE WINNPEG

128 James Avenue #300   **PHONE:** (204) 943-4439
Winnipeg, MB   R3B 0N8

CONTACT: Alison Kirkland   **DESCRIPTION:** Circulation 24,000. Visitor's guide to entertainment, dining, shopping, sightseeing and nightlife for the Winnipeg area. Published 6 times per year.
WRITERS: "All writing is done in-house."
PHOTOGRAPHERS: "We occasionally purchase colour transparencies. Call or write a query letter to the editor. We only pay for cover photography, not the inside shots. We look for major events, sites or landmarks." Photo guidelines are available.

WINDSPEAKER
15001-112 Avenue
Edmonton, AB T5M 2V6

PHONE: (403) 455-2700
FAX: (403)

CONTACT: Linda Caldwell or John Hayes   **DESCRIPTION:** Circulation 15,000.
National aboriginal biweekly news publication offers objective reporting of the issues and
events that affect Canada's Aboriginal peoples. News, sports, entertainment, features, profiles,
opinions etc.
WRITERS: "We are 80% freelance written. We pay by the column inch. If it is a single
source story we pay $3 per published column inch. If it is a multiple source story we pay
$3.60 per published inch. Contact us by phone. We are constantly looking for aboriginal
opinion writers and reviewers. We look for anything that goes into a newspaper: features,
news stories, entertainment profiles. People can send articles on spec or they can phone
and pitch the idea. We don't want poetry or fiction." Writers' guidelines are available.
PHOTOGRAPHERS: "We purchase photos with articles and on their own. We prefer
colour. We pay $50 for the cover and $15 for inside photos. We look for anything to illustrate
an article; photos of a news event; illustrative photos of elders; feature photos; kids doing
neat things; and pow-wow photos."
NOTES: Sample copy available free upon request. Purchases first North American serial
rights.

WINDSPORT
2255B Queen Street East #3266
Toronto, ON   M4E 1G3

PHONE: (416) 698-0138
FAX: (416) 698-8080

CONTACT: Steve Jarrett, Editor   **DESCRIPTION:** Published by True Wind Corp.
Circulation 25,000. Windsurfing magazine features travel and adventure. Also gives consumer
tips and buyers guide to the latest equipment. Published quarterly.
WRITERS: Contact with query letter. Returns unsolicited articles with SASE. Accepts
text/photo submissions. Pay is negotiable. Byline is given. "If you don't know about the
sport of windsurfing, then please don't write for us."
PHOTOGRAPHERS: Contact with query letter. Returns unsolicited colour prints, slides
or transparencies with SASE. Pay is negotiable.
NOTES: Send $2 & 9x12" SASE for a sample copy.

WINE TIDINGS
5165 Sherbrooke Street West, Suite 414
Montreal, PQ H4A 1T6

PHONE: (514) 481-5892
FAX: (514) 481-9699

CONTACT: Tony Aspler, Editor   **DESCRIPTION:** Published by Kylix Media Inc.
Circulation 16,500. Focus is on wine and wine in relation to food and the wine producing
regions of the world. National readership with a large percentage of well-educated
professionals. Published 8 times a year.
WRITERS: Majority assigned to in-house. Contact with query letter and a story outline.
Pay is negotiable. Byline is given.
PHOTOGRAPHERS: Contact with query letter, sample subject list and prices. Returns
unsolicited captioned colour prints or transparencies with SASE. Purchases stock images.
NOTES: Purchases first North American serial rights. Send 9x12" SASE for a sample
copy.

WINGS MAGAZINE
1224 Aviation Park NE #158
Calgary, AB T2E 7E2

PHONE: (403) 275-9457
FAX: (403) 275-3925

CONTACT: Paul Skinner, Editor   **DESCRIPTION:** Published by Corvus Publishing Group. Circulation 11,700. Features domestic and international coverage of the aviation industry. Articles include company profiles, flight training, and commuter and charter operators. Published 6 times a year.
WRITERS: Contact with query letter. Byline is given. Pay is negotiable.
PHOTOGRAPHERS: Contact with query letter. "We accept sample photographs with captions but we do not return them." Occasionally hires photographers on assignment.
NOTES: "Writers or photographers must have an aviation background." Send $4 and 9x12" SASE for a sample copy.

WINTER CITIES NEWS
Box 580
Yellowknife, NT X1A 2N4

CONTACT: Doug Lagore   **DESCRIPTION:** Published by Winter Cities Association. "This international publication takes a look at the top quarter of the world and is based on the premise that the people in the northern zones have a lot in common. Themes are related to cold climate living, architectural planning, sociology etc." Published quarterly.
WRITERS: "All material is written by volunteers. Unsolicited articles will be considered."
PHOTOGRAPHERS: "All photography is contributed by volunteers."
NOTES: For a sample copy send 9x12" SASE.

THE WOMANIST
41 York Street, 3 Floor
Ottawa, ON K1N 5S7

PHONE: (613) 562-4081
FAX: (613) 562-4033

CONTACT: Joan Riggs, Editor   **DESCRIPTION:** Published by Catalyst Research and Communications. Circulation 20,000. National tabloid featuring national and international news from a diversity of women's perspectives. Updates on GATT talks; The NAFTA Agreement; impact of fisheries problems in Newfoundland; book reviews on current books; and problems of women with disabilities are among some of the articles featured. Published quarterly.
WRITERS: Contact with query letter. Does not pay for articles. Byline is given. "We are not open to any kind of outward hatred. We think critical discussion is important but not attacking other people, it doesn't matter what side you are on."
PHOTOGRAPHERS: Contact with query letter. Phone calls also accepted. Cover costs for photographers on assignment, but no other pay is given.
NOTES: Send 9x12 SASE for a sample copy.

WOMEN AND ENVIRONMENTS
736 Bathurst Street
Toronto, ON M5S 2R4

NOTES: Could not locate. Phone number is not in service (416) 514-2379.

WOMEN'S EDUCATION DES FEMMES

47 Main Street
Toronto, ON M4E 2V6

PHONE: (416) 699-1909
FAX: (416) 699-2145

CONTACT: Christina Starr, Editor   **DESCRIPTION:** Bilingual quarterly for the Canadian Congress for Learning Opportunities for Women. Articles include nonsexist education, women in science, government job strategy and the child care needs of women learners.
WRITERS: Unable to pay. Articles between 1,500 and 2,500 words are welcome. Guidelines are available.

WOMEN'S HEALTH CARE see Canadian Journal of Women's Health Care

WOODWORKING

135 Spy Court
Markham, ON L3R 5H6

PHONE: (905) 477-3222
FAX: (905) 477-4320

CONTACT: Maurice Holtham, Editor   **DESCRIPTION:** Published by Action Communications. Circulation 11,000. A tabloid published 7 times a year. Established in 1987.
NOTES: All writing and photography is done in-house. Also publishes Metalworking Production & Purchasing.

WORLD BUSINESS

5480 Canotek Rd. Suite 14
Gloucester, ON K1J 9H6

PHONE: (613) 747-2732
FAX: (613) 747-2735

CONTACT: Douglas MacArthur, Editor   **DESCRIPTION:** Published by World Business Publications. Circulation 15,000. International business publication. Countries are profiled and industrial sector articles are featured. Published monthly. Established in 1990.
WRITERS: 90% assigned to in-house writers. Byline is given. Pay is negotiable. Returns unsolicited materials with SASE.
PHOTOGRAPHERS: All photography is done in-house.
NOTES: Send 9x12" SASE for a sample copy. "Anyone interested can obtain a 12-month editorial schedule showing the countries we will be featuring and the business sectors we will cover."

WORLD OF WHEELS

1200 Markham Road, Suite 220
Scarborough, ON M1H 3C3

PHONE: (416) 438-7777
FAX: (416) 438-5337

CONTACT: Joe Duarte, Editor   **DESCRIPTION:** Published by World of Wheels Publishing. Focus is on new vehicles.
WRITERS: 10% freelance written. Contact with query letter or fax. Do not send unsolicited manuscripts. Pay is negotiable. Byline is given. No sample copies. Purchases all rights.
PHOTOGRAPHERS: 95% assigned to in-house photographers. Contact with query letter or fax. Occasionally purchases stock images. Send colour prints with SASE.
NOTES: Also publishes Canadian Auto World and La Monde.

XTRA!
491 Church St. Suite 200
Toronto, ON M4Y 2C6

PHONE: (416) 925-6665
FAX: (416) 925-6503

CONTACT: Eleanor Brown, Managing Editor   **DESCRIPTION:** Circulation 37,000. Toronto's lesbian and gay bi-weekly. Published 6 times a year.
WRITERS: Over 50% freelance written. Contact this publication by sending or faxing a query letter. Byline is given. Pays $50-$300 for articles. Reserve all rights and the right to reprint for a smaller fee in sister publications in Vancouver and Ottawa. Permission to reprint in other publications may be granted if discussed with the editors.
PHOTOGRAPHERS: Contact this publication by query letter or phone. Local people could make an appointment to show their portfolio. Those from out-of-town could send a small sample portfolio of captioned, colour prints. Pays $60 per photo. "We own the print, but not the negative."
NOTES: "We prefer not to receive completed articles, a query letter is best by way of introduction." Send 9x12" SASE for a sample copy.

YARDSTICK
3C-2020 Portage Avenue
Winnipeg, MB R3J 0K4

PHONE: (204) 885-7798
FAX: (204) 889-3576

CONTACT: Jim Watson, Managing Editor   **DESCRIPTION:** Published by Craig Kelman & Associates. Circulation 1,500. Trade publication for the building supply industry. Features include retail outlets and suppliers. Published 6 times a year.
WRITERS: Majority assigned to in-house writers. Contact with query letter. Pays 20¢ per word. Byline is given.
PHOTOGRAPHERS: Majority assigned to in-house photographers. Contact with query letter. Do not send prints until requested. Pay is negotiable.
NOTES: Considers simultaneous submissions. Send 9x12" SASE for a sample copy. Also publishes Professional Photographers of Canada, Urban Scene, Western Canada Highway News, and Forest Products Carrier.

YES YOU CAN
534 Richmond Street West
Toronto, ON M5V 1Y4

NOTES: NO LONGER PUBLISHED

YOU/VERVE MAGAZINE
37 Hanna Avenue #1
Toronto, ON M6K 1X1

PHONE: (416) 537-2604
FAX: (416) 538-1794

CONTACT: Bettie Bradley or Shirley Ohannessian   **DESCRIPTION:** Published by Family Communications Inc. Circulation over 200,000. A women's magazine focusing on beauty, fitness, health and lifestyle. "You is all about looking good and feeling great." Published quarterly.
WRITERS: "We exclusively purchase lifestyle material that Canadian women are interested in. Contact me with a point form query letter. We assign work of 1,000-1,200 words and we pay $250."

PHOTOGRAPHERS: "We buy mostly from stock." Send query and list of stock subjects plus non-returnable samples.

NOTES: Purchases first North American serial rights. Returns unsolicited materials with SASE. Does not accept simultaneous submissions. Send 9x12" SASE for a sample copy. Also publishes Today's Bride, Expecting, Best Wishes and Baby and Child Care Encyclopedia.

ZOOT CAPRI
Box 18,000
Edmonton, AB   T5J 2P4

NOTES: NO LONGER PUBLISHED

PUBLISHERS

Canada's publishers range from one-man operations to giant multi-national concerns. They publish one-of-a-kind award winning illustrated children's books to hundreds of romance novels a month. The best selling, ever present cookbook and the scholarly literary books all have a place in our society, and all find a publisher somewhere.

The challenge is in finding the market for the type of book you are writing, and once having found the market, convincing them that your book is worth publishing.

Approach your markets carefully, there is little point in pitching a poetry book to a publisher that focuses on self-help books. You will get only rejection if you pitch a cookbook to a publisher of romance fiction, or an adult sci-fi novel to a publisher of children's books. Before you approach any book publisher with a query letter, an outline of your book and sample chapters, you should do your research. Go to the library, ask the librarian for help and locate several of the publishers titles. Spend weeks, or even months searching through your local book store shelves. If you want to have a financial self-help book published, go and look through all the financial books. See who is publishing them and approach those publishers first.

Publishers want you to do your homework. You must know exactly who your audience is (it never is everybody), and they want you to know why your audience should be interested. They want to know how big the audience is, their age range and interests. For example if you were writing a low-fat cook book just before the rash of low-fat cookbooks, you would have to convince the publisher there was an interest in the topic. Now that we know people love low-fat cookbooks, you have to convince the publisher that there still is a market (i.e. it's not saturated), **and** you have to be able to differentiate your book from the dozens already on book store shelves. All of this is your job, and you haven't even begun to write yet!

For the photographer, book publishers can be a good market. Not only do some publishers publish books filled with photos, but they also buy stock photography to illustrate text books, reference books etc. If you have a good stock selection, make a detailed list and send it out with a query letter and some non-returnable samples so that you get on file. If you want assignments, make that known in your query letter and be patient. Books can take years to produce. Don't expect an answer tomorrow, and above all don't give up. There are hundreds of stories from writers who have achieved great success after dozens and even hundreds of rejections. If you think your work has merit and if you have done your homework you too may eventually be on the New York Times best seller list.

AARDVARK ENTERPRISES
204 Millbank Drive SW
Calgary, AB T2Y 2H9

PHONE: (403) 256-4639

CONTACT: J. Alvin Speers, Editor-Publisher **DESCRIPTION:** Publishes on contract and consults with do-it-yourselfers. We advertise books in our catalogue and pay a royalty on that basis. Recent publications include: *Making Poetry Pay: I Did, Maybe You Can Too, How to Do-it-Yourself Publish for Low Cost* and *Death of a Magazine: Reality for Writers* by J.A. Speers, *Down Lundy's Memory Lane* and *More of Down Lundy's Memory Lane* by W. Ray Lundy.
WRITERS: Send a query letter with sample chapter or outline. Average response time 1-2 weeks with SASE. Publishes in 3-6 months. 50% of books published are by first-time authors. Works with unagented writers. Considers simultaneous submissions.
PHOTOGRAPHERS: All photography is done in-house.

AD ASTRA BOOKS
Box 53081
Dorval Station, PQ H9S 5W4

PHONE: (514) 636-6080

CONTACT: Don McVicars, Publisher
NOTES: "I only publish my own books. I will not read outside manuscripts at this time."

ADDISON-WESLEY PUBLISHERS LTD.
26 Prince Andrew Place
P.O. Box 580
Don Mills, ON M3C 2T8

PHONE: (416) 447-5101
FAX: (416) 443-0948

DESCRIPTION: "We are mainly an educational publisher; math, science, chemistry from K to University Level. We have just co-published a math series called *Quest 2000.*"
WRITERS: "We don't look at manuscripts unless they are on math or science. We don't publish fiction. If someone is experienced in our subject areas send in a resumé or part of their manuscript. For K-12 contact the School Department; if it's college level send it attention College Department. Freelancers are sometimes hired on contract."
PHOTOGRAPHERS: "Freelance photographers can send in their brochures with fees to the attention of the editorial department. We use a variety of colour photos to illustrate math and science concepts."

ALCOHOLISM AND DRUG ADDITION RESEARCH FOUNDATION
33 Russel Street
Toronto, ON M5S 2S1

PHONE: (416) 595-6067
FAX: (416) 593-4694

CONTACT: Denise Rochwerg, Publications Manager **DESCRIPTION:** Publishes scientific and lay works in the general field of addictions. Publishes approximately 14 books per year.
NOTES: All writing and photography is done in-house.

ALIVE BOOKS
7436 Fraser Park Drive   **PHONE:** (604) 435-1919
Burnaby, BC V5J 5B9

CONTACT: Siegfried Gursche, Publisher   **DESCRIPTION:** Publishes books on wholistic
health and natural healing. Publishes 5-6 titles per year. Recent publications include: *Fats
That Heal, Fats That Kill* by Udo Erasmus and *Allergies, Disease in Disguise* by Dr. Carolee
Bateson-Koch.
WRITERS: 50% of books published are by first-time authors. Send a query letter with
outline and one or two sample chapters. Average response time 4-8 weeks. Publishes in
6-12 months. Average royalty 10% on retail sales. Advance negotiable.
PHOTOGRAPHERS: Photos used for book covers and dust jackets. Contact this publication
by sending a query letter and sample portfolio to the attention of Siegfried Gursche.

ALLMAPS CANADA LTD.
390 Steelcase Rd. E.   **PHONE:** (905) 477-8480
Markham, ON L3R 1G2   **FAX:** (905) 477-7408

DESCRIPTION: "We publish maps, atlases and streetfinders for Canada."
WRITERS: All writing is done in-house.
PHOTOGRAPHERS: "We buy colour outdoor landscapes and cityscapes of Canadian
locations. We purchase mostly from stock agencies, but would be interested in a stock
list to be kept on file, if the rates are competitive." Prefers slides. Captions are not necessary.
Credit lines are given. Contact Gary Baker, Chief Cartographer.

ALPEL PUBLISHING
Box 203   **PHONE:** (514) 658-6205
Chambly, PQ J3L 4B3   **FAX:** (514) 658-3514

CONTACT: Elie Albala, Publisher-Editor   **DESCRIPTION:** Alpel publishes English
language books about sewing and mail-order sources. Recent publications include: *Catalogue
of Canadian Catalogues* (4th Ed.), *Easy Sewing for Children, Easy Sewing for Adults,
Easy Hallowe'en Costumes for Children and Computer Acronyms and Abbreviations.*
WRITERS: "We might publish first-time authors if they contact us." Works with unagented
writers. Send a query letter with outline or sample chapters. Royalty to be negotiated.
Advance may be negotiated.
PHOTOGRAPHERS: 100% assigned to in-house photographers.
NOTES: "We are always interested in good manuscripts. We are glad to give new writers
information."

ALTITUDE PUBLISHING LTD.
Box 1410   **PHONE:** (403) 678-6888
Canmore, AB T0L 0M0   **FAX:** (403) 678-6951

CONTACT: Stephen Hutchings, Publisher   **DESCRIPTION:** Publishes photographic
and historical guidebooks about British Columbia, Alberta and the Rockies. Publishes 10
new titles a year. Recent publications include: *Greater Vancouver* by Douglas Layton and
Classic Heights of the Canadian Rockies by Graeme Pole. No US Distribution.

WRITERS: 2% of books published are by first-time authors. Works with unagented writers. Average first-time print run 5,000. Send a query letter with manuscript. Response time 4-6 weeks. Considers simultaneous submissions. Gives advance to writer.
PHOTOGRAPHERS: 50% assigned to in-house photographers. Hires photographers on assignment. Submit portfolio of slides with SASE. Reports in 4 weeks.

AND ALL THAT
Box 52614
Mississauga, ON L5J 4S6

NOTES: Could not locate. Phone number is not in service (416) 823-1598.

THE ANGLICAN BOOK CENTRE
600 Jarvis Street
Toronto, ON M4Y 2J6

PHONE: (416) 924-9192
FAX: (416) 968-7983

CONTACT: Publisher: The Rev. Michael Lloyd **DESCRIPTION:** Publishes manuscripts on religious and social issues. Publishes approximately 12 new titles a year. Recent publications include: *Anglican Essentials* edited by George Edgerton; *For All the Saints: Prayers and Readings for Saint's Days According to the Calendar of the Book of Alternative Services of the Anglican Church of Canada* by Stephen Reynolds and *Twelve Stories You and Your Children Need to Know* by William Hockin. US and British Distribution.
WRITERS: 25% of books published are by first-time authors. Works with unagented writers. Contact this publication by sending a query letter and book synopsis with SASE.
PHOTOGRAPHERS: Majority assigned to in-house photographers and illustrators. Contact this publication by sending a query letter.
NOTES: "I'm not sure whether we should be in your book. We get a *lot* of unsolicited manuscripts off our topic area that we have to send back - it takes hours and hours of our time. We receive about 200 manuscripts per year, of which we return 190. Manuscripts should be limited to 'mainline' subject areas for those from Anglican, Roman Catholic, Presbyterian, United, and Lutheran denominations."

ANNICK PRESS LTD.
15 Patricia Avenue
Willowdale, ON
M2M 1H9

PHONE: (416) 221-4802
FAX: (416) 221-8400

CONTACT: Rick Wilks, Editor
DESCRIPTION: Publishes children's literature, picture books and non-fiction. Established in 1975. Recent titles: *From Far Away* by Robert Munsch and S. Askar, art by Michael Martchenko; *Freedom Child of the Sea* by Ricardo Keens-Douglas, illustrated by Julia Gukova.
WRITERS: All submissions must include SASE.
PHOTOGRAPHERS: "We do not use photographs."

ANSON-CARTWRIGHT EDITIONS
229 College Street
Toronto, ON M5T 1R4

NOTES: NO LONGER PUBLISHING BOOKS

AQUILA COMMUNICATIONS LTD.
2642 Diab Street   **PHONE:** (514) 338-1065
St. Laurent, PQ H4S 1E8   **FAX:** (514) 338-1948

CONTACT: Mike Kelada, Managing Editor   **DESCRIPTION:** Specializes in high-interest,
low-vocabulary readers and activities for students of French as a Second Language from
Grade 3 through college. Short, humorous dialogues of daily life for kids and teens in
comic book format. Recent publications include: *Sasquatch, Bermuda Triangle and Psychic
Detectives*. French or English articles considered. US distribution.
WRITERS: 40% of books published are by first-time authors. Works with unagented writers.
Send a query letter with 100 word outline. Average response time 4 weeks. Publishes in
3-6 months. Flat rate paid; royalty negotiable on "school price" of book. Advance negotiable.
PHOTOGRAPHERS: Comic book illustrators are hired. Send photocopies of work.
NOTES: "We are looking for books of 1,200 words in comic book format. Being an
educational market, we cannot accept violence, sex, racism; everything must be gender-free,
bias-free, and anti-authoritarian."

ARNOLD PUBLISHING
Suite 101, 10301 - 104 Street   **PHONE:** (403) 426-2998
Edmonton, AB T5J 1B9

CONTACT: Lynn Carrier   **DESCRIPTION:** Publishes educational books at the
elementary, junior and senior high levels. Recent titles include: *Ordinary People in Alberta's
Past; A New World Emerges; Canada Revisited; Russia Then and Now*. Publishes
approximately 4 titles annually including resource packages.
WRITERS: "We don't accept manuscripts. The material we publish is determined within
the company so we don't accept query letters."
PHOTOGRAPHERS: "We do buy photographs and they are mostly historical or of historical
events. Some are done in-house and the majority is purchased from stock. We don't accept
queries from photographers."

ARSENAL PULP PRESS LTD.
100-1062 Homer Street   **PHONE:** (604) 687-4233
Vancouver, BC V6B 2W9   **FAX:** (604) 669-8250

CONTACT: Brian Lam, Submissions Editor   **DESCRIPTION:** Publishes regional,
sociology, native studies and some fiction. Publishes 15 books per year. Recent titles: *The
Imaginary Indian, Lovely in her Bones and Stony Creek Woman*.
WRITERS: "We appreciate outlines with sample chapters and an SASE. Usually we respond
in 4-8 weeks. 20% first time authors. Takes up to 1½ years after acceptance to publish.
Royalties are 10% on retail. Advances are negotiated." Considers simultaneous submissions.
Writer's guidelines are available. "We are not interested in genre fiction, children's books
or poetry."
PHOTOGRAPHERS: No photography is purchased.

ART METROPOLE
788 King Street West
Toronto, ON M5V 1N6

PHONE: (416) 703-4400
FAX: (416) 703-4404

CONTACT: Stella Kyriakakis **DESCRIPTION:** "We usually publish two books every two years. They include artist books, exhibition catalogues or monograms."
WRITERS: "We don't accept unsolicited material."
PHOTOGRAPHERS: "We always feature the artist's work."

ARTEMIS ENTERPRISES
578 Ofield Road North
Box 54, RR#2
Dundas, ON L9H 5E2

PHONE: (905) 628-0596
FAX: (905) 628-3765

CONTACT: Ann Turner **DESCRIPTION:** "We publish feminist and theological books, about 4-5 per year." Recent titles: *Gathered by the River; Storm and Sanctuary; Out of the Fire; To a Strange Land.*
WRITERS: "We do accept unsolicited manuscripts. We publish mostly women's works." Takes up to 3 months to reply. Almost 100% of our authors are first time authors. We work with unagented authors." Considers simultaneous submissions. "Because we are a small publisher and because we have a fairly specific market we often advise people to sell their work elsewhere. We see ourselves as a voice for women, if someone has access to the bigger markets we encourage them to go after the larger markets. We don't publish fiction or much poetry." Writer's guidelines are available.
PHOTOGRAPHERS: "We accept a queries from photographers. We use a variety of illustration for the works we do and often use photography for cover art. We normally commission a photographer to do work for us." Send a flyer or stock list. Prefers slides.

BALMUIR BOOKS
128 Manning Ave.
Toronto, ON M6J 2K5

PHONE: (416) 603-4199
FAX: (416) 603-3336

CONTACT: Alec Inglis, President-Publisher **DESCRIPTION:** Publishes *Canadian Battle Series* (13 in a series), co-published with The Canadian War Museum. Reprinted twice per year. No US Distribution.
WRITERS: Does not publish first-time authors.
PHOTOGRAPHERS: Photography is obtained from the National Archives.

BARRON'S EDUCATIONAL SERIES
34 Armstrong Ave
Georgetown, ON L7G 4R9

PHONE: (416) 458-5506
FAX: (416) 877-5575

CONTACT: Brian Cox, General Manager **DESCRIPTION:** Publishes educational and trade books. Publishes 50-80 titles per year. Subject areas include children's books, cookbooks, parenting, business, test preparation kits, audio Second Language programs, pet books, literature and general interest. Recent publications include: *Canadian Law Dictionary, Canadian G.E.D., and 501 French Verbs.* US distribution.
WRITERS: Works with first-time authors. Works with unagented writers. Send a query letter with outline and sample chapter; whole manuscript for children's books. Average response time 3-4 weeks. "We publish both spring and fall."

PHOTOGRAPHERS: Photos used for illustration, book covers, and dust jackets. Contact with a query letter, business card, and sample portfolio to be kept on file.
NOTES: "Even though we are US based, we are definitely looking for more Canadian authors. We have received some very nice material from our unsolicited manuscripts. The areas I am very much interested in for Canada would be business books, reference books, and children's books."

BEACH HOLME PUBLISHERS LIMITED
Antonia Banyard, Managing Editor   **PHONE:** (604) 727-6522
4252 Commerce Circle   **FAX:** (604) 727-6418
Victoria, BC   V8Z 4M2

CONTACT: Dave Godfrey, Publisher   **DESCRIPTION:** Publishes fiction and poetry, young adult novels including westerns, northern titles, non-fiction and biography. Formerly Porcepic Books. Established in 1971.
WRITERS: 20% of books published are by first-time authors. Works with unagented writers. Publishes 10 new titles a year. Average first-time print run 500-3,000. Publishes in 12-18 months. Send a query letter (no faxes) with manuscript. Average response time 4-6 weeks. Average royalty 10% on retail sales. Gives advance to writer.
PHOTOGRAPHERS: Majority assigned to in-house photographers. Contact with a query letter. Photos are used for interior illustration. Sample photos returned with SASE.

BEN-SIMON PUBLICATIONS
Box 318   **PHONE:** (604) 652-6332
Brentwood Bay, BC   V0S 1A0   **FAX:** (604) 652-6332

DESCRIPTION: "At this point we are publishing Judaica - books of Jewish interest. We are publishing 1-2 titles a year." Recent titles: *The Old Brown Suitcase, Now You Are Sara.*
WRITERS: "We do not accept unsolicited material. Do not send manuscripts. Send us a query letter and proposal with an SASE. Takes one month to respond. Royalties are negotiated." Considers simultaneous submissions. Works with unagented writers.
PHOTOGRAPHERS: "We don't purchase photography."

BENBEN PUBLICATIONS
1483 Carmen Drive   **PHONE:** (905) 274-4380
Mississauga, ON   L5G 3Z2   **FAX:** (416) 978-5294 **specify BENBEN
                                        on your cover sheet
CONTACT: Taber James   **DESCRIPTION:** Publishes scholarly academic books. Topics include religion, language, architecture. Specializes in Ancient Egyptian studies in Greco-Roman, Christian and Muslim Egyptian time periods. Children's mystery and historical fiction stories are also of interest, in Egyptian setting only. Publishes 4 titles per year. Recent publications include: *The Journal for the Study of Egyptian Archaeology* and *Poetic Reflections in Yiddish Literature.*
WRITERS: 20% of books published are by first-time authors. "I am President of The Egyptological Organization at the University of Toronto; my policy is to get a high percentage of first-time authors, usually students." Send a query letter with outline and sample chapter or portion of a manuscript. Response time 4-6 weeks, September to May; May to August, 3-4 months. Publishes camera-ready material in 1-3 months. "We are registered as a charitable

organization." Authors are given ten free copies of their book. "If we produce children's books, royalties may be negotiable."
PHOTOGRAPHERS: "We are always interested in museum photographs. You must get clearance from the Egyptian Antiquities Service, for use. There is a fee for this." Contact this publication by phone if you feel you have relevant photos. Also interested in artists who can do 3D display work from line-drawings. Knowledge of Quark Express, Aldous Photoshop, and Autocad would be useful." Contact with a query letter and sample graphic art portfolio.

BETWEEN THE LINES
394 Euclid Avenue, Suite 203
Toronto, ON M6G 2S9

NOTES: Could not locate. Phone number is not in service (416) 925-8260.

BLACK MOSS PRESS
Box 143, Station "A"   **PHONE:** (519) 252-2551
Windsor, ON N9A 6L7   **FAX:** (519) 253-7809

CONTACT: Marty Gervais, President-Publisher   **DESCRIPTION:** Publishes poetry and children's picture books and fiction. Publishes only Canadian authors.(40,000 words max.) Publishes 10 new titles a year. Recent publications include: *Child's Portrait of Shakespeare; A Legend of Jacqueline Row* by Dorothy Farmelo; and *Kid's in the Jail* by Paul Vasey.
WRITERS: Contact this publication by query letter only. Average response time 4-8 weeks. DO NOT SEND UNSOLICITED MANUSCRIPTS. Does not work with first-time authors. Advances negotiable. Average royalty 5-10% on wholesale sales. Average first-time print run 300-5,000.
PHOTOGRAPHERS: 100% assigned to in-house photographers.

BLACK ROSE BOOKS
C.P. 1258, Succ. Place du Parc   **PHONE:** (514) 844-4076
Montreal, PQ H2W 2R3   **FAX:** (514) 849-1956

CONTACT: Dimitrious Roussopoulos, Publisher   **DESCRIPTION:** Publishes non-fiction with left-wing, anarchist focus. Subject areas include: media criticism, political and social ecology, political economy, native studies, women's issues, anarchist history and theory, world politics, biographies of political or intellectual leaders and sociology. Recent publications include: *Manufacturing Consent: Noam Chomsky and the Media* by Noam Chomsky and *Aboriginal Peoples Toward Self-Government* by Marie Léger.
WRITERS: 15% of books published are by first-time authors. Works with unagented writers. Average first-time print run 1,000 books. Write for submission guidelines and catalogue with SASE. If you prefer send: Introduction, Preface, Table of Contents, sample chapter, resumé and $25.00 reading fee. Manuscript must be completed. Average response time 8-10 weeks. Publishes in 10-12 months. Average royalty 10% on sales. No advances.
PHOTOGRAPHERS: 100% assigned to in-house photographers.

BLIZZARD PUBLISHING LTD.

73 Furby Street
Winnipeg, MB R3C 2A2

PHONE: 204 775-2923
FAX: 204 775-2947

CONTACT: Peter Attwood   **DESCRIPTION:** Literary publisher specializing in drama and theatre-related books as well as trade non-fiction and children's books. Recent publications include: *The Trials of Ezra Pound* by Timothy Finlay; *Contemporary Issues in Canadian Drama* edited by Per Brask and *Of Two Minds* co-written by Carol Matas and Perry Nodelman. US Distribution. Imprints: Blizzard Publishing and Bain & Cox.
WRITERS: 50% of books published are by first-time authors. Works with 50% agented; 50% unagented writers. Average first-time print run 800-1500 for Blizzard Publishing (drama and theatre-related). Average first-time print run for Baine & Cox imprint (trade non-fiction) is 2000-10,000. Send a query letter with outline or sample chapters. Submission guidelines and catalogue available with SASE. Response time 6-8 weeks. Average royalty 10% on retail sales.
PHOTOGRAPHERS: Contact with a query letter and sample of colour prints to be kept on file. Photos used for illustration and book covers.

THE BOOK ROOM LTD.

P.O. Box 272
1660-66 Granville Street
Halifax, NS B3J 2N7

PHONE: (902) 423-8271
FAX: (902) 423-0398

CONTACT: Charles P. Burchell   **DESCRIPTION:** Publishes 1-2 books annually in the categories of non-fiction trade, travel and regional guides aimed at the Nova Scotia tourist industry. Also publishes and stocks over 300 different scenes of Nova Scotia postcards. No US distribution.
WRITERS: 10% of books published are by first-time authors. Works with unagented writers. Contact with a query letter with outline of 1-2 pages. Do not send manuscript. Average first-time print run 3,000-5,000 books. Average response time 4-8 weeks. Publishes in 6-12 months. Royalty negotiable. No advances. No catalogue available.
PHOTOGRAPHERS: Majority assigned to in-house photographers. Queries from Nova Scotia photographers only. Photos used for book covers.

BOREALIS/TECUMSEH PRESSES

9 Ashburn Drive
Ottawa, ON K2E 6N4

PHONE: (613) 224-6837, 829-0150
FAX: (613) 728-9866

CONTACT: Glenn Clever   **DESCRIPTION:** Publishes poetry, drama, fiction, non-fiction, young adult fiction, history, most general material with Canadian authorship and interest. Publishes 12 new titles a year. Recent publications include: *Journal of Canadian Poetry* and *Canadian Parliamentary Handbook*. US and overseas distribution.
WRITERS: Contact with query letter, a synopsis, writing sample and SASE. 75% of books published are by first-time authors. Works with unagented writers. Average first-time print run 500-1,000 books. Does not read unsolicited manuscripts. Average response time to queries 4-6 weeks. Publishes in 1-2 years. Average royalty 10% on retail sales. No advances. $3.00 & SASE for catalogue and writers' guidelines.
PHOTOGRAPHERS: 100% assigned to in-house photographers.
NOTES: "Our specialty is university level English Literature."

THE BOSTON MILLS PRESS
132 Main Street   **PHONE:** (519) 833-2407
Erin, ON N0B 1T0   **FAX:** (519) 833-2195

CONTACT: John Denison   **DESCRIPTION:** Publishes coffee table, travel, illustrated history and wildlife books. Winner of the Nissan Book Award for the best outdoor book in Canada and winner of the Heritage Canada Communications Award. Publishes 24 titles per year. Recent publications include: *Storytelling Gardens, Wild Things, Canoescapes, Soldiers of the King.*
WRITERS: 40% of books published are by first-time authors. Works with unagented writers. Send a query letter with outline and sample chapter. "We are a strongly visual publication. We would also like to see photocopies of photographs to go inside the books." Average response time 2-8 weeks. Publishes in 6-12 months. Average royalty 10% on retail sales. Advance negotiable.
PHOTOGRAPHERS: "Generally writers supply their own photographs. Photographers can call for an appointment."

BREAKWATER BOOKS LTD.
100 Water Street, Box 2188   **PHONE:** (709) 722-6680
St. John's, NF A1C 6E6   **FAX:** (709) 753-0708

CONTACT: John Andrews   **DESCRIPTION:** Publishes fiction, non-fiction, art, adventure, tourism and natural sites, poetry, drama, cookbooks, humour, academic, Newfoundland culture and history. Established in 1973. Recent titles: *The Work of Newfoundland Artist Gerald Squires*, editors Walsh and Jamison; *Random Passage* by Bernice Morgan; *january, february, june or july* by Helen Fogwill Porter (Winner of the Young Adult Canadian Book Award). Publishes approximately 15 books annually. Takes 6-8 months to publish from acceptance.
WRITERS: Unsolicited manuscripts are not accepted. Contact with query letter. Takes approximately 6 weeks to respond to query. Works with first time and unagented authors.
PHOTOGRAPHERS: Photography is used for covers, inside illustration and in coffee table editions. Formats used include 35mm transparencies and 5x7 b&w prints. Model releases not necessary. Captions are preferred. Credit line is not given. Contact with query letter. Photography contact: Laura Woodford.
NOTES: Unsolicited materials are returned with SASE. Send large SASE for catalogue of books. Guidelines are not available.

BRETON BOOKS
General Delivery   **PHONE:** (902) 539-3817)
Wreck Cove, NS B0C 1H0   **FAX:** (902) 539-9117

CONTACT: Ronald Caplan   **DESCRIPTION:** "We specialize in Cape Breton themes and promote Cape Breton writers." Publishes fiction and non-fiction. Recent children's publication: *Silent Observer* by Cristy MacKinnon. Publishes 4-5 books per year. "Our average print run is 3,000."
WRITERS: "We accept unsolicited manuscripts. The door is open. We like query letters with the first 20 pages of the manuscript. We respond in 2-3 weeks. Authors must remember that Cape Breton is at the heart of what we do and Cape Breton writers are important to us. I will consider any writer if they write about Cape Breton." 20% of writers are first time authors. Works with unagented writers. Pays 10% royalty on retail sales. Advances

negotiated. Published within a year of acceptance. Considers simultaneous submissions. Writers' guidelines are not available.

BRICK BOOKS

431 Boler Road Box 20081　　　　　　**PHONE:** (519) 657-8579
London, ON　N6K 4G6

CONTACT: Kitty Lewis　**DESCRIPTION:** Publishes Canadian poetry, approximately 6 books per year. Recent titles: *Hologram* by P.K. Page; *Riffs* by Dennis Lee. Certain titles distributed in the US.
WRITERS: "We do accept unsolicited material. Send samples or the entire manuscript. Author guidelines are available with a SASE. We prefer not to receive simultaneous submissions although we do get them. It takes us up to 6 months to reply. 30% of our authors are first time authors. We give 10% of the print run which averages 500. Publishes up to 2 years after acceptance. Writers should have a publishing history with literary magazines before they approach us. It really increases credibility."
PHOTOGRAPHERS: All photography is done in-house.

BROADVIEW PRESS LTD.

Box 1243　　　　　　　　　　　**PHONE:** (705) 743-8990
Peterborough, ON　K9J 7H5　　　**FAX:** (705) 743-8353

CONTACT: Michael Harrison, Editor　**DESCRIPTION:** Publishes university and college texts in the arts and social sciences. Subjects include Canadian politics, history, philosophy, women's studies, English literature, ethics, and medieval studies. Distributed world wide. Produces 25 books per year. Prints approximately 2,500 copies per print run. Recent titles: *Criminal Idiots, Women and Minors*; a new version of *The Scarlet Letter* from the Broadview Literary Text series (12 book series) and *Broadview Anthology of Poetry*.
WRITERS: "Some books have a variety of authors and others are by a single author. 40% first time authors. Royalties depend on the type of book. Edited collections range 6-7%. Book written by one author averages 10% of net." Contact with samples of writing, covering letter and Table of Contents. Unsolicited manuscripts or queries will not necessarily be responded to. Considers simultaneous submissions. Writers' guidelines are not available. "We sell to college and university programs. We look at books that have what we call a cross over market; they should have some sort of an academic market. If it has good potential we may go into trade as well but the main focus is academic."
PHOTOGRAPHERS: "We use photos for covers."

BRUNSWICK PRESS

12 Prospect Street West, Box 3370　　**PHONE:** (506) 452-6671
Fredericton, NB　E3B 5A2　　　　　**FAX:** (506) 452-7405

CONTACT: Tom Crowther　**DESCRIPTION:** Publishes works of interest to the Atlantic Provinces.
NOTES: "We are currently not publishing any books. That may change in the future, however, for the present we will not entertain any submissions from authors."

C.D. HOWE INSTITUTE
125 Adelaide Street East
Toronto, ON M5C 1L7

PHONE: (416) 865-1904
FAX: (416) 865-1866

CONTACT: Barry Norris, Director of Publications **DESCRIPTION:** Publishes books on a wide area of economics, business, trade and social policy. Publishes approximately 15 new titles a year. US distribution.
WRITERS: 2% of books published are by first-time authors. Works with unagented writers. Average first-time print run 3,000. Contact with a query letter and outline. Average response time 2-4 weeks. No royalties. Advance after first draft.
PHOTOGRAPHERS: 95% assigned to in-house photographers and artists. Occasional cover shots necessary, as well as photos for annual reports. Contact with a query letter.

CAITLIN PRESS
Box 2387, Station B
Prince George, BC V2N 2S6

PHONE: (604) 964-4953
FAX: (604) 964-4953

CONTACT: Cynthia Wilson **DESCRIPTION:** "We publish books on interior and northern BC. Fiction, non-fiction and poetry. We publish 7 books per year." Titles: *The Traveller's Guide to Northern BC; The Unfriendly Neighbours* by Chilco Choate.
WRITERS: "The best way to contact us is to send a letter of inquiry with a sample of writing and a SASE. A large percentage of our authors are first time authors. We pay 15% on net. I encourage simultaneous submissions. It takes 3-4 months to respond to manuscripts and for inquiries up to a month." Writers' guidelines are available.
PHOTOGRAPHERS: "We do purchase some black & white and colour photography. Photographers can send a letter with resumé and non-returnable samples. We have developed a list of photographers. If they send us information we will add them to our list."

CAMDEN HOUSE PUBLISHING
7 Queen Victoria Road
Camden East, ON K0K 1J0

PHONE: (613) 378-6661
FAX: (613) 378-6123

CONTACT: Tracy Read **DESCRIPTION:** Publishes approximately 8 books and 7 calendars annually in the areas of gardening, agriculture, astronomy, natural history, cooking and "how-to". Publishes full-colour coffee table books.
WRITERS: Works with first time and unagented authors. Royalty negotiated, paid on retail price. Negotiates advance. Query with outline, sample chapters and intended market. Publishes 12 to 18 months after acceptance.
PHOTOGRAPHERS: Uses hundreds of photos annually for calendars, book covers and inside illustration. Query with outline, sample chapters, intended audience, list of available photographs and non-returnable samples. Or, query with detailed subject list of stock available and non-returnable samples, to be kept on file.

CAN-ED MEDIA LTD.
43 Moccasin Trail
Don Mills, ON M3C 1Y5

NOTES: NO LONGER PUBLISHING

CANADA COMMUNICATION GROUP

PUBLISHING DIVISION
45 Sacre-Coeur Blvd., Room A2404
Ottawa, ON K1A OS9

PHONE: (819) 956-4749
FAX: (819) 956-5539

CONTACT: David Fortin, Editor **DESCRIPTION:** Publishes a variety of subjects for Government of Canada Departments plus a few trade and business handbooks. Recent publications include: *Canadian Farm Buildings Handbook and Forage Crops in the Aspen Parklands of Western Canada.* Publishes 500 books annually. **WRITERS:** Works with unagented writers. Government Departments prepare many of the materials for publication. Send a query letter with outline or sample chapters on a trade or business theme. Average first-time print run 500.
PHOTOGRAPHERS: Photos are used for book covers, text illustration and promotional material. Majority assigned to in-house photographers and illustrators. Contact with a query letter.

CANADA LAW BOOK INC

240 Edward St.
Aurora, ON L4G 3S9

PHONE: (905) 841-6472
FAX: (905) 841-5085

CONTACT: Geralyn Christmas, VP of Editorial **DESCRIPTION:** "We publish 30-35 new titles per year covering most facets of practical law and labor." Recent titles: *Preparation of Domestic Contracts; Canadian Pharmacy Law; Practical Guide to the Ontario rules of Civil Procedure; Guide to Workers Compensation in Ontario.*
WRITERS: "Our books are written by lawyers and recognized professionals in their fields. Contact with a query or a phone call if you have an idea. We recognize who the legal whizzes in the industry are so we are actively soliciting on our end."
PHOTOGRAPHERS: "We rarely use photography."

CANADIAN ARCTIC RESOURCES COMMITTEE

1 Nicholas Street, Suite 412
Ottawa, ON K1P 7B7

NOTES: Could not locate. Phone number is not in service (613) 236-7379.

CANADIAN FORUM

35 Britain Street
Toronto, ON M5A 1R7

PHONE: (416) 362-4762
FAX: (416) 362-3939

DESCRIPTION: Publishes 20 non-fiction books per year. Topics include social sciences, politics, and culture, with a Canadian viewpoint. Recent publications include: *Canada's Courts* by Peter McCormick and *Under Seige: The Federal N.D.P. in the Nineties* by Ian Macleod.
WRITERS: 15% of books published are by first-time authors. Works with unagented writers. Send a query letter with outline or sample chapters with SASE. Average response time 6-8 weeks. Publishes in 9-12 months.

CANADIAN MASTER ATHLETE FEDERATION

38 Thornmount Drive, Unit 21　　　**PHONE:** (416) 282-0999
Scarborough, ON　M1B 5P2　　　**FAX:** (416) 282-0999

CONTACT: Liz Roach, Publisher　**DESCRIPTION:** Publishes sports, health, fitness and New Age books. Publishes 1-2 new titles a year. US Distribution.
WRITERS: 100% of books published are by first-time authors. Send a query letter with outline and 3 chapters. Works with unagented writers. Average response time 4-6 weeks. Publishes in 6-12 months. Royalty negotiable. " No advance to first-time writer unless there is art work involved."
PHOTOGRAPHERS: Photographers and illustrators hired for covers and illustrations. "I help authors find illustrations but basically this is considered to be their responsibility. I will keep a business cards and query letters from photographers or illustrators on file so I can refer them when necessary."

CANADIAN PAPERBACKS PUBLISHING LTD.

17 Gwynne Ave.　　　**PHONE:** (613) 722-1171
Ottawa, ON　K1Y 1X1

CONTACT: Colin S. MacDonald　**DESCRIPTION:** Publishes *A Dictionary of Canadian Artists* in seven volumes.
WRITERS: No submissions accepted at the present time.
NOTES: "I compile *A Dictionary of Canadian Artists* containing biographies of 4,000 Canadian artists, both living and dead. I do not take work from other authors."

CANADIAN SCHOLARS PRESS INC.

180 Bloor Street West, Suite 402　　　**PHONE:** (416) 929-2774
Toronto, ON　M5S 2V6　　　**FAX:** (416) 929-1926

CONTACT: Brad Lambertus, Managing Editor　**DESCRIPTION:** Publishes academic textbooks in every discipline from anthropology to zoology. Publishes in English, French and German. US and overseas distribution.
NOTES: "We sell, primarily, to university bookstores and distribute for American and UK publishers including the International Labour Organization and the National Association of Social Workers, based in Washington, D.C."

CANADIAN STAGE AND ARTS PUBLICATIONS LTD.

104 Glenrose Avenue　　　**PHONE:** (416) 484-4534
Toronto, ON　M4T 1K8　　　**FAX:** (416) 484-6214

CONTACT: George Hencz　**DESCRIPTION:** Publishes an average of four books a year. "We publish a lot of children's books, science, arts and some native arts." Some US distribution. Titles from the children's series: *The Adventures of Mickey Taggy* and *For the Love of Simple Line Work.*
WRITERS: "Writers can send ideas in a query letter or an outline of the book and one chapter. I would like authors to stay within our subject area." Replies to queries within one month. "Last year 1 of our 4 authors was a first time author." Works with unagented writers. Royalties negotiated based on wholesale sales.
PHOTOGRAPHERS: "Photography is supplied by the author."

CANAV BOOKS

51 Balsam Ave
Toronto, ON M4E 3B6

PHONE: (416) 698-7559
FAX: (416) 693-4344

CONTACT: Larry Milberry, Publisher DESCRIPTION: "We publish aviation books, 1-2 titles per year. We have done 20 titles since 1981. Generally speaking they are historical books. Titles include: *Canadair: The First 50 Years; RCAF At War: 1939-1945; Aviation in Canada*, in its fifth printing.
WRITERS: "I buy very little. I research and write most of our titles."
PHOTOGRAPHERS: "I know most of the well-know aviation photographers; they supply me with anything I need."

CAPTUS PRESS

4700 Keele Street
North York, ON M3J 1P3

PHONE: (416) 736-5537
FAX: (416) 736-5793

CONTACT: Randy Hoffman DESCRIPTION: Publishes textbooks, scholarly books and trade titles (3-4). Established in 1986. Recent titles: *Personal Financial Planning* by Kwok Ho & Chris Robinson; *Canadian Profile: People, Institution, Infrastructure* (2nd Ed.) by Jerry Dermer; *Getting Back: A Trailwise Guide to Snowmobile Survival* by John Milne; *Journal of Accounting Case Research* by E. Gardner. Imprints: Captus University Publication and Captus Press. Publishes 20-25 books per year. Distributes in the US. Publishes 3 months to one year after acceptance.
WRITERS: Accepts unsolicited manuscripts and replies in 3-12 months. contact with a query letter and book outline with sample chapters. Replies on average 2-4 weeks on queries. Works with first time authors. Royalties are 10-15 % of net sale proceeds. Returns unsolicited materials with a SASE. Writers' guidelines are available.
PHOTOGRAPHERS: Purchases from stock, up to 4 photos annually. Uses photos for book covers and inside illustration. Uses mainly black & white, any format. Model releases and captions are not necessary. Pays up to $100 per photo. Credit line must be negotiated. Contact Pauline Lai with a resumé and business card.
NOTES: For a catalogue send a 9x12 SASE.

CARLETON UNIVERSITY PRESS

160 Paterson Hall, Carleton University
Ottawa, ON K1S 5B6

PHONE: (613) 788-3740
FAX: (613) 788-2893

CONTACT: John Flood, Director & General Editor DESCRIPTION: Publishes scholarly and trade books focusing on Canadian studies. Subjects include women's studies, geography, history, sociology, anthropology and aboriginal people, media studies, political science, law, economics, public administration, literature, art, philosophy, and the classics. US and United Kingdom Distribution.
WRITERS: Must query first. 20% of books published are by first-time authors. Works with agents or unagented writers. "We never accept unsolicited manuscripts." Average response time 6-8 weeks. Publishes in 1-3 years. Average royalty 10% on net receipts. Submission guidelines and catalogue are available, send large SASE.
PHOTOGRAPHERS: All photography is done in-house.

CAVENDISH BOOKS INC

801 West 1st Street, Unit 5
North Vancouver, BC V7P 1A4

PHONE: (604) 985-2969
FAX: (604) 985-2955

CONTACT: Derek Hayes   **DESCRIPTION:** Publishes gardening, craft, sport, hobby and nature books. Publishes 6 books per year. Distributes some books in the US. Average print run 2,000-5,000 copies. Takes approximately 4 months to publish after acceptance. Returns unsolicited materials with a SASE. Considers simultaneous submissions. Imprint: Tavendish. Established in 1983. Recent titles: *Cavendish Encyclopedia of Bonsai; Propogator's Handbook; Garlands and Wreaths.*
WRITERS: Accepts unsolicited manuscripts and replies in one month. Query over the phone or by fax. Replies within a few days. Works with first time authors. Works with unagented authors. Royalties depend on the situation. "We are particularly interested in practical gardening books for Canada."
PHOTOGRAPHERS: Uses photography on book covers and for inside illustration.

CCH CANADIAN LIMITED

6 Garamond Court
North York, ON M3C 1Z5

PHONE: (416) 441-2992
FAX: (416) 444-9011

CONTACT: Terry Hemingway, Managing Editor   **DESCRIPTION:** "We publish legal and business material. We run an updatable legal, business and tax subscription service with about 70 publications. We do purchase outside writing. Contact us by phone and we can determine at that point whether your expertise matches our needs. We look for business writers, people with legal and tax/accounting backgrounds. None of our writers have agents. We pay on a fee for service basis. It takes a few months to complete updatable materials." Publishes first-time writers.
WRITERS: "We don't purchase photography."
PHOTOGRAPHERS: A catalogue of publications is available free upon request.

CENTAX BOOKS AND DISTRIBUTION

1150 - 8th Avenue
Regina, SK S4R 1C9

PHONE: (306) 359-7580
FAX: (306) 757-2439

CONTACT: Margo Embury, Publishing Director   **DESCRIPTION:** Self-publishing service includes cookbooks, self-help and children's titles. Recent publications include: *Grandma's Touch* and *Grandma Today* by Irene Hrechuk and Verna Zasada.
WRITERS: 60% of books published are by first-time authors. Send a query letter with SASE and outline or sample chapters. Contact by phone if you have a completed manuscript. Average first-time print run 10,000 books. Average response time 2-4 weeks. Publishes in 6-12 months. Writers' guidelines and catalogue are available with SASE.
PHOTOGRAPHERS: Contact with a query letter and portfolio of transparencies with SASE. Photos used for illustration, book covers, and food photographs. Photos credited.
NOTES: "We help authors in the editing, re-writing and marketing of their book. We keep inventory, sell on their behalf, collect from the stores and pay the author the discounted price the store pays us. We commission photographers to do food-styling or other photography needed. We set up radio or television talk shows or demos for advertising. We hire home economists, as necessary. Authors can enter a market they could not get into if they went with a regular publishing house." Fiction books are not encouraged for self-publishing.

CHARLEMAGNE PRESS
1384 Hope Road
North Vancouver, BC V7P 1W7

PHONE: (604) 988-7724
FAX: (604) 984-7718

CONTACT: Luman Coad   **DESCRIPTION:** "We publish books on puppetry and related topics." Previous titles: *Marionette Source Book; Puppet Theatre Production* and *Manipulation* by Miles Lee.
WRITERS: "The number of books we publish depends on how many manuscripts we get, usually 1-2 per year. We prefer a proposal first by mail or fax. We respond within 2 weeks if you provide a SASE. We do not accept fiction."
PHOTOGRAPHERS: "Most photography is provided with the author's manuscript."

THE CHARLTON PRESS
2010 Yonge Street
Toronto, ON M4S 1Z9

PHONE: (416) 488-4653
FAX: (416) 488-4656

CONTACT: W.K. Cross   **DESCRIPTION:**   "We publish antique price guides, approximately 30 per year."
NOTES: All writing and photography is done in-house.

THE CHESTNUT PRESS
Box 117, Victoria Station
Montreal, PQ H3Z 2V4

PHONE: (514) 489-6733
FAX: (514) 485-3828

CONTACT: Brian Knight, Editor   **DESCRIPTION:** Consultants for self-publishers. Publishes self-help books, psychology, psychotherapy and hypnosis. Publishes 2 new titles a year.
WRITERS: Send a query letter with outline or sample chapters. Average response time 4-6 weeks.
PHOTOGRAPHERS: Contact with a query letter. Photos used for illustration and book covers.

CHILD'S PLAY
120 Watline Ave, Unit 5
Mississauga, ON L4Z 2C1

NOTES: Could not locate. Phone number is not in service (416) 890-1111.

COACH HOUSE PRESS
50 Prince Arthur Ave., #107
Toronto, ON M5R 1B5

PHONE: (416) 921-3910
FAX: (416) 921-4403

CONTACT: Margaret McClintock, Publisher   **DESCRIPTION:** McClelland and Stewart Imprint
WRITERS: Publishes fiction, translations, and non-fiction; film, drama, poetry, and essays. Publishes approximately 10 - 15 titles per year. Will accept manuscripts through agents only.

PHOTOGRAPHERS: "We don't accept unsolicited manuscripts. We have an editorial board that solicits material. If someone does send something in it literally goes into a slush pile that the editors get to occasionally. Please do not send unsolicited material."

COLES PUBLISHING

90 Ronson Drive
Etobicoke, ON M9W 1C1

PHONE: (416) 243-3132
FAX: (416) 243-8964

DESCRIPTION: Publishes a series of school notes on a variety of topics.
NOTES: No longer publishing books or calendars. Contines to publish "Coles Notes" which are handled in-house.

COMPUTOFACTS

209 Sheppard Ave., East
Willowdale, ON M2N 5W2

PHONE: (416) 222-4361

CONTACT: Marvin Wenner, Editor   **DESCRIPTION:** Publishes computer software instruction books.
WRITERS: "We do not accept unsolicited manuscripts. The only time we will look at anything is if it is about software." Contact with query letter and outline.
PHOTOGRAPHERS: Does not use photography.

COPP CLARK LTD.

2775 Matheson Blvd., East
Mississauga, ON L4W 4P7

PHONE: (905) 238-6074
FAX: (905) 238-6075

CONTACT: Jeff Miller, Publisher   **DESCRIPTION:** Publishes educational (elementary, high school, college and university) and professional titles, as well as trade non-fiction for adults. Publishes 20-25 titles per year. Recent publications include: *The Good Fight, Canadians and World War II* by Jack Granatstein and Peter Neary and *The Money Coach* by Riley Moynes. US Distribution.
WRITERS: 20% of books published are by first-time authors. Works with unagented writers. "We do not want unsolicited manuscripts. If someone queries first, then we will look at their submission when it comes in." Send a query letter with outline, sample chapter and SASE. Publishes 12-18 months after acceptance.
PHOTOGRAPHERS: Photos and art work are used for illustration, book covers, dust jackets. Contact with a query letter, a sample portfolio and SASE. Photography contact: Susan Cline.

CORDILLERA PUBLISHING

Box 46, 8615 Granville Street
Vancouver, BC V6P 4Z9

PHONE: (604) 261-1695
FAX: (604) 266-4469

CONTACT: S.C. Heal   **DESCRIPTION:** "We publish specialty books on shipping, maritime history and aviation." Recent titles: The *Corvette Years* and *A Crossfire of Distant Horizons*.
WRITERS: "We publish about 8 books per year. No advances, we are not big enough for that. Our print runs are about 2,000. 10% royalties."

PHOTOGRAPHERS: "We use a lot of photography in our books. Usually the author provides the photos. We mostly use archival photographs. We have our own large photograph library and we also use photos from the World Ship Society and the Vancouver Maritime Museum. We are not a great market for the freelance photographer."

CORMORANT BOOKS INC.
RR#1
Dunvegan, ON K0C 1J0

PHONE: (613) 527-3348
FAX: (613) 527-2262

CONTACT: Barbara Glen, Assistant to the Publisher **DESCRIPTION:** Publishes adult fiction and trade paperbacks. Produces 7-9 per year. Some are distributed through the US. Average print run is 2,000. Recent titles: *Kitchen Music* by Charles Foran; *Guerrilla Beach* by Oakland Ross; *Frog Moon* by Lola Lemire Tostevin. Established in 1985.
WRITERS: "We prefer to receive completed manuscripts and we respond in 3-6 months. We mostly work with first time unagented writers." Considers simultaneous submissions. Writers' guidelines are not available.
PHOTOGRAPHERS: "We don't purchase photography."

COTEAU BOOKS
2206 Dewdney Avenue, Suite 401
Regina, SK S4R 1H3

PHONE: (306) 777-0170
FAX: (306) 522-5152
E-Mail-coteauatunibase.com

CONTACT: Shelley Sopher, Managing Editor **DESCRIPTION:** Publishes poetry, short stories, novels, books on writers and writing, reader's guides, anthologies, children's stories, women's issues, and drama. Publishes 12 new titles a year. Recent publications include: *Singing Sky* by Margaret Creal and *Stagline: Stories by Men* edited by Bonnie Bernard.
WRITERS: Contact with a query letter to Dave Margoshes, Literary Editor. Reads unsolicited manuscripts. Average response time 4-6 weeks. Publishes in 6-18 months. Average royalty 12.5% on retail sales. "Manuscript completion bonus" for finished manuscript.
PHOTOGRAPHERS: Photos are used for illustrations and book covers. Contact with a query letter. Queries kept on file until needed.

CRABTREE PUBLISHING COMPANY LTD.
Box 898
Niagara-On-The-Lake, ON L0S 1J0

PHONE: (905) 682-5221
FAX: (905) 682-7166

CONTACT: Bobbie Kalman, Publisher **DESCRIPTION:** Publishes 25-30 non-fiction trade and library books annually. Recently published titles include: *Old Time Toys: Games from Long Ago* by Bobbie Kalman and *Crabapples* (series of readers).
WRITERS: Send a query letter with outline, how the book differs from others in that subject area, and the target market of the book. "In two years, we have not printed unsolicited manuscripts."
PHOTOGRAPHERS: Photographers and illustrators hired for illustration, book covers, and dust jacket. Send a query letter with samples and SASE.

CRANE EDITIONS
Box 460
Dundurn, SK S0K 1K0

PHONE: (306) 492-2128
FAX: (306) 492-2202

CONTACT: Delores Reimer,   **DESCRIPTION:** "We are a very small company. We have published one book of short fiction and one book of poetry. The poetry is Danish poetry in translation. We are privately funded so we only publish when we can."
WRITERS: "Some people do send queries but I usually write back telling them we are not currently in the market. We hope to one day publish 8-10 books per year."

CREATIVE BOUND INC.
151 Tansley Drive
Carp, ON K0A 1L0

PHONE: (613) 831-3641
FAX: (613) 831-3643

CONTACT: Gail Pike, Managing Editor   **DESCRIPTION:** Publishes adult non-fiction. Publishes 5-6 new titles a year. Recent publications include: *Hurry Up and Wait: An Inside Look at Life as a Canadian Military Wife* by Diane Collier; *Free to Feel Great: Teaching Children to Excel at Living* by Dr. Terry Orlick and *Tales out of School* by Kathleen O'Ryley Scanlon. US Distribution.
WRITERS: 50% of books published are by first-time authors. Send a query letter with outline or sample chapters. Average response time 6-8 weeks. Publishes in 6-9 months. Does not give advance to writer. Average royalty 10% on retail sales. Writers' guidelines not available.
PHOTOGRAPHERS: Photos occasionally used for illustration and book covers. Contact with a query letter.
NOTES: "Please no poetry, children's and no fiction."

CREATIVE PUBLISHERS LTD.
Box 8660
St. John's, NF A1B 3T7

PHONE: (709) 722-8500
FAX: (709) 722-2228

CONTACT: Donald Morgan, Publisher   **DESCRIPTION:** Publishes books by Newfoundland writers. "The Killick Press imprint is literary; and the Tuckamore Books imprint is for children and young adults. We publish 12 books per year; about 3-4 Killick books and 1-2 Tuckamore per year. The rest are Creative Publishers books with local themes." Distributes in the US. Most recent titles: from Killick: *Their Lives and Times, Women of Newfoundland and Labrador: a Collage* (a women's anthology). From Tuckamore: an illustrated children's book called *There's No Polar Bears Here.* From Creative: *Toll of the Sea; Stories from the Forgotten Coast; Volume III of Shipwrecks of Newfoundland and Labrador.*
WRITERS: "We don't want unsolicited manuscripts for our imprints. We have an editorial committee that solicits material. We will accept a query letter. Manuscripts are more likely to be accepted if they are already on disk in WordPerfect 5.1 or something similar." Less than half of our authors are first time authors. Considers simultaneous submissions. Writers' guidelines are available.
PHOTOGRAPHERS: "Photography is supplied by the author."

DAVIS PRESS
6060 Doulton Avenue   **PHONE:** (604) 277-6003
Richmond, BC V7C 4Y4   **FAX:** (604) 272-5627

CONTACT: Sally Davis, Publisher   **DESCRIPTION:** Publishes children's condensed
classics and picture books for the 2 to 6 year-old set. Averages 1-2 titles per year. Average
first-time print run 2,000. Recent publications include: *Origin of Species (Darwin); A Starry
Night (Van Gogh); Symphony #9 (Beethoven); All The World's a Stage (Shakespeare)*.
WRITERS: "We are not reading manuscripts until the fall of 1995." Send a query letter
with the entire children's book manuscript.
PHOTOGRAPHERS: "We are always looking for illustrators." Contact with a query
letter and samples of work, to be kept on file.
NOTES: "We have requests for the same condensed classics for an older age group."

DC BOOKS
1495 rue de l'Eglise, Box 662   **PHONE:** (514) 843-8130
Montreal, PQ H4L 4V9

CONTACT: Steve Luxton   **DESCRIPTION:** "We are primarily a literary press publishing
poetry, fiction, and memoirs in English." Publishes 2-4 books per year. Distributes in
the US. Average print run 800 units." Recent titles: *The Aftermath* by Henry Lilienheim;
The Beekeeper by Keith Henderson; *Brick, Looking Up* by Grant Loewen; *Small Perfect
Things* by Louis Dudek. "We also publish anthologies; therefore 25% of our authors are
first time authors." Works with unagented writers. Average royalties are 10% of retail.
Send a clean manuscript with no spelling or grammatical errors. "Be serious about format
and presentation if you expect to be taken seriously. I am not crazy about political advocacy
or religious advocacy or anything that is intense advocacy."
WRITERS: "We accept completed manuscripts. It takes us about 6 months to reply."
Considers simultaneous submissions "but let us know." Send SASE's.
PHOTOGRAPHERS: All photography is done in-house.

DETSELIG ENTERPRISES LTD.
Suite 210, 1220 Kensington Road N.W.   **PHONE:** (403) 283-0900
Calgary, AB T2N 1P5   **FAX:** (403) 283-6947

CONTACT: Ted Giles, Publisher   **DESCRIPTION:** Publishes 50% university and
college textbooks and 50% general-interest trade non-fiction. Recent publications include:
Fields of Fire by David Finch and Gordon Jaremko; *The Spirit of Teaching Excellence*
by David Jones and *Women's Work* by Nancy Smith and Sylva Leduc. Publishes 23-25
new titles a year. US Distribution.
WRITERS: 25% of books published are by first-time authors. Send a query letter with
sample Table of Contents and one or two chapters, approximate length, and market for
your book. Average response time 4-12 weeks. Publishes in 6-12 months. Royalty is paid
on retail sales. Advances rarely given.
PHOTOGRAPHERS: Illustrations occasionally used for book covers. Illustrators could
send query letter and sample of work to be kept on file.

DIDACTA INC.
1228 rue St. Mathieu
Montreal, PQ H3H 2H7

PHONE: (514) 931-0707
FAX: (514) 931-0708

CONTACT: Jacques Loudaton, Publisher   **DESCRIPTION:** Publishes English as a Second Language texts for French-speaking people in Quebec and New Brunswick as well as nationally. Recent publications include: *The Sam Series* written by Marise Bosquet and Patricia Brock for E.S.L students in Grades 4-8.
WRITERS: Does not work with first-time authors. Submit a query if you have expertise in the area of writing E.S.L. texts or a degree in English literature.
PHOTOGRAPHERS: Photos used for illustration, book covers. Contact with a query letter, resumé, and business card.
NOTES: "We occasionally need writers with expertise in English literature to write children's texts. We contract and pay for a specific job."

DOUBLEDAY CANADA LTD.
105 Bond Street
Toronto, ON M5B 1Y3

PHONE: (416) 340-0777
FAX: (416) 340-1069

CONTACT: Submissions Editor   **DESCRIPTION:** Publishes general trade non-fiction. Includes current affairs, politics, cook books, fiction, children's fiction and illustrated fiction. Recent titles: *My Jerusalem* by Bronwyn Draney; *Prince of Whales* by Johnathan Dimblebee. Publishes 65 books per year.
WRITERS: Publishes 5-10% from first-time authors. Works with unagented writers. Print runs average 5,000. Takes at least 18 months from acceptance to publish. Considers simultaneous submissions. "We don't accept unsolicited manuscripts. I advise people to send an outline and the first two sample chapters for fiction. For non-fiction send an outline, the Table of Contents and the first two chapters. In the case of a children's book, send the manuscript." Royalties and advances are negotiated. Takes 8-12 weeks for a response.
PHOTOGRAPHERS: "We contact stock agencies or use the work of some freelance photographers. We do not accept a lot of submissions from photographers. We generally work with established photographers."
NOTES: Returns unsolicited materials with a SASE.

DOUGLAS & MACINTYRE LTD.
1615 Venables Street
Vancouver, BC V5L 2H1

PHONE: (604) 254-7191
FAX: (604) 254-9099

585 Bloor Street West
Toronto, ON M6G 1K5

PHONE: (416) 537-2501

CONTACT: Acquisitions Editor   **DESCRIPTION:** Publishes over 100 general trade books on history, biography, art, outdoors, recreation, and Native people. The Greystone Imprint is mainly natural history. The Groundwood imprint, children's books, is published from the Toronto office. D & M Kids is also published from Toronto. Recent titles: *Letter from Vienna* by Claudia Cornwall; *The Black Canoe* with text by Robert Bringhurst and photography by Ulli Steltzer; *British Columbia, A Wild and Fragile Beauty* by Graham Osborne; *Day Trips from Vancouver* by Jack Christie. Toronto Office: 585 Bloor Street West, 2nd Floor, Toronto, ON. M6G 1K5. Contact: Lucy Fraser.
WRITERS: "We prefer query letters or 2-3 chapters. We do not like complete manuscripts. It takes 6-8 weeks to respond and longer in our busy season." Submit adult non-fiction

to Vancouver and fiction and childrens to the Toronto office." Works with first time authors and unagented writers. Royalties vary. "We consider simultaneous submissions as long as they are marked as such. We don't want romance, thrillers, poetry or spiritual."
PHOTOGRAPHERS: "We occasionally purchase photos. We do have a photography file that we can access. Photographers can send a resumé which will be kept on file. Contact: Terry Wershler, Managing Editor, in Vancouver.
NOTES: For a catalogue send 9x12" SASE.

DRAGON HILL PUBLISHING
5541-39 Avenue   **PHONE:** (403) 465-5279
Edmonton, AB   T6L 1B7   **FAX:** (403) 466-3999

CONTACT: Gary Whyte, Publisher   **DESCRIPTION:** "We publish children's books, books promoting understanding between cultures as well as books on self-awareness." Publishes 4 books per year. Recent titles: *Bibi and the Bull* by Carol Vaage illustrated by Georgia Graham. *Telling Tales: Story Telling in the Family* by Gail de Vos and Merle Harris.
WRITERS: 75% of authors are first time authors. Royalties vary from 8-10% on retail. Average print run is 4,000-5,000 copies. "I will accept query letters with a sample of the material by mail or fax. I will not accept full manuscripts unless they are children's books. If possible it is better to call first to confirm that a submission fits my publishing direction." Authors' guidelines are available. Considers simultaneous submissions.

DUNDURN PRESS LTD.
2181 Queen Street East   **PHONE:** (416) 698-0454
Suite 301   **FAX:** (416) 698-1102
Toronto, ON   M4E 1E5

CONTACT: Judith Turnbull, Publisher   **DESCRIPTION:** Publishes approximately 25 books annually in the areas of; history, biography, art & literary criticism, and social issues. Recent publications include: *Poison Chalice: Last Campaign of the Progressive Conservative Party* by David McLaughlin and Light for a Cold Land by Peter Larisey. Publishes 20-25 new titles a year.
WRITERS: 25% of books published are by first-time authors. Submit resumé, one chapter and outline of book. Average response time 6-8 weeks. Publishes in 6-12 months. Average first-time print run 2,000-5,000. Royalty negotiable. Small advances negotiable.
PHOTOGRAPHERS: 100% assigned to in-house photographers. Authors also provide some materials.

DURKIN HAYES PUBLISHING LTD.
3375 North Service Road
Burlington, ON   L7N 3G2

NOTES: NO LONGER PUBLISHING BOOKS

EARTHSCAN CANADA

225 Brunswick Ave.
Toronto, ON M5S 2M6

PHONE: (416) 964-9223
FAX: (416) 964-8239

CONTACT: Sandra Channer **DESCRIPTION:** Publishes environmental and economic trade books. Recent titles: *Property Rights in the Defense of Nature*; *Yangtze Yangtze* and *Odious Debts*. Also distributes Earthscan Publications from the UK.
WRITERS: "We only publish for the Probe foundation. Everything is done in-house."

ECW PRESS

2120 Queen Street East
Toronto, ON M4E 1E2

PHONE: (416) 694-3348
FAX: (416) 698-9906

CONTACT: Jack David **DESCRIPTION:** Publishes non-fiction trade books, biographies, reference volumes and literary criticism on Canadian writers and their work. Publishes 30 new titles a year. Recent publications include: *The Biography of David Cronenberg* by Peter Morriss and *Guide to Law Schools in Canada* by Catherine Purcell.
WRITERS: 30% of books published are by first-time authors. Work with 90% unagented writers. Send a query letter with manuscript proposal. Writers' guidelines are available. Average response time 4-6 weeks. Publishes in 6-12 months. Royalty negotiable. Advance negotiable.
PHOTOGRAPHERS: Photos used for illustration, book covers. Contact with a query letter and business card.

EMOND MONTGOMERY PUBLICATIONS LTD.

58 Shaftesbury Ave.
Toronto, ON M4T 1A3

PHONE: (416) 975-3925
FAX: (416) 975-3924

CONTACT: Paul Emond, President & C.E.O **DESCRIPTION:** Publishes predominantly legal titles: approximately 60% for academic markets - law schools and students; the balance is for environmental, education, corporate counsel and professional groups who want access to legal information. Issues 8-10 new titles a year. Recent publications include: *Religion and the Law* and *Gays and Lesbians and the Law*.
WRITERS: 30% of books published are by first-time authors. Works with unagented writers. Send a query letter with a proposal and sample Table of Contents. "We send an Author's Questionnaire with questions such as markets for the books, potentially competing publications and how this book would distinguish itself from the competition." Average response time 24 hours for really interesting material; 4-8 weeks for something less acceptable. Publishes in 4-10 months. Average first-time print run; 2,500 for academic books; 800-2,000 non-academic books. Average royalty 10% on retail sales. Advance negotiable.
PHOTOGRAPHERS: Photos not used.
NOTES: "It's a complete waste of time if you are not writing on a legal topic, or if you do not have expert academic credentials."

ERGO PRODUCTIONS

Box 4460
London, ON N5W 5J2

PHONE: (519) 432-4357

CONTACT: Winston Schell, Publisher **DESCRIPTION:** Publishes fiction, poetry, humour, and non-fiction by writers from the London, Ontario area. Recent publications

include: *Woodstock Way Back When* by Doug Simons and *Airwave Dreamscapes* edited by Tim and Robin McLaughlin. Publishes 2-3 new titles a year.
WRITERS: Contact with a query letter and a synopsis. Writers' guidelines and catalogue are available with SASE.
PHOTOGRAPHERS: All photography is done in-house.

EVERYDAY PUBLICATIONS INC.
421 Nugget Ave., Unit 2   **PHONE:** (416) 291-9411
Scarborough, ON M1S 4L8   **FAX:** (416) 291-9411

CONTACT: Board of Directors   **DESCRIPTION:** Missionary or Bible study books for Emmaus courses. Distributed free in Third World countries.
WRITERS: "We have an abundance of voluntary help for writing and printing the books. We are not welcoming new submissions."
NOTES: "We are a non-profit, registered charity. The books are written in everyday english for those whose second language is english."

EXILE EDITIONS LTD.
69 Sullivan Street
Toronto, ON M5T 1C2

NOTES: Could not locate. Phone number is not in service (416) 977-7937.

FENN PUBLISHING CO. LTD.
1090 Lorimar Drive   **PHONE:** (905) 670-3366
Mississauga, ON L5S 1R8   **FAX:** (905) 670-3422

CONTACT: Sue Chaiton   **DESCRIPTION:** Publishes trade non-fiction, children's books and cookbooks. Does not publish fiction or poetry. Publishes 25 new titles per year. Recent publications include: *Trolley Cars: Street Cars, Trams, and Trolleys of North America - A Photographic History* by Frank Sullivan and Fred Winkowski; *The Encyclopedia of Pasta, The Quick and Easy Series - Quick and Easy Cookies, Quick and Easy Chocolate, Quick and Easy Pasta Sauces and Quick and Easy Soups; Pop-Up series - Babette Cole's Cats.*
WRITERS: 10% of books published are by first-time authors. Works with unagented writers. Send a query letter with outline, sample chapter and SASE. Average response time 6-8 weeks. Publishes in 6-18 months. Average first-time print run 1,000-2,000. Royalties and advances negotiable.
PHOTOGRAPHERS: Photography and illustrations purchased for inside art, calendars, book covers and dust jackets. Contact with a query letter and samples which can be kept on file.

FERNWOOD PUBLISHING CO. LTD.
Box 9409, Station A   **PHONE:** (902) 422-3302
Halifax, NS B3K 5S3   **FAX:** (902) 422-3179
                                           E-mail:
                                           errol sharpeatdart.matthewsmicro.ns.ca.
CONTACT: Errol Sharpe, Publisher **DESCRIPTION:** Publishes social sciences, native issues and supplementary post-secondary education texts. Publishes 10-12 new titles a year.

Recent publications include: *Basics from Fernwood* a series with topics including farm debt, agriculture and native issues. *Thunder in My Soul* by Patricia Montour Angus; *Constructing Danger: The Misrepresentation of Crime in the News*; and *Politics and the Margins* by Jean Brody. US Distribution.

WRITERS: 10% of books published are by first-time authors. Works with unagented writers. Average first-time print run 1,000-2,000. Write for proposal and writing guidelines with SASE. Then send manuscript proposal of 5-6 pages, Table of Contents, a description of the market and the ideological orientation. If we are interested we will follow-up with a request for a sample chapter. Publishes in 6-18 months. Average royalty 10% on wholesale sales. Occasionally negotiates an advance.

PHOTOGRAPHERS: Photos occasionally used for book covers. Contact with a query letter.

FIDDLEHEAD POETRY BOOKS see Goose Lane Editions

FIFTH HOUSE

620 Duchess Street   **PHONE:** (306) 242-4936
Saskatoon, SK S7K 0R1   **FAX:** (306) 242-7667

CONTACT: Charlene Dobmeier, Managing Editor   **DESCRIPTION:** Publishes general trade books on Western Canadiana, history, biography, and books by and about native peoples. Recent publications include: *The Face Pullers* by Brock Silversides; *The Red Sisters* by Thomson Highway; *Silent Words* by Ruby Slipperjacks and *Firing the Heather: The Life and Times of Nellie McClung* by Mary Hallett and Marilyn Davis. Publishes 10-12 new titles a year. US Distribution.

WRITERS: 10% of books published are by first-time authors. Contact with a query letter, synopsis, and Table of Contents. Average response time 6-8 weeks. Publishes within 9-12 months. Royalty 8-10% on retail sales. Advance negotiable.

PHOTOGRAPHERS: Photos used for illustration, book covers, calendars. Contact with a query letter, sample portfolio with transparencies or colour prints and SASE. Photos are credited.

NOTES: "We do not publish fiction, except for a few native titles. We are always looking for new, fresh photographer and illustrator ideas."

FIRST AVENUE PUBLICATIONS

1328 Avenue Road   **PHONE:** (416) 483-1564
Toronto, ON M5N 2G9   **FAX:** (416) 481-4721

CONTACT: Pravin Singodia   **DESCRIPTION:** "Publishes a travel book on Venezuela called *Venezuela: A Portrait in the Carribean.*" Distributed internationally.

NOTES: All writing and photography is done in-house.

FITZHENRY & WHITESIDE LTD.

195 Allstate Parkway   **PHONE:** (905) 477-9700
Markham, ON L3R 4T8   **FAX:** (905) 477-9179

CONTACT: Robert Read   **DESCRIPTION:** Publishes Canadian adult non-fiction and educational children's books. "We are a general publisher with a focus on education and

non-fiction Canadian subjects in the areas of social studies, history, biography and visual arts. We also publish children's books." Up to 20 books per year. Established 1966.
WRITERS: Contact with a query and outline. Considers simultaneous submissions. Publishes up to one year after acceptance. 10% of writers are first time authors. Royalties are 10% of retail for trade and 10% net on school books. Responds to queries in about 8 weeks.
PHOTOGRAPHERS: "We use some photography. Photographers can send a resumé with a subject list."

FORMAC PUBLISHING CO. LTD.
5502 Atlantic Street   **PHONE:** (902) 421-7022
Halifax, NS B3H 1G4   **FAX:** (902) 425-0166

CONTACT: Carolyn MacGregor   **DESCRIPTION:** Publishes regional titles, history, guidebooks, cookbooks, biographies, and some juvenile and children's novellas ("realistic fiction"). Publishes 8 titles per year. Recent publications include: *The Maritime Flavours Cookbook and Guidebook* by Elaine Elliot; *Dark End of Dream Street* by Lesley Choyce and *Les Editions de la Courte Eschelle*, a series of 16 novels translated from French publisher Gourchelle, for Grade 2-3 readers. Imprint: Goodread Biographies.
WRITERS: 20% of books published are by first-time authors. Works with unagented writers. Send a query letter with outline, sample chapter and resumé along with SASE. Average response time 8-12 weeks. Publishes in 6-12 months. Average first-time print run 3,000-5,000. Royalties and advance negotiable.
PHOTOGRAPHERS: Photos and artwork used for illustration and book covers. Contact with a query letter and sample portfolio with SASE.

FORTRESS PUBLICATIONS INC.
221 Barton St. East, Unit B   **PHONE:** (905) 662-3505
Stoney Creek, ON L8E 2K3   **FAX:** (905) 662-3855

CONTACT: Richard Palimaka, Publisher   **DESCRIPTION:** Publishes Canadian military history and transportation history. Issues 1-2 titles per year. Recent publication: *The Brigade* by Terry Copp.
WRITERS: 10% of books published are by first-time authors. Works with unagented writers. Send a query letter with outline and one or two chapters. Average response time 3-5 weeks. Publishes in 6-12 months. Average first-time print run 3,000-5,000. Average royalty 10% on retail sales. Advance negotiable.
PHOTOGRAPHERS: 100% assigned to in-house photographers. Illustrators could send xeroxed samples of work with query letter, to be kept on file.

FOUR EAST PUBLICATIONS
Box 29   **PHONE:** (902) 823-2279
Tantallon, Halifax County, NS B0J 3J0

CONTACT: Richard Rogers   **DESCRIPTION:** Publishes non-fiction on the Atlantic Provinces.
WRITERS: "I am actively publishing but do not wish to receive manuscripts. I am very small and I have plenty coming in."
NOTES: Do not sent unsolicited manuscripts or photography.

THE FREDERICK HARRIS MUSIC CO. LTD.

529 Speers Road
Oakville, ON L6K 2G4

PHONE: (416) 845-3487
FAX: (416) 845-1208

CONTACT: Trish Sauerbrei, Managing Editor **DESCRIPTION:** Publishes music and musical texts for piano, voice, guitar and violin. Levels from beginner to advanced. Official publisher of The Royal Conservatory of Music. Publishes 20-25 titles per year. Recent publications include: *The Young Pianist Repertoire Series*; *Star Light, Star Bright* by A. Louie and *An Album for Piano* by Stephen Gellman.
WRITERS: 25% of books published are by first-time authors. Send a query letter with outline and sample chapter. Average response time 4-8 weeks. Publishes in 6-12 months. Average first-time print run 1,000. Royalties and advance negotiable.
PHOTOGRAPHERS: 100% assigned to in-house photographers.

FRYE & COMPANY

55 Lismer Street
Ottawa, ON K2K 1A5

PHONE: (613) 592-6226
FAX: (613) 592-9315

CONTACT: Ronald P. Frye **DESCRIPTION:** Publishes secondary and university textbooks. Subject areas include history, political science, geography, land use and policy planning. Recent title: *Analytical Methods in Urban and Regional Planning*.
WRITERS: 2% of books published are by first-time authors. Works with unagented writers. Average response time 4-6 weeks. Royalties negotiated.
PHOTOGRAPHERS: Majority assigned to in-house photographers. Accept query letters from Ottawa-based photographers and illustrators to be kept on file.
NOTES: "Generally, we look for university academics with a great deal of knowledge and expertise on the subject areas we specialize in."

G. R. WELCH COMPANY LTD.

960 Gateway
Burlington, ON L7L 5K7

NOTES: Could not locate. Phone number is not in service (416) 681-2760.

GAGE EDUCATIONAL PUBLISHING

164 Commander Boulevard
Scarborough, ON M1S 3C7

PHONE: (416) 293-8141
FAX: (416) 293-9009

CONTACT: Darleen Rotozinski, Managing Editor **DESCRIPTION:** Publishes educational textbooks. Recent publications include: *Ecosystems* (Grades 4-8); *Civilizations* (High School); *Making Mathematics; MacMillan School Atlas; The Modern Age; Immigrants and Settlers* and *Builders of the Nation*. No US Distribution.
WRITERS: 30% of books published are by first-time authors. School teachers or those with experience in writing educational textbooks may send a query letter. Writers' guidelines are available. Average response time 4-6 weeks. Publishes in 9-24 months. Royalties and advances negotiable.
PHOTOGRAPHERS: Contact with a query letter, resumé and business card. Photos used for inside illustration and book covers.

GARAMOND PRESS
77 Mowat Avenue, Suite 403   **PHONE:** (416) 516-2709
Toronto, ON M6K 3E3   **FAX:** (416) 516-0571
       E-mail garamond@web.apc.org

CONTACT: Peter Saunders   **DESCRIPTION:** Publishes university and academic texts. Subjects include women's studies, cultural and labour studies, education, Third World topics, and ethnicity. Current titles: *Globalization and the Decline of Social Reform; Ghosts in the Machine; Reading Organization Theory, A Critical Approach; The Third World Guide; From Our Eyes, Learning from Indigenous Peoples; Hockey Night in Canada.*
WRITERS: "We solicit writers on campus and accept queries from interested writers." Guidelines are available. "Not that many people can write good academic books." Three copies of an outline are needed for work to be considered. Guidelines available. Publishes 6-8 books per year. Books are distributed in both Canada and the United States.
PHOTOGRAPHERS: Uses very little photography.

GENERAL STORE PUBLISHING HOUSE INC.
1 Main Street   **PHONE:** (613) 432-7697
Burnstown, ON K0J 1G0   **FAX:** (613) 432-7184

CONTACT: Tim Gordon, Publisher   **DESCRIPTION:** Publishes military, self-help, senior's books, cookbooks, sports and regional history. Publishes 30-35 titles per year. Recent publications include: *In the Line of Duty* by Bob Knuckle; *Missing the Kisses of Eloquence* by Michael Dennis.
WRITERS: 50% of books published are by first-time authors. Send complete manuscript, double-spaced cover letter explaining who you are, a quick outline and where you think the market is. NO SASE, NO RESPONSE. Average response time 3-4 weeks. Average first-time print run 1,200-1,500. Royalty negotiable. Rarely gives an advance.
PHOTOGRAPHERS: Majority assigned to in-house photographers. Photos used for illustration, book covers, dust jackets. Contact with a query letter and samples. Will be kept on file.

GILPIN PUBLISHING & DISTRIBUTION LTD.
Box 597   **PHONE:** (705) 424-6507
Alliston, ON L9R 1V7   **FAX:** (705) 424-6507

CONTACT: Wayne Gilpin, Publisher   **DESCRIPTION:** Publishes music books for young children. Publishes 1-2 new titles a year. Recent publications include: *Piano Plus* series (4 vols.); *Colour it Music* (2 vols.) and *The Secret Garden* (full score and script for school use).
WRITERS: "We read unsolicited manuscripts and suggest a publisher where merited."
NOTES: "We rarely publish unsolicited manuscripts. We publish our own books of printed music".

GINN PUBLISHING CANADA INC.
3771 Victoria Park Ave.
Scarborough, ON M1W 2P9

PHONE: (416) 497-4600
FAX: (416) 497-5927

CONTACT: Ferial Suleman or Kathy Doyle, Editors   **DESCRIPTION:** Publishes educational texts. Subject areas are Language Arts, Math and Social Studies for Kindergarten to Grade 9.
WRITERS: 10% of books published are by first-time authors. Send a query letter with outline or sample chapters and Table of Contents. Average response time 6-8 weeks. Publishes in 9-12 months. Royalty negotiated. Advances sometimes negotiated.
PHOTOGRAPHERS: Photographs used for covers and text illustration. Credit line given.

GLOBAL PRESS
164 Commander Blvd.
Agincourt, Ontario M1S 3C7

PHONE: (416) 293-8141
FAX: (416) 293-9009

CONTACT: Susan Girvan, Publishing Director   **DESCRIPTION:** A division of Canada Publishing Corporation. Produces *Who's Who in Canada* and the *Canadian Global Almanac* and reference books and biographies.
WRITERS: "Unsolicited manuscripts are rerouted to MacMillan Publishing."
NOTES: Global Press is a division of Canada Publishing Corporation which is now owned by MacMillan Canada.

GOOSE LANE EDITIONS
469 King Street
Fredericton, NB E3B 1E5

PHONE: (506) 450-4251
FAX: (506) 459-4991

CONTACT: Laurel Boone, Acquisitions Editor   **DESCRIPTION:** Publishes Canadian adult literary fiction, poetry, folklore and non-fiction titles including regional history, guidebooks, nature and the environment. Publishes in French and English. Twelve to fourteen new titles a year. Recent publications include: *Regional Guidebook Series*; *Encyclopedic Guide To Fruits and Vegetables* by Pete Luckett and *Tide's Table*. US Distribution.
WRITERS: 40% of books published are by first-time authors. Works with unagented writers. "FOR ALL QUERIES PLEASE FIRST WRITE FOR GUIDELINES WITH SASE." For non-fiction send a query letter only with SASE. For other titles send a query letter with outline or sample chapters with SASE. First-time print run 500-3,000. Average response time 4-8 weeks. Publishes 10 months after receipt of final manuscript. Average royalty 10% on retail sales. Advance can be negotiated.
PHOTOGRAPHERS: Photos used for illustration and book covers. Contact with a query letter and sample photos with SASE to Julie Scriver, Production Editor.
NOTES: "Do not send us health-related topics, psychology, crime, romances, sci-fi, thrillers or confessional works. We are not reading poetry or short story manuscripts until 1996."

GORMAN AND GORMAN PUBLISHERS LTD.
Box 460
Hanna, AB T0J 1P0

NOTES: Sold to Red Deer College Press.

GREEY dE PENCIER BOOKS

179 John Street #500
Toronto, ON M5T 3G5

PHONE: (416) 971-5275
FAX: (416) 868-6009

CONTACT: Sheba Meland **DESCRIPTION:** Publishes children's books, and general-interest picture books. Emphasis on non-fiction: nature, science, the environment, and children's activities. Imprint Owl books associated with *OWL Magazine*. Uses hundreds of high quality photos. "We publish 8-10 books per year." Recent titles: *A Kids Guide to the Brain* by Jay Ingram & Sylvia Funston; *How Monkeys Make Chocolate* by Adrian Forsyth.

WRITERS: "We prefer to see entire manuscripts. Take a look at the books we publish in your local bookstore or library to get a feeling for the kind of discovery-oriented books we produce for children. Our royalties vary and are based on retail sales. 30% of authors are first time authors. We are interested in books that treat the reader as an equal and we are always looking for fresh and innovative ideas, and a clear and engaging writing style that will be appealing to both children and their families. We publish books for ages 3-12." Responds in 8-12 weeks. May consider simultaneou submissions. Takes 18-36 months to complete a book.

PHOTOGRAPHERS: "All our photography is of a fully professional standard. We sometimes work with authors who are also professional photographers. If people have very high quality photos we would be interested in seeing them. We prefer to deal only with very professional photographers."

GROSVENOR HOUSE PRESS INC.

King West Centre, 2 Pardee Avenue, #203
Toronto, ON M6K 3H5

PHONE: (416) 532-3211
FAX: (416) 532-9277

CONTACT: Ian Burgham **DESCRIPTION:** Publishes medical texts. Written inquiries only. Montreal Office: 1456 Sherbrooke Street West, Suite 301, Montreal, PQ, H3G 1K4, phone: 514 284-1138, fax: 514 284-0415

NOTES: "We do not read unsolicited manuscripts."

GROUNDWOOD BOOKS

585 Bloor Street West, 2nd Floor
Toronto, ON M6G 1K5

PHONE: (416) 537-2501
FAX: (416) 537-4647

CONTACT: Lucy Fraser, Editor **DESCRIPTION:** Publishes children's picture books and novels and a limited amount of non-fiction. Fifteen to twenty new titles a year. Recent publications include: *Out of the Blue* by Sarah Ellis and *Thor* by W.D. Valgardson.

WRITERS: Does not work with first-time authors. Send a query letter with outline and one or two chapters with SASE. Average response time 6-12 weeks.

PHOTOGRAPHERS: Photos used for illustration and book covers. Contact Michael Solomon, Art Editor, with a query letter and samples that can be kept on file.

GUTTER PRESS

100 Richmond Street East, Suite 435
Toronto, ON M5C 2P9

NOTES: Could not locate. Phone number is not in service (416) 777-0400.

HANCOCK HOUSE PUBLISHERS

19313 Zero Avenue
Surrey, BC V4P 1M7

PHONE: (604) 538-1114
FAX: (604) 538-2262

CONTACT: David Hancock, Publisher **DESCRIPTION:** Publishes 20-30 titles annually in the areas of: nature; Indian titles; avaculture and Northern Biographies. Recent publications include: *Wildflowers of the West* by Mabel Chrittendon; *Trout Fishing* by Ed Rychkun; *Salt Water Fly Fishing* by Barry Burnton; *The Gang Ranch: The Real Story* by Judy Alsager.
WRITERS: 30% of books published are by first-time authors. Send a query letter with one or two chapters and Table of Contents and SASE. Average royalty 10% on retail sales.
PHOTOGRAPHERS: Photos used for text illustration and book covers. Contact with query letter, samples of work and SASE.
NOTES: Submission guidelines and a list of titles are available with SASE.

HARBOUR PUBLISHING CO.LTD.

Box 219
Madeira Park, BC V0N 2H0

PHONE: (604) 883-2730
FAX: (604) 883-9451

CONTACT: Howard White, Publisher **DESCRIPTION:** Publishes books on West Coast regional history and culture, both literary and non-fiction, poetry, guides, B.C. authors and women's issues. Publishes 16-18 new titles a year.
WRITERS: Send outline of book, two chapters and SASE. Average response time 4-12 weeks. Publishes in 6-24 months. Average royalty 15% on net sales. Advance negotiable.
PHOTOGRAPHERS: Photos used for illustration, book covers. Contact with a query letter or phone call.
NOTES: Submission guidelines available with SASE.

HARCOURT BRACE & COMPANY CANADA, INC.

55 Horner Ave.
Toronto, ON M8Z 4X6

PHONE: (416) 255-4491
FAX: (416) 255-4046

CONTACT: Heather McWhinney, College Editor
Wendy Cochrane, Elementary Editor
Hans Mills, Secondary Editor
Jean Davies, Director of Publishing **DESCRIPTION:** Educational textbooks for Grades 1-13, psychological tests, medical, college and university titles. Recent publications include: *Bonne route* by Patricia De Méo, James Brown and Edward Gesner and *New Society* by Robert Brym. Imprints: Dryden Press, W.B. Saunders and Holt Rinehart.
WRITERS: Works with unagented writers. Contact with a query letter and resumé. Please note the editor's departments listed above. Average response time 4-6 weeks. Publishes in 6-48 months.
PHOTOGRAPHERS: Contact with a query letter to Jean Davies, Director of Publishing Services. Photos used for text illustrations and book covers.
NOTES: "We solicit authors who have expertise in our specialty areas. Generally we like to do book series."

HARLEQUIN ENTERPRISES LTD.
225 Duncan Mill Road **PHONE:** (416) 445-5860
Don Mills, ON M3B 3K9 **FAX:** (416) 445-8655

CONTACT: Rundle Toye, Submissions Editor **DESCRIPTION:** Publishes paperback novels packed with romance, intrigue and action. Publishes approximately 800-850 new titles a year. EDITORS NOTE: Harlequin Enterprises is a HUGE CANADIAN company with American and UK subsidiaries. The company has many imprints which are each handled out of different offices. Contact the Canadian address for the following imprints: Harlequin Regency, Harlequin Superromance, Harlequin Temptation. Contact the American address for the following imprints: Harlequin American Romance, Harlequin Historicals, Harlequin Intrigue. Contact the UK address for the following imprints: Harlequin Presents, Harlequin Romance. American address: 300 E. 42nd Street, 6th Floor, New York, NY 10017, USA (212) 682-6080. Submissions should include SASE with American postage or International Reply Coupons. UK address: Mills & Boone, Eton House, 18-24 Paradise Road, Richmond, Surrey, TW9 1SR UNITED KINGDOM. (081) 948-0444. Querys should include SASE with International Reply Coupons.
WRITERS: 25% of books published are by first-time authors. Obtain writers' guidelines by sending SASE before submitting any manuscripts. Average response time 3-6 weeks. Publishes in 9-24 months. Royalties negotiable.
PHOTOGRAPHERS: 100% assigned to in-house photographers.

HARPER COLLINS CANADA LTD.
55 Avenue Road, Suite 2900 **PHONE:** (416) 975-9334
West Tower at Hazelton Lanes **FAX:** (416) 975-9884
Toronto, ON M5R 3L2

CONTACT: Virginia Evans, Managing Editor **DESCRIPTION:** Publishes fiction, educational non-fiction and children's books. Publishes approximately 100 titles a year. Recent publications include: *The Piano Man's Daughter* and *Right Honourable Men* by Michael Bliss. Imprint: Pandora Press
WRITERS: Only works with writer's agents. Unsolicited manuscripts are not accepted. "We do not accept unsolicited manuscripts. They are returned unopened. We work through agents. Our editors solicit writers they would like to work with."
PHOTOGRAPHERS: "The use of photographs depends on the mix of books being published. For example we don't use any photos in fiction books." Prefers 35mm transparencies. Can use prints if necessary. "It is useful to send a query with samples we can keep on file."

HARRY CUFF PUBLICATIONS LTD.
94 Le Marchant Road **PHONE:** (709) 726-6590
St. John's, NF A1C 2H2 **FAX:** (709) 726-0902

CONTACT: Robert Cuff **DESCRIPTION:** Publishes approximately 10 textbooks, encyclopedias, dictionaries, and trade books annually. Trade books are about Newfoundland. Recent publications include: *Question of Time* by Jeffrey Cuff and *Out of the Sea* by Kendall & Kendall. US Distribution.
WRITERS: 75% of books published are by first-time authors. Works with unagented writers. Send a query letter with outline or sample chapters and SASE. Average response time 6-10 weeks. Publishes in 6-12 months. Average first-time print run 1,500. Royalties and advances negotiated.

PHOTOGRAPHERS: 50% assigned to in-house photographers, 50% purchased from stock. Buys very limited quantities annually. Contact with query letter and sample portfolio and SASE. Buys one-time rights. Pay negotiated. Uses colour and b&w prints. Photos used for text illustration and book covers.
NOTES: "Check our books out before making queries."

HARTLEY & MARKS LTD.
3661 West Broadway
Vancouver, BC   V6R 2B8

NOTES: Could not locate. Phone number is not in service (604) 738-0644.

HARVEST HOUSE LTD. see University of Ottawa Press

HEIRLOOM PUBLISHING INC.
2233 Argentia Road, Suite 304   **PHONE:** (416) 821-1152
Mississauga, ON   L5N 2X7   **FAX:** (416) 821-1158

CONTACT: Charles J. Humber, Managing Editor
NOTES: All writing and photography is done in-house.

HEMLOCK PRESS
89 Colborne Street East   **PHONE:** (705) 327-2191
Orillia, ON   L3V 1T8   **FAX:** (705) 484-1622

CONTACT: Michael Raggett, Publisher   **DESCRIPTION:** Publishes policy and environmental books. Recent publications include: *The Canadian Environmental Career Resource Manual* by Noel Desautels and *The Village Trap* by Harvey Jones. Publishes 4-8 new titles a year.
WRITERS: 10% of books published are by first-time authors. Works with unagented writers. "We usually solicit writers in a specialty area we want to cover. A query letter with a brief story outline in one of our subject areas would be suitable." Publishes in 2-12 months. Royalties and advances negotiable.
PHOTOGRAPHERS: 100% assigned to in-house photographers and illustrators.

HERITAGE HOUSE PUBLISHING CO. LTD.
Unit #8, 17921 - 55 Ave.   **PHONE:** (604) 574-7067
Surrey, BC   V3S 6C4   **FAX:** (604) 574-9942

CONTACT: Art Downs   **DESCRIPTION:** Specializes in genealogy, history, travel, fishing, and the outdoors in British Columbia. Publishes 6-7 new titles a year. Recent publications include: *Scarlet Tunic* by Robert Tether; *Caribou Chilcotin Pioneer Years* by Irene Stangoe.
WRITERS: 80% of books published are by first-time authors. Phone and approve your manuscript idea with the publisher before you send anything. After approval, send sample of manuscript with SASE. Average response time 1-2 weeks. Average first-time print run 5,000. Royalty and advance negotiable.

PHOTOGRAPHERS: 100% assigned to in-house photographers and illustrators or are provided by the authors.

HIGHWAY BOOK SHOP
R.R.#1, Highway 11   **PHONE:** (705) 679-8375
Cobalt, ON P0J 1C0   **FAX:** (705) 679-8511

CONTACT: Mr. Douglas Pollard, Publisher   **DESCRIPTION:** Publishes adult trade and non-fiction titles on local northern Ontario history and Native history and culture. Majority written by Canadian authors. Recent publications include: *The Age of Steam on Lake Timiskaming* by Bruce Taylor and *Timiskaming Treasure Trails* (8 volume set) by Peter Fancy.
WRITERS: 30% of books published are by first-time authors. Send a query letter with outline or sample chapters. Average response time 4-12 weeks. No advances. Average royalty 10% on retail sales.
PHOTOGRAPHERS: All photos and illustrations provided by the author.

HMS PRESS
Box 340, Station B   **PHONE:** (519) 433-8994
London, ON N6A 4W1

CONTACT: Wayne Ray   **DESCRIPTION:** "We publish books on disk. We have 36 books which are advertised over the Internet." Publishes fiction, romance fiction, autobiographies, biographies, essays and articles. Recent titles include *False Pretences* by Michael MacPherson and *Vanguard Trilogy* by Matthew Soule. Imprint: Books on Disk.
WRITERS: "I take any well-written manuscript submitted on Wordperfect 5.1 or less, no hard copies please. I accept anything as long as it is well-written." Pays 20% royalties. Respond to submissions within a month. "I purchase first time North American computer rights - the author retains the copyright I hold the electronic rights for one year. Writers can still try paper publishing."
PHOTOGRAPHERS: Photos are not used.
NOTES: A catalogue of books is available on disk.

HOLT, RINEHART AND WINSTON OF CANDADA LTD.
55 Horner Ave.   **PHONE:** (416) 255-4491
Toronto, ON M8Z 4X6   **FAX:** (416) 255-4046

DESCRIPTION: Educational textbooks for Grades 1-13, psychological tests, medical, college and university.
WRITERS: Works with unagented writers. Contact with a query letter and resumé. College level materials to Heather McWhinnie; Elementary materials to Wendy Cochrane and Secondary to Hans Mills. Average response time 4-8 weeks. Publishes in 6-48 months, depending on whether it is a single title or series of books.
PHOTOGRAPHERS: Contact with a query letter and samples to Jean Davies, Director of Publishing Services. Photos are used for text illustration and book covers.
NOTES: "We solicit authors who have expertise in our specialty areas. Generally we publish a whole series of books."

HORSDAL & SCHUBART PUBLISHERS

#623-425 Simcoe Street
Victoria, BC V8V 4T3

PHONE: (604) 360-2031
FAX: (604) 360-0829

CONTACT: Marlyn Horsdal **DESCRIPTION:** "We publish about 10 non-fiction books per year, mostly biographies and history." Some distribution in the US. Titles: *Red Serge and Stetsons: 100 Years of Mounties Memories; Winter Shoes in Springtime and The Stars, My Blanket* both by Beryl Smeeton; *Tangled Lines and Patched Waders* by Robert Jones. Photos are used for book covers, dust jackets, text illustration and promotional material.
WRITERS: "We prefer to have a query first describing the material and an approximate length. We appreciate a sample of writing as well. Less than 25% of our authors are first time authors. We develop projects with authors we have worked with in the past. Many of our authors do not have agents. Royalties are based on wholesale sales and depend on the title, subject matter, authors experience and the potential market." Advance is negotiated. Considers simultaneous submissions. Publishes in one year or less if the book is timely. "We are not interested in poetry, avant garde fiction or children's books."
PHOTOGRAPHERS: "We do buy photography. We know a lot of the local photographers and we have used a stock agency. It is difficult for us to deal with people from as far away as Toronto so we prefer to deal with local people. We are always interested in having photographers in our resource file." Send a query letter with stock list.
NOTES: Send SASE for current catalogue.

HOUNSLOW PRESS

2181 Queen Street East, Suite 301
Toronto, ON M4E 1E5

PHONE: (416) 698-0454
FAX: (416) 698-1102

CONTACT: Tony Hawke, Editor-in-Chief **DESCRIPTION:** Publishes coffee-table books, cookbooks, popular non-fiction, business, paranormal, and novels. Publishes 10-12 new titles a year. Owned by the Dundurn Group.
WRITERS: 25% of books published are by first-time authors. Works with unagented authors. Submit resumé, one chapter and outline of book. Average response time 6-8 weeks. Publishes in 6-12 months. Average first-time print run 2,000-5,000. Royalty is negotiable. Small advances are negotiable.
PHOTOGRAPHERS: Publishes coffee-table books and books with a lot of photography and illustration. Authors provide their own photos and illustrations. Query with book outline, sample chapters and photos.
NOTES: Catalogue is available.

HOUSE OF ANANSI PRESS

1800 Steeles Ave. West
Concord, ON L4K 2P3

PHONE: (905) 660-0611
FAX: (905) 660-0676

CONTACT: Michael Davis, Publisher **DESCRIPTION:** Literary titles including some fiction, poetry, drama, short stories, and literary criticism. Does not publish novels or children's books. Publishes 14-16 titles per year. Recent publications include: *Making it Real: The Canonization of English Canadian Literature* by Robert Lecker; *Carrying Slice* by Esta Spalding; and *Dead Men's Watches* by Hugh Hood.
WRITERS: Send a query letter with outline and sample chapter. Average response time 4-8 weeks. Publishes in 6-12 months. Advances negotiable.
PHOTOGRAPHERS: Photos occasionally used for book covers. Contact Martha Sharpe by sending a query letter with sample portfolio and SASE.

HYPERION PRESS LTD.
300 Wales Avenue   **PHONE:** 204 256-9204
Winnipeg, MB R2M 2S9   **FAX:** 204 255-7845

CONTACT: Dr. Mavis Tutiah, Publisher   **DESCRIPTION:** Publishes 10-12 new titles a year. Includes arts, crafts and how-to books for all ages, and children's picture books (under age 12). Recent publications include: *Best Ever Paper Airplanes* by Norman Schmidt and *Somsee and the Magic Elephant* by Jamie Oliviero.
WRITERS: 30% of books published are by first-time authors. Send completed manuscript to publisher. Average first-time print run 10,000. Royalty negotiated. Advances not given.
PHOTOGRAPHERS: Query and resumé accepted from illustrators. Illustrators are hired for children's books.

IMP PRESS
Box 32066   **PHONE:** (519) 653-4813
Cambridge, ON N3H 5M2   **FAX:** (519) 653-4813

CONTACT: Dave Scott, Publisher   **DESCRIPTION:** We publish only non-fiction books, about 5 a year. Titles: *Supporting Myself in Style* by Jill Summerhayes; *Give Up the Ghost* by Victoria Branden.
WRITERS: "We accept queries from writers. An outline is good. Please don't send manuscripts." Publishes approximately one year after acceptance of manuscript. Average print runs are 2,500. Distributes mainly in Canada. 50% first time authors. Works with unagented writers. Royalties based on retail sales. Advances are negotiated and depend on the nature of the book.
PHOTOGRAPHERS: "We use very little photography. We would only be interested if it came directly from the author and it was directly relevant to the book."
NOTES: A catalogue of titles is available with a 9x12 SASE.

INNER CITY BOOKS
Box 1271, Station Q   **PHONE:** (416) 927-0355
Toronto, ON M4T 2P4   **FAX:** (416) 924-1814

CONTACT: Daryl Sharp   **DESCRIPTION:** "We publish only Jungian psychoanalytic books." Publishes 3-5 titles per year. Recent publications include: *Tracking the Gods: The Place of Myth in Modern Life* by James Hollis and *Who Am I Really?* by Daryl Sharp.
WRITERS: "The books must be written by graduate Jungian psychoanalysts." Send a query letter with resumé, outline and one or two chapters.
PHOTOGRAPHERS: Average response time 3-6 weeks. Average first-time print run 3,000. Publishes in 3-12 months. Royalty negotiable. No advance available.
NOTES: All photography is done in-house.

INTERNATIONAL GUIDE
999 8th Street S.W., Suite 222   **PHONE:** (403) 244-7343
Calgary, AB T2R 1J5   **FAX:** (403) 229-2470

CONTACT: Sharon Bell, Managing Editor   **DESCRIPTION:** International Guide is a hotel publication for travellers visiting cities in Western Canada. Articles include attractions, facilities and events. These annual hardcover guides are published for Victoria, Vancouver,

Calgary, and Banff. Photos are used for book covers, text illustration and promotional material.
WRITERS: "We have our own database of writers. If I receive unsolicited material, I keep it on file. If there is a subsequent need in a writer's area of expertise I will contact them."
PHOTOGRAPHERS: "Photographers are welcome to submit a portfolio of 35mm slides, taken in Victoria, Vancouver, Calgary or Banff. Photos are used for book covers and to accompany articles. If we are interested in the photographs we will contact them and negotiate an agreement."
NOTES: "We also publish a digest called Visitor's Choice, one to four times a year, depending on the city. There is also a Japanese Visitor's Choice as well. We are always looking for a fresh perspective on a subject. I will look at queries and previously published articles."

INTERNATIONAL SELF COUNSEL PRESS LTD.
1481 Charlotte Road   **PHONE:** (604) 986-3366
North Vancouver, BC   V7J 1H1   **FAX:** (604) 986-3947

CONTACT: Ruth Wilson, Acquisitions Editor   **DESCRIPTION:** Publishes 16 to 20 new self-help books annually. Subjects include: business, legal, finance, reference, personal self-help, travel and retirement. Recent publications include: *Love Smarts* by Kathy Tait; *Winning Proposals* by Hans Tannenagi; *Crank 'Em Up!!!* by Bruce Fuller; *Separation Kit* for Ontario by Sandra Meyrick and *Fight That Ticket* for British Columbia by Janice Mucalov.
WRITERS: 10-20% of books published are by first-time authors. "We prefer not to receive whole manuscripts. Contact by phone and ask for our submissions guide and a copy of our catalogue." Writers can send an outline, Table of Contents and one chapter with SASE. Writers' guidelines available after contract is signed. Average response time 2-6 weeks. Publishes in 6-12 months. Average first-time print run 5,000-7,000 for first-time authors. Average royalty 10% on retail sales. Advance not available.
PHOTOGRAPHERS: Illustrators are hired for text illustrations. Photographs are used on book covers. Contact with a query letter and samples to be kept on file. Photo contact: Rod Poland, Production Editor.
NOTES: "Our books are now on audio tapes and some are on IBM compatible computer disks."

IPI PUBLISHING
50 Prince Arthur, Suite 708   **PHONE:** (416) 944-1141
Toronto, ON   M5R 1B5   **FAX:** (416) 322-3094

CONTACT: Penny Mallette, Publisher   **DESCRIPTION:** Only publishes legal titles.
WRITERS: Contact with a query letter and synopsis or story outline.
PHOTOGRAPHERS: All photography is done in-house.
NOTES: "Only those with experience in the legal field need apply."

IRWIN PUBLISHING
1800 Steeles Avenue West
Concord, ON L4K 2P3

PHONE: (905) 660-0611
FAX: (905) 660-0676

CONTACT: Norma Pettit   **DESCRIPTION:** Publishes 10 to 15 textbooks, professional books, teacher's resource guides and other educational books annually. Examples of recent titles include: *Irwin Writing Project* (series); *The Art of Teaching Writing* by Lucy McCormick Calkins; and *The Spirit of Math* by Charles Ledger and Fraser Simpson.
WRITERS: 20% of books published are by first-time authors. Works with unagented writers. Send a query letter with outline, a sample chapter and Table of Contents. "We will read whole manuscripts. If there is any particular market for your book, please mention this." Average response time 3-6 weeks. Publishes in 1-2 years. Average first-time print run 3,500-5,000. Royalty 10% on retail sales. Advance negotiable.
PHOTOGRAPHERS: Photos used for text illustration and book covers. Buys 200-300 photos annually. Uses b&w and colour (all formats). Model releases are preferred. Captions are not necessary. Contact with a query letter and samples. Educational illustrations must represent many cultures and ethnic groups; males and females of all ages. Photo contact: Kaari Turk, Production Dept. Director.
NOTES: "Most of our authors have been teachers. It is certainly an advantage to have hands-on experience because we emphasize a practical, hands-on approach."

IS FIVE PRESS
400 Mount Pleasant Road, Suite #4
Toronto, ON M4S 2L6

PHONE: (416) 480-2408
FAX: (416) 480-2546

CONTACT: Tom Scanlan, Publisher   **DESCRIPTION:** Publishes educational books for elementary and secondary schools on social, environmental and education concerns. Issues 1-2 titles per year. Recent publications include: *Development Alternatives* by Brian Nelson, Tom Scanlan; *Treasures in Your Garbage* by Tony Ellis and *I Love My Dad, But...* by Leslie Wright.
WRITERS: Does not work with first-time authors. Send a query letter with outline, a sample chapter and SASE. Average response time 4-6 weeks. Publishes in 10-12 months. Average royalty 10% on retail sales. Rarely gives advances.
PHOTOGRAPHERS: Photos and artwork used for text illustration, book covers, dust jackets. Contact with a query letter and samples; will be kept on file.

ITMB PUBLISHING
736A Granville Street
Vancouver, BC V6Z 1G3

PHONE: (604) 687-3320
FAX: (604) 687-5935

DESCRIPTION: Publishes maps.

J.M. LEBEL ENTERPRISES
10335-61 Ave
Edmonton, AB T6H 1K9

PHONE: (403) 436-8205
FAX: (403) 437-5256

CONTACT: John Lebel   **DESCRIPTION:** Publishes text books in the areas of physics, chemistry and environmental science.
WRITERS: "We accept material from a number of researchers, teachers, scientists and chemists. It is then compiled into a text book. Sources must be legitimate. If you have

something you want to submit make sure to include references that can be checked out, all information must be qualified."
PHOTOGRAPHERS: "Depending on the source contributors will compile various diagrams and photographs and submit them at the same time."
NOTES: Contact with query letter and resumé.

J.P.L. PUBLISHERS
201 Brownlow Avenue, Suite 33
Dartmouth, NS   B3B 1W2

NOTES: Could not locate. Phone number is not in service (902) 468-2682.

JAMES LORIMER & CO. LTD.
35 Britain Street   **PHONE:** (416) 362-4762
Toronto, ON   M5A 1R7   **FAX:** (416) 362-3939

CONTACT: James Lorimer   **DESCRIPTION:** Publishes Canadian trade books including politics, history, economics, social issues; also publishes a limited number of children's books for ages 7-14 years. Publishes 15 titles per year. Recent titles include: *Canada's Courts* by Peter McCormick; *Houses and Homes: Housing for Canadians* by John Sewell; and *Two Minutes for Roughing* by Joseph Romain. US Distribution.
WRITERS: Works with unpublished and unagented writers. Send a query letter with outline and sample chapter plus a resumé and SASE. Average response time 4-8 weeks. Publishes in 6-12 months. Royalties and advances negotiable. Publishes Canadian authors only.
PHOTOGRAPHERS: Photos used for text illustration and book covers. Contact with a query letter, sample portfolio and SASE to James Lorimer or Carolyn MacGregor at 5502 Atlantic St., Halifax, NS, B3H 1G4.
NOTES: Send large SASE for catalogue and writers' guidelines. Parent company Formac Publishing.

JESPERSON PRESS
39 James Lane   **PHONE:** (709) 753-5700
St. John's, NF   A1E 3H3   **FAX:** (709) 753-5507

CONTACT: Editorial Department   **DESCRIPTION:** Publishes educational and trade books; fiction, drama, poetry, novels etc. Publishes about 12 books per year. 50% are first time authors. Average royalties are 10% on retail.
WRITERS: "Completed manuscripts are the best. The time it takes to respond depends on the number of manuscripts we receive. We get about one a day." Considers simultaneous submissions. Publishes within a year of acceptance. Print runs average 1,500. "For educational titles print runs are higher. We run our own press and can reprint anytime. We like to see good manuscripts. As a small company we can't spend a lot of time talking with authors. We prefer a professional approach that gives us time to look at the manuscript."
PHOTOGRAPHERS: "Photography is supplied by the author."

JOHN WHILEY & SONS CANADA LIMITED

22 Worcester Road
Etobicoke, ON M9W 1L1

PHONE: (416) 236-4433
FAX: (416) 236-4448

CONTACT: Carolyn Wells, College Division
Elizabeth Fowler, Trade Division   DESCRIPTION: Publishes college textbooks as well as trade how-to's on business, accounting and finance. 30-50 new titles a year. Recent publications include: *Through the Money Labyrinth* by Shirley Woods and *Have Your Home and Money Too* by P.J. Wade.
WRITERS: 80% of books published are by first-time authors. Send a query letter with outline, Table of Contents and one or two chapters. Average response time 2-4 weeks. Publishes in 6-12 months. Royalties and advances negotiable.
PHOTOGRAPHERS: Photos are used for covers and text illustration. Uses b&w, all formats. Unsolicited material will be returned with SASE. Model releases are preferred. Captions are not necessary. Majority of artwork done in-house. Contact with a query letter to Madhu Ranadive, College Associate Editor.

JUNIPER BOOKS LTD.

RR #2
Renfrew, ON K7V 3Z5

NOTES: NO LONGER PUBLISHING

KEY PACIFIC PUBLISHERS

3rd Floor, 1001 Wharf Street
Victoria, BC V8W 1T6

PHONE: (604) 388-4324

CONTACT: Janice Strong   DESCRIPTION: "We publish visitors guides and information for the travel industry. We cover the Cascadia area. We also publish some meeting planners." Titles: *Where Victoria* (monthly), *The Essential Victoria, Supernatural Islands*, and *Discover Victoria*. Most of them are annuals.
WRITERS: "We do buy freelance material for almost all of our publications, so there are some opportunities. Call us and arrange for a meeting if you are in town, if not send a resumé and some samples." Contact Janice Strong or Kirsten Meinke.
PHOTOGRAPHERS: "We look for scenic photos from the Cascadia area. We also may use generic shopping and dining material plus some business photos." Call for an appointment or send a stock list or flyer. Contact Cathy Leahy.
NOTES: Sample copies of some publications are available free upon request.

KEY PORTER BOOKS

70 The Esplanade, 3rd Floor
Toronto, ON M5E 1R2

PHONE: (416) 862-7777
FAX: (416) 862-2304

CONTACT: Susan Renouf, Managing Editor   DESCRIPTION: Publishes non-fiction titles in the areas of politics, biography, history, natural history, sports, nature, photography, theatre, business, health, the environment and children's books. Publishes 50+ titles annually. Royalties vary 5-15% on retail. Advances can be negotiated $1000 and up. Recent publications include: *The Learning Highway: The Canadian Student's Guide to the Internet* by Trevor Owen, Ronald Owston and Cheryl Dickie; *The Sizeosaurus* by Steven Strauss; and *How on Earth: Question and Answer Book for Kids* by Ronald Orenstein.

WRITERS: "Request writers' guidelines with SASE, then submit an outline with two sample chapters and supporting artwork or photography." Average response time 4-8 weeks. Publishes in 6-12 months. Royalty and advance negotiable.

PHOTOGRAPHERS: Photographers and illustrators used for text illustrations, book covers, and dust jackets. Submit samples of work to Jean Peters, Art Director. Most photography is submitted as part of the book package. Prefers 35mm transparencies.

NOTES: Book catalogue and writers' guidelines available upon request.

KIDS CAN PRESS LTD.
29 Birch Avenue
Toronto, ON M4V 1E2

PHONE: (416) 925-5437
FAX: (416) unpublished

CONTACT: Marie Bartholomew, Art Director   **DESCRIPTION:** Publishes picture books, novels, and non-fiction for children.

WRITERS: Does not accept unsolicited manuscripts. Contact with query letter and samples.

PHOTOGRAPHERS: Photos are used for illustrations and book covers. Submit sample of work to Art Director as above.

KINDRED PRODUCTIONS
4-169 Riverton Avenue
Winnipeg, MB R2L 2E5

PHONE: (204) 669-6575
FAX: (204) 654-1865

CONTACT: Marilyn Hudson, Manager   **DESCRIPTION:** "We work on publications that are resources for churches. Booklets, books, bible study books, devotional books, books that deal with Christian education. We are also looking at drama that can be used in church services. We didn't publish anything last year, but right now we are working on six projects. We plan on publishing 2-3 books per year." Recent titles: *Church in Paegan Society*; *When the Church was Young; A Testament of Joy*. Distributed in the US.

WRITERS: "90% written by first-time writers. Works with unagented writers. Print runs 1000-2000. We like to have a letter from writers with an outline of the book, and a sample chapter or two. If it is a children's book we like to see the whole manuscript. We do a limited amount of children's books. We notify the author immediately upon receipt and we will let them know within 3 months if we are seriously considering it. From there it will go to a reader's panel. The book will be out within 18 months from acceptance." Considers simultaneous submissions. Royalties based on retail sales.

PHOTOGRAPHERS: If photography or illustrations are used they are supplied by the author.

KNOPF CANADA
33 Yonge Street, Suite 210
Toronto, ON M5E 1G4

PHONE: (416) 777-9477
FAX: (416) 777-9470

CONTACT: Editor   **DESCRIPTION:** Publishes trade fiction and non-fiction.

WRITERS: No unsolicited manuscripts. Will accept a query letter only. Prefers to work with writer's agents.

PHOTOGRAPHERS: All photography is done in-house.

KOSOY TRAVEL GUIDES
112 Fairholme Avenue
Toronto, ON M6B 2W9

PHONE: (416) 256-0974

CONTACT: Ted Kosoy   **DESCRIPTION:** Publishes travel guides.
NOTES: All writing and photography is done in-house. Do not send any submissions or queries.

LAMBRECHT PUBLICATIONS
21763 Maple Bay Road, RR#5
Duncan, BC V9L 4T6

PHONE: (604) 748-8722

CONTACT: Helga Lambrecht, Managing Editor   **DESCRIPTION:** Publishes regional history and cookbooks. Publishes 2-3 titles per year. Recent publications include: *Genoa Bay Reckoning* by Gladys MaccGould and *Man of the Land* by Helga Lambrecht.
NOTES: Not publishing new material in 1995. No new material needed at this time.

LANCELOT PRESS LTD.
Box 425
Hantsport, NS B0P 1P0

PHONE: (902) 684-9129
FAX: (902) 684-3685

CONTACT: William Pope, Publisher   **DESCRIPTION:** Publishes non-fiction, specializing in Atlantic Canada, trade books and a few children's and juvenile titles each year. Publishes 12-14 titles per year. Recent publications include: *Ketchum's Folly* by Jay Underwood; *If We Are Spared to Each Other* edited by Raymond Simpson and *No Time* by Margaret Avison. US distribution.
WRITERS: 30% of books published are by first-time authors. Works with unagented writers. Send a query letter with outline and sample chapter. Average response time 4-12 weeks. Publishes in 6-12 months. Average first-time print run 1,000. Average royalty 10% on retail sales. No advance given.
PHOTOGRAPHERS: All photography is done in-house.
NOTES: "Our 1995 calendar is completely filled."

LESTER PUBLISHING LTD.
56 The Esplanade, Suite 507A
Toronto, ON M5E 1A7

PHONE: (416) 362-1032
FAX: (416) 362-1647

CONTACT: Malcolm Lester   **DESCRIPTION:** Publishes general trade books: history, politics, biography, social issues, current affairs, literary fiction, children's picture books, and young adult novels. Averages sixteen books a year. Titles: *Beethoven Lives Upstairs* by Barbara Nichol; *The Story of Canada* by Janet Lunn and Christopher Moore; *Mario* by Lawrence Martin. "We sell rights to the US."
WRITERS: "We accept unsolicited manuscripts. We would prefer a letter of inquiry and a proposal first, to see if we are interested. Children's books should go to Cathy Lowinger; adult books to Malcolm Lester or Janice Weaver. Royalties are a percentage of the retail price. We consider simultaneous submissions and appreciate being told. Takes anywhere from 6-24 months to publish. We work with unagented writers and publish approximately 10% first time authors. Anyone who is submitting should look at our books in the bookstore or request our catalouge to get a sense of what we are doing before they submit."
PHOTOGRAPHERS: "We don't use a lot of photography in our books."

LIFE CYCLE BOOKS LTD.
2205 Danforth Ave.   **PHONE:** (416) 690-5860
Toronto, ON   M4C 1K4   **FAX:** (416) 690-5860

CONTACT: Paul Broughton, Publisher   **DESCRIPTION:** Publishes trade non-fiction on human life issues. Also publishes pamphlets and brochures. Recent publications include: *Help for the Post-Abortion Woman* by Teri Reisser and Paul Reisser, M.D. and *In the Image of God* edited by Gary Thomas. US Distribution.
WRITERS: Works with unagented writers. Send a query letter with outline and one or two chapters. Average response time 4-8 weeks. Publishes in 4-8 months. Average first-time print run 5000. Average royalty 10% on retail sales. Advance up to $500 negotiable.
PHOTOGRAPHERS: Photos used for book and catalogue covers. Contact with a query letter, business card and samples. All submissions to be kept on file.

LITTLE, BROWN & CO.(CANADA) LTD.
148 Yorkville Avenue   **PHONE:** (416) 967-3888
Toronto, ON   M5R 1C2   **FAX:** (416) 967-4591

NOTES: "Most of the publishing is done by our parent company in the United States. We have a very small publishing department, we publish about 4 book per year. We do not accept queries or manuscripts."

LOG HOUSE PUBLISHING CO. LTD.
RR #1   **PHONE:** (604) 629-6521
Pender Island, BC   V0N 2M0   **FAX:** (604) 629-2010

CONTACT: Mary Mackie   **DESCRIPTION:** Specializes in books about log house construction.
NOTES: All writing and photography is done in-house.

LONE PINE PUBLISHING
#206 10426 - 81 Avenue   **PHONE:** (403) 433-9333
Edmonton, AB   T6E 1X5   **FAX:** (403) 433-9646

CONTACT: Jenny Wong   **DESCRIPTION:** Publishes approximately 10 titles annually in the areas of: natural history; recreation guides; gardening: non-fiction trade; wildlife and the environment. Recent tiles include: *Lois Hole's Perennial Favorites; Trees, Shrubs and Flowers to Know in BC and Washington* by Chess Lyons; *Wetland Plants of Washington and Oregon* by Jennifer Guard.
WRITERS: Unsolicited submissions are accepted. Prefers query letter with outline and sample chapter. Royalty negotiated. Average first-time print run 10,000.
PHOTOGRAPHERS: Photography is provided by the author. Photography used in text illustration, and on book covers. Send query letter with detailed stock list to be kept on file.

LUGUS PUBLICATIONS

48 Falcon Street
Toronto, ON M4S 2P5

PHONE: (416) 322-5113
FAX: (416) 484-9512
E-Mail lugust@tvo.org

CONTACT: Gethin James   **DESCRIPTION:** Publishes educational books in the field of guidance and counselling. Includes elementary to adult education, with emphasis on distance education. Publishes 20 titles per year. Also fiction and non-fiction trade titles including some Latin American literature (Spanish-English). Recent publications include: *Employment Groups: The Counselling Connection; Distance Education; The Fundamentals of Photography Conservation* by The National Library of Canada; *The Seven Deaths of Sylvia Plath* by Cora Ramirez. US Distribution.
WRITERS: 50% of books published are by first-time authors. Works with unagented writers. "We want to see completed manuscripts." Average response time 6-8 weeks. Publishes within 2 years. Average first-time print run 1,000. Average royalty 10% on retail sales. Advance negotiable.
PHOTOGRAPHERS: Photos used for illustration, book covers, dust jackets. Contact with a query letter and sample portfolio, to be kept on file.

MACFARLANE WALTER & ROSS

37A Hazelton Avenue
Toronto, ON M5R 2E3

PHONE: (416) 924-7595
FAX: (416) 924-4254

CONTACT: Jan Walter, Publisher   **DESCRIPTION:** Publishes popular non-fiction aimed at Canadian and international audiences. Subjects include politics, business, history, biography, and culture.
WRITERS: Works with 50% unagented writers. Contact with a query letter. Average response time 4-6 weeks. Publishes in 6-12 months. Royalty and advances negotiable.
PHOTOGRAPHERS: Photos used for book covers and dust jackets. Contact with a query letter and sample portfolio to be kept on file.

MACMILLAN CANADA

29 Birch Avenue
Toronto, ON M4V 1E2

PHONE: (416) 963-8830
FAX: (416) 923-4821

CONTACT: Ann Nelles, Managing Editor   **DESCRIPTION:** Publishes non-fiction trade books for and by Canadians. Subjects include business, health, politics, history, sports, finances, biography, law, and cookbooks. "Canada's leading cookbook publisher." Publishes 20-25 titles per year. Recent publications include: *Light Kitchen* by Anne Lindsay; *Global Mafia* by Antonia Nicaso and Lee Lamothe; *Pathways to Performance* by Jim Clemmer; *Passionate Longevity: The Ten Secrets to Growing Younger* by Elaine Dembe and *The Brier: A History of Canada's Most Celebrated Curling Championships* by Bob Weeks.
WRITERS: 10% of books published are by first-time authors. Generally works with unagented writers. Send a query letter with outline, Table of Contents and two sample chapters and SASE to Denise Schon, Publisher. Average response time 8-12 weeks. Publishes in 6-12 months. Royalty and advance negotiable.
PHOTOGRAPHERS: Contact with a query letter and business card with sample portfolio to be kept on file. Send to Laura Williams, Production Editor with SASE. Photos used for text illustrations, book covers, and dust jackets.
NOTES: Catalogue available.

MAXWELL MACMILLAN CANADA INC.

1870 Birchmount Road **PHONE:** (416) 449-6030
Scarborough, ON M1P 2J7 **FAX:** (416) 449-0068

CONTACT: David Jollisse, Managing Editor **DESCRIPTION:** Publishes text books (kindergarten-college/university), reference books, and young-adult fiction. Examples of recent titles: *Series 2000 and The Heritage Book 1996*.
WRITERS: Send a query letter with outline. "A one-pager with the best features of the book, how it differs from similar publications, and the audience it will be marketed to would be best."
PHOTOGRAPHERS: Formats include b&w prints and 35mm transparencies. Uses 100+ photos annually. Purchases from stock. Buys one-time rights. Do not send unsolicited material. Do send resumé and samples which can be kept on file, and a detailed list of stock subjects.
NOTES: Catalogue and writers' guidelines are available, send large SASE.

McCLELLAND & STEWART INC.

481 University Avenue, Suite 900 **PHONE:** (416) 598-1114
Toronto, ON M5G 2E9 **FAX:** (416) 598-7764

CONTACT: Submissions Editor **DESCRIPTION:** Publishes fiction and non-fiction on biography, economics, history, natural history, poetry, religion, sports, mystery, romance, sci-fi, short story collections. Also includes reference books, and college text books. Imprints include: McClelland & Stewart; Stewart House; New Canadian Library. Publishes 50+ titles per year. Recent titles: *The Oracle of the Bones* by Claire O'Neill; *The Figure Skating Calendar*; *Canadian Encyclopedia on Diskette*; *Morning in the Burned House* by Margaret Atwood; *The Uncommon Touch* by Tom Harpur; *Boys Don't Cry* by Darcy Henton with David McCann; *Above the Law* by Paul Palango; *I Dig Up My Heart, Selected poems: 1952-1983*.
WRITERS: Does not accept unsolicited material. Publishes new and unagented writers. Manuscripts can be submitted on disk. Contact with a query and outline. All unsolicited material will be returned unopened.
PHOTOGRAPHERS: Publishes books with extensive photography. These may be supplied by the author. Send query, resumé and samples which can be kept on file.
NOTES: Pays 10% royalty on hardcover editions.

McGILL-QUEEN'S UNIVERSITY PRESS

McGill University, 3430 McTavish Street
Montreal, PQ H3A 1X9 **PHONE:** (514) 398-3750
CONTACT: Philip Cercone **FAX:** (514) 398-4333

Queen's University, 184 Union Street **PHONE:** (613) 545-2155
Kingston, ON K7L 2P6 **FAX:** (613) 545-6822
CONTACT: D.H. Akinson

DESCRIPTION: Publishes scholarly books on Arctic and Northern studies and history. Subject areas extend to English literature, ethnic studies, political science, Canadian urban life, Commonwealth and Canadian literature, architecture, philosophy and religion, North American Native peoples, anthropology, and sociology. Does not publish in the physical sciences or mathematics. Publishes approximately 100 titles per year. Recent publications include: *Arctic Artist* by Stewart Houston and Ian McLaren and *The Secession of Quebec and the Future of Canada* by Robert Young. US Distribution.

WRITERS: 30% of books published are by first-time authors. Works with unagented writers. Send a query letter with outline or sample chapters to either McGill or Queen's University at the above address. Average response time 2-4 weeks if manuscript is accepted for first review. "Peer review" from the Aid to Scholarly Publications Program in Ottawa can delay proceedings up to four months. Final approval by the Publication Review Committee and the author can delay a reply several more weeks. Average first-time print run 1,000-2,500 books. Publishes in 18-48 months. Average royalty 1% on first 1,000 books; 5% thereafter on retail sales. Rarely gives an advance.

PHOTOGRAPHERS: Photos and illustrations used for book covers and dust jackets. Submit small portfolio sample to Suzanne McAdam, Production Editor in the Montreal office. Most samples to be kept on file unless SASE sent and work is specifically requested to be returned.

McGRAW-HILL RYERSON LTD.

Trade and Professional Division
300 Water Street
Whitby, ON L1N 9B6

PHONE: (905) 430-5000
FAX: (905) 430-5020

CONTACT: Joan Homewood **DESCRIPTION:** Publishes adult non-fiction, consumer, business, computer, military history, and personal finance. Established in 1944. Recent titles include: *Infomedia Revolution* by Frank Koelsch; *Jacks on Tax Savings* by Evelyn Jacks; *Corvettes Canada* by Mac Johnston. Imprints include: McGraw-Hill and McGraw-Hill Ryerson. Publishes 70 books annually. Actively pursues co-publishing agreements.

WRITERS: Average first print-run 2,500. Takes up to one year after acceptance to publish. Unsolicited materials will be returned with SASE. Considers simultaneous submissions. Replies within 3 months. Query with book outline and sample chapters. Works with first-time and unagented authors. Average royalty 10% on retail sales. Advance negotiated. "In your query include a profile of the author and professional and personal contacts that are related to your proposal. Also include basic market research, i.e. who should buy this book, how many, why and how is this book unique against its competitors."

PHOTOGRAPHERS: Photography is not used.

THE MERCURY PRESS

Box 446
Stratford, ON N5A 6T3

CONTACT: Beverley Daurio **DESCRIPTION:** Publishes Canadian fiction, non-fiction, and poetry.

MICROMEDIA LTD.

20 Victoria Street
Toronto, ON M5C 2N8

PHONE: (416) 362-5211 extension 2002
FAX: (416) 362-6161

CONTACT: Louise Fast   **DESCRIPTION:** Publishes electronic data in the form of indexes, abstract databases, and printed directories.

WRITERS: "We occasionally use freelance indexers. Call human resources for more information."

NOTES: All writing and photography is done in-house.

MIKA PUBLISHING COMPANY

200 Stanley Street   **PHONE:** (613) 962-4022
Belleville, ON K8N 4A3

CONTACT: Helma Mika   **DESCRIPTION:** Publishes local Canadian city, township and county histories. Publishes 25 titles per year. Recent publications include: *History of Upper Canadian Villages* (in French and English).
WRITERS: "We are not publishing any more books in 1995." Submit a query with outline and sample chapters in 1996.

MOONSTONE PRESS

175 Brock Street   **PHONE:** (519) 524-5645
Goderich, ON N7A 1R4   **FAX:** (519) 524-6185

CONTACT: Peter Baltensperger, Publisher   **DESCRIPTION:** Publishes fiction and non-fiction titles on mysticism and spirituality. Publishes 1-2 titles per year. Recent publications include: *The Shunning* by Mary Anne Paul and *Medusa and Her Sisters* by Clare Braux.
WRITERS: 50% of books published are by first-time authors. Works with unagented writers. Send a query letter with outline and two chapters. Average response time 4-6 weeks. Publishes in 6-12 months. Average royalty 10% on retail sales. Advances are not given.
PHOTOGRAPHERS: Majority assigned in-house. Contact with a query letter and sample portfolio of work. Photographs and illustrations are used for text illustration and book covers.

MOSAIC PRESS/INTERNATIONAL PUBLISHERS INC.

1252 Speers Road, Units 1 & 2   **PHONE:** (416) 825-2130
Oakville, ON L6L 5N9   **FAX:** (416) 825-2130

CONTACT: Howard Aster, Publisher   **DESCRIPTION:** Specialize in trade fiction and non-fiction titles. Publishes 20-25 titles per year. Subject areas are broad, including, social studies, international studies, autobiography, health, literature, novels, poetry, short stories, business, art and literary criticism. Publishes a limited number of children's books. Recent publications include: *Borrowed Time* by Dr. and Mrs. Messenger; *Health and Culture: Exploring the Relationship* by Ralph Massey, Lynette Mensah, and Keith McLeod; and a series called *Cold Blood* edited by Peter Sellers.
WRITERS: 20-30% of books published are by first-time authors. "Phone the editor first to find out if he is interested in your idea. He will let you know if you should send an outline and two or three chapters. If you cannot reach the editor, send a synopsis, and a resumé including other titles you may have in print." Publishes in 2-15 months. Average first-time print run 1,000-2,500. Royalty negotiable. Advances generally not given.
PHOTOGRAPHERS: All writing and photography is done in-house.

MOVING PUBLICATIONS LTD.

44 Upjohn Road, Suite 100   **PHONE:** (416) 441-1168
Don Mills, ON   **FAX:** (416) 441-1641

CONTACT: Lorraine Hunter, Managing Editor   **DESCRIPTION:** Recent publications include *You Choose: A Guide to Canadian Universities* and *You Choose: A Guide to Homes for Seniors in Canada*.
WRITERS: Does not read unsolicited manuscripts.

NOTES: Also publishes Moving To Magazines... for people who are relocating to different Canadian cities.

NAPOLEON PUBLISHING INC.
5334 Yonge Street, #147   **PHONE:** (416) 730-9052
North York, ON M2N 6M2   **FAX:** (416) 226-9975

CONTACT: Sylvia McConnell, Publisher   **DESCRIPTION:** Publishes children's picture books, predominantly in English, also in French. Publishes 4-5 titles per year. Recent publications include: *Thanksgiving Day in Canada* by Lewicki and *Dragon in the Clouds* by Nelson.
WRITERS: "We are not looking for new material until 1996. It's best to call first. We like to see whole manuscript." Average response time 12-16 weeks. Publishes in 10-16 months. Average first-time print run 3,000. Royalty 10% on retail sales. Advance negotiable.
PHOTOGRAPHERS: Photos and illustrations used for text illustration, book covers, dust jackets. Contact with a query letter and samples of work which can be kept on file.

NATURAL HERITAGE/ NATURAL HISTORY INC.
P.O. Box 95, Station O   **PHONE:** (416) 694-7907
Toronto, ON M4A 2M8   **FAX:** (416) 690-0819

CONTACT: Barry Penhale, Publisher   **DESCRIPTION:** Publishes regional histories, environmental, culture, folklore and Canadiana. Recent publications include: *The View From Foley Mountain* by Perry Phillips McQuay; *A Mill Should Be Built Thereon: An Early History of Tod Mordon Mills* by Eleanor Darke and *Caledonia: Along the Grand River* by Barbara Martindale.
WRITERS: 20-30% of books published are by first-time authors. "Contact publisher by phone to discuss your idea before sending anything in the mail. If he is interested he will invite you to send in a manuscript with cover letter and Table of Contents." Publishes in 6-18 months. Average first-time print run 1,000-3,000.
PHOTOGRAPHERS: Photos used for illustration, book covers, and dust jackets. Contact with a query letter and samples.

NC PRESS LTD.
345 Adelaide Street West   **PHONE:** (416) 593-6284
Toronto, ON M5V 1R5   **FAX:** (416) 593-6204

DESCRIPTION: Publishes books on art, economics, history, environment, politics, theatre, women's issues, development, health and cooking. Recent publications include: *Eating Bitterness* by Art Solomon and *Three China's* by Bill Purves.
WRITERS: 20-30% of books published are by first-time authors. Works with unagented writers. Send a query letter with your biography, outline and one or two chapters. Please include what audience your book is targeted to. Average response time 4-12 weeks. Publishes in 6-12 months. Average royalty 10% on retail sales. Small advance available.
PHOTOGRAPHERS: 100% assigned to in-house photographers and illustrators.

NELSON CANADA

1120 Birchmount Road
Scarborough, ON
M1K 5G4

PHONE: (416) 752-9100
FAX: (416) 752-9646

CONTACT: Loren Darroch, Ext. 201 **DESCRIPTION:** Publishes over 100 text books annually. Includes anthologies, workbooks, teacher's guides and manuals.
WRITERS: Send resumé and query.
PHOTOGRAPHERS: Send resumé, samples and detailed stock listing.

NEW CENTURY BOOKS

Box 43093, 4739 Willingdon Ave.
Burnaby, BC   V5G 4S2

PHONE: (604) 521-6524
FAX: (604) 299-4020

CONTACT: Eugene Kaellis, Publisher   **DESCRIPTION:** Publishes trade non-fiction titles. Does not publish poetry or romance. Recent publications include: *The Big Fall* by Sheila Jacobs and *Can Cats Purr* and *Urdu* by Eugene Kaellis.
WRITERS: "It would be a waste of people's time to submit manuscripts right now. We are not looking to publish anything for the rest of this year." In 1996 people may submit a query letter for consideration.
PHOTOGRAPHERS: All photography is done in-house.

NEW WORLD PERSPECTIVES

3652 Avenue Laval
Montreal, PQ   H2X 3C9

PHONE: 514 282-9298
FAX: 514 987-9724

CONTACT: Marilouise Kroker   **DESCRIPTION:** Publishes university-level books on feminism, social and political theory, technology, postmodernism, and popular culture.
WRITERS: "We are not reading unsolicited manuscripts until 1997. We commission authors on the subjects we want to cover."

NeWEST PUBLISHERS LTD.

10359-82 Avenue, Suite 310
Edmonton, AB   T6E 1Z9

PHONE: (403) 432-9427
FAX: (403) 432-9429

CONTACT: Eva Radford   **DESCRIPTION:** Publishes literature and non-fiction pertaining to Western Canada by Western Canadian writers. Publishes 8 books per year. Recent itles: *Poor Superman* by Brad Fraser; *The Klein Revolution* by Mark Lisac.
WRITERS: "We accept query letters and manuscripts, though we prefer to see sample chapters and an outline." Replys in 4-6 weeks. 50% first time authors. Royalties are 10% on retail. Publishes within 9 months to a year. Print runs average 1,800. Considers simultaneous submissions. Author's guidelines are available with an SASE. We are looking for good literary quality from Western Canadian writers on Western Canadian topics."
PHOTOGRAPHERS: "We hardly ever buy photography."

NEWPORT BAY PUBLISHING

356 Cyril Owen Place, RR#4

Victoria, BC V8X 3X1

PHONE: (604) 479-4616

FAX: (604) 479-3836

CONTACT: Don Lindenberg, Publisher **DESCRIPTION:** Publishes non-fiction titles. Issues 2 titles per year.

WRITERS: "We have not published unsolicited material in several years. I read them but generally that's all. Right now we are just publishing calendars."

PHOTOGRAPHERS: Photographs used for text illustration and book covers and calendars. Contact with a query letter and samples; will be kept on file.

NIGHTWOOD EDITIONS

Box 219

Madeira Park, BC V0N 2H0

PHONE: (604) 883-2730

FAX: (604) 885-0212

DESCRIPTION: Publishes children's picture books on west coast themes. Publishes 3-4 titles per year. Recent publications include: *Pucchini and the Prowler* by Adele Wiseman and *The Ferry Boat Ride* by Robert Perry.

WRITERS: 50% of books published are by first-time authors. Works with unagented writers. Send a query letter with outline and sample chapters or whole manuscript with SASE. Average response time for query letter 4-6 weeks. Manuscripts average 12 weeks. Publishes in 6-36 months. First-time print run 2,000-10,000. Royalty 10% on retail sales. Negotiable advance.

PHOTOGRAPHERS: Photographs used for text illustration and book covers. Contact with a query letter and samples.

NIMBUS PUBLISHING LTD.

Box 9301, Station "A"

Halifax, NS B3K 5N5

PHONE: (902) 455-4286

FAX: (902) 455-3652

CONTACT: Dorothy Blythe, Managing Editor   **DESCRIPTION:** Publishes general trade books on Atlantic Canada. Subjects include cultural, natural history, folklore and myth, Native customs, the environment, nautical, cookbooks, children's, and photographic books. No poetry or fiction. Publishes 20-25 titles. Recent publications include: *Calculated Risk* by Dean Job and *Landmarks* by Elizabeth Pacey.

WRITERS: 50% of books published are by first-time authors. Contact with a query letter, sample chapter and outline. Average response time 2-16 weeks. Publishes in 6-12 months. Average first-time print run 3,000-5,000. Royalty 10% on retail sales. Advances negotiable.

PHOTOGRAPHERS: Photos used for illustration, book covers and dust jackets. Contact with a query letter and samples to Joanne Elliott, Production Director.

OBERON PRESS

400 - 350 Sparks Street

Ottawa, ON K1R 7S8

PHONE: (613) 238-3275

FAX: (613) 238-3275

CONTACT: Nicholas Macklem, Publisher **DESCRIPTION:** Publishes Canadian fiction, poetry, history, biography, and art. "We are a literary press so we don't do science fiction or sagas." Recent publications include: *Native Blood* by Judy Smith and *Window Dressing* by Don Bailey. US Distribution.

WRITERS: Works with 2-3 new authors per season and with unagented writers. Send a query letter with outline and 1-2 chapters, or short complete manuscripts with SASE. "Books should not be over 250 pages." Average response time 2-8 weeks. Publishes in 10-12 months. Royalty negotiable. No advance.

PHOTOGRAPHERS: Photos used for book covers and dust jackets. Contact with a query letter and samples to be kept on file.

OCTOPUS PUBLISHING GROUP
75 Clegg Road
Markham, ON L6G 1A1

PHONE: (416) 479-2665
FAX: (416) 479-2826

CONTACT: Publisher: Michael Murton **DESCRIPTION:** Major international book distributor publishes general trade fiction and non-fiction for adults and children. A division of Butterworths Canada and part of Reed International Books.

ONTARIO OUTDOOR PUBLICATIONS
2168 Heridge Drive
Mississauga, ON L5K 1N6

NOTES: Could not locate. Phone number is not in service (416) 823-6158.

OOLICHAN BOOKS
Box 10
Lantzville, BC V0R 2H0

PHONE: (604) 390-4839
FAX: (604) 390-4839

CONTACT: Rhonda Bailey, Publisher **DESCRIPTION:** "We are a literary press that publishes fiction, poetry, non-fiction including history, native titles, an occasional children's book, some general interest, and autobiographies. We publish around 10 titles a year." Titles: *Visible Light* by Carol Windley; *Under Glass* by Grant Buday; *Ed and Mabel go to the Moon* by Aaronn Bushkowsky; *Tracks in the Snow* by Ralph Gustafson; *Trout Tales and Salmon Stories*; *Almost a Lifetime* by John McMahon; and *Borrowed Time*. Distributes in the US. Print runs vary from 750-3,000.

WRITERS: "We prefer writers inquire by mail with a description of their book, a writing sample and SASE. If it is fiction include 3 chapters. It takes us about 2 months to respond. We get about 100 queries per month so we respond in order. Last year 25-30% of our authors were first time authors. We pay 10% on retail." Considers simultaneous submissions if informed. Writers' guidelines are available. "We are looking for more regional history. We are not doing any more children's colour picture books."

PHOTOGRAPHERS: "Normally authors provide photographs for our history titles so we haven't really used freelance photographers."

NOTES: For a catalogue of complete titles send a 9x12 SASE.

ORCA BOOK PUBLISHERS LTD.
Box 5626, Station "B"
Victoria, BC V8R 6S4

PHONE: (604) 380-1229
FAX: (604) 380-1892

CONTACT: Adult/juvenile: Bob Tyrrell, Children's books: Ann Featherstone
DESCRIPTION: Publishes young adult fiction, regional history, guide books, non-fiction and a series of children's books. Established in 1984. Publishes 20 books per year. Distributes

in the US. Average print run is 3,000-5,000. Takes 1-2 years to publish from acceptance. Recent titles: *Deeley, Motorcycle Millionnaire; Eagle Dreams; The Wineries of B.C.; Hound Without Howl.*
WRITERS: Accepts unsolicited manuscripts and replies in 6-8 weeks. Prefers to be contacted with a query letter, outline and sample chapters. Replies to queries in 4-6 weeks. Works with first time and unagented authors. Average royalty is 10%-12% on retail sales. Advances vary. Returns unsolicited materials with a SASE. Does not consider simultaneous submissions. Writers' guidelines are available. "Writers should send for and follow the guidelines."
PHOTOGRAPHERS: "We buy photography on occasion, maybe 2-3 photos per year for a book cover." Text illustrations and text photography supplied by the author.
NOTES: Publishes only Canadian subjects. Guidelines available with a 9x12 SASE.

OTTER PRESS
81 Albert Street
Waterloo, ON N2L 3S6

PHONE: (519) 885-4130
FAX: none

CONTACT: Anne Dagg, Managing Editor **DESCRIPTION:** "We publish non-fiction books by women. Women and biology are our two fields. We publish about 1 a year, we are very small." Recent title: *User Friendly University* by Anne Dagg. Print runs average 500 books.
WRITERS: We don't accept queries from writers. No unsolicited manuscripts please."
PHOTOGRAPHERS: Rarely uses photos.

OUTCROP LTD.
Box 1350
Yellowknife, NT X1A 2N9

PHONE: (403) 920-4652
FAX: (403) 873-2844

CONTACT: Ronne Heming, Vice-President; Marion Levine, Publisher **DESCRIPTION:** Publishes general non-fiction about Canada's North. Publishes 1-5 titles per year. Recent titles include: *The N.W.T. Data Book Annual* and *McDougall's Bash* by Eric Watt.
WRITERS: Works with first time and unagented authors. Royalty averages 10% on retail price. Publishes 10-12 months after manuscript acceptance. Contact with query, outline and sample chapters. Takes up to 12 weeks to reply to queries.
PHOTOGRAPHERS: Photos and artwork are supplied by the author.
NOTES: Book catalogue available.

OWL'S HEAD PRESS
Box 57
Alma, NB E0A 1B0

PHONE: (506) 887-2073
FAX: (506) 887-2346

CONTACT: Allan Cooper **DESCRIPTION:** "We publish only poetry books. We publish established and new Canadian and American poets." Publishes 1-2 books per year. "We publish poetry in the tradition of Robert Bly and Alden Nowlan." Titles: *Ten Poems of Francis Ponge*; *Living In the Cave of the Mouth* by Douglas Burnet Smith.
WRITERS: "We publish one poet at a time. We accept typed double-spaced material. We are not interested in light or humourous verse." Replies in 4-6 weeks. Works with unagented authors. 30% are first time authors. Pays in books; 10% of the print run or as negotiated. Does not consider simultaneous submissions. Publishes within 6 months to one year from acceptance. Contact with manuscript or query and samples.
PHOTOGRAPHERS: Does not use.

OXFORD UNIVERSITY PRESS

Gerry Shkuda, Education Editor
70 Wynford Drive
Don Mills, ON M3C 1J9

PHONE: (416) 441-2941
FAX: (416) 441-0345

CONTACT: Phyllis Wilson, Trade and College Editor   **DESCRIPTION:** Annually publishes 25 trade fiction and non-fiction, school text-books and college text-books. Recent publications include: *Diamonds of the North* by Bill Humber and *A History of Canadian Architecture* by Harold Kalman. US Distribution.
WRITERS: Works with unagented writers. Send a query letter with outline and 1-2 chapters. Publishes in 1-2 years. Royalty and advance negotiable.
PHOTOGRAPHERS: Photos used for illustration, book covers and dust jackets. Contact with a query letter, samples and SASE to Joanna Gertler, Production and Design Dept.

P.D. MEANY PUBLISHERS

Box 118
Streetsville, ON L5M 2B7

PHONE: (905) 567-5803
FAX: (905) 567-1687

CONTACT: Patrick Meany   **DESCRIPTION:** Specializes in scholarly publications. "I only publish 1 to 2 academic books per year usually by people that I personally know." Title: *The Irish Diaspora* by Donald H. Akenson.
NOTES: "I don't accept unsolicited manuscripts and as far as photography and services goes I am not in the market."

P.S.A. VENTURES

80 Empire Street
London, ON N5Y 1G7

PHONE: (519) 659-6279
FAX: none

CONTACT: Paul Liebau   **DESCRIPTION:** "We publish personal growth and education books." Recent titles: *Thoughts on Relationships; Thoughts on the Self; Thoughts on Purpose; Thoughts on Making Dreams Come True; Wheelchairs for Ponies* by Perry Chittick; *Souls Rising* by Rita Benson.
WRITERS: "We don't accept unsolicited material. If someone reads our publications and feels they have something to offer I will have in informal meeting with them." A phone call is welcome. Publishes 1-2 books per year. Royalties depend on the book.
PHOTOGRAPHERS: "I use some photography in my books but I don't accept queries." Photos are supplied by the author.

PACIFIC-RIM PUBLISHERS

Box 5204, Station B
Victoria, BC V8R 6N4

PHONE: (604) 872-7373
FAX: (604) 872-2622

CONTACT: Naomi Wakan, Publisher   **DESCRIPTION:** Publishes educational texts for elementary schools, specializing in social studies and multiculturalism. No fiction titles. Publishes 2-3 titles per year. Recent publications include: *On the Rim Series* including *Puzzling on the Rim* and *Telling Tales on the Rim*.
WRITERS: Contact with a query letter, story outline and SASE. " We don't look at manuscripts unless they come with SASE. We are looking for well-written activity books. How-to books. I like to see art and research activities. I like hands-on stuff." Average response time 6-8 weeks. Publishes in 4-12 months. Royalty and advance negotiable.

PHOTOGRAPHERS: "I don't want to see any space-age stuff. Do not send originals." Contact with a query letter, samples and SASE. Photos used for illustration and book covers.
NOTES: "We also do some critiquing. Authors send me $50.00 with SASE and their manuscript (32 pages or so). I will recommend a publisher to them and sometimes call the publisher and recommend the manuscript if I consider it to be a good one."

PAIDEIA PRESS LTD.
Box 1000
Jordan Station, ON L0R 1S0

PHONE: (416) 562-5719
FAX: (416) 562-7828

CONTACT: John Houltink, Publisher   **DESCRIPTION:** Publishes theological and children's books.
WRITERS: "Not publishing or accepting manuscripts until 1996. Phone before you send anything."

PANORAMA COMMUNICATIONS
128A - 8th Avenue S.W.
Calgary, AB T2P 1B3

PHONE: (403) 264-0404
FAX: (403) 237-0965

CONTACT: Art New   **DESCRIPTION:** Publishes travel-related material and regional guides, also in the corporate and educational areas. Recent publications include: *Alberta Getaways - Banff, Lake Louise, Central Alberta, Jasper, Edmonton, and Northern Alberta* and *How to Have Ten Perfect Vacations in Southern Alberta.*
WRITERS: "We don't accept unsolicited manuscripts. We are in the business of taking on joint projects and ventures with clients."
PHOTOGRAPHERS: Purchases stock images. Photos used for illustration and book covers. Contact with a query letter samples and resumé of where you have been published; to be kept on file.

PEGUIS PUBLISHERS LTD.
Suite 100, 318 McDermott Ave.
Winnipeg, MB R3A OA2

PHONE: (204) 956-1486
FAX: (204) 947-0080

CONTACT: Mary Dixon, Managing Editor   **DESCRIPTION:** Publishes 15 teacher's resource books annually. Recent publications include: *Multi-Age and More* by Colleen Politano and Anne Davies and *Peace in the Classroom* by Hetty Adams.
WRITERS: Works with first-time authors. "We accept unsolicited manuscripts." Send a query letter with outline and sample chapter or whole manuscript. Average response time 4-16 weeks. Average first-time print run 2,000-3,000. Publishing time is variable. Royalty negotiable.
PHOTOGRAPHERS: Photographs and illustrations used for text illustration and book covers. Contact with a query letter and samples; to be kept on file.

PEMMICAN PUBLICATIONS INC.
1635 Burrows Avenue, Unit 2
Winnipeg, MB R2X 0T1

PHONE: (204) 589-6346
FAX: (204) 589-2063

CONTACT: Sue MacLean, Publisher   **DESCRIPTION:** Publishes books of interest to Native and Metis peoples. Specializes in children's books. Publishes 6-9 titles per year.

Recent publications include: *The Spring Celebration* by Tina Umpherville; *How the Turtle Got its Shell - A Nanabosho Legend* by Joan McLellan and *Wolf and Shadows* by Duncan Mercredi.

WRITERS: 20% of books published are by first-time authors. Send a query letter with whole manuscript double-spaced. Average response time 10-16 weeks. Publishes in 10-18 months. Average first-time print run 1,000-3,000. Average royalty 10% on retail sales. Advance negotiable.

PHOTOGRAPHERS: All photography is done in-house.

PENDRAGON HOUSE LTD.
Box 338
Mississauga, ON L5G 4L8

PHONE: (905) 823-0222
FAX: (905) 823-9931

CONTACT: Susan Morrison, Publisher **DESCRIPTION:** Publishes fiction and religious titles. Publishes 1-2 titles per year. Recent publications include: *The Arthuriad* by Darcy Badger and *Prayers of Power* by Darcy Badger. US distribution.

WRITERS: 95% of books published are by first-time authors. Works with unagented writers. Send a query letter with outline or synopsis and 1-2 chapters. Average response time 4-8 weeks. Publishes in 6-12 months. Average royalty 10% on retail sales. Advance negotiable.

PHOTOGRAPHERS: Photographs and illustrations used for text illustration, book covers, and dust jackets. Contact with a query letter and samples to be kept on file.

PENGUIN BOOKS CANADA LTD.
10 Alcorn Avenue, Suite 300
Toronto, ON M4V 3B2

PHONE: (416) 925-2249
FAX: (416) 925-0068

CONTACT: Editorial Department **DESCRIPTION:** Publishes a variety of trade non-fiction in the areas of sports, health, women's, social, and native issues. "We publish very little fiction." Publishes 90 titles per year; 80 non-fiction, 10 fiction. Recent publications include: *The Biography of Robertson Davies* by Judy Skelton Grant and *A Breed Apart: An Illustrated History of Goaltending* by Douglas Hunter.

WRITERS: "We do not accept unsolicited manuscripts. We only consider works which are represented by literary agents or endorsed by published writers. If they are a published author send a query letter, detailing previous publications, and an outline of the book they wish to publish." Roylaties negotiated.

PHOTOGRAPHERS: Photos supplied by the authors, or handled in-house.

PENUMBRA PRESS
435 Stillmeadow Circle
Waterloo, ON N2L 5M1

NOTES: Could not locate. Phone number is not in service (519) 746-8758.

PERFORMANCE PUBLICATIONS INC.
Box 292
Thornhill, ON L3T 3N3

NOTES: Could not locate. Phone number is not in service (416) 889-5242.

PFEIFFER & CO
4190 Fairview Street   **PHONE:** (416) 632-5832
Burlington, ON L7L 4Y8   **FAX:** (416) 333-5675

CONTACT: Acquisitions Editor   **DESCRIPTION:** Publishes human resource books, appealing to managers and trainers in the human relations field. Publishes 6-25 titles per year. Recent publications include: *Annual for Developing Human Resources 1995* (25th edition); *Encylopedia of Team Development*; *Encyclopedia of Team Building*; and *Flawless Consulting* by Peter Block. US, U.K., Amsterdam, South Africa, and Australian distribution.
WRITERS: 10% of books published are by first-time authors. Average first-time print run 1,000-10,000. Send a query letter with outline. "If the book idea fits our mandate, we will ask for the manuscript." Average response time 4-8 weeks. Publishes in 6-15 months. Royalties and advances negotiable.
PHOTOGRAPHERS: All photography is done in-house.

PIPPIN PUBLISHING LTD.
481 University Ave.   **PHONE:** (416) 513-6966
Toronto, ON M5G 2E9   **FAX:** (416) 513-6977

CONTACT: Jonathon Dickson, Publisher   **DESCRIPTION:** Publishes English as a Second Language, from preschool to adult, and teacher resource manuals. Publishes 12 new titles per year. Recent publications include: *Worlds of Wonder* by Paula Kezwer and *My Country, Our History* by Hux et al.
WRITERS: 25% of books published are by first-time authors. Works with unagented writers. Send a query letter with outline, Table of Contents and sample chapter. "We do not read multiple submissions and in return we respond quickly to most authors." Average response time 2-4 weeks. Publishes in 6-15 months. Average first-time print run 3,000. Royalty 10% on retail sales, negotiable. Advance negotiable.
PHOTOGRAPHERS: Photographs and illustrations used for text illustration, book covers, dust jackets. Contact with a query letter and samples, to be kept on file.
NOTES: "We prefer background and experience in the English as a Second Language field."

PLAINS PUBLISHING INC.
17340 - 106A Avenue   **PHONE:** (403) 451-0871
Edmonton, AB T5S 1E6   **FAX:** (403) 455-1388

CONTACT: Acquisitions **DESCRIPTION:** Publishes 5 to 7 books annually specializing in social studies and language arts. Recent examples include: *Culture Canada Upclose*, Dale Ripley; *Adventurous Albertans; Stories from Our Elders, III Volumes*. Uses photos for book covers, dust jackets and text illustration.

PLAYWRIGHTS CANADA PRESS
54 Wolseley Street, 2nd Floor   **PHONE:** (416) 703-0201
Toronto, ON M5T 1A5   **FAX:** (416) 703-0059

CONTACT: Tony Hamill, Editor **DESCRIPTION:** Publishes Canadian plays in single editions, anthologies, and collections. Publishes 6 titles per year. Recent publications include: *Cheatin' Hearts* by Paul Ledoux and *Colonial Tongues* by Mansell Robinson.

WRITERS: Does not work with first-time authors. Works with unagented writers. "In order to become published you must be a member of the Playwrights' Union of Canada and must have at least one play professionally produced." Send manuscript for consideration. Average response time 4-10 weeks. Publishes in 6-18 months. Average royalty 10% on retail sales.
PHOTOGRAPHERS: All photography is done in-house.
NOTES: "If the members' works are not published we distribute them in an unpublished format known as 'copy scripts', photocopying and binding ourselves. The playwright receives $1.10 for each volume sold."

POLESTAR PRESS LTD.
2nd Floor, 1011 Commercial Drive
Vancouver, B.C. V5LK 3X1

PHONE: (604) 251-9718
FAX: (604) 251-9738

CONTACT: Michelle Benjamin **DESCRIPTION:** Publishes fiction, poetry, children's fiction and non-fiction, sports, and general trade non-fiction. No children's picture books. Publishes 10 titles per year. Recent publications include: *Survival Gear* by Rita Moyer; *White Horses and Shooting Stars* by David Greer and *Head Cook at Weddings and Funerals* by Vi Plotnikoff. US distribution.
WRITERS: 30-40% of books published are by first-time authors. "We prefer whole manuscripts." Average response time 6-24 weeks. Publishes in 1-2 years. Print runs are variable. Average royalty 10% on retail sales. Advance negotiable.
PHOTOGRAPHERS: All photography is done in-house.

PORCEPIC BOOKS see Beach Holme Publishers

THE PORCUPINE'S QUILL INC.
68 Main Street
Erin, ON N0B 1T0

PHONE: (519) 833-9158
FAX: (519) 833-9158

CONTACT: Michael Carbert, Managing Editor **DESCRIPTION:** Publishes Canadian literature. Approximately 10 new titles per year. Mostly trade fiction titles, including visual art, young adult, children's and poetry. Recent publications include: *Portraits of Flowers* by Patrick Lima and G. Brender *The Point of the Graver* by Wesley W. Bates.
WRITERS: 40-50% of books published are by first-time authors. Works with 80% unagented writers. "We do not read unsolicited manuscripts."
PHOTOGRAPHERS: All photography is done in-house.

PORTAGE & MAIN PRESS
#100, 318 McDermot Avenue
Winnipeg, MB R3A 0A2

NOTES: Not accepting submissions at this time. Affiliated with Peguis Publishers.

POTLATCH PUBLICATIONS
3 Berry Hill
Waterdown, ON L0R 2H4

PHONE: (905) 689-1632
FAX: none

CONTACT: Robert Nielsen, Managing Editor **DESCRIPTION:** "We publish general trade books." *Generals Die In Bed* is kept in reprint.
WRITERS: "We are not actively publishing right now. We hope to be within one year. We want people to know that we are still operational although we are not accepting queries at the present time. Most of our material comes from unsolicited manuscripts. We work with unagented writers and first time writers."
PHOTOGRAPHERS: "We don't use photography in our books."

POTTERSFIELD PRESS
RR #2
Porters Lake, NS B0J 2S0

PHONE: (902) 827-4517

CONTACT: Lesley Choyce, Publisher **DESCRIPTION:** Publishes general non-fiction, cookbooks, poetry, political cartoons, novels, and books on Atlantic Canada. Publishes 6 titles per year. Recent publications include: *No Friends in High Places* by Athea Moudakis; *Graveyard for Dreamers* by Joan Baxter; *Even at This Distance* by W.P. Consella; *Daring Lady Flyers* by Joyce Springhill; *Visions of Kerouac* by Ken McGoogan and *The Sander's Driftwood* by Budge Wilson.
WRITERS: Send a query letter with outline or synopsis, 1-2 chapters and SASE. Average response time 4-8 weeks. Publishes in 6-12 months. Average royalty 10% on retail sales. $500 advance.
PHOTOGRAPHERS: All photography is done in-house.

THE PRAIRIE PUBLISHING COMPANY
Box 2997
Winnipeg, MB R3C 4B5

PHONE: (204) 885-6496
FAX: (204) 775-3277

CONTACT: Ralph Watkins, Publisher **DESCRIPTION:** Publishes children's books, biographies and Prairie architecture, art, and history. Publishes 3-4 titles per year. Recent publications include: *San-So Blue: The Autobiography of a Thoroughbred* by Edna Emes.
WRITERS: Works with unagented writers. "I do not want to see a sample chapter because my experience has been that the sample chapter is the best chapter. We like to look at the whole manuscript before we can give a commitment. We also like the author to provide some illustrations or photographs, especially for our local histories." Average response time 4-8 weeks. Publishes in 8-12 months. Average first-time print run 500-1,000. Average royalty 10% on retail sales. Advance not given.
PHOTOGRAPHERS: Photographs and illustrations used for illustration and book covers. Contact with a query letter and samples to be kept on file.

PRENTICE-HALL CANADA INC.
1870 Birchmount Road
Scarborough, ON M1P 2J7

PHONE: (416) 293-3621
FAX: (416) 299-2540

CONTACT: David Jollisse, Managing Editor **DESCRIPTION:** Publishes trade non-fiction and all levels of education texts. Subjects include art, self-help, business, current affairs, and politics; must have Canadian focus. Recent publications include: *Balancing Act* by

Joanne Thomas Yaccato; *Building Wealth, and Low-Risk Investing* by Gordon Pape; *Ice Time* by Debbie Wilkes and *The Canadian Internet Handbook.*

WRITERS: Send a query letter with outline, and resumé. "In your query, outline the best points of the book, how it is different from other books in that category and the target market."

PHOTOGRAPHERS: Most photography is supplied by the author. Photographers send query with samples that can be kept on file and a list of stock subjects.

NOTES: "We publish Canadian books and distribute MacMillan computer products." Guidelines available with #10 SASE.

PRESS GANG PUBLISHERS
603 Powell Street
Vancouver, BC V6A 1H2

NOTES: Could not locate. Phone number is not in service (604) 253-2537.

PRIMARY PRESS
Box 372
Peterborough, ON K9J 6Z3

NOTES: Could not locate. Phone number is not in service (705) 749-9276.

PRISE DE PAROLE INC.
P.O. Box 550, Stn. B   **PHONE:** (705) 675-6491
Sudbury, ON P3E 4R2   **FAX:** (705) 673-1817

CONTACT: Denise Truax, Publisher   **DESCRIPTION:** French language publisher. Publishes 8-10 books annually:: French trade literature, including poetry, theatre, and novels. Also publishes school texts (grade 9 to university).

WRITERS: 30% of books published are by first-time authors. "Send a whole manuscript. We have a review committee. If it meets our criteria, then we publish the book." Also works with self-publishers. Response time 6-20 weeks. Rirst-time print run 500-1000. Average royalty 10% on retail sales.

PHOTOGRAPHERS: All photography is done in-house.

PROBE INTERNATIONAL see Earthscan

PROGRESS BOOKS
72 Tecumseh Street
Toronto, ON M5V 2R8

NOTES: Could not locate. Phone number is not in service (416) 368-5336.

PROOF POSITIVE PRODUCTIONS
#1330, 194 - 3803 Calgary Trail   **PHONE:** (403) 435-7831
Edmonton, Alberta T6J 5M8   **FAX:** (403) 434-2888

CONTACT: Melanie Rockett, Editor   **DESCRIPTION:** Publishes trade non-fiction; how-to's for writers, photographers and artists.
WRITERS: "We are looking for how-to information for writers and photographers. Submit entire manuscript and a list or copies (NOT ORIGINALS) of supporting photographic illustration. We would prefer material on disk, IBM Dos Wordperfect 5.1 or 6. We are also looking for personal marketing experience articles for the next edition of *Canadian Markets for Writers and Photographers.*" Include SASE. Pay is negotiated. "We will reply to all manuscripts within eight weeks of receipt. If we are interested in your article it will be kept on file. Final decision will be made prior to publishing the next edition. Once we decide to use an article we will call you to negotiate terms. Please update your phone # and address if you move. If your article is not suitable we will return it within 8 weeks."
PHOTOGRAPHERS: Photographs supplied with manuscript or text/photo package.
NOTES: "This entire book stresses a professional approach. If your submission does not strive for professional perfection I am not interested."

PROSVETA INC.
1565 Montée Masson, Duvermay est   **PHONE:** (514) 661-4242
Laval, PQ H7E 4P2   **FAX:** (416) 661-4984

141 West 7th Ave.   **PHONE:** (604) 872-0860
Suite #202
Vancouver BC V5Y 1L8

CONTACT: Michel Duchesneau, Publisher   **DESCRIPTION:** Publishes general trade non-fiction and philosophy books. Books are printed in France; translated and printed in English.
WRITERS: "We are not reading unsolicited manuscripts in 1995."
PHOTOGRAPHERS: All photography is done in-house.

PURICH PUBLISHING
Box 23032, Market Mall P.O.   **PHONE:** (306) 373-5311
Saskatoon, SK S7J 5H3   **FAX:** (306) 373-5315

CONTACT: Don Purich, Publisher   **DESCRIPTION:** Publishes law books, aboriginal issues, agriculture and western issues. Aimed at the university research markets. Recent publications include: *Aboriginal Self-Government in Canada* edited by John Helton and *The Cypress Hills: The Land and its People* by Brian Hubner and Walter Hildebrandt. Publishes 3-4 titles per year. US Distribution.
WRITERS: 30% of books published are by first-time authors. Works with unagented writers. Send a query letter with outline and the intended audience and SASE. If the material is of interest we will contact the author for sample chapters. Average response time 4-6 weeks. Publishes in 4-6 months. Royalty and advance negotiable.
PHOTOGRAPHERS: All photography is done in-house.

THE QUARRY PRESS
Box 1061, 240 King Street East
Kingston, ON K7L 4Y5

PHONE: (613) 548-8429
FAX: (613) 548-1556

CONTACT: Bob Hilderley, Editor **DESCRIPTION:** Publishes poetry, fiction, educational texts, children's books, rock and pop culture books, theatre and drama manuscripts. Publishes 20-30 titles per year. Recent publications include: *Superman Song: The Story of the Crash Test Dummies* by Stephen Ostick; *The Perfect Cold Warrior* by Gary Geddes; and *I Mention the Garden for Clarity* by Vivian Marple. US Distribution.
WRITERS: 10% of books published are by first-time authors. Works with unagented writers. Send a query letter ONLY with SASE - no outline or sample chapter. Average response time 12-16 weeks. Average first-time print run 1,000 books. Royalty and advance negotiable.
PHOTOGRAPHERS: Contact with a query letter and samples, to be kept on file to, Susan Hannah, Art Director.

QUINTIN PUBLISHERS/ EDITIONS MICHEL QUINTIN
4818 Foster, Box 340
Waterloo, PQ J0E 2N0

PHONE: (514) 539-3774
FAX: (514) 539-4905

CONTACT: Director of English Production: Christiane Debrentani
Director of French Production: Michel Quintin **DESCRIPTION:** Publishes books on Canadian nature and the environment. Some are guides, natural history and stories for both adults and children. Publishes in both English and French. Publishes an average of 10 titles per year. Distributed only in Canada.
WRITERS: Accepts completed manuscripts or queries. Responds in 3-4 weeks. Considers simultaneous submissions. Writers' guidelines are not available.
PHOTOGRAPHERS: Buys photography occasionally. "We don't buy a lot." Send samples to Michel Quintin. Photo guidelines are not available.
NOTES: For a catalogue send 9x12" SASE.

QUON EDITIONS
10103 - 97A Avenue
Edmonton, AB T5K 2T3

PHONE: (403) 428-3333
FAX: (403) 488-3966

CONTACT: Wei Yew **DESCRIPTION:** "We publish primarily special interest design books. For example we have a book on wedding invitations and birth announcements and we have a book on condom advertisements and promotions, a book of the covers that Marilyn Monroe has appeared on, a book on museum and art gallery graphics. Recent titles: *Marilyn Monroe Uncovers; HARDWEAR-The Art of the Condom.*
WRITERS: "We will listen to peoples ideas and evaluate unsolicited manuscripts. We often generate our own ideas and then publish. I don't mind hearing good ideas. We look for interesting graphic design or reference material. People can either write or phone us."
PHOTOGRAPHERS: "We don't buy stock photography."

RAGWEED PRESS INC.
Box 2023
Charlottetown, PE C1A 7N7

PHONE: (902) 566-5750
FAX: (902) 566-4473

CONTACT: Lynn Henry, Editor **DESCRIPTION:** Publishes fiction and non-fiction; Atlantic regional, literature, history, children's books, feminist and lesbian writing. Publishes

12 titles per year. Recent publications include: *Patient No More: The Politics of Breast Cancer* by Sharon Batt and *Rosalie's Catastrophes* by Ginette Anfousse.
WRITERS: 20% of books published are by first-time authors. Works with unagented authors. Send a query letter with outline and one or two chapters. Average response time 8-10 weeks. Publishes in 24-36 months. First-time print run 1,500-3,000. Royalty 10% on retail sales. Advance negotiable.
PHOTOGRAPHERS: Photographs and illustrations used for text illustration and book covers. Illustrators in particular are invited to send a query letter and samples of work, to be kept on file. Contact: Janet Riopelle, Designer.
NOTES: "We are looking for writers in the Atlantic region. Writers from Ontario or the Western Provinces are not given first consideration. We get a lot of unsuitable children's books submissions - query us first."

RANDOM HOUSE OF CANADA LTD.

33 Yonge Street, Suite 210   **PHONE:** (416) 624-0672
Toronto, ON M5E 1G4   **FAX:** (416) 624-6217

CONTACT: Douglas Pepper, Managing Editor   **DESCRIPTION:** Publishes fiction and general trade non-fiction. Includes cookbooks, literature, gardening, history, biography, education, family, Does not publish mystery, romance, children's or poetry. Publishes 50 titles per year. Recent titles: *River of Stone* and *A Discovery of Strangers* by Rudy Wiebe. Imprint: Vintage Canada
WRITERS: "Send a query letter only, we do not have time to read unsolicited manuscripts." Prefers to work with writer's agents. Response time 3-4 months. Publishes in 10-14 months. Photos used for text illustration, book covers, dust covers.

RED DEER COLLEGE PRESS

P.O. Box 5005,   **PHONE:** (403) 342-3321
Red Deer, AB T4N 5H5   **FAX:** (403) 340-8940

CONTACT: Dennis Johnson, Managing Editor   **DESCRIPTION:** Publishes books for the home and garden, adult and juvenile fiction, regional non-fiction, natural history, children's books, poetry and drama. Publishes 14-16 titles per year. Recent publications include: *Children's Illustrated Josefa: A Prairie Boy's Story* by Jim McGoogan and *The Third Suspect: The Roger Warren Story* by Greg Owens and David Staples.
WRITERS: 10% of books published are by first-time authors. Send a query letter with outline and one or two chapters. Average response time 12-24 weeks. Publishes in 18-30 months. Average first-time print run, depending on the subject area, 1,000-6,000. Average royalty 8-10% on retail sales. Advances negotiable.
PHOTOGRAPHERS: Photographs and illustrations used for text illustration and book covers. Contact with a query letter and sample of work, to be kept on file. Contact: Tim Wynne-Jones, Children's Book Editor.
NOTES: "Please note that our children's illustrated and juvenile fiction programs are booked until 1997. WE ARE NOT ACCEPTING MANUSCRIPTS IN THOSE AREAS."

REFERENCE PRESS
Box 70   **PHONE:** (519) 392-6634
Teeswater, ON N0G 2S0

CONTACT: Gordon Ripley, Publisher   **DESCRIPTION:** Publishes non-fiction reference
books as well as large print books. Recent publications include: *Who's Who in Canadian
Literature* and *The Canadian Serials Directory*; *Northern Journey: A Guide to Canadian
Folk Music* (discography and directory) and *The Canadian Periodicals Index*. US distribution
on selected titles.
WRITERS: "We occasionally publish unsolicited manuscripts, mostly indexes and
directories." Send a query letter with outline. Average response time 1-2 weeks. Average
first-time print run 500.
PHOTOGRAPHERS: Photos used for book covers. Contact with a query letter with samples
to be kept on file.

REFERENCE WEST
2450 Central Ave   **PHONE:** (604) 598-0096
Victoria, BC V8S 2S8

CONTACT: Rhonda Batchelor or Charles Lillard   **DESCRIPTION:** "We are a small
press. We have several series of poetry and short stories." Produces 15 books per year.
Authors; Lorna Crozier, Patrick Lane; major Canadian poets as well as unknowns.
WRITERS: "We don't actively solicit manuscripts as the books we produce accompany
a reading series. We will accept queries with a letter and samples of work. Takes one month
to reply. 40% are first time authors, most are in the Victoria region. We pay in books.
Considers simultaneous submissions if informed.
PHOTOGRAPHERS: Does not purchase.
NOTES: A catalogue is available with a 9x12 SASE.

REID PUBLISHING LTD.
Box 69559   **PHONE:** (905) 842-4428
109 Thomas Street   **FAX:** (905) 842-9327
Oakville, ON L6J 7R4

CONTACT: Stan Reid, Publisher   **DESCRIPTION:** Publishes human resource training
materials. We specialize in presentation skills, effective networking, empowerment, organizing
your work space. Publishes 8-10 titles per year. Recent publications include: *Effective
Presentation Skills* and *The Adult Learner*. US Distribution.
WRITERS: 25% of books published are by first-time authors. Works with unagented
writers. "Most of our books average 65-130 pages." Send a query letter with Table of Contents
and one chapter. Average response time 3-4 weeks. First-time print run 3,000-20,000,
depending on the subject. Publishes in 6-12 months.
PHOTOGRAPHERS: Photos are used for illustration and book covers. Contact with a
query letter with samples to be kept on file.

REIDMORE BOOKS INC.
10109-106th Street #1200   **PHONE:** (403) 424-4420
Edmonton, AB   T5J 3L7   **FAX:** (403) 441-9919

CONTACT: Cathie Crooks, Director of Sales and Marketing   **DESCRIPTION:** Reidmore Books is an educational publisher aimed at the elementary and high school markets. "We publish social studies, math and maybe one trade title per year. We publish about 4-5 educational books per year. Recent publications include: *Canada, Its Land and People* (2nd Ed.); *The Sikh Canadian; For King and Country* (trade); *Earth 1995 Calendar.* Takes 8 months or longer to publish once accepted. 70% of authors are first time authors. Considers simultaneous submissions. Some distribution in the US.

WRITERS: "Quite often we will commission a manuscript to be done for primarily educational titles. We assess them to see if there is a market. Queries are fine as long as they specify the market they are targeting and the curriculum they are following." Writers' guidelines are not available. "The most important thing is to do some market research first and tell us who is going to use this book and why they are going to use it. If is an educational title you must state what curriculum it is going to satisfy and what age group."

PHOTOGRAPHERS: "We do accept queries from photographers. The type of image depends on the project. Photographers can send a stock or subject list to Leah-Ann Lymer." Uses both black & white and colour. "It's best to just send a list, no phone calls please."

REPOSITORY PRESS
RR#7, Buckhorm Road   **PHONE:** (604) 562-7074
Site 29, Comp 8   **FAX:** (604) 561-7094
Prince George, BC   V2N 2J5

CONTACT: John Harris, Publisher-Owner   **DESCRIPTION:** Publishes travel guides.

RIVERWOOD PUBLISHERS LTD.
6 Donlands Ave. Box 70   **PHONE:** (905) 478-8396
Sharon, ON   L0G 1V0   **FAX:** (905) 478-8380

CONTACT: Ron Charlesworth   **DESCRIPTION:** Publishes juvenile fiction books for ages 8-13. Recent titles: *Bubsy* by Don Lemma; *Mystery at Meander Lake* by Beverly Bayle; *Ghostly Tales of Mr. Tooth* by Gerald Holt.

WRITERS: "At the moment we are in a holding pattern because we have quite a backlog of material. We are limiting manuscripts to only juvenile fiction. Send in a synopsis with the first 3 chapters. Three quarters of our authors are first time authors. Royalties vary between 5-10% based on retail sales." Replies in 4-6 weeks.

PHOTOGRAPHERS: No photography is purchased.

ROCKY MOUNTAIN BOOKS
#4 Spruce Centre SW   **PHONE:** (403) 249-9490
Calgary, AB   T3C 3B3   **FAX:** (403) 249-2968

CONTACT: Tony and Gillean Daffern, Publishers   **DESCRIPTION:** Publishes books on outdoor recreation including skiing, hiking, climbing, biking, whitewater rafting, guidebooks, history of Alberta, British Columbia, and the Yukon. Recent publications include: *Canmore and Kananaskis Country: Short Walks for Inquiring Minds* by Gillean Daffern;

Scrambles in the Canadian Rockies by Alan Kane and *Sport Climbs in the Canadian Rockies* by John Martin and Jon Jones.
WRITERS: 25% of books published are by first-time authors. Send a query letter with outline and chapters. Average response time 1-4 weeks. Average first-time print run 1,000-2,000. Publishes in 6-12 months. Average royalty 10% on retail sales.
PHOTOGRAPHERS: Photography handled in-house. Illustrations used for text illustration and book covers. Contact with a query letter with samples, to be kept on file.

ROEHER INSTITUTE
4700 Keele Street **PHONE:** (416) 661-9611
Kinsmen Bldg. York University, **FAX:** (416) 661-5701
North York, ON M3J 1P3

CONTACT: Laura Lee, Editor **DESCRIPTION:** Publishes social policy research and issues pertaining to people with disabilities.
WRITERS: We are not reading unsolicited manuscripts. All writing is done in-house.
PHOTOGRAPHERS: All photography is done in-house.

ROLAND & JACOB INC.
52 Hazelton Ave.
Toronto, ON M5R 2E2

NOTES: "We are not actively publishing anymore."

ROSEWAY PUBLISHING LTD.
RR#1 **PHONE:** (902) 656-2223
Lockeport, NS B0T 1L0

CONTACT: Kathleen Tudor **DESCRIPTION:** "We publish all sorts of books. Fiction, non-fiction, poetry, and children's books. We average 2 per year." Recent Titles: *Passionfruit Tea: A Collection of Short Stories* by Eleanor Schönmaier; *Windjammers and Blue Nose Sailors*; *Out of the Depths*. "We are in the process of producing a very fine children's book called *Alexander and the Sky Blue Eggs*, and we are doing a collection of poetry by Sue McLeod which will be out in September." Established in 1990. Distributed in the US.
WRITERS: "We prefer queries with an outline or short description. We don't do anything military, religious or anti-feminist. Everything must include an SASE. Almost 100% of our authors are first time authors. Some of them are first time for literary works." Works with unagented writers. 10% royalties based on retail sales. Considers simultaneous submissions if told upfront. Responds within 3 months maximum.
PHOTOGRAPHERS: "We have used some photos for some books. It depends on the book. I try generally to use local people. If I needed a photographer I would use one from here and I do know a great deal of people here."

ROUTLEDGE
59 Moore Park Cres.
Georgetown, ON L7G 2T5

NOTES: Could not locate. Phone number is not in service (416) 873-2656.

ROYAL ONTARIO MUSEUM
PUBLICATION AND PRINT SERVICES
100 Queen's Park   **PHONE:** (416) 586-5581
Toronto, ON M5S 2C6   **FAX:** (416) 586-5827

CONTACT: Sandra Shaul   **DESCRIPTION:** Publishes manuscripts on the museum's collection. Also published a few books for general readership and children's books. Publishes 2-3 titles per year. Recent publications include: *Legends of Canada* by Fowkes and *Discover Mysteries of the Past and Present; Discover Bones* and *Discover Dinosaurs* all by Katherine Grier.
WRITERS: "Most of our writing is done in-house." Send a query letter with outline. Response time 4-12 weeks.
PHOTOGRAPHERS: All photography is done in-house.

RUBICON PUBLISHING INC.
116 Thomas St. Suite #1   **PHONE:** (905) 849-8777
Oakville, ON L6J 3A8   **FAX:** (905) 849-7579

CONTACT: Maggie Goh, Publisher   **DESCRIPTION:** Publishes school texts and trade titles in the children's and young adult categories and some coffee table books. Publishes 8-10 titles per year. Recent publications include: *Home and Homeland; Companies of Invention; Signs of Thunder; Looking for a Hero; Champlain's Summer* and *On the Lines: The Autobiography of Ron Finn.*
WRITERS: 10% of books published are by first-time authors. Works with unagented or agented writers. Send a query letter with whole manuscript or sample chapters. Average response time 2-6 weeks.
PHOTOGRAPHERS: Average first-time print run 4,000-5,000. Publishes in 9-12 months. Average royalty 10% on retail sales. Advance negotiable.
NOTES: Photographs and illustrations used for text illustration and book covers. Contact with a query letter and samples, to be kept on file.

SCHOLASTIC CANADA LTD.
123 Newkirk Road   **PHONE:** (416) 883-5300
Richmond Hill, ON L4C 3G5   **FAX:** (416) 882-1684

CONTACT: Laura Peetoom, Children's Book Editor   **DESCRIPTION:** Publishes children's books, fiction, and non-fiction from pre-school to young adults. Recent titles include: *Gifts* by JoEllen Bogart, illustrator Barbara Reid; *Just Call Me Boom Boom* by Martyn Godfrey (junior novel); *Big Ben* by Larry Scanlan (non-fiction). "We publish roughly 30 books per year, some are co-published with other companies.
WRITERS: We publish a very low percentage from first time authors, maybe 5% or even less. At the moment we are not accepting unsolicited manuscripts. This has been our policy for the last few years. For now we have lots of material to work with. When it starts running dry we may accept unsoliced manuscripts again."
PHOTOGRAPHERS: "We rarely purchase photos. We may commission or purchase from stock companies."

SECOND STORY PRESS

720 Bathurst Street West, Suite 301   **PHONE:** (416) 537-7850
Toronto, ON M5S 2R4   **FAX:** (416) 537-7850

CONTACT: Liz Martin   **DESCRIPTION:** Publishes approximately 10 non-fiction trade, fiction and children's books annually. Recent publications include: *The Women's Daybook,* updated annually, featuring Canadian women photographers; *Kid Culture: Children and Adults in Popular Culture* by Kathleen McDonnell; *A Friend Like Zilla* by Rachna Gilmore; *Sexual Harassment: High School Girls Speak Out* by June Larkin and *Found Treasures: Stories by Yiddish Women Writers* edited by Freda Forman et al.
WRITERS: 50% of books published are by first-time authors. Works with unagented authors. "Send a query letter with outline and two chapters. Picture book authors could send the whole manuscript." Average response time 12-16 weeks. Royalty and advance negotiable.
PHOTOGRAPHERS: Photos used for illustration, book covers, and dust jackets. Contact with a query letter and samples or colour xeroxes of art work. Photographers should submit a query for the Daybook calendar. "Contact us before August 1st for details about the deadline and theme for the Daybook. The Daybook includes photos from 13 women photographers. One for each month and a cover shot. The theme changes every year. For 1995 it was Women in Creativity and for 96 Mothers. The photos are black & white only."

SIGNET PUBLICATIONS

10 Wingrove Hill   **PHONE:** (416) 239-2629
Etobicoke, ON M9B 2C6

DESCRIPTION: Publishes a very limited number of children's books. "Next year we are planning one book."
NOTES: "Do not send submissions or query. "We are just too small."

SIMON & PIERRE PUBLISHING CO. LTD.

2181 Queen Street East, Suite 301   **PHONE:** (416) 698-0454
Toronto, ON M4E 1E5   **FAX:** (416) 698-1102

CONTACT: Jean Paton, Editor-in-Chief   **DESCRIPTION:** Publishes Canadian drama and theatre titles, literary fiction, criticism and education. Publishes 10-15 new titles a year. Subsidiary of the Dundurn Group.
WRITERS: 25% of books published are by first-time authors. Submit query with resumé, one chapter and an outline of the book. Average response time 6-8 weeks. Publishes in 6-12 months. Average first-time print run 2,000-5,000. Royalty negotiable, usually 10% for trade books, 8% for educational titles. Small advances negotiable.
PHOTOGRAPHERS: Authors provide some materials.

SISTER VISION PRESS

Box 217, Station E   **PHONE:** (416) 595-5033
Toronto, ON M6H 4E2   **FAX:** (416) 533-2397

CONTACT: Makeda Silvera, Editorial and Rights Director   **DESCRIPTION:** "We publishes books by women of colour. We publish fiction, poetry, historical, theoretical and children's books. Approximately 8 new titles per year. Distributed in US.
WRITERS: "Contact us by telephone or by letter. We accept completed manuscripts." Takes 2-3 months to respond. 60-70% first time authors. Works with unagented writers.

Considers simultaneous submissions. Royalty is paid on retail sales. Writers' guidelines are available with an SASE.
PHOTOGRAPHERS: "We use photography in the books and on the covers. We accept queries from photographers. We can set up an appointment as well. Formats include all sizes of colour or black & white." Payment is negotiated. Credit line given. Photo guidelines are available.

SOMERVILLE HOUSE PUBLISHING LTD.

3080 Yonge Street, Suite 5000   **PHONE:** (416) 488-5938
Toronto, ON M4N 3N1   **FAX:** (416) 488-5506

CONTACT: Anna Filippone, Editorial Assistant   **DESCRIPTION:** Publishes general trade books, adult fiction, non-fiction, literature, and metaphysics. Does not publish poetry, children's books, sci-fi or romance. Publishes 4-6 new titles per year.
WRITERS: "We have not to date published an unsolicited manuscript." Contact with a query letter. Average response time 3-6 weeks for a query; 3-6 months for a manuscript.
PHOTOGRAPHERS: Photos used for illustrations and book covers. Contact with a query letter and samples.

SONO NIS PRESS

1745 Blanshard Street   **PHONE:** (604) 382-1024
Victoria, BC V8W 2J8   **FAX:** (604) 382-1575

CONTACT: Darrel Morriss, President Ann West, Publisher   **DESCRIPTION:** Publishes history, biographies, exploration, poetry, and maritime history. Publishes 9-10 titles per year. Recent publications include: *The Skyline Limited* and *The Sicamous and the Naramata: Steamboat Days in the Okanagan* by Robert Turner and *Hard Candy* by Linda Rogers.
WRITERS: 10% of books published are by first-time authors. "We try to do one poetry title a year by a first-time author." Send a query letter with outline, sample chapter and SASE. Average response time 2-4 weeks. "Finished manuscripts take longer." Publishes in 12-15 months. First-time print run varies.
PHOTOGRAPHERS: All photography is done in-house.

SOUND AND VISION PUBLISHING LIMITED

359 Riverdale Ave.   **PHONE:** (416) 465-8184
Toronto, ON M4J 1A4   **FAX:** (416) 465-4163

CONTACT: Geoff Savage, Publisher   **DESCRIPTION:** Publishes music and humour texts. Publishes 2 titles per year. US, UK, and Australian distribution. Recent publications include: *Bark, Beethoven and the Boys: Music History as It Ought to be Told* by David Barber and *Artoons: A Hystery of Art* by Kevin Reeves and *I Want to be Sedated* by Phil Daly and Scott Woods.
WRITERS: 20% of books published are by first-time authors. Works with unagented writers. Send a query letter with outline and one or two chapters. "I respond on the same day if I like the idea. It's not the case that you would wait three months for me to respond." Publishes in 6-12 months. Royalty and advance negotiable.
PHOTOGRAPHERS: All photography is done in-house.

ST. REMY PRESS INC.
Mison Bagg 682 William   **PHONE:** 514 871-9696
Montreal, PQ H3C 1N9   **FAX:** 514 871-2230

CONTACT: Caroline Jackson   **DESCRIPTION:** Publishes approximately 15 trade, non-fiction books per year.
WRITERS: "We do not accept unsolicited manuscripts, we do not do any fiction. We assign writers when we need them and we have writers in-house."
PHOTOGRAPHERS: All photography is done in-house.

STEEL RAIL PUBLISHING
100 Richmond St. East, Suite 435
Toronto, ON M5C 2P9

NOTES: Could not locate. Phone number is not in service (416) 777-0400.

STEWART HOUSE see McClelland & Stewart

STODDART PUBLISHING CO. LIMITED
34 Lesmill Road   **PHONE:** (416) 445-3333
Don Mills, Ontario M3B 2T6   **FAX:** (416) 445-5967

CONTACT: Kathryn Cole, Publisher
Don Bastian, Managing Editor   **DESCRIPTION:** Publishes non-fiction and fiction trade books for adults, young adults, and children. Includes a few picture books. Subject areas: political issues, economics, biographies, autobiographies, health, sports and photography. Publishes 65 titles per year. Recent publications include: *Maple Leaf Against the Axis: Canada's Second World War* by David Bercuson; *The Truth About Breast Cancer* by Claire Hoy and *Empire of the Soul: Some Journeys in India* by Paul William Roberts. Children's titles: *The Tiny Kite of Eddie Wing* by Maxine Trottier; *The Mud Family* by Betsy James; *The Dragon's Pearl* by Julie Lawson.
WRITERS: 20% of books published are by first-time authors. Works with 60% unagented writers and 40% agented authors. Writers' guidelines available with SASE. Send a query letter with outline and two chapters. For children's picture books send the whole manuscript with SASE to Kathryn Cole. Average first-time print run 3,500-5,000. Average response time 2-6 weeks; for children's titles 8-12 weeks. Publishes in 6-12 months. Average royalty 10% on retail sales. Advance negotiable.
PHOTOGRAPHERS: Contact with a query letter and samples with SASE. Do not send originals and state whether you want materials returned with SASE. Photos used for illustration, book covers, and dust jackets.

SUMMERHILL BOOKS
Box 597
Alliston, ON L0M 1A0

NOTES: Purchased by Breakwater Books.

SUMMERTHOUGHT LTD.
Box 1420
Banff, AB T0L 0C0

PHONE: (403) 762-3919
FAX: (403) 762-4126

CONTACT: Gabi Steiner-Wedin, Editor   DESCRIPTION: Publishes non-fiction trail guides and guide books. Also publishes books on animals, birds, flowers, local historic sites and geology. Recent publications include: *Canadian Rockies Trail Guide* and *Parkways to the Canadian Rockies.*
WRITERS: Considers first-time authors. Works with unagented writers. Handles 80% of writing requirements in-house. Send a query letter with outline and chapter. Average response time 3-5 weeks. Print run variable. Royalty negotiable.
PHOTOGRAPHERS: All photography is done in-house.

SUNFIRE PUBLICATIONS LTD.
Box 3399
Langley, BC V3A 4R7

NOTES: NO LONGER PUBLISHING

SYNAXIX PRESS
37323 Hawkins Road
Dewdney, BC V0M 1H0

PHONE: (604) 826-9336
FAX: (604) 820-9758

CONTACT: Lazar Puhalo, Publisher   DESCRIPTION: Publishes non-fiction titles in subject area of Eastern European history and religion. Publishes 4-6 titles per year. Recent titles include: *The Life of Innokenty of Alaska* and *The Soul, The Body and Death: An Eastern Orthodox View* both titles by Lazar Puhalo.
WRITERS: Works with unagented writers. "We occasionally publish others' works if they are restricted within our field of Eastern European culture and history. We have a special interest in Byzantine culture and history. Most of our authors have already published in scholarly journals." Send a query letter with Table of Contents, outline and SASE. Average response time 3-6 weeks. Average first-time print run 1,000. Publishes in 6-12 months. "If people submit on disk we can typeset through Word Perfect." Average royalty 10% on retail sales. No advance given.
PHOTOGRAPHERS: All photography is done in-house.

TALON BOOKS LTD.
1019 East Cordova Street, Suite 201
Vancouver, BC V6A 1M8

PHONE: (604) 253-5261
FAX: (604) 255-5755

CONTACT: Karl Siegler, Publisher   DESCRIPTION: Publishes books on drama, fiction, non-fiction, poetry, women's literature, social issues, and ethnography. Publishes 6-8 titles per year. Recent publications include: *The Ends of the Earth* by Morris Panych;

Tchipayuk: or The Way of the Wolf by Ronald Lavallée, translated by Patricia Claxton; *The Angel of Solitude* by Marie Claire Blais, translated by Laura Hodes; *First Quarter of the Moon* by Michel Tremblay, translated by Sheila Fischman; and *Lost in North America* by John Gray.
WRITERS: 20-30% of books published are by first-time authors. Works with agented or unagented authors. Send a query letter with outline or sample chapters. "Please do not send unsolicited poetry. In terms of drama, we are only interested in plays that have been professionally produced." Average response time 8-16 weeks. Royalties and advances negotiable.
PHOTOGRAPHERS: All photography is done in-house.
NOTES: "We are not publishing anything new until 1997."

TANAGER PRESS
145 Troy Street   **PHONE:** (905) 891-2502
Mississauga, ON   L5G 1S8   **FAX:** (905) 891-6884

CONTACT: J. Neveleff   **DESCRIPTION:** "We publish general interest non-fiction books. We produce about 1 a year." Titles: *Cook Milk in Any Flavour* by the Ontario Milk Marketing Board; *Milk's Microwave Cookbook*.
WRITERS: "We accept queries with an outline, bio details and one sample chapter. We don't accept unsolicited manuscripts." Takes 60-90 days to reply to queries. Works with first time and unagented writers. Royalty payments depend on the type of book. Selected titles are distributed in the US. Average print run 6,000-10,000. Considers simultaneous submissions. Writers' guidelines are not available. "We do a lot of co-publishing."
PHOTOGRAPHERS: "Supporting photography comes as part of the package."

TANTALAS BOOKS
Box 255   **PHONE:** (709) 651-3136
Gander, NF A1V 1W6   **FAX:** (709) 651-3849

CONTACT: Ron Morrison, Publisher   **DESCRIPTION:** Publishes children's picture books. Publishes 1 book per year. Most recent title: *The Spider in the Woodpile* by Ron Morrison.
WRITERS: "For at least two more years I will be self-publishing. That may change in 1997."
PHOTOGRAPHERS: Photos used for illustration, book covers, dust jackets. Contact with a query letter with sample portfolio, to be kept on file.

TELDON CALENDARS
3500 Viking Way   **PHONE:** (604) 273-4500
Richmond, BC V6V 1N6   **FAX:** (604) 273-6100

CONTACT: Monica Vent, Photo Editor   **DESCRIPTION:** Publishes calendars of all types.
WRITERS: "We do not publish books of any type."
PHOTOGRAPHERS: "We need photography and fine art painting or watercolour art for our calendars." Contact this publication by phone, fax or send a query letter, requesting Submission Guidelines. "We need your name, address and phone number. We do not need a SASE. We do not like receiving unsolicited photos. The guidelines indicate how we operate,

what kind of images we are looking for, what our rates are and everything you need to know before we will look at your work."

THEYTUS BOOKS

Box 20040   PHONE: (604) 493-7181
Penticton, BC V2A 8K3   FAX: (604) 493-5302

CONTACT: Greg Young-Ing, Publisher   DESCRIPTION: Publishes First Nation literature, fiction, non-fiction, art, music and educational books by aboriginal authors. Publishes 11 titles per year. Recent publications include: *Opening in the Sky* by Armand Ruffo and *Stones and Switches* by Lorne Simon.
WRITERS: 25% of books published are by first-time authors. "We accept unsolicited manuscripts, either whole or in-part." Average response time 4-12 weeks. Publishes in 6-12 months. Average first-time print run 2,000. Average royalty 10% on retail sales. Gives $200 advance to writer.
PHOTOGRAPHERS: Photos used for illustration, book covers, dust jackets. Contact with a query letter with sample portfolio, to be kept on file.

THISTLEDOWN PRESS LTD.

633 Main Street   PHONE: (306) 244-1722
Saskatoon, SK S7H 0J8   FAX: (306) 244-1762

CONTACT: Patrick O'Rourke   DESCRIPTION: Publishes Canadian poetry, short fiction, and adult and juvenile fiction. Publishes 8-10 titles per year. "This year is our 20th anniversary and we are doing 20 new titles." Recent publications include: *Windshifter* by Linda Smith and *Dance of the Snow Dragon* by Eileen Kernaghan.
WRITERS: "Our *New Leaf* series is dedicated to publishing new authors. There are four authors in each 64-page book of either fiction or poetry." Works with unagented writers. Contact with a query letter." Average response time 4-8 weeks. Publishing time and print-runs vary. Average royalty 10% on retail sales. Rarely give advances.
PHOTOGRAPHERS: Photographers and illustrators used for illustration, book covers, and dust jackets. Contact with a query letter and sample portfolio with SASE. "Generally we keep the work on file for future use, but if we cannot use it we will return with SASE."
NOTES: Submission Guidelines.Guidelines and catalogue are available, please send 9x12 SASE."

THOMPSON EDUCATIONAL PUBLISHING INC.

14 Ripley Ave.   PHONE: (416) 766-2763
Toronto, ON M6S 3N9   FAX: (416) 766-0398

CONTACT: Keith Thompson, Publisher   DESCRIPTION: Publishes textbooks for high school, college and university. Publishes 10-15 titles per year. Recent publications include: *Political Ideologies and Political Philosophies; Ethnicity in Canada; Canadian Social Trends*.
WRITERS: 20% of books published are by first-time authors. Works with unagented writers. Send query letter with resumé and samples of writing.
PHOTOGRAPHERS: Contact with resumé and samples to be kept on file.

TRALCO EDUCATIONAL SERVICES INC
297 Brucedale Ave, East   **PHONE:** (416) 575-5717
Hamilton, ON L9A 1R2   **FAX:** (416) 575-1783

CONTACT: Karen Trainer, Publisher **DESCRIPTION:** Publishes Grade 4-12 material, teacher resource materials for use in English as a Second Language and French as a Second Language programs. Publishes 4-6 titles per year. Recent publications include: *Le Fast Food; Creative Cartoon Capers; Poetry: The Write Reaction* and *Mardi Gras in New Orleans*.
WRITERS: 80% of books published are by first-time authors. "I have a student who is doing a second book, at the age of 18." Average response time 2-6 weeks. Contact with a query letter. Average first-time print run 500-1,000. Publishes in 6-18 months. Average royalty 10% on retail sales. No advance given.
PHOTOGRAPHERS: Illustrators and graphic artists used for borders, design and illustration. Illustrators and graphic artists may send a query letter, business card, sample art, to be kept on file, and SASE.

TREE FROG PRESS LIMITED
10144-89 Street   **PHONE:** (403) 429-1947
Edmonton, AB T5H 1P7   **FAX:** (403) 574-0229

CONTACT: Allan Shute **DESCRIPTION:** Publishes children's books for kindergarten aged kids to young adults. Also publishes some local histories. Publishes 4 books per year. *The McIntyre Liar* by David Bly; *Abaleda Voluntary Firehouse Band* by Dianne Young, illustrated by Barbara Hartmann.
WRITERS: "We like to see completed manuscripts with a 9x12 SASE. We are accepting submissions in the fall of 1995. A good percentage of our authors are first time authors. We prefer not to receive simultaneous submissions. Send $5.00 for writers' guidelines and a catalogue."
PHOTOGRAPHERS: "We sometimes use photography and illustrations. We like to see a very low cost portfolio that we can keep on file; we like to see the flexibility and range of the artist. It takes on average 9 to 18 months to publish a book. Royalties are about 10% of the retail sales. 2,000 would be an average print run, though it really depends on the book. We want to see people's very best work. We don't want to see seasonal stories (Christmas or Halloween)."

TREE HOUSE PRESS INC.
16 Harlowe Road, Unit #2   **PHONE:** (416) 574-3399
Hamilton, ON L8W 3R6   **FAX:** (416) 574-0228

CONTACT: Paul Hannam, Publisher **DESCRIPTION:** Publishes supplementary whole language resource materials for Grades 1-12.
WRITERS: "Not accepting unsolicited manuscripts. All writing is done in-house."
PHOTOGRAPHERS: All photography is done in-house.

TUNDRA BOOKS INC./ LIVRES TOUNDRA INC.
345 Victoria Avenue, Suite 604   **PHONE:** (514) 932-5434
Westmount, PQ H3Z 2N2   **FAX:** (514) 484-2152

CONTACT: Arjun Basu, Managing Editor   **DESCRIPTION:** Publishes children's books and art books in English and French. Publishes 10-12 books per year. Distributes in the US. Titles: *Hockey Sweater; Prairie Alphabet.*
WRITERS: "We accept completed manuscripts with a SASE. 20% are first time authors. Royalties are negotiated. We publish within one year of acceptance. Our average print run is 6,000." Considers simultaneous submissions; must be informed. Writers' guidelines are available. "Writers should be familiar with our books before they contact us."
PHOTOGRAPHERS: No photography is used.

TURNER-WARWICK PUBLICATIONS INC.
892 - 104 Street
North Battleford, Sask. S9A 3E6

NOTES: NO LONGER PUBLISHING

TURNSTONE PRESS LTD.
100 Arthur Street, Suite 607   **PHONE:** 204 947-1555
Winnipeg, MB R3B 1H3   **FAX:** 204 942-1555
                                   E-Mail:
                                   editor@turnstonepress.mb.ca

CONTACT: Jamie Hutchison, Managing Editor   **DESCRIPTION:** Literary trade publisher. Titles range from general non-fiction to fiction; poetry, fiction, and literary criticism. Does not publish children's picture books. Publishes 10-12 titles per year. Recent publications include: *Touch the Dragon* by Karen Connelly and *The Dragon and the Dragon's Princess* by David Arnason.
WRITERS: 30% of books published are by first-time authors. Works with unagented writers. Send a query letter with outline and 30-50 pages of the manuscript. "We prefer E-Mail submissions." Average response time 6-8 weeks. E-Mail response 2-3 weeks. Publishes in 18 months. First-time print run varies according to title, 600-5,000. Average royalty 10% on retail/wholesale sales. Advance negotiable.
PHOTOGRAPHERS: "Generally, photos are included with the book submission, however occasionally we look outside." Photographs and illustrations used for book covers. Contact with a query letter with sample portfolio, to be kept on file.

UBC PRESS
6344 Memorial Road,   **PHONE:** (604) 822-3259
University of British Columbia   **FAX:** (604) 822-6083
Vancouver, BC V6T 1Z2

CONTACT: Jean Wilson, Senior Editor   **DESCRIPTION:** Publishes non-fiction; scholarly, educational, social and natural sciences and general audiences titles. Subjects include environmental, Canadian political science and history, sociology, and native studies. Recent publications include: *A Heart at Leisure From Itself: Caroline Macdonald of Japan* by Margaret Prang; *First Nations Education in Canada: The Circle Unfolds* edited by Marie Battiste and Jean Barman and *Canada and Quebec: One Countries, Two Histories* by Robert Bothwell.

WRITERS: 20% of books published are by first-time authors. Works with unagented writers. Send a query letter with outline and sample chapter. Average response time 2-4 weeks. Publishes in 6-12 months. First-time print run 500-5,000. Average royalty 10% on retail sales. Advances rarely given.
PHOTOGRAPHERS: All photography is done in-house.

UMBRELLA PRESS

56 Rivercourt Blvd.
Toronto, ON M4J 3A4

PHONE: (416) 696-6665
FAX: (416) 696-9189

CONTACT: Ken Pearson, Publisher **DESCRIPTION:** Mainly non-fiction trade and educational reference library products for junior high, high school and university levels. Publishes 6 books per year. Recent publications include: *Mary Ann Shadd; Leading the Way: Black Women in Canada* by Rosemary Sadler and *Struggle and Hope: The Chinese in Canada* by Paul Yee.
WRITERS: 20% of books published are by first-time authors. Works with unagented writers. Send a query letter with outline, sample chapters, market summary and size of finished book. Average response time 3-5 weeks. Publishes in 9-12 months. Average first-time print run 2,000-2,500. Average royalty 10% on retail sales. Advance given upon submission of completed manuscript.
PHOTOGRAPHERS: Illustrators needed for illustration, book covers, dust jackets. Send query letter with repros of work (no originals at all please!) to be kept on file.

UNITED CHURCH PUBLISHING HOUSE

85 St. Clair Avenue East
Toronto, ON M4T 1M8

PHONE: (416) 231-5931
FAX: (416) 925-9692

CONTACT: Peter Gordon White, Editor-In-Chief **DESCRIPTION:** Publishes for church members. Publications include environmental and peace issues, social justice, and ethics.
WRITERS: 20% of books published are by first-time authors. Send a query letter with outline and one or two chapters. Average response time 2-6 weeks.
PHOTOGRAPHERS: Photos used for illustration and book covers. Contact with a query letter and sample portfolio; to be kept on file.

UNIVERSITY OF ALBERTA PRESS

141 Athabasca Hall
Edmonton, AB T6G 2E8

PHONE: (403) 492-0717
FAX: (403) 492-0719

CONTACT: Glenn Rollans, Editor-in-Chief **DESCRIPTION:** Scholarly non-fiction and university level textbooks, history, politics, education, natural sciences, Native studies, literary criticism, Slavic and Eastern European studies, Middle East studies, anthropology, and archaeology. Publishes 8-10 books per year.
WRITERS: "We solicit writers and also accept manuscripts. Writers can phone or write. We don't want a complete manuscript. We prefer an outline with a Table of Contents. We respond within a month. If someone is just canvassing that is fine, but if we want to look at it we want sole exclusivity. Author's guidelines are available.
PHOTOGRAPHERS: "Generally the author supplies all text illustration."

UNIVERSITY OF CALGARY PRESS

2500 University Drive NW   **PHONE:** (403) 220-7578
Calgary, AB   T2N 1N4   **FAX:** (403) 282-0085

CONTACT: Shirley Onn, Director   **DESCRIPTION:** Publishes academically oriented scholarly texts trade texts based on scholarship on a wide range of topics with strengths in Northern studies, natural science and political science. Recent titles: *The Church, A Demon Lover: A Sartrean Analysis of an Institution* by Roberta Imboden; *Doing Things the Right Way: Dene Traditional Justice in Lac La Martre, NWT* by Joan Ryan.
WRITERS: "We look at unsolicited manuscripts." Replies in 6-8 weeks.
PHOTOGRAPHERS: "We use photography for some titles. Photographers can send a resumé and stock list for our files."

UNIVERSITY OF MANITOBA PRESS

Suite 244, 15 Gillson Street   **PHONE:** 204 474-9495/474-9242
University of Manitoba   **FAX:** 204 275-2270
Winnipeg, MB   R3T 5V6

CONTACT: Patricia Dowdall   **DESCRIPTION:** Publishes non-fiction scholarly books in social sciences and the humanities. Subjects include Western Canadian history, Native studies, and women's studies. Publishes 4-5 titles per year. Recent publications include: *O Little Town, Remembering Life in a Prairie Village* by Harlo Jones; *The Ojibwa of Western Canada: 1780-1870* by Laura Peers; *The Iron Rose: The Extraordinary Life of Charlotte Ross M.D.* by Fred Edge.
WRITERS: Publishes 1-2 first-time authors per year. Works with unagented writers. Send a query letter with outline. "If we are interested, we send a two-page information sheet that needs to be completed." Average response time 1-3 weeks. Publishes in 1-2 years. First-time print run 1,000-2,000. "We often do a hardcover as well as a paperback version." Royalty negotiable. Occasionally gives a small advance.
PHOTOGRAPHERS: All photography is done in-house.

UNIVERSITY OF OTTAWA PRESS

542 King Edward Avenue   **PHONE:** (613) 564-2270
Ottawa, ON   K1N 6N5   **FAX:** (613) 564-9284

CONTACT: Suzanne Bosse   **DESCRIPTION:** Publishes scholarly books in English and in French. Publishes 24 books per year. "We have two series in English Canadian Literature, one on French America, on philosophy in translation and a series dedicated to proceedings, social sciences, religions and beliefs, women's studies, education, and medieval text." Recent titles: *Dear Marian Dear You: the MacLennan-Engel Correspondence* edited by Christl Verduyn.
WRITERS: "We have three directors and service committees that work at acquisitions and advertise in the Aid to Scholarly Publications program. Our authors are mostly university professors or professionals working in our fields of interest. Authors can phone or send a Table of Contents, the introduction and conclusion of the manuscript.
PHOTOGRAPHERS: "We very rarely buy photos."

UNIVERSITY OF TORONTO PRESS
10 Saint Mary Street, Suite 700   **PHONE:** (416) 978-2239
Toronto, ON M4Y 2W8   **FAX:** (416) 978-4738

CONTACT: Editorial Department   **DESCRIPTION:** Publishes over 100 text books, reference, non-fiction trade, and encyclopedias per year. "We publish strictly scholarly books. Anthropology, archaeology, architecture, art and art history, medieval studies, collected works, criminology, Canadian history and literature, and native studies." Distributes in the US. Recent titles: *Ocean Bridge*; a series on the correspondence of Bernard Shaw; *A Moscow Literary Memoir: Among the Great Artists of Russia from 1946-1980* by Robert Ford; *Of Passionate Intensity: Right Wing Populace Among the Reform Party of Canada*.
WRITERS: "It is preferable for people to query first. If we are not interested, neither of us wastes postage. We respond to queries within a few weeks. Royalties are based on net sales." Does not consider simultaneous submissions.
PHOTOGRAPHERS: "We use photos; usually the author supplies them."

VANWELL PUBLISHING LTD.
1 Northrup Crescent, Box 2131   **PHONE:** (905) 937-3100
St. Catharines, ON L2M 6P5   **FAX:** (905) 937-1760

CONTACT: Ben Kooter, Publisher   **DESCRIPTION:** Publishes non-fiction and fiction, including historical, regional, military, children's and novels. No poetry or romance. Publishes 4-6 titles per year. Recent publications include: *Her Story* by Susan Merritt; *The Longest Battle* by John Harbron; *Ships of Canada's Naval Forces* by Ken MacPherson.
WRITERS: 20-30% of books published are by first-time authors. Works with unagented writers. Send a query letter with resumé, outline, sample chapters and SASE. Average response time 4-8 weeks. Publishes in 12-18 months. First-time print run 2,000-3,000. Royalty negotiable. Advance not given.
PHOTOGRAPHERS: Photos used for illustration, book covers, and dust jackets. Contact with a query letter and business card, sample portfolio and SASE.

VÉHICULE PRESS
P.O. Box 125   **PHONE:** (514) 844-6073
Place du Parc Station   **FAX:** (514) 844-7543
Montreal, PQ H2W 2M9

CONTACT: Simon Dardick   **DESCRIPTION:** Publishes 12-13 non-fiction trade and literary volumes per year. Does not publish fiction or poetry. Recent publications include: *Despite the Odds: Essays on Canadian Women in Science* by Mary Anne Ainley and *The Book and the Veil: Escape From an Istanbul Harem* by Yeshin Ternar.
WRITERS: 20% of books published are by first-time authors. Works with unagented writers. For non-fiction titles only: query letter with sample chapter, Table of Contents and SASE. Average response time 6-8 weeks. Publishes in 6-12 months. First-time print run 1,000-5,000. Average royalty 10% on retail sales. Advance is given.
PHOTOGRAPHERS: Photos used for illustration, book covers and dust jackets. Contact with a query letter and samples to be kept on file. If you need material returned, state this in your cover letter and send SASE.

VESTA PUBLICATION LTD.
Box 1641   **PHONE:** (613) 932-2135
Cornwall, ON K6H 5V6   **FAX:** (613) 932-7735

CONTACT: Attn: James   **DESCRIPTION:** "We publish poetry, novels, non-fiction and fiction. Presently we are publishing two books, we have 130 books in print."
WRITERS: "Authors can contact us with a query letter and we will respond in 6-8 weeks. 50% of our authors are first time authors. Royalties are 10% of retail sales paid at the end of the year. We don't want to see terrorism or violence or pornography. Otherwise we are pretty open."
PHOTOGRAPHERS: Photography is not purchased.

VOYAGEUR PUBLISHING
Maple Pond, Maple Ave., R.R.#2   **PHONE:** (613) 925-2111
Prescott, ON KOE 1P0   **FAX:** (613) 925-0029

CONTACT: Sean Fordyce, Publisher   **DESCRIPTION:** Publishes trade non-fiction with a small amount of fiction. Specializes in political and social commentaries. Recent publications include: *We Stand on Guard for Thee* by Marjorie Bowkers; *In the Public Interest* by Stephen Langdon, Rosemary Worsket and Judy Rebick; *A N.A.C. Voter's Guide*; *Misconceptions* by Lippman, Eichler, and Basen; *Treason of the Intellectuals* by Robin Matthews and *Arctic Smoke and Mirrors* by Gerard Kenney. Publishes 5-10 titles per year.
WRITERS: "We read unsolicited manuscripts. We prefer whole manuscripts."
PHOTOGRAPHERS: Average response time 4-6 weeks. Publishes in 2-18 months. Average royalty 10% on retail sales. No advances.

W.B. SAUNDERS COMPANY CANADA LTD.
55 Horner Avenue   **PHONE:** (416) 255-4491
Toronto, ON M8Z 4X6   **FAX:** (416) 255-4046

CONTACT: Heather McWhinney   **DESCRIPTION:** Publishes books on medicine, nursing, dentistry, and health and veterinary sciences. Recent publications include: *Community Nursing: Promoting Canadians' Health* by Marion Stewart; *Managing a Veterinary Practice in Canada* by Jack and *Ethical and Legal Issues in Canadian Nursing* by Keating.
WRITERS: Works with unagented writers. Send a query letter with outline and sample chapters. Average response time 2-6 weeks. Publishes in 6-36 months. Average royalty 10% on retail sales.
PHOTOGRAPHERS: Photos occasionally used for book covers and text illustration. Contact with a query letter to Jean Davies, Director of Publishing Services.

WALL & EMERSON INC.
6 O'Connor Drive   **PHONE:** (416) 467-8685
Toronto, ON M4K 2K1   **FAX:** (416) 696-2460

CONTACT: Byron Wall, Publisher   **DESCRIPTION:** Publishes college and university textbooks. Subject areas include adult education, history, philosophy, mathematics and English as a Second Language. Recent publications include: *Aftermath* by Ed Barbeau and *Cooperative Education and Experiential Learning* by Jeffrey A. Cantor. Publishes 5-6 titles per year.

WRITERS: 60% of books published are by first-time authors. Send a query letter with the market you are targeting, outline, sample chapters and resumé. Average response time 6-8 weeks. Publishes in 10-15 months. First-time print run 500-2,000. Average royalty 10% on retail sales. No advance.
PHOTOGRAPHERS: All photography is done in-house.

WARWICK PUBLISHING

24 Mercer Street, Suite 200   **PHONE:** (416) 596-1555
Toronto, ON M5V 1H3   **FAX:** (416) 596-1520

CONTACT: Nick Pitt, Publisher   **DESCRIPTION:** Publishes non-fiction titles, including sports, business, how-to's, and cookbooks. A small amount of fiction. Recent publications include: *Today in History* by Bob Johnson; *Maple Leaf Moments* by Howard Berger and *The Niagara Winery Cookbook* by James Bruce. US distribution.
WRITERS: 40% of books published are by first-time authors. Works with unagented writers. "We publish only one or two fiction titles per year. We accept unsolicited manuscripts happily." Send a query letter and resumé with outline and sample chapter, and SASE. Average response time 6-8 weeks. "If we reject the manuscript, we will try to let you know why." Publishes in 9-18 months. Royalty and advance negotiable.
PHOTOGRAPHERS: 90% assigned to in-house photographers. Contact with a query letter, business card and samples of work to be kept on file.

WATSON & DWYER PUBLISHING LTD.

905 Corydon Avenue, Box 86   **PHONE:** (204) 284-0985
Winnipeg, MB R3M 3S3   **FAX:** (204) 453-8320

CONTACT: Gordon Shillingford, Publisher   **DESCRIPTION:** Publishes Canadian history.

WEIGL EDUCATIONAL PUBLISHERS LTD.

1902 - 11 Street S.E.   **PHONE:** (403) 233-7747
Calgary, AB T2G 3G2   **FAX:** (403) 233-7769

CONTACT: Linda Weigl, Publisher   **DESCRIPTION:** Publishes text books and teacher guides. Subject areas include social studies, math, Canadiana, science, language arts, C.A.L.M., and multicultural. Publishes 10-15 titles per year. Recent publications include: *Career Connection* (series).
WRITERS: 90% of writing is in-house and by contract. Send a query letter with outline and SASE. Average response time 6-8 weeks. Publishes in 12-24 months. Royalties and advances negotiable.
PHOTOGRAPHERS: 90% assigned to in-house photographers. Contact with a query letter, sample portfolio and SASE.

WESTCOAST PUBLISHING
1496 West 72nd Avenue   PHONE: (604) 266-7433
Vancouver, BC   V6P 3C8   FAX: (604) 263-8620

CONTACT: Michael Skogg, Publisher   DESCRIPTION: Publishes a marine directory.
NOTES: "We only publish The Commercial Marine Directory. It is reprinted once a year.
We do not read unsolicited manuscripts, unless it is for our magazine publications."

WHITECAP BOOKS LTD.
351 Lynn Avenue   PHONE: (604) 980-9852
North Vancouver, BC   V7J 2C4   FAX: (604) 980-8197

CONTACT: Colleen Macmillan, Publisher   DESCRIPTION: Publishes local guides
and historical books. Also includes nature, gardening the environment, colour scenic, cooking,
parenting, railways, and full colour tourist giftbooks and calendars. Publishes 30 titles
per year. Recent titles: *The Creative Container Gardener* by Elaine Stevens; *The Presence
of Whales* by Frank Stewart and *Sky Dancers* by Diane Swanson, ILlustrated by Douglas
Penhale.
WRITERS: Send for Submission Guidelines with SASE. "Anyone from the US or overseas
needs an international money order."
PHOTOGRAPHERS: Photos are used for calendars, text illustration, book covers, and
dust jackets. Contact with a query letter, business card and sample portfolio to be kept
on file.

WILFRID LAURIER UNIVERSITY PRESS
75 University Ave. West   PHONE: (519) 884-1970
Wilfrid Laurier Univ.   FAX: (519) 725-1399
Walterloo, ON   N2L 3C5

CONTACT: Sandra Woolfrey   DESCRIPTION: Publishes scholarly books in the
humanities and social sciences. Also general interest books on film, culture, and the
environment. Subjects include literary criticism, women's studies, religious studies, Canadian
studies, and history. Publishes 12-15 titles per year. Recent publications include: *Going
By the Moon and the Stars: Stories of Two Russian Mennonite Women* by Pamela E. Klassen;
The Language of Canadian Politics: A Guide to Important Terms and Concepts - Revised
Edition by Ron McMenemy and *The Collected Writings of Michael Snow* with a by Michael
Snow.
WRITERS: 10% of books published are by first-time authors. Authors should have funding
for their book. Send a query letter with outline and one or two chapters. Average response
time 2-4 weeks. Manuscripts go to an Editorial Review Committee. Publishes in 6-18 months.
Royalty 6% of net sales. No advances.
PHOTOGRAPHERS: All photography is done in-house.

WILLIAM STREET PRESS
Box 21114   PHONE: (519) 263-5973
Stratford, ON   N5A 7V4   FAX: (519) 263-5973

CONTACT: Patricia Wilson, Publisher   DESCRIPTION: "We have always done travel
books but this year we are publishing two children's books. We publish specifically bed
and breakfast books; how-to and the bed and breakfast book for Ontario and Canada."

Titles: *The Ontario Bed and Breakfast Book; Alice of Wonderfarm Goes to the Races* Ann Nelles. Publishes on average 3 books per year.

WRITERS: "Writers should contact us by mail with a query letter. If we are interested we will follow-up." Works with first time authors. So far 100% first time authors. Works with unagented writers. Royalties based on retail sales. Advances vary. Publishes about 6 months after acceptance. Considers simultaneous submissions. Responds in about two weeks.

PHOTOGRAPHERS: "We have never used photography; only for something very specific for a cover."

WILLIAMS-WALLACE PUBLISHERS INC
Box 756
Stratford, ON N5E 4A0

NOTES: Could not locate. Phone number is not in service (519) 271-7045.

WINDFLOWER COMMUNICATIONS
844-K McLeod Avenue
Winnipeg, MB R2G 2T7

PHONE: (204) 668-7475
FAX: (204) 661-8530

CONTACT: Gilbert Brandt, Publisher **DESCRIPTION:** Publishes fiction and non-fiction titles. Subject areas include biography, history, and juvenile (13-17). No children's books or poetry. Publishes 4-5 titles per year. Recent publications include: *Without Shedding of Blood* by Kevin Block and *An Orphan's Song* by Hilda Dueck.

WRITERS: 10-20% of books published are by first-time authors. Send a query letter with outline or sample chapters. Average response time 2-4 weeks. Publishes in 9-12 months. First-time print run 1,500-2,500. Average royalty 15% on net sales. No advance given.

PHOTOGRAPHERS: All photography is done in-house.

WOLSAK AND WYNN PUBLISHERS LTD.
Box 316, Don Mills P.O.
Don Mills, ON M3C 2S7

PHONE: (416) 222-4690
FAX: (416) 445-1816

CONTACT: Maria Jacobs **DESCRIPTION:** Publishes about 5 poetry books per year. Recent titles: *Hero of the Play* by Richard Harrison; *Connect the Dots* by Nicole Markotic; *Loveruage* by Ashok Mathur; *Cantos From a Small Room* by Robert Hilles (winner of the Governor General's award.)

WRITERS: 40% of authors are first time authors. Publishes within the year of acceptance. Does not consider simultaneous submissions. Print runs start at 500 copies. Royalties are 10% on retail sales. "We prefer that an author queries first with a sample of their work. If we like what we see then we will ask for a complete manuscript. Writers' guidelines are available. People should allow 4-6 months for a response. I want authors to read the best poets going and if they think their writing compares, then we would like to have a look at their work. They have to be good judges of their own work before they start sending material out. We get a lot of material that really doesn't satisfy any needs. It is a waste of time for us. All material must have a SASE with sufficient postage."

THE WOMEN'S PRESS
517 College Street, Suite 233
Toronto, ON M6G 4A2

PHONE: (416) 921-2425
FAX: (416) 921-4428

CONTACT: Ann Decter, Fiction Editor
Martha Ayim, Non-fiction Editor. **DESCRIPTION:** Publishes books on social criticism,
fiction, non-fiction, translation, lesbian issues, children's and adolescent literature. Most
books written by women. Also publishes The *Every Women's Almanac.* Titles: non-fiction:
By, For and About; Feminist Cultural Politics an edited collection by Wendy Waring.
Adolescent fiction novel: *My Aunt is a Pilot Whale* by Anne Provoost. Publishes 8 books
per year. Works with mostly unagented writers. Average print run is 2,000. "We are a
collective so the process for assessing it is probably the longest part. Takes 3 months to
get an initial response from us and 6 months for the assessment process. It would probably
take 2 years before something was actually published."
WRITERS: "We ask people to query with a letter and ask whether they should submit
their work. Writers' guidelines are available with a SASE.
PHOTOGRAPHERS: "We use photography maybe once a year, and we have contacts
in our neighbourhood."

WOOD LAKE BOOKS INC
10162 Newene Road
Winfield, BC V4V 1R2

PHONE: (604) 766-2778
FAX: (604) 766-2736

CONTACT: David Cleary and Bonnie Schlosser, Publishers   **DESCRIPTION:** Publishes
religious works on protestant Christianity. Recent publications include: *True to You* by
Donald C. Pasterski; *There's Got to be More* by Reginald Bibby and *These Evangelical
Churches of Ours* by Lloyd Mackey.
WRITERS: Send for Writers' guidelines, then send a query letter with outline and sample
chapter.
PHOTOGRAPHERS: 90% assigned to in-house photographers. Contact with a query
letter and sample portfolio to be kept on file.

WOODSWORKS
7-A Vickery Road
Victoria, BC V9B 1M3

NOTES: NOT CURRENTLY PUBLISHING

YORK PRESS LTD.
Box 1172
Fredericton, NB E3B 5C8

PHONE: (506) 458-8748
FAX: (506) 458-8743

CONTACT: Dr. Saad Elkhadem **DESCRIPTION:** Publishes dictionaries, college-level
educational texts, scholarly publications, reference books, and manuscripts on literary criticism
and comparative literature. Publishes 6-8 titles per year. Recent publications include: *Garcia
Marquez and Cuba* by H. D. OberHelman and *Life Work and Criticism* by Graham Greene.
WRITERS: Does not work with first-time authors. Works with unagented writers. Send
a query letter with outline or sample chapters. Average response time 1-2 weeks. Publishes
in 3-6 months. Average first-time print run 500-1,000. Average royalty 10% on retail sales.

STOCK AGENCIES

Stock agencies collect, catalogue and market the photographs of anywhere from one to dozens of photographers. Stock agents use their contacts in the book, magazine, advertising, paper products and special interest markets, to handle the "business" end of negotiating deals and selling images. Some stock agencies prefer to remain small and to represent a few photographers, or to specialize in a certain subjects such as a nature or regional files. Other agencies have grown into internationally connected companies, handling dozens of photographers and millions of images.

A stock agency is of value to photographers who want to get out and photograph on a regular basis, but who are not interested in contacting buyers, making submissions and negotiating the fine details of a sale. They are of special interest to photographers who are devastated by rejection. If you like getting involved in the sales aspects of the business, and have the ability to consistently make submissions, keep in contact with editors and do the necessary paperwork, you may be able to do a better job of selling your own images. Why? Simply because when you send out a submission yourself, all the images are your own. When a stock agency sends out a submission, your photos may be mixed in with the images of six other photographers, or worse yet, your photos may not even make it into the submission.

If you sign with an agency, you will be expected to supply them with new images on a regular basis. Your images must keep pace with the trends and the market place. You must be prepared to wait for results. It takes time to catalogue and file your images, it takes time for your images to get the kind of exposure that results in an annual, or if you are lucky, quarterly cheque. You cannot unrealistically expect to make a living by selling stock ... few photographers ever do.

Most agencies take a 50% commission ... and some of them do a great deal for their 50%: they print sales brochures and advertising material; make long distance phone calls; supply file space; pay for insurance; pay the photo librarians and researchers; cover the cost of packaging and courier fees and they represent you, trying always to get the best deal for each sale.

Getting represented by an agency is not easy. The competition is fierce. Your photos have to stand against the best in the world. Your photos must be current and reflect the trends of the day. You will have to convince the agency that you will be supplying them with stacks of new images on a regular basis.

If you are interested in selling your own stock, or want to be represented by an agency you must do your homework. Nothing annoys agents more than having to educate you over the phone. Their assumption is that if you have not taken the time to find out about the industry, you are not likely to consistently spend the time supplying them with their needs. One of the best books on the subject is Rohn Engh's *SELL AND RE-SELL YOUR PHOTOS*, get it at your local library, bookstore or call 1-800-361-2349 for the Creative Source Bookshop mail-order service.

CANADA IN STOCK
109 Vanderhoof Avenue #214
Toronto, ON M4G 2H7

PHONE: (416) 425-8215
FAX: (416) 425-6966
internet ottmar bierwagen
@ canrem com

CONTACT: Ottmar Bierwagen   **DESCRIPTION:** "We have 100,000 images in our library with good files in Canadiana, International travel, model-released people, food and concept. We represent 40 photographers and 5 illustrators and sell in both Canada and the US. Clients are in advertising, corporate, and editorial. Established in 1994.
PHOTOGRAPHERS: "We accept any format, 99.9% of our files are colour. We have exclusive contracts with most of our photographers." Pays 50% commission. Prices per photo can range from $250-$2,000 depending on its use. The average is between $400-$500 based on North American sales. "The rights we sell depend on the clients needs and the amount of exposure a photo gets. We require model and property releases and have a captioning kit that our photographers use. We negotiate credit lines on editorial; rarely on advertising photography. We consider previously published work. The more it sells the more profitable it is. We need medical, corporate and industrial. Contact us with a phone call. Most slides should be in groups and organized by subject matter. For a sampling I would like to look at approximately 200 transparencies."

CANAPRESS PHOTO SERVICE
36 King Street East, Suite 402
Toronto, ON M5C 2L9

PHONE: (416) 364-0321
FAX: (416) 364-9283

CONTACT: Ron Welch **DESCRIPTION:** Photo Service News library, with both recent colour, b&w photos, and archival photography: and assignment photography. Clients include: ad agencies; graphic designers; magazines; publishers and corporations. "Our network of freelance photographers makes it possible for us to handle on-location or event photography for clients in any centre across Canada and in most foreign countries" Canapress is a division of The Canadian Press.
PHOTOGRAPHERS: "We don't rep individual photographers any more for stock. We sell only our own Canadian Press and Associated Press photographs and represent various other news agencies around the world. We still use photographers for freelance assignments around the world on a contract or freelance basis. We look for experienced news photographers or studio photographers.If you are interested in doing work with us I would be happy to discuss it. Write or fax us with resumé of relevant experience."

COMSTOCK
49 Bathhurst Street #401
Toronto, ON M5V 2P2

PHONE: (416) 504-9177
FAX: (416) 504-6619

CONTACT: Carlos Maningas **DESCRIPTION:** General stock agency with over 4 million images on file. Serves ad agencies, graphic designers, publishers, calendar companies and text book companies. Comstock has offices in New York, London, Paris and Berlin.
PHOTOGRAPHERS: "We accept queries but no unsolicited submissions. We are always looking for lifestyle people photography and industrial photography." Model and property releases required. Captions preferred. Credit line negotiated for editorial. Sells one-time non-exclusive rights. Commissions vary. "Contact us by letter with a description of the type of work you have." Replies to queries in a couple weeks. "We are looking for photographers to represent worldwide exclusively, they can't be with any other agencies. We use mainly 35mm but we have photographers that submit everything up to 4x5. We have limited black & white."

COREL CORPORATION   **PHONE:** (613) 728-8200 ext. 1168
1600 Carling Avenue
Ottawa, ON K1Z 8R7

CONTACT: Kirsten Watson   **DESCRIPTION:** Buys thousands of photos for use on CD Rom's. Publishes 100 new CD's a year. "We presently have about 400 individual CD's. All photographs are on Kodak CD photo format." Distributed world wide. Titles include: autumn, bridges, fishing, helicopters, Italy, military vehicles, Ottawa, textures, underwater reefs, winter and Yellowstone National Park.
PHOTOGRAPHERS: "We buy our photos from both stock agencies and individuals. Call our number to access our voice mail system. Leave your name or fax number to get an application. When you send in your application and slides we with either purchase them or return them." Ask for number 85080.

FIRST LIGHT ASSOCIATED PHOTOGRAPHERS
One Atlantic Avenue, Suite 204   **PHONE:** (416) 532-6108
Toronto, ON M6K 3E7   **FAX:** (416) 532-7499

CONTACT: Pierre Guevremont   **DESCRIPTION:** Stock agency with a general interest file, files specializing in Canadiana, green themes and natural history subjects. Also carries a wide range of topics including: people, business, industry, global abstracts, sports, concepts and still life. Over 800,000 photos in the collection. Represents 50 Canadian photographers and a number of international associated libraries including agencies in New York, Los Angeles, the UK and Spain. "Our strength is our Canadiana."
PHOTOGRAPHERS: "We are looking for photographers to shoot main stream commercial subjects. Contact us with a large SASE and we will send our information package within a week. Contracts vary, we pay the standard commissions, require model releases, property releases where it makes sense, and certainly captions. We negotiate credit lines. Photographers are advised to read the last two years worth of Photo Life magazine. The column on stock photography is written by our partner Julia Day. The market is a very different place at this time and you should know something about the marketplace before trying to get into it. I would require that as essential preliminary reading."

HOT SHOTS STOCK SHOTS INC.   **PHONE:** (416) 441-3281
309 Lesmill Road   **FAX:** (416) 441-1468
Toronto, ON M3B 2V1

CONTACT: Christine Frazer   **DESCRIPTION:** "We cover the whole range of stock including lifestyle, people, scenics. We sell all through Canada and the US and have affiliates overseas. Our clients are advertisers, publishers etc."
PHOTOGRAPHERS: "We prefer 35mm, 120 or 4x5 colour transparencies. We have exclusive contracts with our photographers. Commissions vary between affiliates and photographers. Generally we pay 50% commission on gross, and we pay quarterly upon collection. We sell one-time rights; if the client wants to use an image again they must contact us. We sometimes negotiate credit lines. We definitely need model releases and property releases. We like everything captioned." Present needs: people, scenics, Canadian scenics and especially lifestyle. "Photographers should call us first and we will screen over the phone." Photo guidelines are available with SASE.

THE IMAGE BANK CANADA
40 Eglinton Avenue East
Suite 307
Toronto, ON M4P 3A8

PHONE: (416) 322-8840
FAX: (416) 322-8855

DESCRIPTION: "The Image Bank as a worldwide organization with 65 offices around the world and 20 million pictures on file. The Dallas Texas office signs agreements with photographers: 5221 North O'Connor Blvd #700, Irving Texas 75039, phone 214-432-3900. The current contact is Linda Smith." The Image Bank Toronto office has guidelines available; phone or write for a copy.

IMAGE FINDERS PHOTO AGENCY
now affiliated with Tony Stone.

IMAGE MAKERS
337 West Pender #301
Vancouver, BC V6B 1T3

PHONE: (604) 688-3001
FAX: (604) 688-3005

CONTACT: Joy Huston **DESCRIPTION:** "We have 200,000 images on file including a large file of international wildlife. We have pictures from throughout the world including scenic and tourist photos. We also stock photos on all the major stock categories including:agriculture, people, sports, industry, scenics, transportation, the environment, seasonals, etc. We service mostly commercial clients and sell internationally. We have agreements with several overseas agencies." Represents 82 photographers.
PHOTOGRAPHERS: "We use 35mm slides or 8x10 black & white prints. Current needs include: people in industry, trades, major cities, tourist shots and cliché shots, children. No more wildlife, scenic or flowers please." Pays 50% commission. Sell one time or multiple rights. Requires model releases and property releases, marked on the slide. "Send us a letter, give us a phone call or fax us. Make sure you are really into taking people pictures."

IMAGE NETWORK
#300, 1955 Wylie Street
Vancouver, BC V5Y 3N7

PHONE: (604) 879-2533

CONTACT: Trudy Woodcock **DESCRIPTION:** "We have access to over 350,000 slides. Currently we are contracted with over 13 photographers. We have a general file specializing in west coast imagery. We service clients worldwide.
PHOTOGRAPHERS: "Most of our library is 35mm slides but we have 4x5, 70mm, and panoramas. We do have some black & white but not an enormous amount." Pays 50% commission. "Our contracts are image exclusive." Sells one-time rights. "Ideally we would like to have every single image model and property released and captioned as well." Credit lines are negotiated. "People photography is something we can never get enough of. If your material is of excellent quality we would be interested in seeing it. Call us or write. We prefer a phone call. Talk to us and let us help you guide your photography in a way that is marketable and would work for stock photography. We would be interested in speaking to photographers across Canada."

KEYSTONE ACENCE DE PRESSE
664 Grovenor
Westmount, PQ H3Y 2S8

PHONE: (514) 482-5312
FAX: (514) 482-5312

CONTACT: Lyde Moynier **DESCRIPTION:** "We are very international. We have 1 million black & white and over 500,000 colour transparencies. We cover every subject: international sports, politics, movie stars, geography etc. We have correspondents in England, California and Europe." In Canada since 1960.
PHOTOGRAPHERS: "Let me know what you have in stock." Pays 60% commission.

MACH 2 STOCK EXCHANGE
204-1409 Edmonton Trail NE
Calgary, AB T2E 3K8

PHONE: (403) 230-9363

CONTACT: Pam Varga **DESCRIPTION:** "We are a general agency with 100,000 images on file. We specialize in agriculture, oil and gas. We promote commercial, illustrative and advertising. We world wordwide though various affiliates."
PHOTOGRAPHERS: "My present needs are lifestyle, technology, and business from across Canada. I am in dire need of Ontario and Quebec material. I am not looking for any scenic or wildlife. I use any format. They can write or phone me. I prefer them to phone. Send a SASE. I want submissions in separate vinyl pages, not binders. I require model and property releases to be kept on file. I need captions with dates, locations and information that is not self- explanatory. Use the narrow edge of the slide for that. We are willing to look at portfolios of about 300 images."

MASTERFILE
175 Bloor Street East
South Tower 2nd Floor
Toronto, ON M4W 3R8

PHONE: (416) 929-3000
FAX: (416) 977-8162

CONTACT: Linda Crawford, Artist Liaison **DESCRIPTION:** General collection of tightly-edited contemporary photos and illustrations: some historical; no news, features or trash. Clients include all categories of commercial users - worldwide. Masterfile has agents throughout Europe, the Far East and Australia. All North American business is handled directly from Toronto, which means our artists get maximum royalties from the world's largest market. Masterfile is the largest stock agency in Canada and one of the major international players.
PHOTOGRAPHERS: 40-50% royalties paid monthly upon collection. Artists share in some costs of duplication and catalogue participation. Usage fees for individual images range from $100 to $10,000 according to media; best sellers have accumulated well over $50,000 in aggregate sales. Colour transparencies only - all formats accepted. Send query letter. "Masterfile charges a handling fee to view portfolios - this helps to eliminate the deadbeats. Contact us by mail or telephone for details on how to submit your work. We are only interested in worldwide exclusive representation." Photos guidelines are provided quarterly to artists under contract. Needs: Exceptional images in all categories, but particularly model released: lifestyle, sports, recreation and industry. "Masterfile is a tough agency to get into ... but well worth the effort. We provide a financial return to our photographers and illustrators which far surpasses the international industry standard. We accomplish this by concentrating our considerable efforts on representing a select group of talented individuals - talented, not necessarily famous; that comes later."

MEGAPRESS IMAGES   **PHONE:** (514) 528-6048
777 Gilford   **FAX:** (514) 528-6048
Montreal, PQ H2J 1N8

CONTACT: Helen Porada **DESCRIPTION:** "We are a general agency with an emphasis on wildlife, and illustration shots of people including children, and medical activities. We sell across Canada, into the US and we have a representative in France selling to the European market. We have over 100,000 slides on file. We represent around 20 regular photographers plus 30 others. We sell to magazines, publishers, some postcard companies, some ad agencies and private clients."
PHOTOGRAPHERS: Uses 35mm transparencies only. Pays 50% commission. Requires model and property releases. Each slide must have the name of the photographer and the subject, if it is wildlife it has to be very well captioned with the common and the Latin name. No longer accepting black & white. "We always try to negotiate credit lines. We don't accept less than 500 pictures at one time." Submit a collection of at least 500 slides; very well captioned and very tightly edited. If we like them it is easy to put them on the market right away. We will respond in roughly a month." Photo guidelines are available with a 9x12 SASE. All material must include a SASE with enough postage to return material (or courier information). Sells one time rights. Exclusive contracts. "We need wildlife at the moment, portraits of animals, very sharp pictures of animals in their habitat. There is a lot of competition so they have to be good. We look for material from all across the world. We sell a lot of people, children, couples, and beauty shots. Children and babies are great sellers. We also sell pet pictures like cats and dogs. We do sell flowers however we have enough right now. No phone calls please unless you are very serious about submitting more than 500 slides carefully edited and captioned."

PHOTO SEARCH LTD.   **PHONE:** (403) 425-3766
10130-103 Street #107   **FAX:** (403) 425-3766
Edmonton, AB T5J 3N9

CONTACT: Gerry Boudrias **DESCRIPTION:** "We are a general stock agency covering industry and commerce, people, agriculture, sports, wildlife, entertainment, adventure, education, science, and technology, with a special emphasis on images of Western Canada and Western Canadians." Established in 1991. 75,000 images on file. "The type of image we have breaks down to two very broad categories, one of which is very regionally oriented and has to do with things specific to the city of Edmonton and the natural beauty of Alberta. The other area is generic stock images: model released images of people working, playing, family, the lifestyle type of things. We sell to advertising agencies, graphic designers, publishers, and business communicators. We represent 30 photographers. We have a regional exclusivity which gives us Alberta rights to photographers work.
PHOTOGRAPHERS: Handles only colour transparencies. Pays 50% commission. Generally sells one-time non-exclusive rights. "We absolutely require model releases and property releases. Captions should contain locations, particularly if there is something that is not obvious to a photo editor. I negotiate credit lines and often discount for credit lines. If we add one or two people this year that will be more than enough. I am looking for a lot more lifestyle material. Model released studio quality images of people at work, at play, industry shots. All well lit, well composed and specifically shot for stock. I have little use for anything else. Photo guidelines are available with an SASE. I need to know if photographers are professional shooters, where they are in their careers, how much material they have, what kind of material it is, and how much they are willing to submit on a regular basis. Every photographer who is thinking of stock should research the stock industry. The stock industry is different than any other part of the photography industry."

PHOTOGENICS FINE PHOTOGRAPHY
1510 Broadway Avenue **PHONE:** (306) 665-7721
Saskatoon, SK S7H 2A9

CONTACT: Reg Coulter **DESCRIPTION:** "We have about 25,000 images. If I don't have it we photograph it. We have a lot of outdoor and nature from Saskatchewan, Canada, the United Kingdom; people pictures, seniors in a healthy lifestyle, and children. We have an Large number of black & white images available."
PHOTOGRAPHERS: "I accept queries from photographers. Some of my photographers have exclusive contracts. I have six photographers that I can call upon at any one time. Write me and tell me what your goal is, how long you have been photographing and what you do. The library is mainly 35mm slides but we are trying to build up more medium format images. As a rule we pay 50% but depending on the situation it may be more. It has to be fair to both of us. I am looking for images from across Canada especially from Ontario west. It helps if photographers query first. I must always have model released photos especially when there are minors in the photograph. 99.9% of the time I negotiate credit lines however there are some cases where it is not possible." Photo guidelines are available with a SASE

PONOPRESSE INTERNATIONALE
2177 Masson **PHONE:** (514) 528-9825
Montreal, PQ H2H 1B1 **FAX:** (514) 528-9826

CONTACT: Michel Ponomareff, President **DESCRIPTION:** "We are a press photo agency that represents foreign press agencies in Canada. We also shoot news photos here and syndicate them worldwide. We have a stock agency section that cover politics, show biz, human interest stories, sports and science."
PHOTOGRAPHERS: "The best way for a photographer to contact us is to send us a letter and explain what they have, what they are looking for, how long they have been shooting, and whether they have colour slides or negatives. We work 90% with colour slides." We normally pay a 50% commission. If the photographer went to the other side of the world and invested time, money and film to do a story we may pay more than 50%. We definitely require model and property releases. Captions are good whenever possible.

PUBLIPHOTO
797 Champajneur **PHONE:** (514) 273-4322
Outremont, PQ H2V 3P9

CONTACT: Michel Faugere **DESCRIPTION:** "We are a general agency that also represents 21 international agencies in different fields like zoology, medical, sports, cinema, archives and so on. We represent 107 Canadian photographers.
PHOTOGRAPHERS: "We are open to hearing from photographers especially if you have animals, Canadian fauna and fantastic shots of Canada. We are always searching, but are very selective. We are looking for very high quality images that are good enough to be sold in Japan, Australia and all of the countries in which we are represented. We need at least a couple-of-hundred very high quality images. Write a letter first and then send a selection of images. We have exclusive contracts with our photographers. We use any format, though we prefer scenics in medium format. Our photographers must shoot regularly and be very involved in shooting for stock. That is very important. We pay 50% commission.

REFLEXION PHOTOTHEQUE   **PHONE:** (514) 876-1620
Suite 307, 1255 Square Phillips
Montreal, PQ H3B 3G1

CONTACT: Michel Gagne **DESCRIPTION:** "We carry 100,000+ images on file and represent about 20 photographers as well as world wide agencies. We are a general agency that sells across Canada and the US."
PHOTOGRAPHERS: Pays 50% commission. Average payment $150-$500. Sells one-time rights. Model and property releases are required. Captions are very important. "The best way to query is to call or send a letter explaining what you do and from there we will see. Photo guidelines are available or we will give them over the phone. Limit your selection to 100 images. A professional approach will result in a professional response."

THE STOCK LIBRARY   **PHONE:** (416) 362-7767
275 King Street East, Suite #18   **FAX:** (416) 362-9417
Toronto, ON M5A 1K2

CONTACT: Stan Pagonis **DESCRIPTION:** Established in 1994. We represent 3 companies so our total offering is a little over two and a half million images. One distinct thing we have done is set up the Canadiana library. By the time the Canadiana library is complete we are looking at 50-60,000 images.
PHOTOGRAPHERS: "Our needs are primarily regional, business life in Canada, a little more social life especially in the regional areas. We don't stock much black & white. We prefer 35mm slides but will take medium and large formats." Commission depends on the photographer and whether the contract is exclusive or not. It can range anywhere from 35%-60%. Credit lines are negotiated. "Contacting me is by phone at 1-800-362-0833. We can discuss whether we are interested in what you are offering. If we are interested we will negotiate from that point. It's an exciting time, everything is changing. We are working on going on-line, digitizing shots and working on CD roms for some people."

SUPERSTOCK /FOUR BY FIVE   **PHONE:** (514) 849-2181, 1-800-363-1664
417 St. Pierre, Suite 800   **FAX:** (514) 849-5577
Montreal, PQ H2Y 2M4

CONTACT: Monique Denis **DESCRIPTION:** We stock generic images related to lifestyle, travel, industrial, business, a fine art collection, and a vintage collection. We have over 500,000 images on file. We sell only in Canada. We are affiliated with Super Stock International in Jacksonville Florida. We service designers, ad agencies, designers, publishers, government etc.
PHOTOGRAPHERS: We use 4x5 or 70mm and a small amount of 35mm. Our vintage collections are in black & white but the contemporary materials are colour.
"We are a sales office here in Canada. All the photographers are contracted in Florida. We usually do a preliminary selection over the phone. A direct phone call is appropriate. Call the Montreal number and we will direct them to the florida office 1-800-363-1664."

TAKE STOCK INC.
516-15th Avenue S.W.
Calgary, AB T2R 0R2

PHONE: (403) 229-3458
FAX: (403) 541-9104

CONTACT: Judy Teare **DESCRIPTION:** 90,000 images on file. Represents 30 Canadian photographers and 7 other agencies from around the world. We are very strong in people, lifestyle, business, industry and Alberta.
PHOTOGRAPHERS: We use anything from 35mm to 4x5 transparencies; very little black & white. We have exclusive contracts for geographical areas. Pays 50% commission and sells one time rights. Model and property releases required. Captions required. Credit lines are negotiated for editorial. Needs: anything to do with lifestyle, business and the areas as listed above. I do need Eastern Canada images, scenics, skylines etc. Phoning us is the best way to make contact. A letter is fine as well.

TONY STONE WORLDWIDE
161 Eglinton Avenue East
Suite 501
Toronto, ON M4P 1J5

PHONE: (416) 488-9495
FAX: (416) 488-9448

CONTACT: Andrea Spoule **DESCRIPTION:** "We are a sales office only. All photography is processed through our Los Angeles office."

VALAN PHOTOS
Clayton Lake Road
Clayton, ON K0A 1P0

PHONE: (613) 256-5294
FAX: (613) 256-5296

CONTACT: Valerie Wilkinson **DESCRIPTION:** Specializes in editorial stock including: wildlife, environment, pets, pollution, people and lifestyle, Canada, the world, geography, science, industry, agriculture, horticulture, etc. Clients include books, magazines, calendars and advertising agencies, etc. We have 250,000 photos in stock.
PHOTOGRAPHERS: We use 35mm colour slides; no black & white. We pay 50% commission quarterly. Sells one-time rights. We don't usually require model releases and property releases are not essential. Captions are not essential because we do a lot of editorial. Credit lines are normally given. "Photographers can contact us by letter with their personal information and a stock list. We don't supply guidelines unless we are interested. If they ask for guidelines we send them a questionnaire."

VIEWPOINTS WEST PHOTOFILE LTD.
238 East 2nd Avenue
Vancouver, BC V5T 1B7

PHONE: (604) 873-4883
FAX: (604) 873-6696

CONTACT: Kaj Svensson **DESCRIPTION:** "We are a general stock photography agency. Our strength is BC and in particular the forest industry but we have images of the whole Pacific Northwest: BC, AB, Washington, Oregon, Idaho, and California." We represent 19 photographers and service ad agencies, designers, publishers, magazines etc.
PHOTOGRAPHERS: "We are always looking for new photographers or new material. Either phone us to set up an appointment or write us a letter. We prefer a phone call." Pays 50% commission. "It's to the photographer's advantage to provide releases because they make way more money that way. Captions are a must. We use colour transparencies." Photo guidelines are available.

VISUAL CONTACT PHOTOSOURCE INC
67 Mowat Avenue #247   **PHONE:** (416) 532-8131
Toronto, ON M6K 3E3   **FAX:** (416) 532-3792

CONTACT: Tom Freda or Laura Chen **DESCRIPTION:** We have over 25,000 images on file and represent 44 photographers. We have a general file but the area of best representation would be Canadian scenics and international travel. Our client base is all over North America and we service calendar companies, magazines, book publishers, advertising agencies and design firms. Established in 1990.
PHOTOGRAPHERS: "We need photography in all categories. We accept all formats. Most of our scenics are in medium and large format but we will accept work in anything from 35mm and up; no black & white." Pays 50% commission. Exclusive contracts. Sells everything from regional to world rights. Model and property releases whenever possible. Captions are very important. Credit lines are negotiated; for editorial and calendars they are required. Contact Laura Chen by mail for guidelines and want list. "We also have a newsletter." Replies within 4 weeks. "We find it difficult to get Canadian winter scenes. This seems to be a continuing request by clients. If you have winter activities we would be interested in looking at your images. We also need people and lifestyle shots. We will look at all quality work."

NEWSPAPERS

Canadian daily and weekly newspapers provide an excellent (though low paying) market for the freelance writer or photographer. Every day there are timely news events that need to be recorded. Newspaper staff try to cover the bulk of known and happening events, but there is always room for the freelancer.

If you are a photographer, nothing is more important than being in the right place at the right time. Luck plays a large part. If you are the first at the scene of an event, don't give up if the staff photographer shows up. Phone the news editor, tell him what you have and if he is interested get the film there quickly. If the newsroom is interested they will develop them in-house in order to save time. It's hard to put a price on news photos. A photographer on the scene at the Oklahoma bombing, saw his photo of a firefighter carrying a child splashed on front pages across the world. I'm not sure that I ever want that kind of "luck," but if you are interested in news photography you have to be prepared for anything, including negotiating a good price. It may seem wrong to make money from human misery, but let's be realistic, that's what most news photography is about. According to the New York Times, LIFE magazine paid between $25,000 and $40,000 to Abraham Zapruder for his 8mm movie film of the assassination of John F. Kennedy. This is the exception! Most news shots will get approximately $50 ... however, it is up to you to negotiate the best price possible. If you have a great newsworthy photo, don't forget the TV stations. If news crews aren't on location they may be interested.

Writers also can sell regularly to newspapers. Though most of the hard news is handled by staffers, you can break into some of the special interest areas. Food columns; gardening; finance; house and home; travel; and opinion columns are often handled by freelancers. Some newspapers even purchase fiction from time to time!

Freelancers with both writing and photography skills have a real edge in the articles market simply because they make the editor's job easier.

As always, approach the market professionally. Make your queries short and to the point, be prepared to negotiate a price and when you commit to a project make sure you meet the deadlines.

ASSOCIATED PRESS
36 King Street East, 2nd Floor
Toronto, ON M5C 2L9
PHONE: (416) 368-1388

BARRIE EXAMINER
16 Bayfield Street
Barrie, ON L4M 4T6
PHONE: (705) 726-6537

BELLEVILLE INTELLIGENCER
45 Bridge Street East
Belleville, ON K8N 1L5
PHONE: (613) 962-9171

BRANDON SUN
501 Rosser Avenue
Brandon, MB R7A 5Z6
PHONE: (204) 727-2451

BRANTFORD EXPOSITOR
53 Dalhousie Street
Brantford, ON N3T 5S8
PHONE: (519) 756-2020

BROCKVILLE RECORDER AND TIMES
Box 10, 23 King Street West
Brockville, ON K6V 5T8
PHONE: (613) 342-4441

CALGARY HERALD
215 - 16 Street SE
Calgary, AB T2P 0W8
PHONE: (403) 235-7505

CALGARY SUN
2615 - 12th Street NE
Calgary, AB T2E 7W9
PHONE: (403) 250-4200

CAPE BRETON POST
Box 1500, 255 George Street
Sydney, NS B1P 6K6
PHONE: (902) 564-5451

CAMBRIDGE REPORTER
26 Ainslie Street South
Cambridge, ON N1R 3K1
PHONE: (519) 621-3810

CARAQUET L'ADADIE NOUVELLE
476 Boul. St. Pierre O
Caraquet, NB E0B 1K0
PHONE: (506) 727-4444

CHARLOTTETOWN GUARDIAN AND PATRIOT
165 Prince Street
Charlottetown, PE C1A 4R7
PHONE: (902) 629-6000

CHATHAM DAILY NEWS
Box 2007, 45 Fourth Street
Chatham, ON N7M 2G4
PHONE: (519) 354-2000

CORNER BROOK WESTERN STAR
Box 460, West Street
Corner Brook, NF A2H 6E7
PHONE: (709) 634-4348

CORNWALL STANDARD-FREEHOLDER
44 Pitt Street
Cornwall, ON K6J 3P3
PHONE: (613) 933-3160

LE DEVOIR
2050 de Bleury Street
Montreal, PQ H3A 3M9
PHONE: (514) 985-3333

LE DROIT
47 Clarence Street Suite 222
Box 8860, Station T
Ottawa, ON K1G 3J9
PHONE: (613) 560-2747

EDMONTON JOURNAL
Box 2421, 10006 - 101 Street
Edmonton, AB T5J 0S1
PHONE: (403) 429-5400

EDMONTON SUN
#250, 4990 - 92 Avenue
Edmonton, AB T6B 3A1
PHONE: (403) 468-0100

FINANCIAL POST
333 King Street East
Toronto, ON M5A 4N2
PHONE: (416) 350-6000

FREDERICTON DAILY GLEANER
Prospect Street at Smythe
Box 3370
Fredericton, NB E3B 5A2
PHONE: (506) 452-6671

THE GLOBE AND MAIL
444 Front Street West
Toronto, ON M5V 2S9
PHONE: (416) 585-5411

GUELPH MERCURY
8-14 Macdonnell Street
Guelph, ON N1H 6P7
PHONE: (519) 822-4310

**HALIFAX CHRONICLE-HERALD/
MAIL-STAR**
1650 Argyle Street
Halifax, NS B3J 2T2
PHONE: (902) 426-2898

HAMILTON SPECTATOR
44 Frid Street
Hamilton, ON L8N 3G3
PHONE: (416) 526-3333

LE JOURNAL DE MONTREAL
4545 Frontenac
Montreal, PQ H2H 2R7
PHONE: (514) 521-4545

LE JOURNAL DE QUEBEC
450 Bechard Avenue
Vill Vanier, PQ G1M 2E9
PHONE: (418) 683-1563

KAMLOOPS DAILY NEWS
393 Seymour Street
Kamloops, BC V2C 6P6
PHONE: (604) 372-2331

KELOWNA DAILY COURIER
550 Doyle Avenue
Kelowna, BC V1Y 7V1
PHONE: (604) 762-4445

KENORA DAILY MINER AND NEWS
Box 1620, 33 Main Street South
Kenora, ON P9N 3X7
PHONE: (807) 468-5555

KINGSTON WHIG-STANDARD
306 King Street East
Kingston, ON K7L 4Z7
PHONE: (613) 544-5000

KITCHENER-WATERLOO RECORD
225 Fairway Road
Kitchener, ON N2G 4E5
PHONE: (519) 894-2231

LETHBRIDGE HERALD
504 - 7th Street South
Lethbridge, AB T1J 3Z7
PHONE: (403) 328-4411

LONDON FREE PRESS
Box 2280, 369 York Street
London, ON N6A 4G1
PHONE: (519) 679-1111

MONCTON TIMES-TRANSCRIPT
Box 1001, 939 Main Street
Moncton, NB E1C 8P3
PHONE: (506) 859-4900

MONTREAL GAZETTE
250 St. Antoine West
Montreal, PQ H2Y 3R7
PHONE: (514) 987-2399

NANAIMO DAILY FREE PRESS
223 Commercial Street, Box 69
Nanaimo, BC V9R 5K5
PHONE: (604) 753-3451

NEW GLASGOW EVENING NEWS
352 East River Road
New Glasgow, NS B2H 5E2
PHONE: (902) 752-3000

NIAGARA FALLS REVIEW
4801 Valley Way
Niagara Falls, ON L2E 6T6
PHONE: (905) 358-5711

NORTH BAY NUGGET
Box 570, 259 Worthington Street West
North Bay, ON P1B 8J6
PHONE: (705) 472-3200

LE NOUVELLISTE
1920 Bellefeuille Street
Trois-Rivieres, PQ G9A 3Y2
PHONE: (819) 376-2501

OAKVILLE BEAVER
467 Speers Road
Oakville, ON M2H 2N8
PHONE: (416) 493-1300

ORILLIA PACKET AND TIMES
31 Colborne Street East
Orillia, ON L3V 1T4
PHONE: (705) 325-1355

OSHAWA TIMES
44 Richmond Street West
Oshawa, ON L1G 1C8
PHONE: (905) 723-3474

OTTAWA CITIZEN
Box 5020, 1101 Baxter Road
Ottawa, ON K2C 3M4
PHONE: (613) 829-9100

OTTAWA SUN
380 Hunt Club Road
Ottawa, ON K1G 5H7
PHONE: (613) 739-7000

OWEN SOUND SUNTIMES
290 - 9th Street East
Owen Sound, ON N4K 5P2
PHONE: (519) 376-2250

PEMBROKE DAILY NEWS
Box 10, 86 Pembroke Street
Pembroke, ON K8A 6X1
PHONE: (613) 735-3141

PEMBROKE OBSERVER
186 Alexander Street
Pembroke, ON K8A 4L9
PHONE: (613) 732-3691

PENTICTON HERALD
186 Nanaimo Avenue West
Penticton, BC V2A 1N4
PHONE: (604) 492-4002

PETERBOROUGH EXAMINER
400 Water Street, Box 3890
Peterborough, ON K9J 8L4
PHONE: (705) 745-4641

LA PRESSE
7 St. Jacques Street
Montreal, PQ H2Y 1K9
PHONE: (514) 285-7306

PRINCE ALBERT DAILY HERALD
30 10th Street East
Prince Albert, SK S6V 5R9
PHONE: (306) 764-4276

PRINCE GEORGE CITIZEN
Box 5700, 150 Brunswick Street
Prince George, BC V2L 5K9
PHONE: (604) 562-2441

LE QUOTIDIEN
1051 Talbot Blvd.
Chicoutimi, PQ G7H 5C1
PHONE: (418) 545-4474

RED DEER ADVOCATE
2950 Bremner Avenue, Bag 5200
Red Deer, AB T4N 5G3
PHONE: (403) 343-2400

REGINA LEADER POST
1964 Park Street
Regina, SK S4P 3G4
PHONE: (306) 565-8211

SAINT JOHN TELEGRAPH JOURNAL\EVENING TIMES GLOBE
210 Crown Street, Box 2350
Saint John, NB E2L 3V8
PHONE: (506) 632-8888

ST. CATHARINES STANDARD
17 Queen Street
St. Catharines, ON L2R 5G5
PHONE: (905) 684-7251

ST. JOHN'S TELEGRAM
Columbus Drive, Box 5970
St. John's, NF A1C 5X7
PHONE: (709) 364-6300

SARNIA OBSERVER
Box 3009, Box 140 S. Front Street
Sarnia, ON N7T 7M8
PHONE: (519) 344-3641

SASKATOON STAR PHOENIX
204-5th Avenue North
Saskatoon, SK S7K 2P1
PHONE: (306) 664-8340

SAULT STE. MARIE STAR
Box 460, 145 Old Garden River Road
Sault Ste Marie, ON P6A 5M5
PHONE: (705) 759-3030

SIMCOE REFORMER
Box 370
Simcoe, ON N3Y 4L2
PHONE: (519) 426-5710

LE SOLEIL
390 St. Vallier Street East
Quebec City, PQ G1K 7J6
PHONE: (418) 647-3270

STRATFORD BEACON-HERALD
Box 430, 108 Ontario Street
Stratford, ON N5A 6T6
PHONE: (519) 271-2220

SUDBURY STAR
33 Mackenzie Street
Sudbury, ON P3C 4Y1
PHONE: (705) 674-5271

SUMMERSIDE JOURNAL PIONEER
Box 2480, 4 Queen Street
Summerside, PE C1N 4K5
PHONE: (902) 436-2121

SYDNEY CAPE BRETON POST
Box 1500
Sydney, NS B1P 6K6
PHONE: (902) 564-5451

THUNDER BAY TIMES-CHRONICLE JOURNAL
75 South Cumberland Street
Thunder Bay, ON P7B 1A3
PHONE: (807) 343-6200

TORONTO STAR
1 Yonge Street
Toronto, ON M5E 1E6
PHONE: (416) 869-4000

TORONTO SUN
333 King Street East
Toronto, ON M5A 3X5
PHONE: (416) 947-2222

LA TRIBUNE
1950 Roy Street
Sherbrooke, PQ J1K 2X8
PHONE: (819) 564-5450

TRURO DAILY NEWS
Box 220
Truro, NS B2N 5C3
PHONE: (902) 893-9405

VANCOUVER SUN\THE PROVINCE
2250 Granville Street
Vancouver, BC V6H 3G2
PHONE: (604) 732-2944

VICTORIA TIMES-COLONIST
2621 Douglas Street, Box 300
Victoria, BC V8W 2N4
PHONE: (604) 380-5211

WELLAND-PORT COLBORNE TRIBUNE
228 East Main Street
Welland, ON L3B 3W8
PHONE: (416) 732-2411

WHITEHORSE STAR
2149-2nd Avenue
Whitehorse, YK Y1A 1C5
PHONE: (403) 668-2002

WINDSOR STAR
167 Ferry Street
Windsor, ON N9A 4M5
PHONE: (519) 255-5711

WINNIPEG FREE PRESS
1355 Mountain Avenue
Winnipeg, MB R2X 3B6
PHONE: (204) 697-7000

WINNIPEG SUN
1700 Church Avenue
Winnipeg, MB R2X 3A2
PHONE: (204) 694-2022

WOODSTOCK-INGERSOLL DAILY SENTINAL
Box 1000, 16 Brock Street
Woodstock, ON N4S 8A5
PHONE: (519) 537-2341

INDEX

Printed in Canada by
Hignell Printing Ltd.,
Winnipeg, MB, R3G 2B4